SYSTEMES
ET SERVICES
A PETITS SATELLITES

SMALL SATELLITES
SYSTEMS
AND SERVICES

CÉPADUÈS-ÉDITIONS

DANS LA MÊME COLLECTION
IN THE SAME SERIES

Dépôt légal : janvier 1993

N° éditeur : 346

ALLOCUTIONS

Monsieur le Ministre, Messieurs les Directeurs généraux, Mesdames, Messieurs,

C'est comme on le dit traditionnellement, mais croyez-le avec beaucoup de vérité, que je vous accueille en toute sympathie à Arcachon.

Dans ce palatium, inauguré l'année dernière, et qui est un outil que nous pensons assez performant, et dont je suis sûr que vous allez nous permettre de le démontrer ; tant, et c'est déjà fait, par le nombre de ceux qui viennent assister à ce symposium, que je dirai, par la qualité des participants.

La ville d'Arcachon est une station qui a vocation d'accueil et celui-ci se traduit par un tourisme important et aussi par des nécessités d'aménagement, qui rendent la vie agréable à toutes celles et ceux qui viennent fréquenter notre cité. Mais elle a aussi une vocation laborieuse au travers de l'administration, de tout ce qui constitue les services, et sa petite population de 12 000 habitants, en fait, recouvre une activité bien plus grande à travers tout son secteur d'activité. Je voudrais également vous accueillir, non seulement en tant que maire d'Arcachon, mais en tant que député européen, et vous exprimer cette satisfaction de voir que l'Europe de l'espace que vous représentez, est l'exemple même de l'Europe qui marche et qui préfigure l'Europe de demain. Ceci est vrai par la multiplicité des programmes engagés, cela est vrai aussi par le titre 15 d'un traité dont on parle beaucoup en ce moment, de Maastricht ; cela est vrai aussi parce que c'est un secteur exemplaire pour l'avenir, et que, au travers des Agences Spatiales Européennes, se préfigure et s'annonce la forme que prendra certainement l'Europe du XXIᵉ siècle.

Alors je voudrais, en vous assurant de l'amitié de la ville, vous exprimer des remerciements très sincères pour l'avoir choisie, afin de pouvoir y tenir cette importante réunion, et vous dire que, en toutes choses, elle demeurera non seulement attentive à ce que vous ferez, mais surtout tout à fait ouverte aux besoins que vous pourrez exprimer.

For English speaking people, may I add just a few words in English: a very hearty welcome to this city. Translations will be available as from this afternoon, until then, a very hearty welcome on behalf of Arcachon, thank you.

M. LATAILLADE
Maire d'Arcachon

Monsieur le Ministre, Monsieur le Maire, Mesdames et Messieurs,

Le thème de ce colloque est « les petits satellites ».

Au début de l'ère spatiale, on en faisait sans en parler, aujourd'hui on en parle beaucoup et on fait des projets. Passera-t-on demain à la réalisation concrète ?

Pourquoi ce mouvement d'intérêt qui amène tant de participants à ce colloque, organisé conjointement par le Centre National d'Etudes Spatiales, par l'Agence Spatiale Européenne, par l'Ecole Nationale Supérieure de l'Aéronautique et de l'Espace et par l'Ecole Nationale Supérieure des Télécommunications ?

Déjà, la récente conférence de la CAMER, la Conférence Administrative Mondiale des Radiocommunications, qui s'est tenue à Malaga en mars 1992, a lancé le débat sur les petits GEO et les gros LEO. Les petits GEO ont pour nom Ordcom, Star6, Vital, Eosat etc., les gros LEO, Iridium, Globalstar, Aries, Elitsat, Odyssée etc.

Les satellites et systèmes de ce genre occupent des pages entières dans les journaux spécialisés, le plus souvent illustrées par des photos d'artiste, car les réalisations concrètes sont encore bien rares. Le sujet soulève un grand intérêt, tant dans les pays qui maîtrisent déjà les technologies spatiales, que dans les pays qui souhaitent entrer dans l'aire du spatial.

Pour les uns, c'est la recherche de missions à faible coût, avec des délais d'attente réduits pour prendre en compte des idées nouvelles de mission, avec l'espoir de certains industriels d'entrer dans le club des fournisseurs spatiaux par ce créneau. C'est aussi le souci de retrouver une certaine flexibilité, en glissant des grains de sable d'innovation dans les plans à long terme des grandes agences spatiales.

Pour les autres, les pays qui n'accèdent pas encore à la technologie spatiale, c'est la possibilité d'apprendre à faire et d'entrer, par une démarche progressive, dans le cercle des pays spatiaux.

L'organisation d'un tel colloque repose sur un présupposé favorable aux petits satellites. Pour vérifier la robustesse de cette hypothèse de travail, il nous faudra obtenir des réponses à un certain nombre de questions.

Tout d'abord, question primordiale, y a-t-il des missions pour les petits satellites ? Autrement dit, les petits satellites ont-ils un créneau d'excellence particulière ? Peut-on faire, grâce aux progrès des technologies, avec des petits satellites, ce que l'on pouvait faire avec des grands ? Petit est-il synonyme de pas cher ? L'économie d'échelle qui peut exister pour des systèmes de petits satellites, existe-t-elle aussi pour des satellites isolés ?

Les méthodes de travail, les organisations industrielles du spatial, qui ont tendance à se sophistiquer et à devenir donc très coûteuses, doivent-elles être revues, voire profondément bouleversées, par un autre parti pris sur les risques du spatial ? Y a-t-il une spécificité du métier de constructeur de petits satellites par rapport aux gros ? Ou ce créneau des petits satellites ne prépare-t-il pas l'arrivée sur le marché de nouveaux constructeurs de gros satellites ? Ce colloque apportera, sur tous ces sujets, son lot de controverses, de réponses argumentées provisoires ou définitives.

Son importance se mesure déjà au nombre de propositions reçues par les organisateurs, au nombre d'exposants et au nombre de participants. Toutes les conditions sont réunies pour que les confrontations et les chocs des idées se produisent, et produisent des conclusions intéressantes. Vous apprécierez, j'en suis sûr, le cadre de travail que nous offre la ville d'Arcachon.

Diverses manifestations ont été organisées pour permettre de nouer, en marge du colloque, des contacts amicaux qui sont la tradition de notre famille spatiale.

Puisque je m'exprime au nom de l'Agence Française de l'Espace, à l'ouverture de ce colloque, je rappellerai brièvement sur quels acquis nous fondons, au CNES, notre réflexion sur les petits satellites, sur quels projets nous travaillons actuellement, quelles sont les attentes des utilisateurs français. Au début de ses 30 ans d'existence, le CNES a bien sûr commencé son activité par la réalisation de petits satellites et d'ailleurs aussi de petits lanceurs.

De nombreux projets ont ainsi vu le jour, parfois en coopération, dans les deux premières décennies de la vie de ce jeune organisme. Ils s'appelaient D2A, D2B, Eole, Symphonie, D5A, D5B. Ces projets du CNES n'étaient certainement pas isolés de leur contexte du moment, si on se rappelle que Intelsat a lancé en 1965, avec Intelsat 1 Early bird, un satellite de 65 kg au lancement. En 1967 Intelsat a lancé également Intelsat 2, qui faisait 162 kg, en 1968, Intelsat 3 qui faisait 293 kg ; donc déjà une course à la taille, si on se rappelle aussi le satellite OTS ou le satellite Météosat.

Les années 80 ont été pour nous des années où les forces spatiales françaises étaient surtout orientées vers des gros satellites, tels que Spot, TDF 1, TDF2, Telecom 1, Telecom 2, et il faudra attendre cette année 92 pour que le CNES fasse un retour vers les petits satellites, puisque nous avons développé le satellite expérimental S80T, qui fait de l'ordre de 50 kg et qui sera lancé en août 92, en passager de la mission CNES/NASA Topex/ Poséidon, que nous avons soutenu le développement, en coopération avec la Délégation Générale pour l'armement mais également avec l'Agence Spatiale italienne, d'un satellite Arsène qui fait environ 150 kg, et qui devrait être lancé à la fin de cette année.

C'est donc un retour limité mais réel de l'Agence Spatiale française, qui a acquis ses galons de professionnalisme sur de grands programmes, vers un créneau qui n'était occupé, en France, que par des satellites étudiants.

D'autres projets existent en France. Ils feront l'objet, tout au long de cette semaine, de présentations faites par le CNES, par d'autres organismes ou par les industriels impliqués. Se rechercheront et se dessineront peut-être ici, les contours d'une politique plus affirmée dans ce secteur. Déjà, nous constatons qu'il existe une demande pour des missions technologiques et des missions d'apprentissage. Il faut aussi que se précise la demande des scientifiques.

Notre Comité National des programmes scientifiques a manifesté à plusieurs reprises son intérêt pour des petits satellites, et nous nous sommes engagés à faire un point devant ce comité à la mi-93. Ce sera l'occasion d'évoquer des missions scientifiques dans le prolongement de notre programme Ballon, d'évoquer la suite de Topex/Poséidon, sujet déjà évoqué par la NASA, d'évoquer aussi des satellites de surveillance sismique ou de mesure du champ magnétique, ou du champ de potentiel de la Terre.

Au-delà des missions proprement scientifiques, les missions tournées vers les applications, et qui pourraient trouver, à terme, des débouchés de marché, doivent également être précisées. Elles intéresseront les radiocommunications, l'observation de la Terre, la météorologie. Comme vous le pressentez, notre réflexion ne serait pas complète, si nous ne la rebouclions pas sur les moyens de lancement des petits satellites.

Jusqu'à présent, en Europe tout au moins, les petits satellites ont été placés en « piggyback », à la marge des grosses missions. Cette solution a le mérite d'exister, et les dispositifs techniques, pour que les risques de la mission principale ne soient pas accrus par une mission secondaire, ont été qualifiés – par exemple, sur le lanceur européen Ariane. Encore faut-il ne pas avoir pour la mission secondaire, des exigences trop fortes, que ce soit en termes de date de lancement ou d'attitude ou d'inclinaison des orbites.

Plus on ira vers des exigences fortes, et vers des missions opérationnelles, et plus on entrera dans la logique de lanceurs dédiés aux petits satellites. Des lanceurs adaptés à ce nouveau marché font l'objet de nombreuses études, y compris en Europe, y compris en France, et on peut espérer que les réflexions qui, pour l'instant, sont menées en parallèle sur les petits satellites et sur les petits lanceurs, convergeront vers une vision claire de l'avenir.

Nous attendons donc beaucoup de ce colloque pour apprécier l'intérêt et la faisabilité des systèmes et services à petits satellites. Je souhaite bien sûr à tous les participants de fructueux échanges, et pour ceux qui ne connaissent pas la région, le plaisir de la découvrir. Je remercie tous les participants, conférenciers, présidents et vice-présidents de session, comités de programme, exposants, interprètes (qui ne sont pas encore à l'œuvre), organisateurs de l'accueil, pour la contribution qu'ils ont apportée et qu'ils continueront à apporter tout au long de cette semaine, à un colloque, qui je l'espère, fera date dans les annales. Merci de votre attention.

M. Jean-Daniel LEVI
Directeur Général du CNES

Monsieur le Ministre, Monsieur le Maire d'Arcachon, Mesdames Messieurs,

C'est pour moi un grand plaisir que d'assister à l'ouverture de ce symposium international sur les petits satellites, qui se tient dans un cadre aussi séduisant.

J'ai noté, en étudiant le programme, que nous sommes parvenus avec tous nos co-organisateurs, le CNES, l'ENSAL, l'ENST à mettre au programme de ce symposium un vaste ensemble de sujets, qui vont de questions aussi diverses que les services de lancement, l'économie, et l'accès à la technologie spatiale, aux sujets les plus classiques, que sont les sciences et les télécommunications spatiales. Les quelques 90 communications qui y seront faites, et la présence de participants de 15 nationalités différentes vous permettront, j'en suis convaincu, de passer en revue une large part des possibilités d'utilisation de ces petits satellites, afin de pouvoir nous permettre, dans l'avenir, de prendre les décisions adéquates.

Petits, ils pèsent généralement moins d'une tonne, mais il semble bien que l'interprétation de ce terme dépend beaucoup de la discipline considérée, et aussi d'une certaine classification en terme de moyens de lancement nécessaires. Je suis heureux, cher Jean-Daniel, qu'il se trouve parmi les communications faites ici, des résultats de travaux menés par nos deux organisations. Vous n'ignorez pas, et ceux qui m'écoutent apprécieront, j'en suis convaincu, d'apprendre que lors d'une récente réunion du Comité Programme scientifique de l'ESA, l'exécutif a présenté un document de réflexion sur l'utilisation de systèmes à petits satellites pour les missions de science spatiale. Nous avons eu à ce sujet une discussion fort intéressante et l'une des conclusions a été qu'il semble possible de mener à bien, avec de petits instruments, des missions scientifiques valables et originales.

L'Agence Spatiale Européenne est disposée à contribuer, toutes les fois où elle le pourra, à stimuler la réalisation de tels petits satellites, y compris au niveau national. Dans le domaine des petits satellites, il ne faut pas oublier l'impulsion donnée par un autre événement, la Conférence Administrative Mondiale des Radiocommunications de 1992, qui s'est tenue cette année à Torremolinos.

Cette conférence a eu lieu à un moment particulièrement opportun pour les petits satellites de télécommunication de type boîte postale, et j'ai la grande satisfaction de savoir, qu'aux Etats-Unis, l'un des premiers concurrents en ligne pour ce type de service entretient d'étroites relations avec l'Europe.

Pour ce qui est des télécommunications en particulier, je constate une expansion de l'étroit marché des petits satellites équipés de charges utiles relativement modestes, appelés par exemple à fournir des services à un certain nombre de pays en voie de développement. Si les sciences et les télécommunications sont les premiers domaines qui viennent à l'esprit dans ce contexte, il est probable que d'autres disciplines, comme l'observation de la Terre, pourraient, elles aussi, tirer parti, dans des cas bien déterminés, des petits satellites, et je vois qu'une large place est faite à ce sujet dans le programme du symposium. On notera également, avec satisfaction, le vif intérêt de l'industrie pour ce symposium, qui transparaît dans l'exposition organisée parallèlement au colloque.

Outre les quatre organisations parrainant cette manifestation, on comptera parmi les exposants plus de 25 autres sociétés. On soulignera à juste titre, qu'à la différence des autres colloques, celui-ci trouve sa raison d'être dans les besoins des utilisateurs civils, comme c'est le cas de la majeure partie des travaux réalisés en Europe dans ce domaine. C'est ce que confirme la liste des organismes qui construisent et lancent des petits satellites. De plus, ces premières initiatives qui ont surgi dans toute l'Europe, ont en commun le fait de devoir leur succès, pour une large part, au dynamisme des individus et des organismes qui en sont à l'origine. Les relations étroites qu'ils entretiennent avec des établissements d'enseignement sont bien entendu d'une importance capitale aux yeux de l'ESA et des organisations similaires, eu égard aux besoins de l'industrie spatiale en ingénieurs et techniciens, ce qui explique l'intérêt marqué que les différentes agences spatiales accordent à ces projets.

C'est pourquoi je tiens, Mesdames et Messieurs, à former tous mes vœux pour que vos délibérations soient fructueuses et j'espère bien avoir connaissance des résultats de la conférence, qui se refléteront dans les débats de la table ronde prévue jeudi après-midi. Encore une fois merci.

M. Jean-Marie LUTON
Directeur Général de l'Agence
Spatiale Européenne

Mesdames, Messieurs,

Je suis comme vous tous heureux d'assister à cette ouverture d'un important colloque, heureux qu'il se tienne à Arcachon.

Merci Monsieur le Maire de nous accueillir dans cette belle cité et dans ce bel établissement. J'ai retenu dans votre discours, Monsieur le Maire, une phrase qui nous a fait à tous plaisir : « l'Europe de l'espace ça marche ». Et oui ça marche, et déjà depuis longtemps, et beaucoup d'entre nous, qui sommes ici aujourd'hui, ont fait d'énormes efforts pour que ça marche, et nous avons le plaisir de pouvoir donner cette Europe de l'espace en exemple à toutes les autres Europes qui se construisent actuellement et que nous appelons de nos voeux. Comme les orateurs qui se sont exprimés, je voudrais bien sûr remercier le CNES, l'ESA, Suptélécom et Sup'aéro qui ont organisé ce colloque, remercier tous les participants qui ont bien voulu consacrer leur début de semaine à cette réunion, une réunion importante sur les petits satellites.

Dans les affaires spatiales, comme dans les activités humaines et en particulier scientifiques et techniques, il y a des effets de mode et vous pourriez dire, on pourrait dire : « Oh maintenant parler des petits satellites, c'est à la mode ». Alors à part ça, les petits satellites ! Bon, oui mais la mode c'est important. C'est ce qui donne des idées, si j'ose dire. Que l'on retienne ces idées-là ou que l'on ne les retienne pas, c'est une autre chose. Mais dès l'instant qu'il y a un effet de mode, cela entraîne une réflexion, une certaine excitation, un intérêt nouveau, et pourquoi ne pas profiter de cet intérêt nouveau pour aller jusqu'au fond des choses et voir vers où l'on peut effectivement s'orienter. D'ailleurs vous savez cet effet de mode pour le petit quand on est habitué au gros, ce n'est pas l'espace qui en a ni la primeur ni l'exclusivité. Dans tous les autres domaines scientifiques nous assistons à cela.

Moi qui suis physicien, dans tous les domaines de la physique on a ça. Pendant un moment, on ne rêvait que d'énormes machines à faire des neutrons pour tout le monde, et maintenant chacun rêve d'avoir ses petits neutrons à soi, chez soi. C'est tout à fait naturel, mais pourquoi ne pas avoir les deux : ses petits neutrons à soi chez soi et puis les gros neutrons ensemble, en même temps, autour de la grosse machine. Les justifications pour l'un et pour l'autre sont évidentes. Je parle de neutrons, mais je pourrais parler de n'importe quelle particule à accélérer. Les très grands accélérateurs quand on veut faire des gros chocs et puis les petits accélérateurs chez soi, quand on a des petites manips bien dédiées, bien définies et qui nécessitent des conditions un peu particulières et qu'on peut très bien réaliser dit-on, au moins au départ, à moindres frais.

Mais d'ailleurs, il se trouve de temps en temps que ça se réalise effectivement à moindres frais. Donc, regarder les petits instruments ou les petits systèmes alors que les gros ont déjà fait leurs preuves, n'est pas du tout une démarche vaine, bien au contraire c'est une démarche de complémentarité qui me paraît absolument indispensable, et je vous suis très reconnaissant de bien vouloir vous livrer à cet exercice. D'ailleurs mes collègues l'ont déjà fait remarquer, quand on parle de petits satellites, la chose est toute relative parce que M. Luton vient de nous dire à l'instant : « Pour moi les petits satellites ce sont des satellites dont la masse est inférieure à une tonne ». Mais rappelez-vous un temps qui n'est pas si ancien, il y a une quinzaine d'années, une vingtaine d'années peut-être au maximum, un satellite d'une tonne c'était déjà le bon gros satellite ! Et nous avons commencé les uns et les autres, et M. Lévi nous donnait quelques chiffres tout à l'heure, avec des satellites qui étaient d'un demi-quintal, un quintal, deux quintaux, etc. Et on est arrivé, à ce moment-là la tonne c'était le méga, et maintenant c'est pas le micro mais c'est le mini.

Alors le micro c'est, je comprends bien que c'est à peu près 50 kg, 100 kg, c'est le type S80T, le type Arsène ou d'autres encore, et ce n'est pas une nouveauté actuellement, c'est une réalité puisque M. Lévi nous l'a fait remarquer, en Europe, on lance bon an mal an, au moins un de ces satellites – S80T en 92, Arsène, vous avez dit fin 92 c'est peut-être 93. Pour la facilité de ma démonstration, j'en mets un par an, voyez. Donc, janvier 93 et puis un autre un peu militaire en 94 etc., etc. Donc, déjà les petits satellites sont sur nos programmes. Donc pas d'opposition entre, les petits satellites c'est beaucoup mieux que les gros, et ou, les gros remplacent les petits, ce n'est pas du tout cela.

C'est la complémentarité que nous cherchons et des vocations particulières pour les petits satellites. Alors vocations particulières, la première évidemment qui vient à l'esprit, c'est la vocation de satellites d'apprentissage, satellites de vocation technologique. Nous en avons eu beaucoup, par le passé, des petits satellites qui étaient simplement des satellites de validation. On avait une idée, on voulait tester tel type de matériel, tel type de matériau, et on les embarquait dans des satellites de petite taille et de petit prix.

Et puis ensuite, bien sûr, viens la réalisation de plus gros satellites qui doivent être, eux, opérationnels. Et c'est peut-être là la difficulté, c'est de passer d'un satellite petit, qu'on a conçu comme un satellite de démonstration, à une utilisation opérationnelle. Est-ce qu'il faut garder à ce moment-là le même type de satellite, est-ce qu'il faut changer d'échelle pour réaliser la même mission, mais opérationnelle, au lieu d'être démonstrative, c'est aussi un point qui me paraît important.

Il y a bien sûr un deuxième type d'application des petits satellites, ce sont les missions scientifiques. On conçoit bien que des missions scientifiques spécifiques peuvent assez souvent se satisfaire de satellites de taille relativement modeste. Taille relativement modeste, mais là aussi il y a une discussion intéressante. C'est que, en général, quand on conçoit un satellite scientifique, on pense à une mission, et puis les discussions très souvent font penser qu'avec le même engin on peut réaliser en même temps une autre mission. Et puis ça croît comme ça et on arrive à la limite du petit et du moyen. Et alors là, il y a les deux écoles.

L'école qui dit, oh mais c'est bien mieux d'avoir des satellites complètement dédiés pour une seule mission : on les fait plus légers, plus souples, plus faciles d'exploitation, et s'il y a deux missions on fait deux satellites. Et puis l'autre école qui a aussi ses arguments qui dit : mais non, c'est plus astucieux d'avoir des satellites qui sont à deux missions, à trois missions, parce que si ces missions sont relativement voisines du point de vue de leur impact scientifique, on a intérêt à les exploiter sur la même plate-forme parce que par exemple, s'il s'agit de différents types d'observation d'un objet, que cet objet soit la Terre, l'atmosphère ou tel ou tel objet extra-terrestre, la simultanéité des observations, qui est assurée par la contiguïté des instruments sur la même plate-forme, peut être un avantage et là, alors on voit qu'on dérive du petit satellite dédié vers le moyen satellite un peu moins dédié. C'est aussi une discussion qui me paraît intéressante. Alors, ces deux types de petits satellites, les petits satellites de caractère technologique et probatoire, les petits satellites de caractère scientifique, ne nous empêchent pas de penser aussi aux petits satellites de caractère opérationnel et pour lesquels il y a un marché avec des productions en série.

On peut penser évidemment aux deux grands thèmes d'exploitation qui sont : observation de la terre et télécommunications. Observation de la Terre et télécommunications, il faut naturellement que l'on s'interroge et vous vous interrogez, nous nous interrogeons sur l'avenir plus ou moins immédiat, des satellites de petite taille dans ces deux domaines. Par exemple, un satellite de télécommunications en orbite basse est le plus souvent conçu en essaim, je ne sais pas si l'on dit maintenant essaim ou constellation. On dit essaim ? Constellation. Très bien. Et en anglais c'est swarm, non ?

Bref, vous voyez bien ce que je veux dire. Alors là, quand on pense à ce type de satellite qui se démarque assez fortement des satellites géostationnaires, des gros satellites et qui ne cessent de grossir, gros satellites de télécommunications, on entre assez clairement en compétition directe avec tous les satellites, non pardon, tous les moyens de télécommunications basés à terre. Donc là, on imagine des systèmes qui sont complémentaires et intermédiaires entre les satellites géostationnaires et l'ensemble des moyens de télécommunication à terre, et c'est là aussi un beau et gros sujet qui mérite, je pense, d'être étudié à fond.

Et puis lorsqu'on parle de petits satellites, et les Directeurs Généraux du CNES et de l'ESA l'ont fait remarquer il y a un instant, on ne peut pas ne pas parler de petits lanceurs. Qui pense petits satellites pense aussi, pas nécessairement, mais doit penser accessoirement à petits lanceurs. Voilà un autre sujet de discussion et je ne peux pas rencontrer moi les responsables de telle ou telle grande Agence Spatiale nationale ou internationale, ou tel ou tel responsable de grande firme industrielle fabricant et mettant sur le marché des lanceurs, sans leur poser la question.

Où en êtes-vous de vos réflexions sur les petits lanceurs ? Alors les uns me disent : non, les petits lanceurs ce n'est pas notre affaire, nous, nous avons notre créneau de lancement de satellites pour 10, 15 ans et nous n'avons pas l'intention de nous en démarquer parce que nous avons une certaine clientèle à laquelle nous sommes habitués. Et puis d'autres nous disent : oui, on y pense dès maintenant ou bien on y pense pour plus tard. C'est un sujet qui mérite aussi que l'on s'y attache mais il faut essayer de définir là, quel est véritablement le marché, à quelle échéance ce marché se manifestera, pour ajuster les programmes.

Nous avons déjà dans nos différentes agences et en particulier en Europe, des programmes assez chargés comme vous le savez, à la limite de l'essoufflement financier – j'ai dit à la limite, je n'ai pas dit au-dessus ou en dessous – pour que nous nous chargions très rapidement de nouveaux types de programmes, en particulier de programmes de petits lanceurs. Cela ne veut pas dire du tout qu'il ne faille pas y penser. Il faut bien sûr, dès maintenant, y penser et voir comment cela peut s'accommoder des programmes que nous avons actuellement. Voilà. Le seul point que je voulais ajouter, c'est un point qui me paraît important, c'est que sur ces sujets comme sur tous les autres, nous constatons dans le monde et plus spécialement sur notre continent européen, une bonne connivence des efforts de chacun. Je me réjouis en particulier, qu'ici, pour ce congrès, nous voyions travailler ensemble et de façon très bien engrenée, le CNES et l'Agence Spatiale Européenne. Ce travail en commun, c'est évidemment ce que nous appelons de nos vœux.

Et puis, Monsieur le Maire, nous ne voulons pas terminer la série de ces discours quasi-officiels – je ne sais pas pourquoi je dis quasi, ils sont tout à fait officiels – sans rendre à nouveau un hommage à Arcachon et tenez, je vais si vous me le permettez, évoquer les dunes qui vous entourent. Les dunes qui entourent Arcachon me font penser un peu au travail que nous faisons nous, dans nos efforts spatiaux. Pour franchir un mètre quand on monte sur une dune, il faut faire au moins cinq pas. A aucun pas on ne recule, mais il faut en faire cinq pour franchir un mètre. Il faut avoir de la continuité et de l'opiniâtreté et c'est ce que nous avons.

M. Hubert CURIEN

Ministre de la Recherche
et de l'Espace

SPEECHES

Minister, Managing Directors, Ladies and Gentlemen,

The expression is traditional, but said with sincerity – I wish you an extremely warm welcome to Arcachon.

Welcome too to this conference centre, inaugurated last year. We believe it to be an extremely well-adapted facility. This is already borne out by the number and, I would add, the quality of the participants at this symposium.

The town of Arcachon is a resort catering for a considerable level of tourism. This requires the development of amenities which make life pleasant for all those who come to visit. But the town also has a working population, particularly through the administrative and other services. Its small population of twelve thousand inhabitants has an extremely wide range of activities.

But I extend my welcome to you not only as Mayor of Arcachon, but also as European Member of Parliament, and I am happy to see that the European space industry you represent is the very example of Europe's success and an indication of its bright future. This holds good by virtue of the number of programmes undertaken and also through heading number 15 of a treaty which is subject to much discussion at the moment, the Treaty of Maastricht. The space sector is also exemplary in that, through the European Space Agencies, the form Europe will certainly take in the twenty-first century can also be foreseen.

Mr LATAILLADE
Mayor of Arcachon

Minister, Your Worship the Mayor, Ladies and Gentlemen,

The theme of this symposium is "small satellites".

At the beginning of the space age these were built without discussion, while nowadays we talk a lot about them and draw up projects. Will we actually get down to producing them in the near future?

Why this surge of interest leading to such high level of participation in this symposium, organized jointly by the Centre National d'Etudes Spatiales, the European Space Agency, by the Ecole Nationale Supérieure de l'Aéronautique et de l'Espace and by the Ecole Nationale Supérieure des Télécommunications?

The recent World Radiocommunications Administrative Conference, held in Malaga in March 1992 kicked off debate on small GEOs and large LEOs. Small GEOs with names like Ordcom, Star6, Vital, Eosat, etc., and large LEOs like Iridium, Globalstar, Aries, Elitsat, Odysée, etc.

Satellites and systems of this type take up whole pages in specialised journals, usually illustrated by artists' impressions, as real examples are still extremely rare. The subject arouses considerable interest, both in countries which already master space technologies and in countries which seek to enter the space scene.

For some, the aim is to carry out missions at low cost with short lead times allowing new ideas for missions to be taken on board, while certain industrial organizations seek to join the club of space equipment suppliers through this niche. There is also the desire to recover a certain level of flexibility, by introducing grains of sand into the complicated machinery of the major space agencies, in the form of innovative projects and ideas.

For those countries which have not yet mastered space technology, small satellites offer the possibility of acquiring know-how and gradually finding their place among the circle of those countries active in space.

Organizing such a symposium suggests a favourable attitude to small satellites. To check out this working assumption, a certain number of questions must be answered.

Firstly, the main question is to know whether there are missions appropriate to small satellites. In other words, do small satellites have an area in which they provide best performance? Thanks to technological progress, can small satellites be used to do what we could do with large satellites? Will they lead to greater economy? Does the economy of scale that can be achieved by small satellite systems also apply to isolated satellites?

Should the working methods and industrial organizations of the space sector, which tend to become more and more sophisticated and costly, be subjected to review, or even completely rethought out on new lines and a new purpose with respect to analysis of risk in space? Is the role of small satellite manufacturer distinct from that of large satellite manufacturer? Or is the small satellite niche simply a way in for a new wave of large satellite manufacturers? This symposium will bring its range of controversies and interim or final conclusions on all these subjects for discussion.

Its importance can already be gauged by the number of proposals received by the organizers, the number of exhibitors and participants. Everything has been arranged such that the battle of ideas will take place and exciting conclusions be reached. I am sure, too, that you will appreciate the working environment offered by the town of Arcachon.

Very much in the tradition of the family atmosphere which prevails in the space community, various events have been organized to allow friendships to develop around the symposium.

As, for the opening of this symposium, I am speaking on behalf of the French Space Agency, I will briefly recall on what bases we develop our thinking at CNES on the question of small satellites, the projects we are currently working on and describe the expectations of French users. At the beginning of its thirty years of existence, CNES obviously started by developing small satellites, together with small launch vehicles.

Many projects were successfully developed, sometimes in cooperation, during the two first decades of the young body's existence. They were called D2A, D2B, Eole, Symphonie, D5A and D5B. These CNES projects were certainly not isolated from their current context, remembering that Intelsat was launched in 1965, with Intelsat 1 Earlybird, a satellite weighing 65 kg on launch. In 1967 Intelsat also launched Intelsat 2, weighing 162 kg and in 1968 Intelsat 3 weighing 293 kg. Thus, we were already making a rush for greater and greater scale − think also of the OTS or the Meteosat satellites.

The 80s was a decade in which French space sector energies were mainly directed towards larger satellites such as Spot, TDF1, TDF2, Telecom 1 and Telecom 2. It was not until this year 1992, that CNES returned to small satellites, with the development of the experimental satellite S80T, which weighs about 50 kg and will be launched in August 92 as a passenger on the CNES/NASA Topex/Poseidon mission, while, in cooperation with the Délégation Générale de l'Armemement but also with the Italian Space Agency, we have also supported development of a satellite called Arsène weighing about 150 kg. This satellite should be launched at the end of the year.

Thus, we can see a real, though limited, return by the French Space Agency, which has proved its professional competence on major programmes, towards a niche which, in France, was occupied only by student project satellites.

But other French projects exist. They will be covered, throughout this week, by presentations by CNES, by other bodies or by the industrialists involved. A more clearly defined policy in this sector will perhaps emerge from the proceedings here. We can already observe a demand for technological missions and training missions. The scientists' demands must also be made explicit.

Our National Committee for scientific programmes has shown its interest on a number of occasions for small satellites, and we have committed ourselves to providing a report to this Committee by mid-1993. This will be an opportunity to evoke scientific missions taking our Ballon Programme further, to bring to your attention the continuation of Topex/Poseidon, which has already been brought up by NASA, and also seismic monitoring, magnetic field and Earth potential measurement satellites.

Beyond purely scientific missions, missions oriented towards applications liable to find future market outlets must also be mentioned. These will concern radiocommunications,

Earth observation and meteorology. As you may already be thinking, our consideration of these matters will not be complete without going back to the question of launch methods for these small satellites.

Until now, in Europe at least, small satellites have been in a "piggyback" position, part of the background to major missions. This solution has the advantage of being available, and technical arrangements to avoid risks to the main mission being increased by secondary missions have been quantified, for example on the European Ariane launcher. But over-heavy demands on the secondary mission, whether in terms of launch date or orbit attitude and inclination must be avoided.

The further we go along the path to greater demands, and towards operational missions, the more we will be heading towards the logic of launchers being dedicated to small satellites. Launchers adapted to this new market are the subject of a large number of studies, including in Europe, and in France. It can be hoped that thinking going on in parallel on small satellites and small launchers will converge towards a clear vision of the future.

We therefore have great expectations of this symposium in order to appreciate the interest and the feasibility of systems and services for small satellites. I hope all participants will enjoy fruitful exchanges and that those who don't know this region will have the pleasure of discovering it. I would like to thank all the participants, lecturers, session chairmen and vice-chairmen, programme committees, exhibitors, interpreters (who have not yet started) and reception organizers for the contribution they have made and will continue to make throughout the week, to this symposium which, I hope, will be a milestone in the field. Thank you for your attention.

Mr Jean-Daniel LEVI
Managing Director of CNES

Minister, Your Worship the Mayor of Arcachon, Ladies and Gentlemen,

It gives me great pleasure to attend the opening of this international symposium on small satellites, which is being held in such a charming environment.

I noticed, studying the programme, that we have managed with all the co-organizers, CNES, ENSAL and ENST, to bring into the symposium a vast number of subjects, ranging from such varied questions as launch services, the economics and means of access to space technology to more classical themes such as space sciences and telecommunications. The 90 or so contributions which will be made, and the presence of participants with 15 different nationalities will allow you, I am sure, to cover major ground in the possibilities for use of these small satellites so as to allow us, in the future, to make the right decisions.

Small satellites weigh less than a ton as a general rule, but our understanding of the term "small" satellite would seem, however, to depend largely on the branch considered and also to a certain classification of the launch facilities needed. I am glad, dear Jean-Daniel, that among the communications made here, there are the results of work carried out by our respective organizations. You will not be unaware, and those listening will, I am sure, appreciate the fact that during a recent meeting of the ESA Scientific Programme Committee, the executive put forward a discussion document on the use of small satellite systems for space science missions. We had a highly interesting discussion on this matter and one of the conclusions was that it would seem to be possible to carry through valid and original scientific missions with small-scale instruments.

The European Space Agency is so minded to contribute, wherever it can, to encouraging the development of such small satellites, including on a national level. Neither, in the field of small satellites, should the stimulus provided by another event, the 1992 World Radiocommunications Administrative Conference held this year in Torremolinos, be forgotten.

This conference took place at a particularly appropriate time for small post-box type telecommunications satellites, and I am delighted that, in the United States, on of the leading competitors for this type of service maintains close relations with Europe.

As far as telecommunications in particular are concerned, I note that the narrow market for small satellites equipped with relatively modest payloads, called on, for example, to provide a certain number of services to developing countries, is expanding. While sciences and telecommunications are the fields which first come to mind in this context, other fields, such as Earth observation, could probably also benefit, in closely defined cases, from small satellites, and I can see that a considerable part of the symposium programme is devoted to this subject. We can also derive satisfaction from the keen interest of industry for this symposium, as evidenced by the exhibition organized alongside the symposium.

Besides the four organizations sponsoring this event, we can number more than 25 other companies exhibiting.

I would also stress the fact that, unlike other symposia, the present one finds its justification in the needs of civil users, as is the case for most work carried out in Europe in this field. This is confirmed by the list of bodies building and launching small satellites. Further, these first initiatives which have emerged across Europe commonly owe their success to the dynamism of the individuals and the bodies which initiated them. The close relations they maintain with teaching institutions are, of course, of prime importance from ESA's point of view and similar organizations, given the needs of the space industry for the supply of engineers and technicians. That goes a long way to explaining the pronounced interest the different space agencies devote to these projects.

That is why, Ladies and Gentlemen, I would like to express my wish that your deliberations be fruitful and I hope to learn of the results of the conference which will be reflected in the debates of the open discussion planned for Thursday afternoon. Thank you again.

Mr Jean-Marie LUTON

Managing Director of the European Space Agency

Ladies and Gentlemen,

Like you, I am extremely pleased to attend the opening of this major symposium, and glad that it is taking place in Arcachon.

Thank you, Your Worship the Mayor for welcoming us to your beautiful town and these fine premises. In your speech, Your Worship the Mayor, I took special interest in a sentence which pleased us all "the European space industry. Europe's success". Yes indeed, Europe as a success. This success has been proved over a number of years now, and many of us who are here today have made huge efforts to contribute thereto. We are happy to give this image of Europe in space as an example to all the other European entities currently under construction and which we wish every success. Like the previous speakers, I would, of course, like to thank CNES, ESA, Suptélécom and Sup'aéro who organized this symposium, and thank all the participants who were willing to devote the beginning of their week to this meeting, a major meeting on small satellites.

In space matters, as in other human activities, particularly scientific and technical, there are current trends, and we could say : "Oh yes, talk about small satellites is just the latest fashion". But as for small satellites themselves, that's another matter! But the trend is significant. That's where ideas spring from, in a manner of speaking. Whether the ideas are held onto or not is another matter. But as soon as there is a general trend, thought results, with a certain excitement, a new interest, and why not take advantage of this new interest to go into things in greater depth and see in what direction we may actually take things. Indeed, you understand the trend effect which leads us to look at the smaller entities when we are used to the large scale, and the space sector has no exclusive rights in the matter. We can see the same thing happening in all areas of scientific activity.

Speaking as a physicist, we can see this happening in all areas of physics. For a time, we dreamt only of gigantic machines to make neutrons for the whole world, and now everyone aspires to having their own little neutrons for oneself. Which is quite natural, but then why not have the best of both worlds: small neutrons for oneself at home and big neutrons together, simultaneously, around the big machine. The justifications for both are clear. I'm referring to neutrons, but I could be talking about any particle to be accelerated. The large-scale accelerators for major impacts and the small accelerators kept on a domestic basis to be used when small, highly dedicated and well-defined manipulations requiring rather specific conditions and which, at least at the beginning, can be carried out at relatively low cost are needed.

What's more, from time to time, such work can really be carried out on a low budget. So, considering small instruments or systems when the larger ones have already been proved and tested is not at all a vain exercise, but on the contrary a complementary approach which seems to me to be absolutely indispensable; I am indeed grateful to you for devoting your time to this matter. Moreover, as my colleagues have already observed, the question is relative, as M. Luton has just made it clear: "For me, small satellites are those whose weight is lower than one ton". But if we look back a little, maybe fifteen to twenty years at most, a satellite weighing one ton was already considered to be a large satellite! And, after all, we all started, as M. Lévi's figures have just shown us, with satellites weighing half a hundredweight, a hundredweight, two hundredweight and so on. And then we got to the ton which was the ultimate, while now while it is not on micro level, we can call it a minisatellite.

The microsatellite, as I understand it, is around 50 or 100 kg, of the S80T, Arsène or similar types. And there is nothing new here, but as M. Lévi has demonstrated, it is a matter of fact that in Europe, year in year out, at least one of these satellites is launched - S80T in 92, Arsène, at the end of 92 or the beginning of 93 as you told us. To simplify matters, let's say that one a year will be launched. One in January 93, then another, of a somewhat military nature, in 94, and so on and so on. So we can see that small satellites already form part of our programmes. So let's not fall into the false dichotomy of saying that small satellites are much better than large ones, and/or that large satellites can replace small ones. That is far from being the case.

What we are seeking is rather a complementarity and specific purposes for small satellites. And when we are talking about specific purposes, obviously, the first that come to mind are training satellites and satellites with a technological purpose. In the past, we had a lot of such small satellites, which were simply validation satellites. Where we had an idea or wanted to test a particular type of equipment or material we would put them on-board a small and relatively cheap satellite.

Then, of course, came the development of larger satellites which had to be operational. And herein lies the difficulty, in going from a small satellite designed for demonstration purposes, to operational use. At this stage, should we keep the same type of satellite or change scale to accomplish the same mission, operational this time rather than for demonstration. This seems to me to be an important point.

Of course, there is a second type of application for small satellites – carrying out scientific missions. We can readily understand that specific scientific missions may often enough make do with relatively small satellites. Relatively small, but there again there is an interesting matter for discussion, in that, generally, when one designs a scientific satellite, one has a mission in mind, and then discussion often leads to thinking that one could also carry out another mission at the same time, using the same vehicle. And the thing grows until we get to the limit between the small and the medium scale. There are two schools of thought in this matter.

One school maintains that it is much better to have satellites completely dedicated to a single mission. They can be lighter, more flexible, easier to run. And if you have two missions, you build two satellites. While the other school, which is not short of good arguments, says: no, it's better to have satellites with two or even three missions as, if the missions are fairly close in terms of their scientific impact, we have everything to gain by running them on the same platform as, for example, if different types of observation of the same object are involved, whether the object be the Earth, the atmosphere or whatever heavenly body, the simultaneousness of observation, ensured by the contiguous situation of the instruments on the same platform, can be advantageous. Here, we go from a dedicated satellite to the medium-scale and rather less dedicated satellite. This too seems to me to be an interesting discussion. So these two types of small satellite, those with a technological and probatory character and those with a scientific character, do not prevent us from thinking of small satellites of an operational nature for which there is a market for series production models.

Of course, we can also think in terms of the two main operational themes : Earth observation and telecommunications. Earth observation and telecommunications must naturally form part of our thinking on the nearer or more long-term future of small satellites in these fields. For example, a low orbit telecommunications satellite is most often designed on a swarm concept (I believe that is the correct English term). Or we could talk about a satellite constellation.

To be brief, I think you can see my point. When we consider this type of satellite, which can clearly be distinguished from geostationary satellites, large satellites which keep on growing and major telecommunications satellites, we are clearly going into competition with all satellites, sorry, with all ground-based telecommunications facilities. So here we can imagine complementary and intermediate systems between geostationary satellites and all ground-based telecommunications facilities. Here too is a fine and interesting matter for debate which, I believe, deserves to be gone into in depth.

And then, when we talk about small satellites, and the Managing Directors of CNES and ESA made the point just a few moments ago, we can't avoid going into the matter of small launchers. As soon as you think about small satellites, you should, even though in reality this is not always the case, think about small launchers. Here is another subject for discussion, and there is no way I can meet the managers of a major national or international space agency, or a major industrial organization building and marketing launchers without bringing the matter up.

What is the current state of your thinking on small launchers ? Some people tell me : no, small launchers are none of our business. We have our niche for satellite launching in 10 to 15 years and we don't intend to deviate from that as we have our customers who are used to our present way of working. Others say: yes, we're already thinking about the matter or will be doing so shortly. It's a subject worthy of interest but we have to define clearly the market and its timescale so as to adjust our programmes.

As you know, our different agencies, particularly in Europe, have fairly heavily loaded programmes, tending towards an exhaustion of financial resources (note that I have not talked in terms of overspending or underspending). This situation is hardly propitious for us to take on the burden of new types of programmes, particularly programmes for small launchers. Which certainly does not mean that we should refrain from thinking on those lines. We should, of course, start thinking about the matter right now, and try to see how we could accommodate such work with the programmes we are already working on. Such are my thoughts on the matter. The only point I would add, which seems to me to be important, is that on these matters, as on so many others, we can see worldwide, and more particularly on our European continent, a high level of collaboration in our efforts. It gives me special pleasure to see that for this congress, CNES and the European Space Agency can be seen to be working together extremely closely. This joint effort is obviously something we welcome with all our heart.

Finally, Your Worship the Mayor, we would not wish to end this series of semi-official speeches (in fact, I should say official speeches, for they are that) without paying tribute again to Arcachon. And with your permission, I would like to mention the dunes which surround you. The duns around Arcachon make me think of the work we are accomplishing in our space research. To climb a metre up a dune, you have to take five steps at least. You don't slide back, but you still have to take five steps to gain a metre. You have to have a sense of continuity and stubbornness to get on, and we have plenty of that.

Mr Hubert CURIEN

Minister for Research and Space

INTRODUCTION

Ce premier symposium « 4 S », Small Satellite Systems and Services, s'est déroulé du 29 juin au 3 juillet 1992 à Arcachon (France).

Proposé par le Centre National d'Etudes Spatiales (CNES), et organisé par le CNES, l'Agence Spatiale Européenne (ESA), les Ecoles Nationales d'Ingénieurs, Sup'Aéro et Télécom-Paris (site de Toulouse), ce symposium a réuni plus de 350 participants de toutes origines (19 pays représentés).

M. le Ministre français de la Recherche et de l'Espace, Hubert CURIEN, M. le Directeur Général de l'Agence Européenne, Jean-Marie LUTON, M. le Directeur Général du CNES, Jean-Daniel LEVI et M. le Député Maire d'Arcachon, M. LATAILLADE ont procédé à l'ouverture des travaux et à l'inauguration de l'Exposition Industrielle, M. Jean-Jacques SUSSEL, Directeur Général Adjoint du CNES ayant procédé à la clôture des travaux.

Le succès de cette manifestation montre l'intérêt porté par les participants au sujet traité. « Les petits satellites » sont en effet redevenus un sujet d'actualité après une longue période d'éclipse relative qui a vu le développement de missions plus ambitieuses reposant sur des « gros satellites et des gros lanceurs » : Homme dans l'espace, missions scientifiques astronomiques, satellites d'observation de la Terre, satellites régionaux, nationaux et internationaux de Télécommunication...

Les petits satellites offrent l'espoir que, progrès technique aidant, on pourra réaliser des missions attractives pour un coût, un délai, une flexibilité bien meilleurs que dans le cas des satellites plus gros. Le Symposium « 4S » a permis de confronter études et réalisations, clients et fournisseurs, concepteurs et utilisateurs, petits et gros industriels...

Les travaux ont été organisés autour de 11 sessions comprenant plus de 70 présentations :

– Analyses Systèmes et Simulations,
– Moyens de Lancement,
– Sciences de l'Univers,
– Observation de la Terre,
– Moyens Sol,
– Systèmes de Radiocommunications et leurs applications,
– Architecture Satellite,
– Technologie des Sous-Systèmes,
– Accès à la Technologie Spatiale,
– Aspects Economiques,
– Session Poster.

A côté des conférences, une exposition industrielle réunissait une quinzaine d'exposants.

Cet ouvrage incorpore les différents documents fournis par les présentateurs ainsi qu'une synthèse par thème effectuée par les animateurs des sessions et présentée à la table ronde de conclusion. Il apparaît que l'activité bouillonne sur les petits systèmes mais que la situation n'est pas encore stabilisée : produits, fabricants, moyens de lancements, missions restent à décanter. Nul doute que les réalisations en cours contribueront à cette clarification aussi bien que les réflexions des organismes clients ou utilisateurs et des fournisseurs potentiels.

Les enquêtes réalisées au terme de cet événement on montré un excellent niveau de satisfaction des participants tant sur le contenu que sur les conditions matérielles de réalisation. Un large consensus s'étant dégagé sur la nécessité de réaliser périodiquement ce symposium, les organisateurs vous donnent rendez-vous à la prochaine édition du « 4S » ainsi qu'à d'autres événements qu'ils pourraient organiser sur le même thème.

INTRODUCTION

This first "4S", Small Satellite Systems and Services symposium was held from 29th June to 3rd July in Arcachon (France).

This idea was proposed by the French national space agency (CNES), and the event was organized by CNES, the European Space Agency (ESA), the national engineering schools, Sup'Aéro and Télécom-Paris (Toulouse establishment).

The symposium was attended by more than 350 participants from all over the world (19 countries represented).

The French Minister of Research and Space, Hubert CURIEN, the Directeur Général of the European Space Agency, Jean-Marie LUTON, the Director General of CNES, Jean-Daniel LEVI, and the Deputy Mayor of Arcachon, Mr LATAILLADE, opened the symposium and inaugurated the Industrial Exhibition, the working sessions being closed by the Assistant Directeur Général of CNES, Jean-Jacques SUSSEL.

The success of this event demonstrates the interest the participants have in the subject. "Small satellites" have indeed come back into the limelight after a relatively long period of obscurity during which more ambitious missions were developed, based on "large satellites and heavy launchers": man in space, scientific astronomy missions, Earth Observation satellites, regional, national and international telecommunications satellites, etc.

Small satellites provide the hope that, technical progress fulfilling its promises, attractive missions will be possible with lower costs, shorter delays and greater flexibility than is the case for larger satellites. The "4S" symposium brought together studies and products, customers and suppliers, designers and users, large and small industrial firms.

Work was organized around 11 sessions comprising over 70 presentations:
– Systems analysis and simulations,
– Launch facilities,
– Sciences of the universe,
– Earth observation,
– Ground facilities,
– Radiocommunication systems and their applications,
– Satellite architecture,
– Subsystem technology,
– Access to Space Technology,
– Economic aspects,
– Poster session.

Alongside the conferences, fifteen or so industrial firms took part in the commercial exhibition.

The present work incorporates the various documents provided by the speakers, together with a synthesis of each theme made by the session leaders and presented at the concluding round table. It seems that small systems are a very active area of interest but that the situation has not yet stabilized; products, manufacturers, launch systems and missions still need clarification. There is no doubt that the work in progress will contribute to this, as will the thoughts of customer and user organizations, and potential suppliers.

A survey performed at the end of the symposium showed a very high level of satisfaction concerning the content of and the practical arrangements for the event. In view of the widespread opinion that the symposium should be held at regular intervals, the organizers will be happy to see you at the next "4S" and at other events that may be organized on the same theme.

TABLE DES MATIERES

CONTENTS

SESSION III : Sciences de l'univers
Space sciences

Chairperson: F. GAMPE *(ESA, The Netherlands)*

SESSION IV : Observation de la Terre
Earth observation

Co Chairpersons: M. ARNAUD *(CNES, France)*
M. GHIZONI *(INPE, Brésil)*

SESSION V : Moyens sols
Ground infrastructure

Co Chairpersons: B. ESCUDIER *(ENSAE, France)*
K. DEBATIN

SESSION VI : Systèmes de radiocommunications et leurs applications
Radiocommunications systems and applications

Co Chairpersons: K. GALLIGAN *(ESA, The Netherlands)*
M. JAI SINGH *(INMARSAT, UK)*

SESSION VII : Architecture satellite
Satellite architecture

Co Chairpersons: J.-M. BOUSQUET *(ENSAE)*
J. HAMELIN *(MRE, France)*

SESSION VIII : Technologie des sous-systèmes
Subsystems technology

Co Chairpersons: G. BELLAICHE *(CNES, France)*
J. DORADO *(INTA, Spain)*

COMITE DE PROGRAMME
PROGRAMME COMMITTEE

Président – *Chairman*

D. HERNANDEZ
CNES, Toulouse – France

Membres – *Members*

M. ARNAUD
CNES, Toulouse – France

G. BELLAICHE
CNES, Toulouse – France

M. BOUSQUET
ENSAE, Toulouse – France

M. CLAUTRIER
CNES, Toulouse – France

B. ESCUDIER
ENSAE, Toulouse – France

K. GALLIGAN
ESA/ESTEC, Noordwijk – The Netherlands

F. GAMPE
ESA/ESTEC, Noordwijk – The Netherlands

H. LAPORTE-WEYWADA
CNES, Evry – France

G. MARAL
TELECOM-PARIS, Toulouse – France

J. MAX
CNES, Toulouse – France

C. SALMON
CNES, Toulouse – France

COMITE D'ORGANISATION
ORGANIZING COMMITTEE

Président – *Chairman*

C. SALMON
CNES, Toulouse – France

Membres – *Members*

G. MARAL
TELECOM-PARIS, Toulouse – France
R. STRONOCK
CNES, Toulouse – France
C. TAILHADES
Groupe EUROPA, Toulouse – France

Ce symposium a été organisé
par le Centre National d'Etudes Spatiales (CNES).

*This Symposium has been organized
by the Centre National d'Etudes Spatiales (CNES).*

SESSION I

ANALYSES SYSTEMES
ET SIMULATION

SYSTEMS ANALYSES
AND SIMULATIONS

SMALL SATELLITE CONSTELLATION SYSTEM: OPTIMIZATION CRITERIA

B.Pavesi P.Palmucci

TELESPAZIO - V.Tiburtina 965 - Rome (Italy)

ABSTRACT

In the present environment the adoption of small satellites based constellation seems very attractive for a large number of commercial applications. The network architecture design shall be conditioned by the service requirements, therefore a suitable system implementation will have to follow a sistematic approach.
In the paper, the key parameters responsible for the optimal mission definition will be identified. On the basis of the assessment of the service requirements, the system efficiency and availability will be quantified. The economical aspects will be taken into account in the evaluation of the system feasibility and of the potential market acceptability.

1 - INTRODUCTION

Many commercial applications can look to satellite systems as favourable candidates for their implementation. The adoption of small satellites is attractive both for user's suitability and for economic convenience, allowing flexibility to custom services, reducing the system complexity and spreading the investments according to the gradual increase of the service demand.
Because of the economic advantages due to low initial and further gradual investments, the competitiveness of the service cost with respect to traditional systems can become true.
In fact, in order to achieve these advantages, it is necessary to optimize the system architecture considering separately all the related aspects such as payload architecture, constellation parameters and network components. Once identified the criteria for the selection of the overall system, by evaluating the right weights of each trade-off, the optimal path among the various combinations of alternatives will be defined.

2 - METHODOLOGY

The service-system optimal phasing approach shall follow the dynamic structure of the complex problems connected both to the service requirements and to the system configuration.
One of the potential approch to generalize the optimization problem is the formulation of a multiobjective program. Infact the multiobjective programming deals with the optimization problems with many objective functions; this approach seems well suited to the constellation optimization criteria, providing the means to select for each item the best compromise solution.

The partitioning will identify the different subsystems and the various level of the problems. In each sub-unit the required iterative processes are identified and the individual tools or the function representative of the subsystem shall be determined. The transition from the lower level blocks to the above one can be obtained by building a function where all the variables are optimally weighted (see Table 1).

In conclusion, consider an objective function as the economic optimisation of the system and a set of constraints as the limits of the single variables and the requirements of integration balances. If the integrated optimisation problem is formulated by including the constraints through either Lagrange multipliers or penalty terms or logical weighted evaluation, the conversion to a multilevel form is done by:

- choosing a set of coordinating variables (indipendent or combined) assuming these to be fixed, thereby producing a first level of the optimisation problem;
- assigning to the second level the task determining the optimal values of the coordinating variables;
- deriving the appropriate algorithm by which the second level unit may improve its estimate of the optimal interaction variables.

This teorethical approach has been tempted to the real problems of optimising a small-satellite system .

3 - KEY PARAMETERS

In the tentative of identifying the objectives of the optimization logic the following key parameters, impacting on the architecture selection, are highlighted:

. Service and traffic Requirements
. Constellation Parameters
. System Parameters
. Economic costraints

Only a balance in terms of optimal performaces for each item can drive to the definition of a complete architecture achieved therefore as a good compromise among different partial alternatives.

4 - SERVICE AND TRAFFIC REQUIREMENTS

The main parameters relevant to service and traffic are the applicable field of services and the acceptable grade of service. For the application field, for example, implications relevant to integration or competitiveness with analogous terrestrial system have to be taken into account.
For the service acceptability, the grade of service has to be considered in terms of coverage areas, service and quality, time to be waited from the moment in which the communications demand arises, to the moment in which the information flow reaches the addressee.

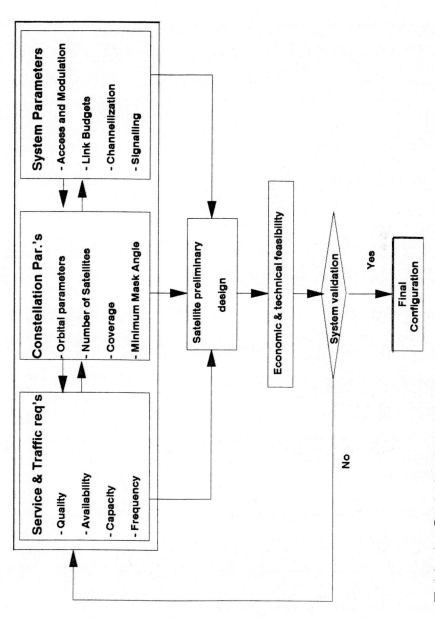

Table 1 - Optimisation process

5 - CONSTELLATION PARAMETERS

For the "objective- constellation design", the main parameters to be defined are: orbit altitude, orbit inclination, number of spacecraft per orbit, conditioned by the coverage requirements.
The candidate orbits considered in this model are geostationary orbit, low circular earth orbit and high elliptical orbit.
The service area considered could be both regional or global; typically, as in the mobile communications scenario, a full-time coverage is required. The coverage time is defined as the time percentage in which the area is in visibility.

In case of GEO satellite if regional coverage is required, the area is full-time served by one satellite, for global coverage two satellites located in opposite side on the geostationary arc can fullfil the requirement except for the polar regions where the geometrical visibility is not possible.

In case of LEO and HEO orbits both the regional and global coverages can be defined by means of envelope of istantaneous coverages, particular algoriths shall be implemented to optimize this problem. The satellite altitude, the inclination and the minimum mask angle are the parameters responsible of the istantaneous coverage.

For HEO constellation, for example, depending on the apogee and perigee altitude, it is possible to change the orbital period and to optimize the service availability by: phasing the repetition of the ground track, estending the operating time of the each satellite in view of the selected service area, and trying to reduce the zooming effects.
These constellations seem very attractive for regional services to be provided medium or high latitude zones.
LEO constellations, based on circular orbits, instead, are more suitable for providing global coverage services expecially if polar orbits are considered. The satellites number for these constellations is depending on the satellite altitude and on the widness of the coverage area. The evolution of the global coverage achieved from a constellation of low and polar orbit satellites and the identification of the overlapping areas, which depend on the adopted satellite orbit altitude, are the main steps of the optimization criteria for the constellations selection.
In the following table, an example of the results of an algorithm implemented to define the satellites number required to achieve global coverage full-time at different quotes is shown. This analysis is limited to constellations where the satellites on polar orbit are distributed symmetrically and in equal number on each plane, and the planes are equispaced, similar algorithm can be improved decresing the angle among the counter rotating planes, in order to facilitate the hand-off procedure excluding the case of switching between counter-rotating planes.. The number of satellites and the orbital planes are optimized to provide global coverage with 100% timeavailability.
Results of optimisation process for LEO satellites constellation is shown as an example in table 2. The concept adopted is the "street of coverage", applied to a system where the satellites are positioned on different co-rotating planes with optimised phase.

N° TOTAL SATELLITES

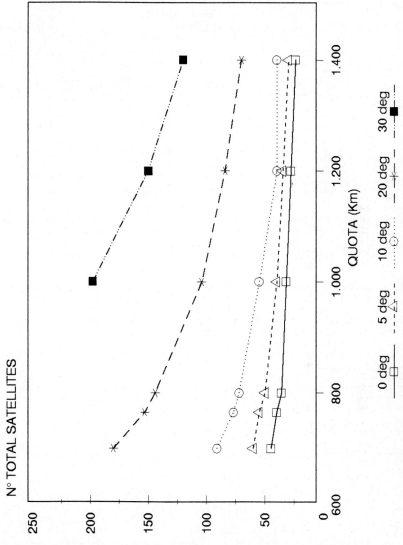

Table 2 - Total Sat. Number for different Mask angles

	MASK ANGLE (deg)					
QUOTE (Km)		0	5	10	20	30
700	planes	5	6	7	10	---
	sat.	9	10	13	18	---
765	planes	5	5	7	9	---
	sat.	8	11	11	17	---
800	planes	4	5	6	9	---
	sat.	9	10	12	16	---
1000	planes	4	5	5	8	11
	sat.	8	8	11	13	18
1200	planes	7	7	8	12	10
	sat.	4	5	5	7	15
1400	planes	4	5	5	7	8
	sat.	6	6	8	10	15
10000	planes	---	---	2	3	3
	sat.	---	---	4	4	6

6 – SYSTEM PARAMETERS

For the general aspects of the communications system the main variables identified are the following:

* Access and Modulation Techniques
* Link Budgets
* Channellization
* Signalling
* Antenna configuration

Each subject is analysed as an indipendent subsystem: the link budgets and the optimal frequency plan are objective functions which can be mathematically formulated, while access and modulation are selected on the basis of improving the satellite capacity, reducing the economic impact for the on-board complexity and being limited by maximum power available. The signalling procedures are selected emphasizing the advantages achievable throught standardization and market proved technology adoption.

Access and Modulation Techniques

Access technique selection, strictly related to the service requirements, has a strong impact on the payload architecture. The most usual and reliable techniques are based on the CDMA, TDMA and FDMA access.

A trade-off is necessary in the optimization process. Along with a consideration of access selection, the modulation technique must also be considered.

The selection of access technique is achieved considering carefully the optimisation of the spectum availability, the on board power limitation and the user-terminal constraints. The FDMA access implyies a low cost user terminal but is not optimised from the bandwidth point of view, the CDMA scheme is adopted to solve user safety requirements and offers the best performances in terms of power and spectrum utilisation, but is not yet a cost-effective system due to the status of the technology. The TDMA access is usually used for the fixed communications because the aspects of the call synchronisation impose a sophisticated management.

The best modulation technique is selected on the basis of key performance. examples are the optimal spectrum occupancy, the maximization of the output power, the minimization of the waveform distorsion due to the non linear behaviour of filter masks and non linear effects of adopted amplifiers producing crosstalk and intersymbol interference.

Of course the modulation technology to be adopted in the system will weight on the overall economical analysis, the ratio improving characteristics/cost effectiveness should be considered, in terms of additional complexity or cost increase inspite of the optimization of the system performance.

Qualitative evaluation of the major key parameters is sketched in table 3.

Link Budgets

Optimization criteria for the system link budget shall be based on the evaluation of different cases for the various types of satellite configurations, as function of the service quality, access and modulation techniques.

Infact depending on the satellite constellations, specific link budgets has to be developed. In case of LEO, in addition to the atmospheric fadings, the variability of earth-satellite range leads to significant time-variations of satellite elevation, range and coverage. The communications are also affected by doppler problems.

The link budget shall be based on the worst case condition in the entire visibility period of each satellite. Therefore in the link evaluation the system geometry and the related characteristics can be considered as fixed, depending on the orbit selection, as shown in table 4, while the communications parameters can be changed depending on the optimisation objective.

Neverthless technological constraints condition the variation process, fixing the acceptablee range of each parameter (as RF power, efficiency, antenna configuration, etc.)

Channellization

Various problems shall be approched under this topic.

- Mobile link: the service characteristics shall be met and managed on board throught the needed channelization process for the intersatellite link at different transmission rates.

- ISL link : the techniques for compressing or compacting the channels received on board shall be identified, eventual IDR

	Spectrum Efficiency	Waveshape distorsion	S/N Constraints	Cost
MSK	Low	Low	High	Low
BPSK	High	High	Low	High
O-QPSK	High	High	Low	High

Table 3 - Modulation Key Parameters

Orbit	LEO	GEO	HEO
Range	Low	High	Very High
Doppler	Yes	No	Yes
Zoom	No	No	Yes
Delay	Low	High	Very High
Mask Angle	5° - 10°	5° - 10°	45° - 55°

Table 4 - Link Budget Key Parameters

methods or particular filtering processing or optimal time frames organization shall be outlined and selected.

- Feeder link : the organization of the channelization for this kind of connection shall be defined considering the routing of the channels in common carrier directed to the same gateway, and the criteria of multiplexing them without increasing too much the on board functions.

- General channel utilization: The optimization algorithm for channel assignment, the selection of frequencies allocation , the organization of carriers bringing channels with different information rates and structures shall be defined considering the available technology and the easiest approach for the implementation.

Signalling

The attention of this optimization aspect have to be addressed to these topics:

- Identification of the standard procedures adopted for the selected architecture configuration;

- Optimization of channel assignment

- Particular procedures for the set-up of the communications, the channel assigment request, the establishment of the connection throught the optimal path and the hand-off procedures.

Each of this problem impact on the complexity of the overall system management and on the software required on-board. Indirectly also the hardware architecture is conditioned, then a best compromise shall be identified, case by case, to guarantee the system performance efficiency.

Antenna configurations

The antenna system performances are function of the orbital constellation, in fact the link geometry and the coverage requirements are the key parameters in the selection of the optimal configuration. Some typical items has to be considered in the system analysis have been outlined for three orbit configurations.
. GEO configuration: The antenna FOV from a geostationary satellite is equivalent to the geometrical coverge if the global coverage will be required and it is 17,4 deg, it is narrower in case of regional coverage. Moreover this is a narrow beam and the configuration providing the best performances in terms of peak gain, side lobe level, geographical isolation and minimum encumbrance is the aperture antenna system. The selected frequency band for the feeder and user links is the key-parameter in the definition of the aperture size and then in the definition of the optimum antenna design parameter.
. HEO configuration: the definition of some important aspects on antennas are considered, like:
- User antenna: the user antenna has to provide a narrow beam to reject the mutipath effect, but at the same time it is required to

provide a beamwidth large enough to have the satellite in visibility during its orbital path without any steering mechanism.
- On board antenna: the antenna coverage changes with the variation of the orbit altitude, this effect is called zooming and is more evident in orbit with high eccentricity. If the regional and continuos coverage is required a tracking mechanism to maintain a fixed pointing boresight direction shall need.
It means that the useful coverage is the envelope of multiple istantaneous coverages which are the intersection between the earth and the antenna field of view. Of course, from a fixed observer point of view, when the satellite is at the apogee, the boresight direction is the same of the subsatellite point and the istantaneous coverage is circular, otherwise it is deformed with a shape depending on the angular distance between the antenna boresight and the subsatellite point.
A coverage provided by a multispot antenna could be required in order to achieve an increase of the antenna gain and to permit frequency reuse among the spots. The steering and the adaptivity of the coverage are problems arising in this case.
The minimum elevation angle on the selected coverage area and the satellite number are key parameters strictly correlated and their requirements condition the constellation parameters.
. LEO configuration: the on board antenna has to fulfil the characteristics of link geometry deriving from the orbital constellation parameters. The path loss at the center of the coverage are lower than at the edge; to compensate this effect a shaped beam antenna can be used. If cellular service is one of the system objective, the multibeam antenna configuration is suitable and the footprint distorsion becomes one of the most critical aspect in the overall system management.
The table 5 summarizes a list of antenna configurations typical for satellite applications and their correspondent performances; on the basis of coverage and orbit characteristic requirements the most suitable configuration can be selected adopting the optimization criteria as shown in table 6.

7 - ECONOMIC VALIDATION

The definition of the economic convenience of a satellite system is based on the identification of the cash-flow items for the evaluation of the expected revenues derived from the proposal service.
The scheme to be used for the calculation depends on the alternative strategies selected for the sharing among the actors and the criteria adopted for the recovery of the investments.
The reduction of the complexity in the management, the minimization of the infrastructure costs increase the advantages of the small satellite systems.
A simple example of the organization scheme could be the following:
- a space system corporation, responsible of the overall space segment implementation (purchasing the space vehicle, the launch, the in-orbit control, the TT&C, the insurance, the maintenance, etc), getting the profit from the lease of the in orbit capacity, and refunding the share holders financing the mission, paying the profit on its earnings and the reimbursement of the capital borrowed from the banks;

Antenna Configuration	Bandwidth	Dual Polarization	Gain	Volume
Reflector	Wideband	Yes	High	Large
Array	Narrow	Difficult	High	Large
Horn	Narrow	Yes	High	Small
Helix	Narrow	One sense	Medium	Large
Crossed Yagis	10 %	Yes	Medium	Large
Turnstile	10 %	Yes	Low	Small

Table 5 - Antenna System Key Parameters

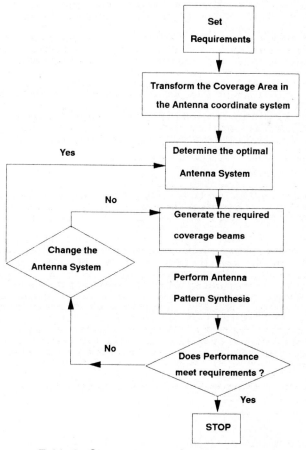

Table 6 - Optimal Antenna System

- a service provider corporation , responsible for the NCC, and for providing and commercialising the service. This corporation will have to provide the billing to the single user or to the CUGs (Closed User Group).

In the economic validation process, once the financing policy has been fixed, the first step is the identification of the major cost items for space and ground segments. The overall costs must be divided in: non recurring, recurring and operational costs.
In a small satellite constellation the major advantages can be derived: from the adoption of already proved technologies impacting on the non-recurring costs; from the reduction of the integration requirements for each units, from the possibility of batch production for space segment and of mass production for user segment, allowing low recurring costs. The simplicity of the network and the low requirements of satellite control can also maintain acceptable the operational costs.
The second step consists of the selection of the methodology to be applied for the verification of the profitability of the potential mission and of the preparation of the matematical model.In fact an instrument to compute the cash-flow, to derive the return of investment curve, and to localize the break-even point is developed identifying an economical index as objective function. For the final comparison the Minimum Annual Revenue (MAR)concept shall be adopted.
The key elements of the models are the various costs (space segment, ground segment, launch, insurance) distributed during the time implementation plan, the expected traffic demand derived from market assessment, the selection of the strategies of the different actors and the definition of the values of the major economic drivers (desirable profit, interest rate, discount rate and amortization plan).
On the basis of the values of the economic index obtained for different system design, it can be possible to insert significant information in the feedback process for the final optimization.

8 - CONCLUSION

The small-satellite system complexity requires an optimization process. This optimization can be obtained by adopting an analytical model, flexible enough to support the decision maker process and organized in hierarchical layers to allow the adaptability to different approaches.
On the basis of the objective functions identified as key parameters of the system and of the service requirements, the best compromise solution can be derived. The economic validation must confirm the system attractiveness.
The effective convenience of implementing a system shall be quantified on the basis of the interest of potential actors to join the project, in the perspective of promising revenues, achievable only throught an optimised architecture. An attractive business-plan will have to guarantee a quick service penetration, phasing optimally the available on board capacity and the service demand, with a ROI encuraging the investors to risk in a satellite business.

AMIGAU:

PROTOTYPE D'OUTIL D'ANALYSE DE MISSION POUR

SATELLITES ET CONSTELLATIONS DE SATELLITES

Jacques FOLIARD [1], Alain LAMY [1], Stéphane PASCAL [2]

Résumé

Les études menées actuellement en Mécanique Spatiale sur les mini-satellites à défilement, ou sur les constellations de mini-satellites, montrent que malgré leur diversité, les problèmes relevant de l'analyse de mission sont similaires (étude de phasage, héliosynchronisme, bilan d'ergol, stratégies de manœuvres, précision de localisation,...).

Il apparait donc nécessaire de disposer d'un produit unique (une boîte à outils de fonctionnement aisé et homogène) regroupant les différentes fonctionnalités indispensables à l'analyse de mission.

Pour cela, le CNES dispose d'un vaste patrimoine de modules de calcul de Mécanique Spatiale développés dans le cadre d'analyses de mission ou pour les opérations.

Un prototype d'outil d'analyse de mission (AMIGAU: Analyse de Mission par Graphiques Abaques et Utilitaires) est en cours de développement à la division MS.

Son objectif est de montrer la faisabilité d'un système général, devant être utilisable par des spécialistes ou non, selon différents niveaux de complexité, avec par exemple, la génération d'abaques, de calculs unitaires ou enchaînés de façon automatique ou non.

(1)   C.N.E.S   (Centre National d'Etudes Spatiales)
      18 Avenue Edouard Belin - 31055 TOULOUSE Cedex - Tél: 61.27.38.73

(2)   SEMA GROUP
      Innoparc voie 2 BP 46 - 31675 LABEGE Cedex - Tél: 61.39.93.89

Introduction

Malgré la diversité et les spécificités des missions, les études de mécanique spatiale qui interviennent pour chacune d'entre-elles révèlent souvent de grandes similitudes, que ce soit dans les analyses préliminaires, ou dans la mise au point de stratégies opérationnelles. Par exemple, des sujets tels que l'évaluation du coût de maintien à poste, l'étude de la précision de restitution d'une orbite et des moyens associés, la détermination de paramètres orbitaux optimisant certains critères connus (répétitivité, accessibilité, maillage au sol, élévation solaire,...) apparaissent pratiquement systématiquement dans les études de nouveaux projets. Il s'avérait donc judicieux de pouvoir disposer d'un environnement d'analyse de mission, regroupant les différents outils nécessaires en un système unique.

Une réflexion un peu plus poussée montre qu'un tel système pouvait avoir deux objectifs distincts:

- simplifier le travail du spécialiste qui répond habituellement aux demandes d'analyse de mission. Ceci suppose de disposer d'un environnement ouvert et évolutif, qui ne sera efficace que s'il permet de s'adapter de manière très simple à tout nouveau problème, en facilitant la réutilisation optimale de ce qui existe, et en favorisant l'introduction dans l'environnement de nouveaux outils (nouveau modèle d'extrapolation d'orbite, programme d'application de haut niveau,...).

- assister le non-spécialiste dans la phase de définition d'une nouvelle mission. Dans ce cas, une plus grande convivialité est nécessaire, et le besoin de flexibilité n'est pas aussi grand que dans le cas précédent.

AMIGAU (Analyse Mission par Graphiques, Abaques et Utilitaires) vise ces deux objectifs en tirant parti des puissants moyens qu'offrent aujourd'hui les stations de travail dont l'environnement est particulièrement adapté aux besoins de l'analyse de mission: interactivité très grande, outils graphiques, utilitaires performants de l'environnement UNIX.

Les parties I et II de ce papier, décrivent succinctement les différents domaines qui peuvent être abordés dans des études d'analyse mission de mécanique spatiale, puis brièvement le contexte dans lequel s'effectuent ces études. Ces deux parties expliquent comment l'idée d'AMIGAU, qui est décrite plus en détail dans la partie III, est apparue. Enfin la partie IV montre quelques exemples courants d'analyses de mission qui peuvent être traités sans difficultés dans le contexte AMIGAU.

I. Analyse de mission

L'analyse de mission, au sens "Mécanique spatiale" a principalement comme objectifs de:
- déterminer l'orbite et les moyens nécessaires qui sont compatibles avec la mission,
- déterminer les stratégies qui seront mises en oeuvre pendant les phases opérationnelles.

En fait, le cheminement qui conduit de l'idée initiale d'une mission jusqu'à sa définition finale n'est souvent pas direct:

Dans une phase d'analyse préliminaire, des résultats simples et généraux, pouvant être disponibles sous forme d'abaques, suffisent la plupart du temps à fixer rapidement certains ordres de grandeurs, ou à déterminer les domaines admissibles des principaux paramètres clés. A ce stade de l'étude, la mission n'est souvent définie que par de grandes lignes directrices, et le champ d'investigation est par conséquent très ouvert. L'analyse de mission doit donc permettre d'avoir une vision globale du problème afin d'aider à le préciser davantage en mettant en évidence des solutions réalisables.

Cette analyse préliminaire permet d'avoir une idée un peu plus précise du type d'orbite que l'on peut envisager, qui soit à la fois compatible avec l'objectif que l'on se fixe et avec les moyens que l'on peut espérer mettre en oeuvre. Le but de l'analyse de mission est alors de préciser les hypothèses et de vérifier complètement la faisabilité de la mission. Cette étude peut impliquer une modélisation plus fine des phénomènes en vue de la définition des stratégies opérationnelles.

Malgré la diversité des missions rencontrées, on peut rapidement constater que les problèmes soulevés lors d'analyses de mission de satellites à défilement, et parfois plus largement[1] sont souvent très similaires. On est ainsi amené à résoudre des problèmes-types, qui répondent à l'essentiel des questions soulevées, et dont on peut dresser un inventaire non exhaustif:

- Détermination d'orbites ayant des propriétés particulières
  . héliosynchronisme
  . minimisation des variations d'altitude (périgée "gelé")
  . phasage - répétitivité - accessibilité

- Résultats concernant
  . visibilités (avec des stations sol - inter-satellites)
  . couvertures

- Détermination de constellations optimisant certaines propriétés

- Maintien à poste
  . évaluation du coût en ergol
  . évolution naturelle des orbites
  . stratégie de correction d'orbite
  . maintiens à poste multiples

- Mise à poste
  . correction d'erreurs d'injection
  . mises à poste multiples

- Précision de restitution d'orbite
  . évaluation de la précision - moyens nécessaires

- Prévisions d'événements divers
  . visibilité de senseurs embarqués
- etc...

Ces problèmes-types définissent les bases de l'analyse de mission; leur résolution a priori permet de proposer des solutions connues, et d'accélerer les phases de définition.

II. Contexte d'analyse de mission

Au CNES, la division TE/IS/MS a pour rôle de servir de support dans la résolution de problèmes liés à l'orbitographie, et en particulier, de résoudre les problèmes d'analyse de mission que peuvent lui soumettre les groupes-projets.

La résolution d'un problème d'analyse de mission met donc en rapport le groupe projet qui donne le cadre général du projet et spécifie certaines hypothèses et contraintes, et le spécialiste de mécanique spatiale qui fournit les résultats souhaités, ces derniers permettant de confirmer et d'affiner

---

1. Les missions planétaires (notamment autour de Mars) peuvent rentrer dans ce cadre

les hypothèses, ou à l'inverse de les modifier, ou encore de relâcher certaines d'entre elles.

Afin de répondre aux problèmes posés, la division MS possède un vaste patrimoine d'outils réalisés à l'occasion d'analyses de missions précédentes et/ou d'opérations, de programmes de simulations élaborées, ou encore de programmes graphiques, qu'ils soient très généraux (tracé de courbes) ou plus spécifiques (visualisations de trajectoires 3D). Des études (R&D en particulier) peuvent également être menées pour résoudre des problèmes nouveaux; les sujets abordés concernent par exemple les théories analytiques d'extrapolation d'orbite à très long terme (études en collaboration avec le CERGA), ou le calcul de stratégies optimales de maintien à poste de constellations.

Du fait de leur développement dans des cadres parfois différents, ces outils manquent souvent d'homogénéité (chaque outil a ses spécificités, du fait de son développement dans un contexte particulier) et ne sont pas, en général, regroupés en un endroit unique; ceci tend à rendre plus difficile la résolution d'un problème d'analyse de mission.

D'autre part la tendance actuelle pour les missions spatiales est de rechercher des solutions légères à coûts réduits (micro-satellites, constellations,...). L'accumulation de tels projets sature rapidement le potentiel humain susceptible de répondre aux problèmes d'analyse de mission, que chaque projet espère voir résoudre en un temps le plus bref possible. Il devient ainsi difficile de répondre aux analyses de missions courantes, et en parallèle d'étudier des solutions à des problèmes nouveaux.

Il devenait donc impératif de rationnaliser l'analyse de mission, d'une part pour faciliter l'obtention de réponses à des questions standard, mais également afin de permettre aux demandeurs de répondre eux-mêmes à une bonne partie des questions qui se posent dans les phases d'études préliminaires; c'est l'objectif d'AMIGAU.

III. AMIGAU: environnement d'analyse de mission

L'objectif d'AMIGAU (Analyse de Mission par Graphiques, Abaques, et Utilitaires) peut être défini naturellement à partir de ce qui a été présenté précédemment: regrouper, harmoniser, standariser les outils d'analyse de mission.

Une constatation simple est à l'origine du projet AMIGAU: malgré la complexité de certains problèmes du fait du nombre parfois important de paramètres à déterminer, ou du grand nombre de contraintes qui interviennent, il est souvent possible d'obtenir les résultats souhaités grâce à des représentations pertinentes de certains paramètres du problème, et par des recoupements astucieux. Souvent, les différences entre deux demandes venant de projets distincts ne portent pas sur les outils qui interviennent dans la résolution des problèmes (extrapolation d'orbite, transformation de paramètres, calcul de certains paramètres en fonctions d'autres...), mais plutôt sur la façon de représenter le problème, de manière à mettre en évidence les contraintes de la mission, et d'en déterminer certains paramètres-clés.

Ainsi, un environnement efficace d'analyse de mission devra contenir un grand nombre d'outils, chacun ayant une fonction précise, avec la possibilité de les enchaîner, de tracer les paramètres désirés, de filtrer les résultats selon certains critères, plutôt que quelques logiciels "à-tout-faire", qui ne sont dans la pratique jamais assez souples, ni assez modulables pour pouvoir résoudre le problème particulier qui se pose.

Pour faire le lien entre tous les programmes d'applications, les utilitaires de filtrage et de tri de l'environnement UNIX peuvent être largement utilisés. Ils permettent le tri des données à tracer, ou celles en entrée d'autres programmes. Ils permettent également d'enchaîner des programmes simples existants pour en faire des programmes plus complexes ou ciblés pour une application particulière.

Les composants de AMIGAU sont:

- une bibliothèque de sous programmes fondamentaux sur lesquels reposent les applications. Celle-ci contient d'une part des définitions élémentaires, mais aussi des sous-programmes de plus haut niveau d'abstraction qui rendent aisé l'accès à des familles de fonctionnalités (modèles d'extrapolation, transformation de paramètres,...). Cette approche simplifie les programmes d'application et les rend plus puissants puisqu'ils peuvent bénéficier spontanément de toutes les fonctionnalités de haut niveau de la bibliothèque,

- des utilitaires de mécanique spatiale permettant à tout moment d'avoir des réponses immédiates à des questions courantes. Ces utilitaires peuvent être accessibles au moyen d'un système de saisie évolué, ou bien être utilisés dans l'écriture de procédures plus complexes d'enchaînement de différentes fonctionnalités,

- des outils de tracé généraux permettant une grande adaptabilité, si ils sont utilisés en conjonction avec d'autres utilitaires de sélection des données à tracer,

- des programmes spécifiques qui répondent aux questions les plus fréquentes. Ceux-ci sont figés et servent de "base de connaissance" pour l'analyse de mission. Si un développement est nécessaire pour résoudre un nouveau problème, il devra s'effectuer en utilisant au mieux ce qui existe, en généralisant si besoin la fonction remplie, de façon à créer un nouveau programme à but ciblé dans la base de programmes,

- des programmes divers de visualisations ou d'animations graphiques, qui permettent de résoudre certaines questions plus directement (visualisation de cercles de visibilités stations-satellites par exemple), ou qui permettent une meilleure compréhension d'un problème (par exemple: visualisation 3D des mouvements d'attitude d'un satellite),

En outre, une partie des utilitaires pourra disposer de moyens de saisie conviviaux; ceci afin de:
- permettre un accès centralisé à tous les utilitaires et avoir une vision globale de tous les problèmes que l'on sait résoudre,
- permettre à n'importe quel utilisateur (indépendamment du problème de l'interprétation des résultats) d'utiliser les outils d'analyse de mission.

Pour assurer cette convivialité, il est prévu d'utiliser le système GENESIS[1]. Il permet de définir des écrans de saisie ou d'affichage de données au moyen d'un langage de haut niveau. Parmi ses avantages, on peut remarquer que:
- l'utilisateur a à sa disposition des moyens de saisie et d'affichage évolués (menus déroulant, boutons...),
- le fait que GENESIS génère du code compilable permet d'inclure des contrôles et des actions arbitrairement complexes dans les fichiers de description des écrans de saisie,
- certains utilitaires pourront consister en un unique fichier descripteur incluant des appels à des fonction de haut niveau de la bibliothèque,
- l'utilisateur est déchargé de la mise au point laborieuse d'interfaces graphiques, de plus l'écriture d'écrans descripteurs est aisée et relativement naturelle.

Le dernier point important à mentionner concernant AMIGAU est sa nécessité de fonctionner

---

1. GENErateur de Systèmes d'Interfaces de Saisie - en cours de développement

dans un cadre multi-projets. En effet, il est souhaitable que des analyses de missions parallèles puissent être menées sans qu'il y ait d'interaction des unes sur les autres; chacune devant avoir son propre environnement d'exploitation.

IV. Exemples d'applications

Les deux exemples qui suivent exposent certains problèmes que l'on peut fréquemment rencontrer lors d'analyses de mission.

Le premier montre comment des recoupements entre quelques représentations de paramètres bien choisis (étude du phasage, de l'accessibilité, de l'heure locale) aboutissent à la définition de l'orbite, chacun des programmes utilisés correspondant à une application qu'il est immédiat de lancer dans l'environnement AMIGAU.

Le second, plus proche des programmes opérationnels, présente l'analyse du coût du maintien à poste d'un satellite à défilement.

Exemple 1: détermination de l'altitude et de l'heure locale de l'orbite héliosynchrone phasée d'un satellite d'observation.

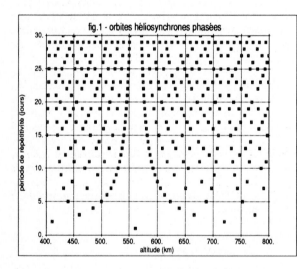

fig.1 - orbites héliosynchrones phasées

A partir de cinq paramètres principaux que sont:

- le phasage (période de répétitivité fixée),
- l'accessibilité (nombre de jours maximum séparant deux passages en visibilité d'un point de latitude donnée),
- l'angle de débattement maximum de l'équipement d'observation,
- le minimum d'éclairement requis pour l'instrument de prise de vue (i.e. la distance zénithale[1] maximum),
- le nombre minimum de jours dans l'année pendant lesquels l'éclairement sous satellite à une latitude donnée est suffisant,

il est possible en choisissant judicieusement certaines applications de l'environnement AMIGAU de déterminer l'altitude et l'heure locale de l'orbite.

En effet, l'altitude peut être simplement déterminée à partir des conditions de phasage (fig.1) et d'accessibilité (fig.2).

Par exemple, pour une période de répétitivité de 8 jours il ressort de la figure 1 que les altitudes admissibles sont: 450, 525, 600, 680 et 760 km; on déduit alors de la figure 2 que pour un angle de débattement maximum de 35 degrés et une accessibilité à l'équateur de 3 jours, l'altitude correcte serait 760 km.

---

1. distance zénithale: angle entre la direction du soleil et la verticale locale; cet angle est nul lorsque le soleil est au zénith

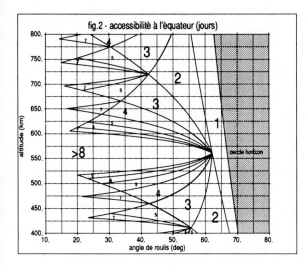

fig.2 - accessibilité à l'équateur (jours)

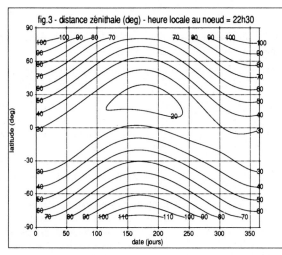

fig.3 - distance zénithale (deg) - heure locale au noeud = 22h30

De même, connaissant la limite d'éclairement minimum de l'équipement de prise de vue et la durée minimum dans l'année de visibilité à une latitude donnée, il est possible de sélectionner l'heure locale du noeud ascendant en retenant parmi plusieurs réseaux de courbes iso-distance zénithale (fig.3) - tracées pour différentes heures locales -, la plus adaptée aux spécifications.

Ainsi, pour une distance zénithale limite de 80 degrés et un minimum de 300 jours en éclairement suffisant à 60 degrés de latitude, on s'aperçoit (fig.3) qu'une heure locale au noeud ascendant de 22^h30 (valeur retenue pour le réseau représenté) est admissible car l'éclairement est correct du 25ème au 325ème jour de l'année.

N.B: Les courbes de la figure 3 tiennent compte du mouvement réel du soleil (l'équation du temps et la déclinaison sont modélisées) et de la position du satellite sur l'orbite (à une latitude donnée correspond une heure locale du satellite).

Exemple 2: étude du maintien à poste d'un satellite à défilement sur une orbite héliosynchrone phasée.

Pour un satellite à défilement, l'altitude nominale est calculée à partir d'un modèle du potentiel terrestre limité aux termes en J_2 et J_3 de façon à définir un maillage régulier de l'équateur (réseaux de traces phasées). Or dans la réalité, les perturbations affectant le satellite sont responsables d'un décalage du réseau de traces réelles par rapport au réseau de traces nominales; le contrôle de cet écart est l'objectif principal du maintien à poste des satellites à défilement.

L'exemple choisi présente l'étude de ce contrôle, qui comprend deux étapes.

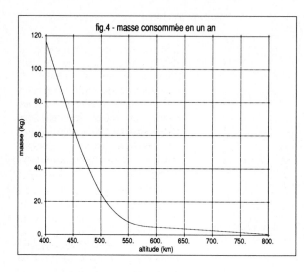

fig.4 - masse consommée en un an

La première consiste à obtenir une évaluation simple du coût en fonction de l'altitude.

Après avoir estimé l'effet du frottement sur le demi-grand axe de l'orbite pour différentes altitudes, il est possible d'évaluer la masse d'ergols nécessaire pour maintenir les traces phasées au passage à l'équateur.

La figure 4 donne les résultats obtenus sur une période d'un an. Cette évaluation de la consommation servira de base pour le dimensionnement des réservoirs. En outre, il apparait que pour des altitudes inférieures à 450 km, le coût en ergols est prohibitif.

La seconde étape consiste à simuler le maintien à poste de façon plus réaliste pour tester les stratégies de maintien et obtenir des fourchettes de consommation plus fines.

Les figures 5 et 6 présentent les résultats d'une simulation sur le satellite SPOT1 entre 1986 et 1991 pour laquelle il a été tenu compte du flux solaire réel (flux instantané, flux moyen et indice géomagnétique) et de la stratégie retenue.

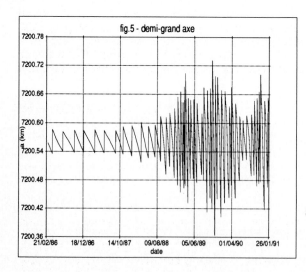

fig.5 - demi-grand axe

On dispose ainsi de l'évolution du demi-grand axe (fig.5) et de l'écart à la trace nominale au passage à l'équateur (fig.6) sur la période considérée. Ces courbes mettent en évidence les problèmes rencontrés dans les périodes de forte activité solaire (1989-1990) avec la stratégie retenue, puisque la spécification pour l'écart à la trace (3 km) n'est pas toujours tenue. La stratégie choisie pour cette simulation n'est donc pas parfaite; il s'agira de l'affiner en vue d'une application opérationnelle.

Dans le cadre de l'analyse de mission, une telle simulation est intéressante à double titre:

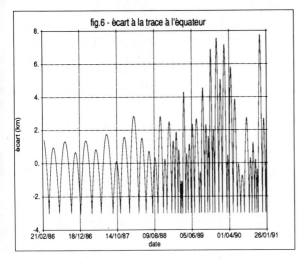

fig.6 - écart à la trace à l'équateur

- d'une part, les fourchettes de consommation, calculées en tenant compte des incertitudes sur les manœuvres (efficacité des tuyères), sur l'activité solaire estimée et sur les modèles d'atmosphère utilisés, sont réduites par rapport aux estimations classiques mais restent tout aussi fiables,

- d'autre part, la préparation des opérations de maintien à poste est facilitée par une meilleure connaissance des performances de la stratégie (fiabilité, fréquence des manœuvres, précision de l'évaluation des effets du frottement, etc...).

Ces deux exemples illustrent l'efficacité d'AMIGAU qui permet de répondre rapidement aux questions des projets.

Conclusion

L'intérêt de disposer d'un système centralisé pour résoudre les problèmes d'analyse de mission de mécanique spatiale est indéniable; le regroupement des outils donne une vision globale des produits existants et augmente la simplicité d'utilisation et de développement. L'utilisation systématique d'AMIGAU permettra d'assurer la cohérence entre tous les programmes d'analyse mission qu'il regroupe et ainsi de définir un standard servant de base à l'approche de tout nouveau problème.

Ainsi, les fonctionnalités d'AMIGAU amènent une simplification des tâches d'analyse de mission. Il devient plus facile de traiter en détails les points délicats en éliminant rapidement les faux problèmes. La collaboration entre les équipes projets et les équipes chargées de l'analyse mission est plus efficace du fait de la mise en commun des moyens disponibles. Les groupes projets pourront par exemple s'impliquer dans la phase préliminaire de définition de l'orbite en limitant les interventions des experts en analyse mission.

Le système AMIGAU est donc très bien adapté aux orientations actuelles dans le domaine spatial, les nombreux projets de mini-satellites et de constellations de satellites étant les exemples typiques de projets nécessitant des outils simples et conviviaux.

De plus, son champ d'activité ne se limite pas aux seuls satellites terrestres puisque les problèmes rencontrés pour les missions interplanétaires (MARS 94, V.A.P.,...) sont souvent identiques.

LOW EARTH ORBIT CONSTELLATIONS: ORBIT CONTROL OR NOT

José RADZIK
Dassault Aviation
Centre Spacial Dassault, Immeuble Pythagore
17, Avenue Didier Daurat - BP 23
31701 Blagnac, Cedex

Gérard MARAL
TELECOM Paris, Site de Toulouse
10, avenue Edouard Belin
BP 4004, 31028 Toulouse

ABSTRACT

When defining a communication network using low earth orbit satellites (altitudes below 2000 km), one of the main concern is the adoption of orbit control or not. The aim of this study is to list the arguments which will allow a final choice. The first two sections discuss the number of uncontrolled satellites necessary to reach a given probability of visibility. The third gives a comparison between non-controlled satellite constellations and controlled satellite ones defined thanks to the Walker format, in the case of very low altitudes (below 800 kilometers).

The first section gives a semi-analytical calculation of the probability of visibility with minimum elevation angle of a single satellite (end-of-life performance), which can be used for altitudes below 2000 kilometers. In section 2, thanks to a simple but realistic hypothesis about the repartition of satellites in space, it is possible to evaluate the number of non-controlled satellites in order to guaranty a given probability of visibility for the whole constellation.

In section 3, a comparison is given between non-controlled and controlled constellations in the case of very low altitudes (below 800 kilometers). When looking for the probability of communication of one or more non-controlled satellites, the main problem raised by such altitudes is the effect of atmospheric drag, since it can reduce significantly the coverage performances of each satellite at its end of life. The first step of this section consists in evaluating the semi-major-axis contraction and excentricity evolution with time. Then, non-controlled satellite constellations can be defined. As a reference basis, controlled Walker-type constellations are chosen so that they offer the same overall probability of visibility as the non-controlled constellations. Eventually, a study of long-term behavior of the satellites is conducted in order to give an objective comparison between the two options.

INTRODUCTION

The growing difficulties induced by the use of geostationnary satellites (growing cost, long development cycles,...) lead to a recent renewed interest in low earth satellites constellations, especially for cellular telephony (IRIDIUM, GLOBALSTAR, ...). This type of service implies the definition of whole coverage constellations, where the probability of visibility (probability for any point of the service zone to be able to establish a communication with a satellite) is equal to 100%. In this context, only a few types of constellations can maintain such a performance, and a control of satellites is an absolute necessity.

Nevertheless, low earth satellites can also be well suited to other services, e.g. delayed paging or local communications. Most often, only a niche market is reachable, so that the reduction of the system cost must be extreme. For this reason, small satellites launched in low altitude circular orbits is most often the best solution (small cost of satellites and low capacity launchers, direct injection into orbit). In this case, it is of no use to offer a very high probability of visibility, 50 to 80% could be enough. This special aspect of such services raises the problem of adopting orbit control or not. Two criterions of performance are used: the overall visibility probability, and the maximum waiting time exceeded for more than 1% of the time. Thanks to the analysis of these two parameters, it is possible to obtain an objective comparison of controlled and non-controlled constellations.

The content of this paper is as follows:
- Section 1 gives a convenient way of estimating the probability of visibility with minimum elevation angle of a single satellite.
- Section 2 discusses the number of satellites which will be needed in a global constellation in order to reach a given probability of visibility.
- Section 3 gives a comparison of controlled and non-controlled constellations in the case of very low altitudes (less than 800 kilometers): estimation of the atmospheric drag influence, number of satellites, average performance, maximum waiting time, main constraints.

1 - PROBABILITY OF VISIBILITY WITH MINIMUM ELEVATION ANGLE

In order to estimate the coverage performance of a non-controlled satellite constellation, it is necessary to calculate the probability of visibility of a non-controlled satellite by an earth station over a large observation time. As the trajectory of the satellite is observed for a long time (typically several days), the successive ascending nodes (intersection of the satellite trajectory when moving south to north and the equator) can be assumed to be uniformely distributed over the terrestrial equator. This uniform law for ascending nodes is the fundamental hypothesis of the calculation.

Nevertheless, a complete simulation of the satellite movement will lead to large computer time, since many configurations must be analysed in order to reach an uniform distribution of ascending nodes, or long time behavior must be simulated (simulation of several days flight). On the contrary, an analytical method [ROT76] leads to a far reduced computer time and offers a sufficient accuracy for this study. The calculation described below enables the determination of visibility times (rise and set times) of one satellite by an earth station for a given ascending node.

1.1 - Definition of the needed parameters

The first step is the determination of the satellite position in a station-linked coordinates system. Three coordinates systems will be used:
- inertial equatorial (O,x,y,z), with Ox in direction of vernal point γ
- geocentric (O,x',y',z')
- station-linked (O,x",y",z"), with Oz" giving the local vertical direction.

The position of the earth station is given by the following parameters: sideral time θ (angle between the axes (Ox) and (Ox')), latitude λ (angle between (Ox') and (Oz")). The position of a satellite is given by:
- Ω ascending node angle
- ω perigee argument
- i inclination
- v true anomaly
- a semi-major-axis
- e eccentricity

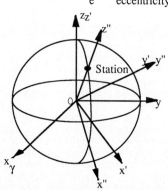

Station coordinates
Figure 1

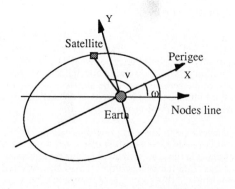

On orbit satellite coordinates
Figure 2

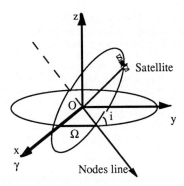

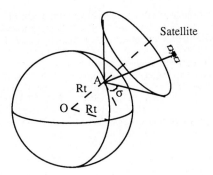

Orbital plane coordinates	Satellite minimum view angle
Figure 3	Figure 4

The on-orbit coordinates (figure 2) are defined by:

$$X = a.(\cos E - e)$$

$$Y = a.\sqrt{1 - e^2}.\sin E$$

where E is the excentric anomaly. It can be expressed as a fonction of v (true anomaly):

$$E = \cos^{-1}\left(\frac{e + \cos v}{e.\cos v - 1}\right)$$

1.2 - Visibility equation

A satellite is considered as "visible" by an earth station if the local elevation angle (view angle) becomes greater than a minimum value generally imposed by electro-magnetic wave propagation conditions and corelated antenna design (figure 4). This constraint leads to a visibility equation thanks to the following calculation:

The satellite coordinates are expressed in the station-linked coordinates system.

$$\begin{vmatrix} X_{sat} \\ Y_{sat} \\ Z_{sat} \end{vmatrix} = M . \begin{vmatrix} a.(\cos E - e) \\ a.\sqrt{1 - e^2}.\sin E \\ 0 \end{vmatrix}$$

where

$$M = R\left(\phi - \frac{\pi}{2}, Oy\right) . R(\theta, Oz) . R(-\Omega, Oz) . R(-i, Ox) . R(-\omega, Oz)$$

and $R(\theta, Oz)$ is a rotation matrix with rotation angle θ about the Oz axis.

The matrix M is described with the coefficients (a_{ij}), $i \in [1,3], j \in [1,3]$.

The visibility equation can then be written as:

$$\frac{Z_{sat} - D}{(X_{sat}^2 + Y_{sat}^2)^{1/2}} = tg\ \sigma .$$

with D = Earth radius + Earth station altitude, and σ = minimum view angle (figure 4).

The development of this equation as a fonction of E eventually gives a quadratic expression:

$$\mathcal{A}.\cos^4 E + \mathcal{B}.\cos^3 E + \mathcal{C}.\cos^2 E + \mathcal{D}.\cos E + \mathcal{E} = 0$$

A numerical resolution leads to 4 real solutions in the case of an actual trajectory. The condition $Z_{sat} \geq D$ suppresses the extra solutions. A dedicated software has been developed which rapidly provides the rise and set times versus two parameters: the station position, and the value of the ascending node angle Ω. However, it must be noted that the calculation is made with a non-rotating earth. Hence, an iteration is also necessary to take into account the evolution of the θ parameter as the satellite flies over the arc E. A precision of 10 seconds imposes two iterations.

The software delivers visibility diagrams (see [HAN90] for other applications of such diagrams). In the following example (figure 5), rise and set times have been computed as fonctions of the ascending node. The earth station is located at 0° longitude and 20° latitude, its minimum elevation angle is 10°. The satellite altitude is 1250 kilometers, the inclination is 45°. Negative rise time values indicate that the satellite becomes visible before it crosses the equatorial plane. The visibility probability of one satellite from the considered earth station is then simply the surface ratio between in visibility surfaces and the observation surface (figure 6). In this example, this probability Pc[1] is 5%.

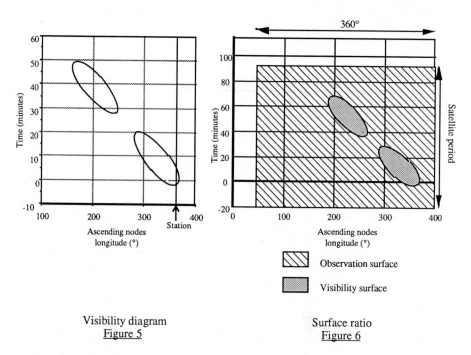

Visibility diagram	Surface ratio
Figure 5	Figure 6

2 - NUMBER OF SATELLITES REQUIRED IN A NON-CONTROLED CONSTELLATION

At this point, it is possible to calculate the number of satellites N needed in a constellation to reach an overall probability of visibility Pc[N]. In order to take into account the instants of time where many satellites are visible simultaneously by a given earth station, it is necessary to lead the calculation with the probability of non-visibility Pnc[N]. Then the following equations are straightforward:

$$Pnc[N] = \prod_{i=1}^{N} Pnc[1] = \prod_{i=1}^{N} (1 - Pc[1])$$

so that

$$Pc[N] = 1 - Pnc[N] = 1 - \prod_{i=1}^{N} (1 - Pc[1]) = 1 - [\,1 - Pc[1]\,]^N$$

The number N of satellites needed in the constellation in order to reach an overall probability of visibility Pc[N] is:

$$N = \frac{\ln(1 - Pc[N])}{\ln(1 - Pc[1])}$$

This set of equations allows an analysis of the number of satellites in various situations. For example, figure 7 gives the required number of satellites for altitudes between 400 and 1000 kilometers and inclination between 40° and 90°. The probability of visibility is set equal to 40%. The orbits are considered to be circular and the constellation is observed by a station based on the equator with a 10° minimum elevation angle. It can then be inferred that a wide service zone leads to a great number of satellites (about 30 at an altitude of 700 km). It is also of great interest to observe the evolution of the number of satellites with the required probability of visibility. In figure 8, the altitude is set to 700 kilometers and the inclination to 60°.

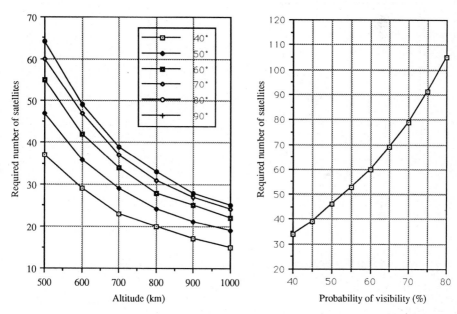

Required number of satellites versus altitude	Number of satellites versus probability
Figure 7	Figure 8

It seems quite clear that the non-linear increase of the required number of satellites with the visibility probability makes it quite indesirable to over-evaluate the quality of service asked for.

3 - COMPARISON BETWEEN CONTROLED AND NON-CONTROLED CONSTELLATIONS IN THE CASE OF LOW ALTITUDES

A comparison between non-controlled and controlled satellite constellations allows the determination of the conditions where the lack of orbit control can be acceptable or not. he first step is to determine the "worst case" for non-controlled satellites. In this example, where only low altitudes are considered (altitudes below 800 kilometers), the long-term evolution of the semi-major-axis is not influenced by relatively high level pertubating effects (J2,J3 and J4 terms of the earth gravity development)[KOZ74]. On the contrary, the atmospheric drag yields weak , but cumulative forces, which effect is a significant semi-major-axis contraction with time. It must be mentionned that the fundamental hypothesis presented in section 1 (uniform distribution of satellite positions in space) is also valid for higher altitude satellite orbits, as shown in a companion paper, where the incertainty of orbit injection induces the randomness [DER92].

3.1 - End-of-life coverage performance of non-controlled satellites

An analytic theory of atmospheric drag is given by Vinh and al. in [VIN79]. Applied to a 70 kg and $1m^2$ drag surface satellite launched on a 550 km altitude orbit (inclination 60°), it gives the following evolution of orbit parameters with time (figure 9):

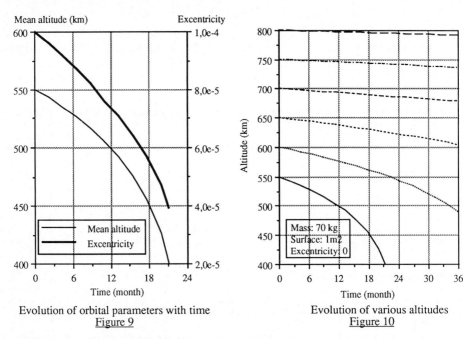

Evolution of orbital parameters with time
Figure 9

Evolution of various altitudes
Figure 10

The evolution of various circular orbits is given by figure 10 (inclination 60°). It shows the importance of the atmospheric drag in the case of very low altitudes. Satellites launched below 600 kilometers cannot even provide the expected 3 years life-time. For satellites above 800 kilometers, atmospheric drag is no longer the most critical pertubating force. For such satellites, more detailed movement model is needed to evaluate the minimum value of semi-major-axis reached during the satellite life-time.

3.2 - Performance comparison

In this study, the controlled satellite constellations will be "Walker compliant", that is they will be described thanks to the classical T/P/F scheme (T: total number of satellites, P: number of orbital planes, F: index of phasing for satellites in adjacent planes)[WAL70]. In the following sections, the initial altitude of the satellites will be 700 kilometers and the inclination 60°.

3.2.1 - Probability of visibility

For each given visibility probability, Table 1 gives the required number of non-controlled satellites at end of life, and the parameters of an "equivalent" phased constellation. What is meant by "equivalent" is that this constellation ensures an overall probability of visibility at least equal to the desired performance. The constellation is also designed in order to minimize the number of planes. The effective behavior of such a constellation will be discussed in the next section.

Visibility probability	40%	45%	50%	55%	60%	65%	70%	75%	80%
Required number of non-controlled satellites	32	38	44	50	58	66	76	87	101
Definition of a Walker-type constellation (T/P/F)	27/3/0	30/3/0	30/3/0	36/3/0	42/7/0	42/7/0	49/7/1	49/7/1	56/7/2

Table 1

It can seen from Table 1 that the parameter F remains null for constellations with low performance (up to 65% visibility probability). In fact, the Walker-type constellations are so designed that satellites on one orbital plane offer a dense coverage. Then the orbital planes are placed in order to reach the wanted performance. Optimal phasing for satellites in adjacent planes is then only needed if the planes are close enough and the number of satellites per plane is high. These two conditions become true in the case of constellations with overall visibility probability over 70% (see discussion in the next section). In any cases, the non-controlled satellite constellation entails more satellites. Nevertheless, the difference is small enough for a low visibility probability to make non-control an interesting alternative.

3.2.2 - Maximum waiting time

As underlined in the introduction, the visibility probability is not the only important parameter. In designing a telecommunication service, the maximum waiting time (time when no satellites are visible) is also to be considered. This parameter cannot be defined in the same way for controlled and non-controlled satellite constellations. In the case of non-controlled satellite constellations, a probabilistic approach is necessary. The results obtained here are computed using the analytical calculation of section 1, the ascending node of each satellite being chosen thanks to a pseudo-random generator (48 bit-sequences). The performance of each constellation is estimated in 1000 different configurations. It is then possible to obtain the cumulative probability to observe a maximum waiting time (figure 11). In the case of a 32 satellite constellation, the maximum waiting time exceeded for 1% of time is 190 minutes (more than 3 hours).

On the contrary, for controlled satellite constellations, the maximum waiting time is defined in an absolute way, since the positions of satellites follow a deterministic scheme. In fact, this time is mainly determined by the disposition of the orbital planes for the low performance constellations given in table 1. For example, in the case of the 27/3/0 Walker constellation, the gap of visibility between satellites on a given plane does not exceed 10 minutes, since such satellites are separated by only 40° (the course of this arc is 11 minutes). Now the time for an earth station to see the satellites of one plane, then the satellites of the next plane as the Earth rotates below the constellation is much larger than the previous one (166 minutes). However, it is possible to reduce this time with the same number of satellites by increasing the number of orbital planes. For example, a 28/14/3 constellation provides a maximum waiting time of 29 minutes only. In fact, the main advantage to reduced number of planes is the multi-launch opportunity. The trade-off between launch options and quality of service should then be explored.

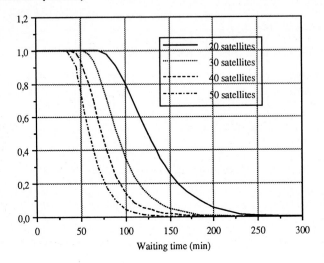

Cumulative probability to reach a given waiting time
Figure 11

3.3 - Constraints comparison

In any case, a non-controlled satellite constellation displays poorer performances than a controlled satellite one. However, when only low coverage performance is asked for, this can be an interesting alternative. In fact, the constraints induced by each option are quite different.

For non-controlled constellations, two main constraints can be encoutered:
- interference problems can arise, since more than one satellite may be visible at one time. This constraint is dramatically reduced for controlled satellite constellations, since they can be designed so that only one (two in the case of high performance constellations) satellite will be visible at one time by an earth station.
- the probability of a very degraded coverage performances is very low, but cannot be excluded.

Controlled constellations face quite different constraints, mainly due to the presence of an orbit control system.
First of all, the occurence of orbit control in the case of low altitude satellites can be very frequent. In order to maintain a proper phasing, the satellite position must be kept within a narrow window. In the case of the 27/3/0 constellation described above, a correction occurs every 15 days and follows the scenario shown on figure 12. It is then possible to estimate the needed ergol mass.

The total mass requested for orbit control is as follows:

$$Mp = (1+k).Me + Ms + M(L,F,n)$$

where:
Me is the mass of propergol
Ms is the dry mass associated with the existence of attitude and orbit control
M is a function of the size of the spacecraft L, the thrust level F, the number of thrusters n
k is a ratio between tank mass and propergol mass.

The propergol mass for a single manoeuver is given by:

$$Me = Mf - Mi = Mi.(1 - e^{-\frac{\Delta V}{g_0 Isp}})$$

where Mf is the satellite mass after manoeuver, Mi the initial mass, g_0 the gravity constant and Isp the specific impulse of the selected propellant.

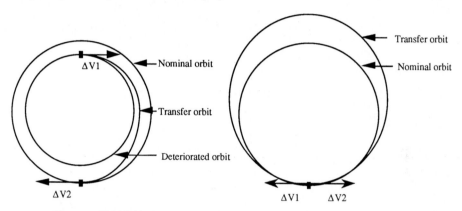

Recapture of initial altitude   Re-phasing

Figure 12

Let us consider an altitude of 700 kilometers and the following set of parameters:

        life-time: 3 years
        thruster: catalytic hydrazine thrusters, F=0.5 N
        initial mass: Mi = 70 kg
        surface: S = 0.35 m2

The following results can be obtained for the total ΔV in the case of one orbit correction considering that the tranfer orbit for re-phasing is travelled over 5 times: ΔV = 2,5 m/s. The propergol mass needed for the whole life-time is Me = 5.5 kg. The overall mass of the control system will then be about 9 kg (k = 0.15, Ms+M(L,F,n) = 3kg). This means that out of a global mass of 70 kg, about one seventh are needed for orbit control. What is more, such frequent control operations lead to an important work load for the control station staff.

Others contraints should also be taken into account:
- phasing infers launch constraints. This may lead to a reduction of the number of orbital planes, with the consequences on performance as mentionned in section 3.1.2.
- the launching incertainty requires orbit correction with increased propellant consumption
- a study of sensitivity of performance to a shortfall of one satellite in the constellation must be conducted, since controlled satellite constellations can be thought to present a greater sensitivity to such shortfalls than non-controlled ones.

4 - CONCLUSION

This study has presented the main arguments for the choice between controlled or non-controlled satellite constellations. In spite of lower performances, non-controlled satellite constellations can be an interesting alternative, since only quite simple satellites and ground segment can provide a satisfying service for worldwide messaging for example. Orbit control becomes a necessity when high performance is asked for: overall visibility probability over 60% or fixed maximum revisit times.

BIBLIOGRAPHY

[BEN61] DETERMINATION OF THE REQUIRED NUMBER OF RANDOMLY SPACED COMMUNICATION SATELLITES
Floyd V. Bennett, Thomas L. Coleman, John C. Houbolt
Langley Research Center
NASA technical note D-619, January 1961

[DER92] IMPACT DES INCERTITUDES DE LANCEMENT SUR LES PERFORMANCES DE VISIBILITE DE CONSTELLATIONS DE SATELLITES DE TELECOMMUNICATIONS SANS CONTROLE D'ORBITE
J.J. De Ridder, G. Maral, C. Tamisé
Small Satellite Systems and Services International Symposium (ESA/CNES)
June 29th, July 3th 1992, Arcachon, France

[HAN90] DESIGNING GOOD PARTIAL COVERAGE SATELLITE CONSTELLATIONS
John M. Hanson, Maria J. Evans, Ronald E. Turner
4th Annual AIAA/USU Conference on Small Satellites, Logan (UTAH, USA)
August 27-30, 1990

[KAU80] FIRST ORDER SEMIANALYTIC SATELLITE THEORY WITH RECOVERY OF THE SHORT PERIOD TERMS DUE TO THE THIRD BODY AND ZONAL PERTIRBATIONS
B. Kaufman
International Astronautical Federation, International Astronautical Congress, 1980
Vol. 31, n°80-E-204

[KOZ74] ANALYTICAL THEORIES OF THE MOTION OF ARTIFICIAL SATELLITES
G.I. Hori, Y. Kozai, G.E.O. Giacaglia
Satellite Dynamics, 19-21 June 1974, pp.1-15

[ROT76] RISE AND SET-TIME AND MAXIMUM ELEVATION OF A SATELLITE
E.A. Roth
ESA Scientific and Technical Review 1976, n° 2, pp 11-24

[VIN79] ANALYTIC THEORY OF ORBIT CONTRACTION DUE TO ATMOSPHERIC DRAG
N.X. Vinh, J.M. Longuski, A. Busemann, R.D. Culp
Acta Astronautica, 1979
Vol. N°6, pp. 697-723

[WAL70] CIRCULAR ORBIT PATTERNS PROVIDING CONTINUOUS WHOLE EARTH COVERAGE
J.G. Walker
Royal Aircraft Establishment Technical Report 70211
Novembre 1970

IMPACT DES INCERTITUDES DE LANCEMENT SUR LES PERFORMANCES DE VISIBILITE DE CONSTELLATIONS DE SATELLITES DE TELECOMMUNICATIONS SANS CONTROLE D'ORBITE

Jean Jacques DE RIDDER et Gérard MARAL
Ecole Nationale Supérieure des Télécommunications (TELECOM Paris),
BP4004, 31028 Toulouse Cedex, France

Chantal TAMISE
Université Paul Sabatier
Toulouse, France

RESUME

L'utilisation de constellations de satellites en orbite basse pour des missions de télécommunications civiles et militaires apparait aujourd'hui comme une possibilité technologique et une alternative économique intéressante face aux satellites géostationnaires.

Durant les vingt dernières années, de nombreuses études ont été menées pour déterminer des types de constellations optimales en terme de nombre de satellites pour assurer une couverture donnée. Cependant, la plupart des auteurs ont proposé des solutions basées sur des constellations de satellites phasés, ce qui signifie que la position relative des satellites est invariante au cours du temps, et implique donc l'utilisation de systèmes de contrôle d'orbite à bord de chaque satellite.

En l'absence d'un tel système, du fait des imprécisions d'injection sur orbite des satellites d'une constellation, ceux-ci vont subir des dérives orbitales différentes et leurs positions relatives sont amenées à varier au cours du temps. Il en résulte nécessairement des dégradations quant aux performances de visibilité des satellites par un observateur terrestre.

Cet article propose une analyse et une modélisation statistique des constellations de satellites sans contrôle d'orbite, ainsi que des résultats de simulations numériques des performances de visibilité sur quelques cas de constellations en orbite basse.

Les résultats présentés permettront au concepteur d'un système de se prononcer quant à la nécessité d'un contrôle d'orbite en fonction des contraintes de service et économiques de la mission.

ABSTRACT

The use of low earth orbiting satellite constellations for commercial and military communication applications seems to be an interesting technological and economical alternative to the geostationnary satellites systems.

During the past twenty years, many studies have been made to find optimal coverage constellations in terms of number of satellites. However, most authors proposed solutions based on phased satellite constellations, which means that the relative position of satellites is not time depedent, and implies orbit control of each satellite.

Without orbit control, and because of the inaccuracy of orbit injection of each satellite of a constellation, the spacecrafts are submitted to different orbital drifts and this results in a variation of their relative position in time. Necessarily, visibility performance degradations are to be expected.

In this paper, a statistical analysis and modeling of satellite constellations without orbit control is proposed, and is illustrated by numerical simulation results of visibility performance for a few cases of low earth orbit constellations.

The exposed results will enable the system designer to make up his mind about the necessity of orbit control, according to the service and economical constraints of the mission.

INTRODUCTION

L'utilisation de constellations de satellites en orbite basse circulaire pour des missions de télécommunications civiles et militaires apparait aujourd'hui comme une possibilité technologique et une alternative économique intéressante face aux satellites géostationnaires. Durant les vingt dernières années, de nombreuses études ont été menées pour déterminer des types de constellations optimales en terme de nombre de satellites pour assurer une couverture donnée. Cependant, la plupart des auteurs ont proposé des solutions basées sur des constellations de satellites phasées, ce qui signifie que la position relative des satellites est invariante au cours du temps.[WALK-70] [WALK-77][BES-78][RID-85][RID-86].

Le phasage d'une constellation est assuré grâce à un contrôle d'orbite qui permet d'une part de compenser les imprécisions d'injection sur orbite liées au lanceur, et d'autre part les dérives orbitales séculaires durant la mission.

En l'absence de contrôle d'orbite, les paramètres orbitaux de chaque satellite vont dépendre de la précision d'injection, et être soumis à des forces perturbatrices qui induisent des variations temporelles des paramètres orbitaux. Ces forces sont par ordre d'importance :
- irrégularités du potentiel terrestre (harmoniques d'ordre 2)
- irrégularités du potentiel terrestre (harmoniques supérieurs à 2)
- les attractions luni-solaires
- la pression de radiation solaire.

Il faudrait également mentionner les forces de frottement atmosphérique. Celles-ci dépendent de l'altitude des satellites. On considérera dans cette étude que l'altitude est suffisamment élevée (supérieure à 1000 km) pour les négliger. Le cas des satellites soumis à ces forces de frottement est discuté dans un autre article de cette conférence [RAD-92].

On considérera ici que le mouvement du satellite sur son orbite résulte de la force d'attraction centrale et des forces dues aux irrégularités du potentiel terrestre (harmonique d'ordre 2), qui sont largement prépondérantes par rapport aux autres forces perturbatrices.

Les imprécisions d'injection sur orbite affectent principalement l'altitude et l'inclinaison des plans orbitaux de chaque satellite. Or, ces deux paramètres interviennent dans les variations temporelles des paramètres orbitaux et de ce fait les dérives orbitales de chaque satellite seront différentes et la constellation sera rapidement déformée au cours du temps. Il en résulte que les performances de visibilité des satellites de la constellation, en un lieu géographique donné, seront modifiées dans le temps.

L'objectif de cet article est donc d'évaluer l'impact des incertitudes de lancement sur les performances de visibilité en analysant l'évolution temporelle des paramètres orbitaux des satellites de la constellation, en l'absence de contrôle d'orbite.

Une analyse et une modélisation statistique du problème sont proposées, ainsi que des résultats de simulation numérique des performances de visibilité sur quelques cas de constellations en orbite basse. Les résultats présentés permettront au concepteur d'un système de se prononcer quant à la nécessité d'un contrôle d'orbite en fonction de l'appréciation qu'il aura de la perte de performances de couverture, comparativement à une constellation phasée ayant le même nombre de satellites. Le compromis est ici, à couverture donnée, entre un nombre plus grand de satellites sans contrôle d'orbite, et un nombre plus faible de satellites à orbite controlée.

Le paragraphe 1 permet de définir la visibilité d'un satellite par une station terrienne ayant un angle d'élévation minimum donné. Puis, le paragraphe 2 présente le modèle de Lagrange du mouvement orbital d'un satellite. Le paragraphe 3 présente une modélisation des incertitudes sur l'altitude des satellites dues aux imprécisions d'injection sur orbite. Le paragraphe 4 présente ensuite les résultats des calculs statistiques des critères de performance de visibilité ainsi que la méthode numérique retenue pour l'évaluation de ces critères . Enfin, le paragraphe 5 illustre la mise en oeuvre de la méthode en exposant les résultats de simulations numériques effectuées pour une constellation.

1 - VISIBILITE D'UN SATELLITE : DEFINITION ET CALCUL

Un point géographique sera dit en visibilité d'un satellite de la constellation, si à un instant t, le satellite se trouve dans le cône d'angle solide $(2\pi-2\alpha)$ où α est l'angle de site minimum requis pour établir une liaison radioélectrique (Cf. Figure 1).

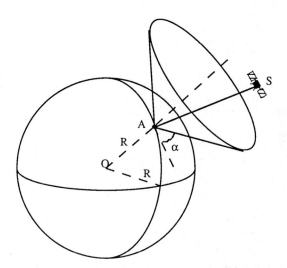

Figure 1 - Visibilité d'un satellite de la constellation.

L'expression mathématique du critère de visibilité du satellite de coordonnées (X_t, Y_t, Z_t) à l'instant t par la station A est la suivante :

$$f(Xt, Yt, Zt) \geq 0 \qquad (1)$$

avec :

$$A \begin{bmatrix} X_A \\ Y_A \\ Z_A \end{bmatrix} \begin{array}{c} \text{Coordonnées de la station A} \\ \text{dans un repère galliléen} \\ \text{à l'instant t} \end{array} \qquad S \begin{bmatrix} X_t \\ Y_t \\ Z_t \end{bmatrix} \begin{array}{c} \text{Coordonnées du satellite S} \\ \text{dans un repère galliléen} \\ \text{à l'instant t} \end{array}$$

et :

$$f(X_t, Y_t, Z_t) = X_A X_t + Y_A Y_t + Z_A Z_t - R^2 - R \cos(\frac{\pi}{2} - \alpha) \sqrt{(X_t - X_A)^2 + (Y_t - Y_A)^2 + (Z_t - Z_A)^2}$$

Où R est le rayon terrestre moyen.

2 - MODELISATION DU MOUVEMENT DU SATELLITE

Le mouvement du satellite résulte du mouvement képlerien correspondant à la force d'attraction centrale et des perturbations produites par les forces énoncées dans l'introduction. Les forces de perturbations gravitationnelles sont dominées par l'harmonique d'ordre 2 du potentiel terrestre (terme en J2) et le mouvement du satellite peut alors être décrit en première approximation par le modèle de Lagrange :

$$e = e_0$$
$$a = a_0$$
$$i = i_0$$

$$\Omega = \Omega_0 - \frac{3\,n_0\,J_2}{2} \cdot \frac{R^2 \cos i_0}{a_0^2\,(1 - e_0^2)^2} \cdot (t-t_0)$$

$$\omega = \omega_0 - \frac{3\,n_0\,J_2}{4} \cdot \frac{R^2\,(1 - 5\cos^2 i_0)}{a_0^2\,(1 - e_0^2)^2} \cdot (t-t_0)$$

$$M = M_0 + n_0 \cdot (t-t_0) + \frac{3\,n_0\,J_2}{4} \cdot \frac{R^2\,(3\cos^2 i_0 - 1)}{a_0^2\,(1 - e_0^2)^{\frac{3}{2}}} \cdot (t-t_0)$$

avec :

$$n_0 = \left(\frac{G.M_T}{a_0^3}\right)^{\frac{1}{2}}$$

J_2 harmonique d'ordre 2 du potentiel terrestre.
R rayon terrestre moyen
t_0 instant initial de mise en orbite
G constante universelle de la gravitation
M_T masse de la terre
e (e_0) excentricité de l'orbite à l'instant t (t_0)
a (a_0) demi-grand axe de l'orbite à l'instant t (t_0)
i (i_0) inclinaison du plan orbital à l'instant t (t_0)
Ω (Ω_0) longitude du noeud ascendant à l'instant t (t_0)
ω (ω_0) angle noeud-périgée à l'instant t (t_0)
M (M_0) anomalie moyenne à l'instant t (t_0)

Ces équations nous montrent que les variations temporelles des paramètres orbitaux d'un satellite sont entièrement liées aux paramètres initiaux (indices 0) et donc à la précision d'injection sur orbite. Par conséquent, les dispersions sur le demi grand-axe, l'inclinaison et l'excentricité des orbites, dûes aux imprécisions d'injection, à linstant t_0, résulteront en des perturbations différentes pour chacun des satellites d'une constellation. Aussi, si les orbites ne sont pas contrôlées, la position relative des satellites d'une constellation initialement phasée varie au cours du temps et implique une modification des performances de couverture de cette constellation.

Notons que les imprécisions d'injection sur le demi-grand axe seront prépondérantes pour la déformation de la constellation puisque la période de révolution des satellites est directement liée à celui-ci.

3 - MODELISATION DES INCERTITUDES DE LANCEMENT

Les incertitudes de lancement liées aux injections sur orbite d'un satellite dépendent du type de lanceur utilisé et sont répercutées sur l'ensemble des paramètres orbitaux du satellite. Cependant, il a été montré [DER-90] que c'est l'incertitude sur le demi grand-axe de l'orbite de chaque satellite qui aura le plus de conséquences sur les performances de couverture de l'ensemble des satellites d'une constellation. Par conséquent, seule l'incertitude sur l'altitude est modélisée et prise en compte dans cette étude pour l'analyse de performance de couverture de constellations.

Suivant le lanceur, la précision sur l'altitude des satellites obtenue lors de la mise à poste est de l'ordre du kilomètre à la dizaine de kilomètres.

L'altitude initiale de chaque satellite est modélisée par une variable aléatoire de loi normale de moyenne m et de variance σ^2. La relation entre l'écart type σ et l'incertitude ε sur le demi-grand axe a pour que la probabilité que l'écart à la moyenne soit supérieur à ε, soit inférieure à 10^{-3} est donnée par:

$$\sigma = \frac{\varepsilon}{3} \quad \text{pour} \quad P(|a-m| > \varepsilon) \leq 10^{-3}$$

Le tableau 1 expose quelques valeurs numériques de σ^2 et ε.

Tableau - 1 - Correspondance entre la variance σ^2 et l'incertitude ε sur le demi-grand axe a.

σ^2	ε (km)	σ^2	ε (km)
500	67	100	30
277	50	44	20
178	40	3	5,2

4 - CALCULS STATISTIQUES DES CRITERES DE PERFORMANCE DE VISIBILITE

4.1 - Probabilité pour qu'un des satellite soit en visibilité instantanée de la station

L'altitude de chaque satellite étant modélisée par une variable aléatoire de loi normale de moyenne m et de variance σ^2, une station A est en visibilité du iéme satellite de la constellation, S_i de coordonnées (X_t^i, Y_t^i, Z_t^i), à un instant t, si l'inégalité (1) est vérifiée. La solution de l'inéquation (1) se présente sous forme de l'union de n intervalles d'altitudes :

$$(\text{la station A est en visibilité du satellite } S_i) \equiv f(X_t^i Y_t^i Z_t^i) \geq 0$$

$$\equiv a \in [a_0, a_1] \cup [a_2, a_3] \cup \ldots [a_{2.(n-1)}, a_{2.(n-1)+1}]$$

La probabilité P_t^i pour que le satellite S_i soit en visibilité de la station A à l'instant t s'exprime alors par :

$$p_t^i = p(f(X_t^i Y_t^i Z_t^i) \geq 0) = p(a \in [a_0, a_1] \cup [a_2, a_3] \cup \ldots [a_{2.(n-1)}, a_{2.(n-1)+1}])$$

$$\boxed{p_t^i = \sum_{j=0}^{n-1} \left(\int_{a_{2j}}^{a_{2j+1}} g_{(m,\sigma^2)}(a)\, da \right)} \quad (2)$$

Où $g_{(m,\sigma^2)}$ est la densité de probabilité d'une loi normale de moyenne m et de variance σ^2:

$$g_{(m,\sigma^2)}(a) = \frac{1}{\sqrt{2\pi\sigma^2}} \exp\left(\frac{-(a-m)^2}{2\sigma^2}\right)$$

4.2 - Nombre instantané de satellites en visibilité

On note X_t^i la variable caractérisant la visibilité du satellite i d'une constellation de N satellites à l'instant t. Elle vaut 1 si le satellite S_i est en visibilité et 0 sinon. C'est une variable aléatoire de Bernouilli de paramètre p_t^i. On a alors :

$$p(X_t^i = 1) = p_t^i \text{ et } p(X_t^i = 0) = 1 - p_t^i$$

Le nombre N_t de satellites en visibilité à un instant t est alors une somme de variables aléatoires de Bernouilli définie par :

$$N_t = \sum_{i=1}^{i=N} X_t^i \qquad (3)$$

On en déduit le nombre moyen de satellites en visibilité à l'instant t, qui est l'espérance mathématique de N_t :

$$E(N_t) = \sum_{i=1}^{i=N} p_t^i \qquad (4)$$

4.3 - Probabilité de visibilité instantanée d'au moins 1 satellite

La probabilité de visibilité d'au moins 1 des N satellites d'une constellation à un instant t par une station terrienne A est un des critères de performance de couverture les plus importants. On la note $p1_t$ et du fait que les satellites sont indépendants (pas de contrôle d'orbite), elle peut s'exprimer par :

$$p1_t = 1 - \prod_{i=1}^{i=N} \left(1 - p_t^i\right) \qquad (5)$$

On peut en déduire la probabilité de ne voir aucun satellite à l'instant t, $\overline{p1}_t$:

$$\overline{p1}_t = 1 - p1_t = \prod_{i=1}^{i=N} \left(1 - p_t^i\right) \qquad (6)$$

4.4 - Probabilité de visibilité instantanée de k satellites simultanément à l'instant t

La probabilité pour que le nombre de satellites en visibilité soit k à un instant t s'exprime en fonction de la variable aléatoire N_t définie par (3). Ainsi, pour une constellation de N satellites :

$$p(N_t = k) = \sum_{i=1}^{C_N^k} \left(\prod_{j=1}^{j=k} p_t^{i+j-1} \right) \left(\prod_{j=k+1}^{j=N} \left(1 - p_t^{i+j-1} \right) \right) \quad (7)$$

avec :

$$C_N^k = \frac{N!}{k! \, (N-k)!}$$

4.5 - Temps moyen de visibilité d'au moins 1 satellite avec une probabilité supérieure à p

La formule (5) permet de calculer la probabilité de visibilité d'au moins 1 satellite à un instant t. Le temps moyen de visibilité d'au moins un satellite entre les instants 0 et T, avec une probabilité supérieure à p, s'exprime par :

$$T_m = \frac{1}{T} \int_0^T \mathbb{1}_{p1_t > p} \; dt \quad (8)$$

avec :

$$\mathbb{1}_{p1_t > p} = 1 \;\; \text{si} \;\; p1_t > p$$
$$= 0 \;\; \text{sinon}$$

4.6 - Méthode numérique d'évaluation des critères de performance de visibilité

Les calculs des critères de performance de visibilité définis ci-dessus dépendent tous de la probabilité de visibilité instantanée d'un satellite i de la constellation p_t^i. Le problème du calcul de l'ensemble des critères de performance de visibilité se ramène donc au calcul de p_t^i (Cf. formule (2)).

La première étape de ce calcul consiste à trouver les solutions de l'inéquation (1), c'est à dire à trouver les intervalles d'altitude pour lesquels on a visibilité, à un instant t donné. Il ne semble pas possible actuellement de résoudre cette inéquation de façon analytique.
On peut cependant trouver les intervalles d'altitude de façon numérique en définissant à chaque instant t une fonction de visibilité VS(a) évaluée par itérations sur l'altitude :

$$VS(a) = 1 \;\; \text{si le satellite est en visibilité à l'instant t pour l'altitude a}$$
$$= 0 \;\; \text{sinon}$$

C'est une variable aléatoire de Bernouilli de paramètre p_t^i. Une fois l'évaluation de la fonction VS(a) effectuée sur une plage d'altitude (a_{final} - $a_{initial}$) et pour un pas d'itération sur l'altitude correctement choisis, p_t^i peut être déduit de (2) sous la forme :

$$p_t^i = \sum_{j=0}^{n-1} \left(\int_{a_{2j}}^{a_{2j+1}} g_{(m,\sigma^2)}(a)\, da \right) = \int_{a_{initial}}^{a_{final}} g_{(m,\sigma^2)}(a) \cdot VS(a)\, da$$

La loi de probabilité de a étant une gaussienne très resserrée, il est suffisant de prendre la plage de variation suivante:

$$a_{initial} = m - 2\,\varepsilon \quad \text{et} \quad a_{final} = m + 2\,\varepsilon$$

Le pas d'intégration doit être choisi de façon à être assez fin pour obtenir une valeur correcte de l'intégrale, tout en tenant compte des limitations imposées par les temps de calcul.

5 - EVOLUTION DES PERFORMANCES DE VISIBILITE D'UNE CONSTELLATION SANS CONTROLE D'ORBITE

5.1 - Conditions de simulation

Dans cet exemple d'application, on évalue les performances de visibilité à long terme, d'une constellation initiale de type WALKER (24/3/2) [WALK-70] [WALK-77] de 24 satellites répartis sur 3 plans orbitaux. L'inclinaison des plans orbitaux est de 50° et l'altitude moyenne des satellites est de 1500 kilomètres.
Une étude paramètrée a été menée afin d'examiner l'influence de 3 des paramètres les plus significatifs suivants sur les performances de visibilité :

— Variance sur l'altitude : Elle modélise la dispersion en altitude des satellites de la constellation dûe à l'injection sur orbite, autour de l'altitude moyenne. Les variances sur l'altitude pour lesquelles les performances ont été examinées sont exposées dans le tableau 1. Les imprécisions d'injection correspondantes varient de ± 5.2 km à ± 67.1 km.

- Latitude du point d'observation : Les performances de visibilité des constellations dépendent essentiellement de la latitude du point d'observation terrestre et peu de la longitude. Les performances de visibilité ont donc été examinée pour des latitudes de 0°, 20°, 40° et 50° pour une longitude de 0°.

- Date d'observation : Les performances de visibilité sont évaluées sur des périodes d'observation de 24 heures aux dates de début de simulation suivantes : 0 jours (constellation initiale phasée), 5 jours, 6 mois et 1 an.

Par ailleurs, l'angle d'élévation minimum au lieu de chacun des observateurs terrestres est constant pour l'ensemble des simulations et vaut 10°.

5.2 - Influence de la variance sur l'altitude

Les figures 2 - a , b et c montrent les courbes du temps moyen de visibilité d'au moins 1 satellite avec une probabilité supérieure à 70%, 80% et 90% (Cf. § 4.5), en fonction de la variance sur l'altitude σ^2, ceci pour des simulations aux différentes dates énoncées ci-dessus et pour une latitude de 0°. Le temps moyen de visibilité décroît lorsque la variance croît, c'est à dire lorsque les incertitudes sur l'altitude dûes à l'injection sur orbite croissent. La performance est d'autant plus dégradée que la date de simulation est éloignée de la date initiale où la constellation est encore phasée.
La comparaison des courbes a,b,c, montre que pour des probabilités supérieures à 80% et 90%, le temps moyen de visibilité converge vers 0%, alors que pour une probabilité supérieure à 70%, il converge vers 50%.

Cela signifie qu'à l'équateur, on pourra au plus espérer établir une communication pendant la moitié du temps avec une chance de succès d'environ 70%. Ceci, quelles que soient les incertitudes d'injection.

Les figures 3 - a, b et c représentent la même performance pour une latitude de 20°. Les tendances observées sont identiques à celles observées précèdemment pour une latitude de 0° . Cependant, le temps moyen de visibilité converge toujours vers une valeur supérieure à 0% et plus élevée que pour le cas précédent.

5.3 - Influence de la latitude du lieu d'observation

La figure 4 montre le temps moyen de visibilité d'au moins 1 satellite en fonction de la latitude pour le cas déterministe (constellation à orbite contrôlée et phasée) et pour des probabilité de 90% à des dates de simulation de 5 jours et 1 an, et des variance sur l'altitude de 3 et 100.
La comparaison du cas déterministe (pas d'incertitude sur l'altitude à l'injection) et des cas aléatoires (loi gaussienne sur l'altitude de variance 3 et 100) montre une dégradation importante des performances. Cette dégradation est d'autant plus grande et plus rapide que la variance est grande : perte d'environ 20% au bout de 5 jours pour une variance de 3 et d'environ 50% au bout de 5 jours pour une variance de 100.
Dans le cas déterministe, le temps moyen de visibilité d'au moins 1 satellite est compris entre 80% et 100% pour des latitudes comprises entre 0° et 60°.
Dans le cas aléatoire, au bout d'un an, et pour des latitudes comprises entre 20° et 40° le temps moyen de visibilité d'au moins 1 satellite avec une probabilité p>0,9 est compris entre 20% et 40%. Pour les latitudes inférieures à 20° et supérieures à 40°, le temps moyen est inférieur à 20%.

6 - CONCLUSIONS

La modélisation des incertitudes de lancement liées à l'injection sur orbite a permis de définir et de calculer des critères statistiques de performances de visibilité pour des constellations sans contrôle d'orbite. L'implémentation informatique de cette méthode permet en outre d'évaluer les performances de visibilité de ce type de constellation.
Les résultats obtenus mettent en évidence l'évolution des performances des constellations sans contrôle d'orbite en fonction de l'imprécision d'injection. Ainsi les performances de visibilité d'au moins un satellite sont d'autant plus rapidement dégradées que l'imprécision d'injection sur l'altitude est grande. Pour des valeurs réalistes de précision d'injection, la dégradation des performances de visibilité au bout de seulement 5 jours est telle qu'il est inutile d'envisager une constellation initialement phasée sans contrôle d'orbite.
Cette étude ne tient compte que des imprécisions de lancement sur l'altitude. Une analyse plus détaillée devrait considérer les imprécisions sur les autres paramètres orbitaux. Cependant, ces améliorations ne pourront se faire qu'au détriment de la simplicité de modélisation et de calcul des performances, et, compte tenu de la dégradation rapide des performances de visibilité, il apparait inutile d'affiner ce modèle qui s'avère suffisant pour permettre au concepteur d'un système de se prononcer quant à la nécessité d'un contrôle d'orbite, selon le service désiré.
Les constellations sans contrôle d'orbite ne semblent pas adaptées à un service nécessitant la visibilité permanente d'au moins un satellite, si ce n'est en augmentant le nombre de satellites. Cependant les constellations sans contrôle d'orbite sont envisageables pour des services ne nécessitant qu'une visibilité intermittente des satellites (messagerie par exemple).
La modélisation présentée dans cet article constitue un outil simple d'évaluation des performances de visibilité d'une constellation de satellites sans contrôle d'orbite. Pour un service donné, elle permet de déterminer, soit le lanceur le mieux adapté à l'injection sur orbite d'un nombre de satellites donné, soit le nombre de satellites nécessaires si le lanceur est imposé.

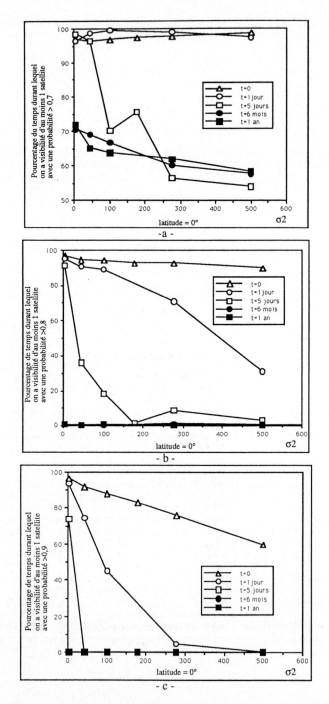

Figure 2 - Influence de la variance sur l'altitude pour un lieu d'observation situé à l'équateur.

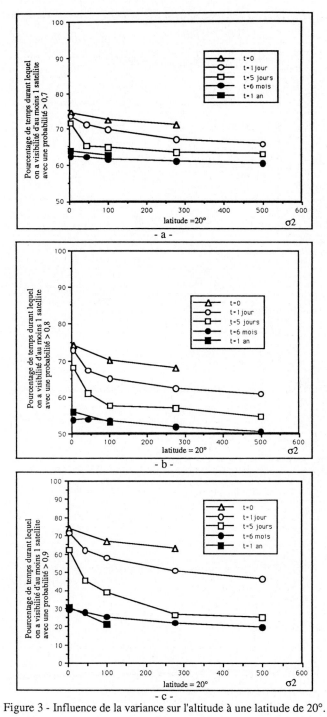

- a -

- b -

- c -

Figure 3 - Influence de la variance sur l'altitude à une latitude de 20°.

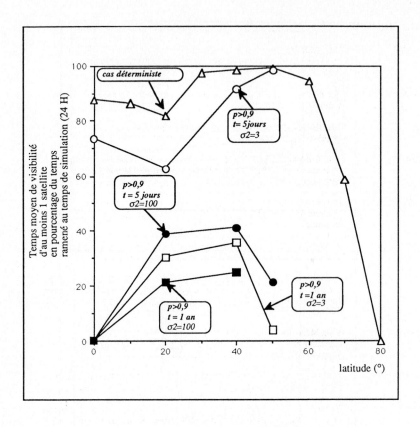

Figure 4 - influence de la latitude du lieu d'observation

BIBLIOGRAPHIE

[BES-78]   D.C. BESTE, "Design of satellite constellations for optimal continuous
                coverage", IEEE Trans; on Aerospace and Electronic Systems, Vol.
                AES-14,N° 3, pp. 466-473; May 1978.

[CNES-83]   "Le mouvement du satellite. Conférences et exercices de mécanique spatiale",
                CEPADUES-EDITIONS.

[DER-90]   J.J. DERIDDER, "Etude des performances d'une constellation de 24 satellites
                en orbite basse", rapport final, contrat CNES : 802/CNES/90/0803

[EMA-77]   H.E. EMARA, C.T. LEONDES, "Minimun number of satellites for three
                dimensional continuous worldwide coverage", IEEE Transactions on
                aerospace electronics systems, mars 1977, vol AES-13, N°2, pp-372-380.

[FLO-61]   FLOYD, BENNET, THOMAS, COLEMAN, John C. HOUBOLT,
                "Determination of the required number of randomly spaced communication
                satellites", NASA IN D-619, Jan 1961.

[KOMP-59]   R. KOMPFNER, J.R. PIERCE, "Transoceanic communication by means of
                satellites", Proceedings of the IEEE, Mars 1959, pp 372-380.

[LAW-87]   J.A. LAWTON, "Numerical method for rapidly determining satellite-satellite
                and satellite ground station in view periods", Naval Surface Weapons Center,
                Dalghren, VA, USA, J. Guid. Control and Dyn., jan-feb 1987, vol 10, N°1, pp
                32-36.

[MAM-60]   W.L. MAMMEL, F.W. SINDEN, "Geometric aspects of satellite
                communication", IRE Trans. on space electronics and telemetry, SET-6, N°3-
                4, pp146-157, september-december 1960.

[MAR-91]   G.MARAL, JJ . DERIDDER , "Basic concepts of low earth orbit satellite
                systems for communications", N: 91/01, Telecom Paris ENST 1991.

[MAR-91]   G. MARAL, J.J. DE RIDDER, B .G. EVANS, M. RICHHARIA, "Low earth
                orbit satellite systems for communications", International Journal of Satellite
                Communications, Vol 9, No 4, pp 209-225, 1991.

[REI-63]   S.H. REIGER, "A study of passive communication satellites", Rand. Corp.
                Rept. R-415-NASA, feb. 1963.

[RID-85]   L. RIDER, " Optimized polar orbit constellations for redundant earth
                coverage", The Journal of the Astronautical Sciences, Vol. 33, N°2, pp.
                147-161; April-June 1985.

[RID-86]   L. RIDER, " Analytic design of satellite constellations for zonal
                coverage using inclined circular orbits",The Journal of the Astronautical
                Sciences, Vol. 34, N°1, pp. 31- 64; January - March 1986.

[ROT-76]   E.A. ROTH, "Rise and set time and maximun elevation of a satellite", ESA
                Scientific and technical review 1976, N°2, pp 11-24.

[TAM-91]   CHANTAL TAMISE, "Etude des performances de visibilité de constellations
                de satellites sans contôle d'orbite", R: 91/04, Télécom Paris - Site de
                Toulouse - (ENST) , 1991.

[WALK-70]   J.G. WALKER, "Circular orbit patterns providing continuous whole earth
                coverage", RAE Technical report 70211, 71p, 1970.

[WALK-77]   J.G. WALKER, "Continuous whole earth coverage by circular orbit satellite
                patterns", RAE Technical report 77044, 78p, 1977.

[ZAR-87]   ZARROUATI, "Trajectoires spatiales", CEPADUES-EDITIONS 1987.

ASPECTS RADIOCOMMUNICATIONS DANS UN SYSTEME DE LOCALISATION ET MESSAGERIE BIDIRECTIONNELLE EN VHF/UHF PAR SATELLITES EN ORBITE BASSE

par

G. LESTHIEVENT et M. MARGERY

Centre National d'Etudes Spatiales - Toulouse

1 - RESUME

Un service de localisation et messagerie dénommé S80 est en cours d'études au CNES. L'utilisation des constellations mini-satellites en orbite basse pour des liaisons VHF/UHF entre des centres de mission et des mobiles équipés de terminaux impose des contraintes spécifiques au système de radiocommunication.

Nous passerons en revue les différents paramètres du système en proposant une approche "descendante" pour étudier le comportement des liaisons. Cette étude portera sur l'analyse approchée des bilans de liaison, puis présentera des modèles pour simulation informatique permettant une évaluation statistique des performances en terme de taux d'acquisition des messages transmis.

2 - INTRODUCTION

Le système S80 (voir /1/) propose un service de localisation (précision de 1 km à σ) et de transmission de messagerie légère bidirectionnelle (256 bits maximum et 32 bits en moyenne). Les liaisons sont établies dans les bandes VHF/UHF vers 150 et 400 MHz, avec une capacité d'adressage pour environ 700 000 terminaux par région (Europe ou Conus). Les constellations choisies à l'heure actuelle utilisent cinq mini-satellites judicieusement phasés sur des orbites circulaires inclinées à 57° et à environ 1200 km d'altitude.

Ces choix imposent un ensemble de contraintes pour les émetteurs et les récepteurs (centres de missions et terminaux) ainsi que pour le "canal de transmission" :

a) Visibilités mutuelles réduites à 15 mn en moyenne avec un maximum de 17 mn pour un Centre de Mission à Toulouse et des terminaux sur la zone Europe.

b) Canal VHF/UHF caractérisé par des parasites divers, des évanouissements par masquage ou multi-trajets, des scintillations et erreurs ionosphériques ainsi que des brouillages causés par d'autres systèmes.

c) Effet Doppler/Fizeau important : écart Doppler maximum de 3 kHz vers 150 MHz et 8,5 kHz vers 400 MHz, rampe Doppler maximum de -19 Hz/s vers 150 MHz et -50 Hz/s vers 400 MHz.

d) Aspects réglementaires : choix des fréquences, flux au sol et rayonnement toléré hors bandes. Attributions de fréquence issues de la CAMR 92 :

$$
\left.
\begin{array}{l}
148 - 150{,}05 \text{ MHz} \\[2pt]
137 - 138 \text{ MHz} \\
400{,}15 - 401 \text{ MHz}
\end{array}
\right.
$$

148 - 150,05 MHz   **montant** sol/satellite

137 - 138 MHz
400,15 - 401 MHz   **descendant** satellite/sol avec :

- flux max. au sol dans la bande allouée = -125 dB(W/m^2/4 kHz)

- flux max. au sol (radioastronomie de 150,05 à 153 et 406,1 à 410 MHz) = -223 dB(W/m^2/4 kHz)

e) Mini-satellites donc Charge Utile (CU) et servitudes (TTC) à consommation, coût, masse et encombrement réduits (85 W disponibles pour l'alimentation de la CU avec 100 W max).

f) Terminaux peu chers et de faible consommation.

Cette étude est focalisée sur les effets perturbateurs du canal de transmission cités au point b) ci-dessus, les autres paramètres étant soit fixés par la mission (visibilité, effet Doppler, aspects réglementaires) soit imposés par ailleurs (choix industriels, technologiques, etc ...). Une synthèse des résultats obtenus au cours de travaux récents (voir bibliographie) sera effectuée, avec application aux bandes de fréquences retenues pour S80. Une validation ultérieure de ces résultats est prévue aux moyens des mesures qui seront réalisées avec le micro-satellite technologique S80T, dont le lancement est prévu au mois de juillet 1992, en association avec une simulation logicielle basée sur l'outil SPW (Signal Processing Workpackage) de Comdisco.

3 - EFFETS PERTURBATEURS DU CANAL DE TRANSMISSION

Les problèmes de propagation que l'on rencontre habituellement dans les bandes 150 MHz et 400 MHz sont abondamment traités dans la littérature ainsi qu'au CCIR pour des systèmes terrestres ; par contre peu d'études ont été conduites pour des systèmes par satellite (/3/).

Ces effets peuvent être regroupés en deux familles :
. les effets **additifs**,
. les effets **multiplicatifs**.

3.1 - LES EFFETS ADDITIFS

Ils correspondent à l'influence du bruit thermique du récepteur et des bruits galactiques, parasites industriels et brouilleurs captés par l'antenne de réception.

3.1.1 - Le bruit thermique

Il se caractérise statistiquement par un processus aléatoire continu à répartition d'amplitude gaussienne centrée $N(0, \sigma_t^2)$ et une densité spectrale de puissance constante dans la bande équivalente de bruit B_r du récepteur (/4/ et /5/) :

. $b(t) = b_s(t) . \sin(2\pi.f_o.t + \Theta) + b_c(t) . \cos(2\pi.f_o.t + \Theta)$
b_s et b_c étant des processus aléatoires indépendants de loi Normale $(0, \sigma_t^2)$

. $S_b(f) \begin{cases} = No_{th} = k.T_{rec} = \sigma_t^2/B_r & \text{pour } f \in [f_o - B_r/2, f_o + B_r/2] \\ = 0 \text{ ailleurs} \end{cases}$

3.1.2 - Le bruit galactique

Ce bruit de fond provient essentiellement de la ceinture galactique et intègre donc toutes les sources radioélectriques qui y sont actives.

Ce bruit peut être modélisé comme le bruit thermique par un bruit centré blanc gaussien à bande étroite de variance : $\sigma_g^2 = k . T_g . B_r$ avec $T_g \simeq 290$ K à 150 MHz et 50 K à 400 MHz. (voir /2/)

Ces résultats permettent de faire une première estimation de la température d'antenne hors brouilleurs et bruits impulsionnels pour une antenne de type "fouet quart d'onde" ou pour une antenne à gain élevé (> 12 dBi) :

. T_{gal} **(λ/4)** $= 1/4\pi \int_{\Omega} g . T \, d\Omega \quad \simeq 1/4\pi (2\pi.0,4.T_{terre} + 2\pi.1,6.T_g) \simeq 0,8.T_g + 0,2.T_{terre}$
$\simeq$ **290 K à 150 MHz** et **100 K à 400 MHz**

. T_{gal} **(ge)** $\simeq T_g \simeq$ **290 K à 150 MHz** et **50 K à 400 MHz**
Lorsque l'antenne à gain élevé est pointée sur le centre galactique (rare), cette température peut monter vers 700 K à 150 MHz et 150 K à 400 MHz.

3.1.3 - Les bruits parasites artificiels

Ces bruits de nature impulsionnelle très riches en harmoniques ont des origines variées, comme les allumages automobiles, les interrupteurs industriels, les appareillages à commutation souvent mal anti-parasités. Les effets sont de type "proximité" donc différents en importance entre les zones rurales et urbaines (/2/). Leur influence sera donc différente sur le centre de mission, les terminaux et le satellite.

La modélisation, même statistique, de ce type de bruits est délicate car ils sont généralement non stationnaires.

De plus, il est difficile de définir un modèle général représentatif pour des simulations en raison du nombre élevé de paramètres (temps, fréquence, densité du trafic automobile, caractéristiques RF du récepteur, emplacements des émetteurs et récepteurs, etc ...).

Au niveau statistique, on rencontre essentiellement trois variables aléatoires (voir /6/, /7/) :

- la **distribution** de l'**amplitude S** des **impulsions** (souvent considérée comme gaussienne) = "Amplitude Probability Distribution" (**APD**) et "Noise Amplitude Distribution" (**NAD**) ;

- la **distribution temporelle** ou **occurrence p** (souvent approximée à une distribution poissonnienne avec une densité λ allant de 1 à 500 000 impulsions par seconde) = "Pulse Interval Distribution" (**PID**) ;

- la **durée** des **impulsions** pour différents niveaux d'amplitude (doit retranscrire la décroissance en 20 dB par décade de la densité spectrale de puissance du bruit, surtout intéressant en très large bande) = "Envelope Pulse Width Distribution" (**EPWD**).

Les modèles simplifiés ne prennent en compte qu'une partie de ces aspects (NAD et PID pour /6/ et APD seulement pour /7/) mais les validations terrain associées ont montré que les phénomènes moyens peuvent être approximés à l'aide d'un modèle de type bruit thermique additif (AWGN) caractérisé par une température équivalente de bruit dans une bande donnée.

Pour valider ce choix, deux campagnes de mesures ont été effectuées. L'une utilise un ballon observant les bandes montantes (148 - 150 MHz) avec une antenne représentative ; elle a permis d'évaluer la blancheur du bruit moyen observé (par analyse spectrale rapide avec ou sans moyennage) et le caractère quasi-gaussien ainsi que la mise en évidence de brouilleurs discrets. Ceci a permis par homothétie de distance de considérer, au 1er ordre, que le bruit impulsionnel vu par le satellite est un bruit thermique (additif) de température équivalente $T_{an\ sat} \simeq 2000\ K$ dans une bande de bruit d'environ 3 MHz.

L'autre campagne a permis d'évaluer de la même manière les contributions mêlées (bruits galactiques, bruits impulsionnels) pour la bande descendante (137 - 138 MHz). Une $T_{an\ station} \simeq 2000\ K$ a été constatée pour un site "calme" et une antenne directive (Yagi 4 éléments avec Gmax $\simeq$ 16 dBi en polarisation circulaire) ainsi qu'une $T_{an\ terminal} \simeq 5000\ K$ en milieu sub-urbain avec une antenne quart d'onde quasi-omnidirectionnelle en polarisation verticale. Ces éléments sont représentatifs de l'équipement station et mobile futur avec une bande de bruit d'environ 3 MHz (voir résultats en figure 1).

Ces résultats sont en accord avec les travaux de Skomal (/8/) lesquels s'écartent sensiblement des informations contenus dans les rapports du CCIR (/2/). En effet, Skomal constate une réduction du facteur de bruit équivalent F_a de 22 à 10 dB en moyenne.

$F_a = 10 \log (T_{an}/T_{amb})$ donc $T_{an} = T_{amb} \cdot 10^{(Fa/10)}$

Les **modèles de simulation** pour le **terminal** et la **station** actuellement comparés sont au nombre de deux ; le premier modèle (/6/) correspond à l'expression suivante du bruit impulsionnel :

$$b_i(t) = \sum_n S_n \cdot \delta(t - p_n) + b_{it}(t)$$

- S_n est l'amplitude des impulsions de durée 1/Fe, caractérisée par une densité de probabilité p_{Sn} (L) telle que :
p_{Sn} (L) = $10/Fe\ (2.A^2)/L^3$ avec $L \in [A/10 ; A]$, sachant que A =

66 dBµV/MHz (urbain)
56 dBµV/MHz (sub-urbain)
46 dBµV/MHz (rural)

- p_n est l'instant d'apparition de l'impulsion n. L'intervalle de temps $\delta p_n = p_n - p_{n-1}$ suit une loi exponentielle $f_{\delta pn}(u)$ telle que :

$f_{\delta pn}(u) = \lambda.\exp(-\lambda.u)$

- Fe est le fréquence d'échantillonnage qui doit être suffisamment élevée devant la bande du signal pour pouvoir simuler des impulsions fines et représenter correctement les filtrages et non-linéarités :

Fe = 32 . B_{signal} soit 32 MHz

- $b_{it}(t)$ est un bruit thermique de variance : $\sigma_{it}^2 = k \cdot T_{it} \cdot B_r$

  B_r étant la bande équivalente de bruit du récepteur

  $T_{it} \simeq$ | 4500 K en zone urbaine et sub-urbaine
  | 1800 K en zone rurale

Le second modèle (/7/) s'exprime sous la forme : $b_i(t) = \text{Re}[(b_{pr}(t) + b_r(t)) \cdot e^{j\Theta}]$

avec : | . b_{pr} composante impulsionnelle de l'amplitude du bruit modélisée par une distribution
"Power-Rayleigh" caractérisée par un rayon R et sa puissance $\alpha \simeq 0,49$ (Cf./2/, /7/).

| . b_r composante amplitude du bruit de fond modélisée par une distribution de Rayleigh
(équivalent à un bruit thermique) caractérisée par un rayon $R_o = 2\sigma_r^2$.

| . Θ est une phase aléatoire équirépartie sur [0, 2π[.

Pour le satellite, son antenne à grande ouverture fait tendre la statistique de l'amplitude du signal reçu vers une loi Normale $N(0, \sigma_{i\,sat}^2)$ avec (théorème "central limit") :

$$\sigma_{i\,sat}^2 = k.(T_{an\,sat} + T_{rec\,sat}) \cdot B_{sat}$$

B_{sat} étant la bande équivalente de bruit du satellite (environ 3 MHz mais peut être abaissée à 1,5 MHz par utilisation de filtres étroits, de type SAW par exemple).

3.1.4 - Les brouillages par d'autres systèmes

C'est bien entendu la part de perturbation la plus difficilement évaluable.

Un examen des assignations de fréquence effectuées par l'IFRB dans la bande 148 - 150,05 MHz (accès satellite) donne un nombre considérable d'utilisateurs déclarés (2500 pour CONUS, 1400 pour l'Europe, et 300 environ pour l'Asie).

L'utilisation de la bande est quasi régulière sauf pour l'ex-bande Transit (149,9 - 150,05 MHz). Pour **CONUS**, la **puissance isotrope rayonnée par les usagers** se répartit approximativement entre **10** et **26 dBW** avec une moyenne d'environ **18 dBW** ; pour l'**Europe** on constate plutôt une moyenne de **10 dBW**.

Sachant que les systèmes déclarés sont de type **téléphonie** avec 16 kHz ou 36 kHz de bande occupée, le taux d'occupation crète E_{br} (en Erlangs) des systèmes brouilleurs peut être évalué par :

$$E_{br} = N_b \cdot O_j \cdot T_p = \begin{array}{l} 62 \text{ pour CONUS} \\ 35 \text{ pour l'Europe} \end{array}$$

. N_b nombre de brouilleurs potentiels dans la bande = nombre d'utilisateurs déclarés (voir IFRB).

. $O_j \simeq 1h/\text{jour} \simeq 0,05$ occupation moyenne du canal par jour par brouilleur.

. $T_p \simeq 0,5$ taux de parole par transaction.

On a donc le résultat intéressant suivant donnant la **PIRE moyenne de brouillage dans le canal du satellite** :

$$PIRE_{\text{brouilleur vu par le satellite à 1 Erlang}} = PIRE_{\text{moyenne brouilleur}} \cdot E_{br}$$

$$\simeq \begin{array}{l} 36 \text{ dBW pour CONUS} \\ 25 \text{ dBW pour l'Europe} \end{array}$$

Ces estimations sont bien entendu inquiétantes mais il semble aussi que bon nombre de ces systèmes déclarés ne soient que très peu ou même plus du tout utilisés. Un coefficient d'érosion peut chiffrer cet usage et il semble qu'il vaille au moins **2** ou **3**. De plus, les brouilleurs étant quasiment équirépartis sur la bande, on peut appliquer un facteur correctif moyen d'environ **3 dB** de part la forme en sinc^2 du lobe principal de nos modulations en étalement de spectre. La segmentation de la bande en canaux diminue aussi le taux d'occupation en taux d'occupation élémentaire par canal. Les expérimentations à venir sur S80T devront permettre de lever l'incertitude et déterminer ainsi la stratégie à adopter.

Le brouillage dans les autres bandes (137 - 138 et 400,15 - 401 MHz) devrait se limiter à des effets de proximité. Côté terminal, il sera probablement important dans les zones urbaines.

Lors des essais cités précédemment, on a pu observer des brouilleurs à bande étroite (< 12 kHz) avec des rapports $I/(k.T_{an\ terminal}.B_r)$ de l'ordre de 10 à 15 dB dans la bande. Mais surtout, il faudra veiller à assurer une bonne réjection des brouilleurs adjacents tels que les émetteurs radios FM vers 108 MHz et les émetteurs TV vers 176 MHz, car les puissances mises en jeu (PIRE $\geq$ 40 dBW) peuvent provoquer des intermodulations très gênantes (non-linéarités) dans la partie Radiofréquence du récepteur terminal.

En ce qui concerne le centre de mission, le brouillage sera de même type mais avec des niveaux sûrement plus importants aux faibles élévations (< 15°). Ces aspects devront être pris en compte dans les choix d'architecture.

3.2 - EFFETS MULTIPLICATIFS

On trouve dans /3/ un bon résumé des effets multiplicatifs : scintillations et effets ionosphériques, évanouissement et multi-trajets qui peuvent s'appliquer sur le signal dans le cas S80.

3.2.1 - Scintillation, effets ionosphériques

Les transactions bidirectionnelles sont caractérisées par une **double** traversée de l'ionosphère avant d'être **démodulée** (messagerie) et **triple** ou **quadruple** traversée avant d'être utilisée pour la **localisation** (mesure Doppler et mesure de temps de transit).

Les scintillations correspondent à des variations rapides du signal (amplitude et phase) dues à des variations de l'indice de réfraction dans les couches traversées. Cet effet est bien connu (/9/, /10/, /11/) et dépend du Contenu Electronique Total de l'atmosphère traversée (C.E.T. ou T.E.C.). Le CET chiffre le nombre d'électrons libres présents dans une section unité (pour un trajet quelconque ou avec l'indice v pour un trajet vertical) dans les couches D, E, F_1, F_2 de l'ionosphère entre 100 et 1000 km. Le profil de cette densité est complexe et variable dans le temps (/9/) comme le montre la figure 2.

Des réflexions sur les couches ionosphériques peuvent avoir lieu pour des incidences rasantes, ce qui limite l'élévation minimale utilisable par les stations à 5° dans 99 % des cas.

3.2.1.1 - Etude de la scintillation

La modélisation de la scintillation a surtout concerné les zones d'anomalies géomagnétiques (pôles, équateur voir /11/) mais à nos latitudes (45, 50°) les effets ne sont pas à négliger. En résumé (/10/, /11/) :

. **pour l'amplitude :**

Les scintillations ont un indice S4 = $\sqrt{1/m} \simeq 0,17$ (m = 35). Ceci correspond à des évanouissements supérieurs à 1 dB pendant environ 15 % du temps. Les indices S4 maxima (de 21 h à 3 h et vers 12 h) valent 0,24 (m = 17) et les minima sont égaux à 0,14 (m = 51).

Ces scintillations sont modélisables par des distributions m de Nakagami (voir /5/) bien que pour les valeurs de m élevées, on puisse utiliser une approximation par une loi $N(1 - 1/2m, \sigma_s^2)$ avec :

$$\sigma_s = \frac{1}{\sqrt{2\pi}} \cdot \frac{(m-1)\,!}{2\,.\,m^m.(1-1/2m)^{m-1/2}\exp[-(m-1/2)]}$$

Au niveau spectral, le spectre est plat jusqu'à $f_{cs} \simeq 0,05$ Hz (corrélation importante) puis décroît avec une pente en $f^{-3,4}$.

. **pour la phase :**

Les scintillations suivent approximativement (/11/) une loi Normale $N(\delta\varnothing, \sigma_\varnothing^2)$ avec :

. $\delta\varnothing = -(8,44.10^{-9} \cdot CET/f)$ en radians

. $\sigma_\varnothing = 0,2$ rad en moyenne avec 0,12 en minima et 0,3 en maxima.

3.2.1.2 - Etude des effets ionosphériques

Les effets ionosphériques sont très importants pour l'aspect précision de localisation du système (mesures Doppler et surtout de temps de trajet au sol). Des modèles de type Klobuchar (1er ordre) ou Bent (plus complexe) permettent de corriger partiellement l'erreur correspondante (60 à 80 % de la valeur obtenue par calcul brut).

. retard de temps de trajet :

$$\delta t' = \frac{1,34.10^{-7} . CET_V}{f^2 . \sin[Arccos(\cos Eo/1,055)]}$$

. décalage Doppler :

$$\delta f \simeq - (d\delta t'/dt) . f \qquad \text{(écart relatif} < 2.10^{-3} \text{ à 150 MHz)}$$

Afin d'obtenir la classe de précision recherchée ($\simeq$ 1 km) l'utilisation d'un réseau de balises (9 à 10 par région) mesurant le CET (via S80 ou via GPS par exemple) à différentes inclinaisons est envisagée.

3.2.2 - Evanouissements et multitrajets

Dans la liaison satellite/terminaux, les conditions de propagation sont surtout de nature statistique puisque l'environnement est variable. Ces phénomènes peuvent être scindés en deux catégories (voir /12/, /14/), correspondants à des variations lentes et des variations rapides des phénomènes observés.

Les variations lentes sont dans notre cas quasi-déterministes (élévation station $\geq$ 5° et élévation terminaux $\geq$ 10°) puisque dépendantes de l'évolution géométrique de la constellation. Elles sont dues à une compensation imparfaite des pertes d'espace (libre) par le diagramme de l'antenne satellite ou à un masquage sur une certaine portion de trajectoire du satellite (pour un terminal quasi fixe) sachant qu'à nos latitudes (CONUS ou Europe), celui-ci a une vitesse angulaire apparente de 3,4°/min dans le plan (donc des masquages possibles de sa trajectoire sur plus d'1 mn).

Les variations rapides (pour un mobile en mouvement) sont décomposables en deux situations (/13/) qui se combinent dans la pratique :

a) masquage

La présence d'un obstacle sur la droite satellite/terminal cause un masquage du trajet direct (exemple, le passage à 60 km/h sous un pont de 15 m de large cause un masquage d'environ 1 s).

b) multitrajets (ou fading de Rayleigh)

Des réflexions multiples sur le sol et des objets proches du mobile (la zone de Fresnel est importante en VHF/UHF) créent un réseau d'ondes stationnaires. L'amplitude du signal reçu au niveau du terminal suit alors deux types de statistique suivant la **présence** (distribution de **Rice**) ou **non** (distribution de **Rayleigh**) du trajet direct.

Le modèle donnant la densité de probabilité p(S) de la puissance S du signal reçu et qui représente le plus correctement cet ensemble de situations est le modèle de **Lutz** (/13/) :

$$p(S) = \sqrt{2S} . \{(1 - A).r.e^{-r(S+1)}.I_o(2r\sqrt{S}) + A.\int_o^\infty e^{-S/S_o}.10/[\sqrt{2\pi}.\sigma_l.\ln(10).S_o^2].\exp[-(10\log S_o - \mu)^2/2\sigma_l^2].dS_o\}$$

avec

A :	probabilité de masquage
r :	facteur de Rice (puissance signal direct/somme des puissances réfléchies)
μ :	moyenne de la décroissance de puissance
σ_l^2 :	variance de la décroissance de puissance

Les valeurs de A, r, μ, σ_l actuellement connues (/13/) le sont pour la **bande L** et indiquent une forte **dépendance** de **A** et de **r** avec l'**élévation au sol**. Les expérimentations **S80T** vont permettre de caractériser ces valeurs pour les bandes **VHF**.

La mise en forme spectrale du modèle est nécessaire pour le rendre conforme à son comportement à bande étroite tel que (/12/ et /15/) :

$$S(f) = 1/[\pi.\sqrt{f_d^2-(f-f_i)^2}] \quad \text{et} \quad 0 \quad \text{ailleurs, avec :} \quad \begin{array}{l} f_i \text{ fréquence instantanée porteuse} \\ f_d \text{ l'effet Doppler} \end{array}$$

Ce modèle est théoriquement valable (/12/ et /14/) pour un signal à bande étroite c'est-à-dire sans étalement important des retards t_i et ce pour des échelles de temps de l'ordre de 0,2 µs car alors la sélectivité en fréquence (effet sur l'amplitude modélisée en $|\cos[\pi(f-f_o)t_i]|$ correspond à l'ordre de grandeur de la largeur du canal disponible ($0 < |f-f_o| < 500$ kHz).

La réponse impulsionnelle du canal peut se représenter en une somme de Dirac aux instants t_i ce qui en environnement dégagé (zone rurale) se réduit en un seul Dirac (variations de ± 0,1 µs). Par contre, pour des zones suburbaines et urbaines (ville), la réponse s'étale beaucoup plus encore (voir exemple à Paris tiré de /14/ en figure 3). On y retrouve environ 10 Diracs supérieurs à -15 dB jusqu'à 4,5 µs.

Le modèle pour la bande utile (1 MHz) consistera en la mise en parallèle de 5 modèles de Lutz, chacun étant associé à un retard différent (allant de 0,2 à 3 µs) à caractériser par l'expérimentation S80T.

Pour l'amplitude, il est possible de calculer un temps entre nul pour le réseau d'ondes stationnaires. En considérant le cas d'école d'une seule réflexion sur un obstacle quasi-conducteur (béton armé à ces longueurs d'onde), on trouve :

$$t_{\text{entre nul}} = \frac{\lambda \pm 2.d.\delta_{\text{entre nul}}(\cos E_o)}{2.R_o.w.\cos E_o} \quad \text{avec} \quad \begin{array}{ll} E_o & \text{élévation en réception mobile} \\ d & \text{distance mobile - obstacle} \\ w & \text{vitesse angulaire relative satellite / mobile} \\ R_o & \text{rayon de la Terre} \end{array}$$

Ce résultat prouve que la forme du réseau varie en fonction du temps (déformation géométrique de l'ensemble satellite - mobile). Compte tenu de l'élévation moyenne de travail des mobiles ($\simeq 30°$) et de l'éloignement ou du rapprochement (cas pire) du satellite vis à vis de l'obstacle, on a les valeurs suivantes :

170 µs (rapprochement) $\leq \overline{t_{\text{entre nul}}} \leq 235$ µs (éloignement) et **200** µs moyen à 150 MHz, d $\in [0;30$ m]

60 µs (rapprochement)$\leq \overline{t_{\text{entre nul}}} \leq 80$ µs (éloignement) et **70** µs moyen à 400 MHz pour d $\in [0;10$ m]

On peut définir aussi la durée moyenne d'un évanouissement par (voir /12/) :

$$\overline{t_{\text{eva}}} = \frac{e^{\mu^2} - 1}{\mu . f_d \sqrt{2\pi}} \quad \mu \text{ étant la moyenne de l'évanouissement en puissance (/13/).}$$

Pour μ = -8 dB on a $\overline{t_{\text{eva}}} \simeq 57$ µs à 150 MHz et **20** µs à 400 MHz

Ces résultats auront bien sûr une grande importance pour le choix des modulations et codages pour chaque liaison.

4 - LES ARCHITECTURES

4.1 - INTRODUCTION

Le choix des architectures du système de transmission (/1/) a été guidé par les contraintes évoquées au paragraphe précédent.
En ce qui concerne la liaison **aller**, **trois scénarii** se sont dégagés des études effectuées (cf. Fig 4). Deux d'entre eux (scénarii A et C) utilisent l'étalement de spectre mais se distinguent par les bandes de fréquence employées (VHF ou UHF). Le troisième (scénario B) est basé sur une liaison à bbande étroite. Pour la liaison **retour**, l'Accès Multiple à Répartition de Code (AMRC) a été retenu pour les raisons essentielles suivantes :

- le canal de transmission doit être partagé de façon aléatoire par plusieurs utilisateurs simultanés

- la mission de localisation des mobiles, qui nécessite de réaliser des mesures de pseudo distance et Doppler sur des signaux de référence appropriés,
- les propriétés intéressantes de l'étalement de spectre en présence de trajets multiples,
- l'amélioration de la compatibilité avec d'autres systèmes dans la même bande et une bonne résistance aux brouillages.

4.2 - DIMENSIONNEMENT DE LA LIAISON RETOUR (terminaux vers centre de mission)

La modulation retenue est une modulation de phase du type NRZ/MSK/DS-SSMA ou NRZ/OQPSK filtré/DS.SSMA avec un rythme bribe (R_{bribe}) égal à 1 Mbribes/s. Ce choix permet aussi de concentrer l'énergie utile dans la bande de 1 MHz disponible et minimiser les flux hors-bandes émis par le satellite (voir /16/ pour des informations sur l'étalement de spectre par séquence directe et /17/ pour les aspects modulations / codage). Les sessions de communication s'effectuent au moyen de messages courts ("burst") de durée inférieure à la longueur du (ou des) code PN d'étalement. Un préambule dont la durée est de 8 bits permet l'acquisition des signaux ainsi que la mesure Doppler sur une durée suffisante (test d'hypothèses en réception station). Le message moyen comprend 100 bits environ qui subissent un brassage et un codage correcteur d'erreurs (code convolutionnel, voir /18/).

Le choix du rythme de bit est le résultat d'un compromis entre la charge du système et les caractéristiques des éléments de transmission. En effet, un rythme faible entrainera des messages longs d'où un temps d'occupation du canal plus élevé par mobile et en conséquence une réduction de la capacité du système. En ce qui concerne l'acquisition du code d'étalement préalable à toute opération de traitement sur le signal reçu (voir /16/), le résultat de la corrélation en réception est sensible à la différence de fréquence entre la valeur attendue, le début et la fin du préambule (influence du Doppler non-connu a priori sur le signal reçu). En conséquence et pour optimiser l'efficacité de la liaison, cette séquence devra être aussi courte que possible mais caractérisée toutefois par une énergie suffisante afin de détecter le signal : ceci necessite un rapport $(C/No)_t$ plutôt élevé auquel correpond un rythme élevé.

En outre, la précision requise sur la mesure de distance (estimation de retard) et Doppler (estimation de fréquence) nécessitent un rapport $(C/No)_t$ suffisant en réception mais une durée D_m de présence signal compatible avec les exigences ;

$$\hat{\sigma_f} = f[(C/No)_t^{-1}] / D_m \quad \text{et} \quad \hat{\sigma_\tau} = g[(C/No)_t^{-1}, D_m^{-1}]$$

Donc un rythme de bit rapide implique de fortes puissances à émettre ce qui va à l'encontre des contraintes de coût et de consommation sur les terminaux. Il doit permettre une longueur de message suffisante pour effectuer la localisation.

Dans le satellite, l'essentiel de la puissance est utilisée pour amplifier du bruit et/ou des brouilleurs lorsque la charge moyenne C_m (en Erlang) des terminaux est faible (< 10) ce qui n'est pas très efficace.

Cela impose aussi une bonne linéarité du répéteur satellite car les faibles signaux sont les plus sensibles à l'écrêtage. Malgré cette linéarité, la forte variation de charge sur l'étage de puissance du répéteur due au facteur de crête important des parasites (bruit et brouilleurs) induit une modulation parasite de phase (pente AM/PM supérieure à 4° par dB de variation de puissance instantanée d'entrée) pouvant être néfaste pour la localisation et la démodulation à la station. Pour C_m supérieure à 10, le satellite fonctionne plus efficacement mais le problème se reporte au centre de mission qui doit démoduler plus de 10 terminaux simultanément donc avec un auto-brouillage important.

De plus l'antenne satellite devra compenser au mieux les pertes d'espace libre pour éviter de favoriser en réception ("near-far effect") les terminaux proches (peu nombreux) au détriment des terminaux plus éloignés (la majorité).

Des alternatives sont d'effectuer une démodulation à bord mais celle-ci est difficilement envisageable pour un mini-satellite ou d'effectuer un traitement bord pour éliminer (partiellement) les perturbateurs. En réception (centre de mission) on essayera aussi d'utiliser les avantages qu'offrent le filtrage adaptatif pour la réjection de brouilleurs à bande étroite et donc accroître le $(C/No)_t$ (voir /19/ pour des développements intéressants).

4.3 - DIMENSIONNEMENT DE LA LIAISON ALLER (centre de mission vers terminaux)

Les contraintes sur la liaison aller sont beaucoup plus sévères, la partie descendante satellite vers terminaux étant sujette aux évanouissements et multitrajets. Les propriétés de l'étalement de spectre permettent une réduction des marges nécessaires (sorte de diversité de fréquence). Le flux informationnel aller total, composé des interrogations et des transactions, a été évalué (voir /1/) à R_b = 14 kbits/s.

La réutilisation du même transpondeur satellite conduit à un premier scénario (voir figure 4) utilisant lui aussi la modulation NRZ/MSK/DS.SSMA (ou NRZ/OQPSK filtré/DS.SSMA) avec le même rythme bribe R_{bribe} mais un code d'étalement orthogonal à celui des terminaux. Il est alors possible d'assurer, par la transmission d'une trame aller continue servant de base de temps et de fréquence, un rendement radiofréquence du répéteur satellite plus intéressant (25% pour une puissance brouilleurs équivalente de 18 dBW au sol en direction du satellite). De plus, cette liaison assure alors un point de fonctionnement plus stable à l'étage de puissance du répéteur (moins de conversion AM/PM).

Malheureusement, cette modulation avec étalement de spectre ne favorise pas la simplicité du terminal et elle lui impose des stratégies plus complexes de réveil pour économiser ses ressources en énergie (batteries ou piles) qui sont limitées. La simplification du terminal peut être obtenue par des modulations type NRZ/BFSK/DS.SSMA avec démodulation non cohérente (proposé dans /20/), mais leurs performances déjà limitées en canal Gaussien ne permettent guère de les envisager.

Pour résister aux évanouissements dans le canal, le choix du code correcteur d'erreur est important (voir /15/,/18/,/21/). Pour ce scénario, divers codes convolutionnels seront comparés en simulation.

Compte tenu des récents efforts autour des associations étroites modulation/codage et pour mettre à profit le "calme" relatif de la bande 149,9-150,05 MHz, des modulations en bande étroite ont été envisagées. Suite aux travaux de Massey et d'Ungerboeck, des études ont mis en exergue un excellent comportement des Modulations Codées en Treillis ("Trellis Coded Modulations" ou TCM) dans les canaux à évanouissements (voir /15/,/18/,/22/). La base de modulation de ces TCM est essentiellement les M-PSK ($M \geq 2^3$). De part leur constellation de M secteurs de phase de $2\pi.\log_2 M$ de large, ces modulations, surtout économes en bande occupée (efficacité importante), imposent des contraintes fort gênantes de linéarité de phase pour la liaison. De même, elles entraînent une certaine complexité des terminaux, malgré les premiers développements industriels en cours. De plus, ces modulations ne semblent pas très adaptées à la localisation ; les terminaux ne disposent pas d'une base de temps suffisamment précise pour permettre une réémission dans une fenêtre connue à partir du début d'une trame numérotée.

Sur la base des investigations théoriques précédentes (voir §3), on peut remarquer que l'évanouissement dans la liaison aller est rapide et à forte occurence (rapport 3,8 à 150 MHz et 4 à 400 MHz du temps moyen entre nul au temps moyen d'évanouissement à -8 dB). On peut faire une évaluation de la perte de puissance moyenne causée par les évanouissements :

$$\text{Pertes}_{\text{puissance moyenne}} \simeq 2/\pi \int_{Arccos \frac{1}{\sqrt{\pi}}}^{o} \cos\Theta.d\Theta . (\overline{t_{\text{entre nul}} - t_{\text{eva}}})/\overline{t_{\text{entre nul}}} \simeq 3,7 \text{ dB à 150 MHz et 400 MHz}$$

Cette expression s'applique :
- aux modulations à bande étroites pour des rythmes de bits faibles (inférieurs à 4500 bits/s pour 150 MHz et 12500 bits/s pour 400 MHz)en raison de l'intégration sur la durée d'un bit,
- aux modulations à étalement de spectre où cette perte intervient dans le calcul de l'intercorrélation sur une longueur de quelques bits entre le code reçu partiellement atténué et le code local.

Par contre, les limitations connues sur le TEB dues à l'effet doppler (voir /12/ et /15/) pour les modulations de phase différentielles DPSK (/21/,/23/) et surtout les modulations directes de fréquence M-FSK (voir /23/ et /24/) nous imposent l'usage d'un rythme symbole important et donc d'une $\text{PIRE}_{\text{satellite}}$ pour la voie aller élevée ; d'où selon /12/ :

$$TEB_{\text{irréductible}} = 0,5 . (\pi.f_d/\Delta.R_s)^2 \quad \text{en BFSK, avec } \Delta \text{ l'indice de modulation}$$

La bande occupée peut alors dépasser les 150 kHz disponibles en jouant sur Δ ou R_s. Ces modulations restent intéressantes car elles permettent une démodulation simple au niveau des terminaux ainsi qu'une amplification non-linéaire (donc à meilleure rendement dans le satellite) avec une quasi-absence de brouilleurs. Les mesures doppler nécessitent un préambule de porteuse pure d'une centaine de millisecondes (pour une variance suffisamment faible) ; les mesures de pseudo-distance sont limitées par les performances de la synchronisation en FSK (environ 10 à 15% du rythme symbole R_s aux $(C/N_o)_t$

moyens). Les résultats en terme de bilans de liaison sont moyens mais une investigation plus poussée est envisagée (scénario B de la figure 4).

Pour s'affranchir des problèmes de bruits divers importants de la VHF, tout en restant avec un mini-satellite à charge utile simple, la bande UHF peut être utilisée pour les voies aller et retour descendantes (scénario C de la figure 4). Si l'effet doppler important (8,5 kHz maximum) peut être compensée par le centre de mission, il n'en va pas de même pour les terminaux. Ceux-ci doivent alors travailler dans des conditions difficiles (évanouissements, fort effet doppler) mais les liaisons sont envisageables en NRZ/MSK/DS.SSMA (ou NRZ/OQPSK filtré/DS.SSMA) puisque les bilans sont plus favorables.

5 - LES BILANS DE LIAISON

Une analyse approchée de la faisabilité du système peut être conduite par le biais des bilans de liaison. Trois scénarii (voir fig 4) ont été étudiés pour permettre d'évaluer l'influence des différentes contributions. On retrouve çi-dessous comme exemple les bilans de liaison aller et retour du scénario A (cas moyens).

Pour la voie aller, un codage convolutionnel (7,1/2) a été choisi, le décodeur (par algorithme de Viterbi) étant un composant (VLSI) ou une fonction (informatique) d'usage courant donc envisageable pour les terminaux. Par contre, aucune optimisation n'a été faite pour vérifier que ce code est réellement adapté (comparaison prévue par simulations). La charge moyenne C_m a été prise égale à 4. Les autres valeurs ont été discutées dans les paragraphes précédents. Les performances en gain des antennes ainsi que les PIRE ont été confirmées comme possible par des industriels.

La contribution totale des bruits, brouillage interne et brouillage externe a été calculée à partir des contributions élémentaires suivant les formules classiques suivantes. La validité de celles-ci dépend du choix satellite qui est un répéteur à gain constant ajustable, travaillant en régime linéaire (classe A) avec un rendement RF/DC de 25% environ et dont la consommation est limitée à 82 W sur le bus d'alimentation (les 3 W restants sont utilisés par le reste de la Charge Utile).

$$(C/N_o)_t^{-1} = (C/N_o)_m^{-1} + (C/N_o)_d^{-1} + (C/I_o)^{-1}{}_{stat.\ et/ou\ term.} + (C/I_o)^{-1}{}_{brouilleurs}$$

avec

$(C/N_o)_m = PIRE_{sol}.Affaiblissements.G_{satellite} / k.T_{eq\ rec\ satellite}$

$(C/N_o)_d = PIRE_{utile\ satellite}.Affaiblissements.G_{rec\ sol} / k.T_{eq\ rec\ sol}$

aller $(C/I_o)_{terminaux} = PIRE_{station}.R_{bribe} / 2/3.C_m.PIRE_{terminal}$

retour $\begin{cases} (C/I_o)_{station} = PIRE_{terminal}.R_{bribe} / 2/3.PIRE_{station} \\ (C/I_o)_{autres\ terminaux} = R_{bribe} / 2/3.(C_m-1) \end{cases}$

$(C/I_o)_{brouilleur} = PIRE_{utile}.R_{bribe} / PIRE_{brouilleur}.R_{symb}$

en moyenne avec porteuses proches mais non-cohérentes et même rythme bribe

Pour ces expressions, les terminaux brouilleurs et les brouilleurs externes sont reçus par le satellite avec le même niveau de puissance relative. Ceci suppose qu'ils se situent en moyenne à l'intérieur d'une zone géographique où le diagramme d'antenne satellite compense les pertes d'espace libre.

Coté localisation, sur la base de ces bilans de liaison, quelques simulations informatiques pour la liaison retour (la plus délicate) ont permis d'obtenir les performances d'estimateurs d'écart de fréquence et d'écart de temps suivantes:

$m_{\hat{f}} = 0,1 \pm 0,025$ Hz	$m_{\hat{T}} = 2\%$ de $T_{bribe} = 20 \pm 5$ ns	pour $(C/N_o)_t = 38$ dBHz , $C_m = 4$
$\sigma_{\hat{f}} = 0,5 \pm 0,1$ Hz	$\sigma_{\hat{T}} = 3,5\%$ de $T_{bribe} = 35 \pm 10$ ns	et $D_m \simeq 110$ ms (préambule de 8 bits)

Ces performances tiennent compte du canal satellite (filtrage, non-linéarités) et supposent aucune incertitude sur la fréquence ni sur le temps de transit du satellite et du terminal. De plus, il faut signaler des performances en taux d'acquisition faibles (0,5 ± 0,06 pour une seule unité de traitement) qui vont nécessiter la mise en parallèle d'un grand nombre d'unités de traitement (> 6 pour $C_m = 4$) ainsi qu'une unité de gestion associée au niveau du centre de mission.

S80, Liaison Aller Montante, scénario A

Flux total sur la voie Aller	kb/s	14,0
••••••• CARACTERISATION DU SIGNAL		
Fréquence bribes	kHz	1000,0
Fréquence symboles	kHz	28,0
Bande utile	kHz	1000,0
••••••• EMISSION		
Gain antenne émission	dBi	16,0
PIRE	dB(W)	12,8
••••••• PROPAGATION		
Fréquence	MHz	149,0
Pertes de propagation (espace libre)	dB	147,4
••••••• RECEPTION		
Pertes polarisation	dB	2,0
Gain antenne reception	dBi	3,0
Température de bruit antenne	K	2000,0
Facteur de mérite récepteur	dBI/K	-30,5
(C/No)montant	dBI(Hz)	61,5
S80, Liaison Aller Descendante, scénario A		
••••••• CARACTERISTIQUES REPETEUR		
Gain répéteur (hors antennes)	dB	143,5
PIRE	dB(W)	11,8
••••••• PROPAGATION		
Fréquence	MHz	138,0
Pertes de propagation (espace libre)	dB	145,6
••••••• RECEPTION		
Pertes polarisation	dB	3,0
Pertes par évanouissements	dB	2,0
Gain antenne reception	dBi	1,0
Température de bruit antenne	K	5000,0
Facteur de mérite récepteur	dBI/K	-36,2
(C/No)descendant	dBI(Hz)	53,5
••••• BROUILLEURS INTERNES S80		
Nombre moyen de terminaux brouilleurs		4,0
(C/Io)terminaux	dBI(Hz)	68,6
••••• DEMODULATION DECODAGE		
(C/No)total	dBI(Hz)	52,8
Pertes d'implémentation	dB	2,0
Eb/No	dB	9,3
Eb/No requis	dB	4,4
Marge	dB	4,9
Bilan de puissance de la Charge Utile		
Puissance RF émise par canal	dB(W)	10,3
Puissance RF émise par terminal	dB(W)	-4,5
Puiss. totale consommée par la Charge Utile	W	84,6

S80, Liaison Retour Montante, scénario A

Flux total sur la voie Retour	kb/s	4,4
••••••• CARACTERISATION DU SIGNAL		
Durée de message	ms	100,0
Fréquence bribes	kHz	1000,0
Fréquence symboles	kHz	2,4
Bande utile	kHz	1000,0
••••••• EMISSION		
Gain antenne émission	dBi	1,0
PIRE	dB(W)	-1,1
••••••• PROPAGATION		
Fréquence	MHz	149,0
Pertes de propagation (espace libre)	dB	146,3
••••••• RECEPTION		
Pertes polarisation	dB	3,0
Gain antenne reception	dBi	1,9
Température de bruit antenne	K	2000,0
Facteur de mérite récepteur	dBI/K	-31,6
(C/No)montant	dBI(Hz)	46,7
S80, Liaison Retour Descendante, scénario A		
••••••• CARACTERISTIQUES REPETEUR		
Gain répéteur (hors antennes)	dB	143,5
PIRE	dB(W)	-2,0
••••••• PROPAGATION		
Fréquence	MHz	138,0
Pertes de propagation (espace libre)	dB	146,7
••••••• RECEPTION		
Pertes polarisation	dB	2,0
Pertes par évanouissements	dB	2,0
Gain antenne reception	dBi	16,0
Température de bruit antenne	K	2000,0
Facteur de mérite récepteur	dBI/K	-17,6
(C/No)descendant	dBI(Hz)	58,3
••••• BROUILLEURS INTERNES S80		
(C/Io)canal	dBI(Hz)	44,9
Nombre moyen de terminaux brouilleurs		3,0
(C/Io)terminaux	dBI(Hz)	57,0
••••• DEMODULATION DECODAGE		
(C/No)total	dBI(Hz)	42,4
Pertes d'implémentation	dB	2,0
Eb/No	dB	9,6
Eb/No requis	dB	4,4
Marge	dB	5,2

6 - CONCLUSION

Des modèles théoriques du canal VHF/UHF pour un système de transmission et de localisation ont été présentés. L'expérimentation S80T va permettre de donner des paramètres réalistes à ces modèles. Une première approche par l'intermédiaire de bilans de liaison a permis de dégager quelques scénarii. Leurs caractéristiques ainsi que les choix définitifs seront effectués à la suite de simulations informatiques, par une approche plus fine sur la base des modèles précédemment décrits.

BIBLIOGRAPHIE

/1/ "Taos (S80) : un système LEO-MSS pour des services de localisation et de télégestion"
A. Gautier, P. Dumont - CNES - Colloque SSSS - 1992

/2/ "Protection ratios and minimum field strengths required in the mobile services"
Rapport 358-5, section 8A, rapports du CCIR - 1990

"Niveau minimal de bruit interne : spécification mondiale 0,1 Hz à 100 GHz"
Rapport R670-1, section 1D, rapports du CCIR - 1990

/3/ "Propagation considerations in Satellite Communication Systems"
G. Brossaard, D.V. Rogers - Proc. of the IEEE, vol 78 n° 7 - july 1990

/4/ "Mathematical Analysis of Random Noise" "Statistical Properties of sine wave plus random noise"
S.O. Rice - Bell System Technical Journal, vol 23 et vol 24 - July 1944 et January 1945

/5/ "Lois de probabilité dans la propagation des ondes radioélectriques"
Rapport 1007-1 - rapports du CCIR - 1990

/6/ "Simulation of man-made noise in 100 MHz to 3 GHz band" H.A. Masoum, J.G. Gardiner
Proc of 8th Conference on European Satellite Communications - December 1991

/7/ "Ignition Interference in land mobile environnements : measurements, characterization & models"
A.V.H. Sheikh - Proc 1984 IEEE National Symposium on Electromagnetic Compatibility - April 84

/8/ "A long term trend in urban zone man made radio noise & the UHF automotive ignition resonance"
E.N. Skomal-IEEE 1985 Intern. Symp. on Electromagnetic Compatibility Record, pp 312/317 - 85

/9/ "Ionospheric effects on modern electronic systems"
J.H. Goodman, J. Aarons - Proc of the IEEE, vol 78 n° 3 - March 1990

/10/ "Mid-latitude ionospheric scintillation of geostationnary satellite signals at 137 Mhz"
E.N. Bramley, R. Browning - Journal of Atmospheric and Terrestrial Physics, vol 40 - 1978

/11/ "Ionospheric scintillation"
R.K. Crane - Proc. of the IEEE, vol 65 n° 2 - February 1977

/12/ "Systèmes de Radiocommunications avec les mobiles"
J.G. Remy, J. Cueugniet, C. Siben - CNET - Masson 1990

/13/ "The land mobile satellite communication channel - Recording, Statistics, and Channel Model"
E. Lutz, D. Cygan, M. Dippold, F.Dolainsky et W. Papke
IEEE Trans on Vehicular Technology, vol 40 n° 2 - May 1991

/14/ "Propagation avec les mobiles en milieu urbain"
A. Maloberti - L'Echo des Recherches n° 142 - 4ième trim. 1992

/15/ "Modulation and Coding for satellite and space communications"
J.H. Yuen, M.K. Simon, W. Miller, F. Pollara, C.R. Ryan, D. Divsalar, J. Morakis
Proc. of the IEEE, vol 78 n° 7 - July 1990

/16/ "Coherent spread spectrum systems"
J.K. Holmes - Wiley & sons - 1982

/17/ "Eléments de communications numériques"
J.C. Bic, D. Duponteil, J.C. Imbeaux - Dunod - 1986

/18/ "A comparison of Trellis Coded versus Convolutionally coded spread spectrum Multiple Access systems"
G.D. Boudreau, D.D. Falconer, S.A. Mahmoud - IEEE Journal on
Selected Areas in Communications, vol 8 n° 4 - May 1990

/19/ "Signal Processing for interference rejection in spread spectrum communications"
L.B. Milstein, R.A. Iltis - IEEE ASSP Magazine - April 1986

/20/ "Spread spectrum ASIC eases design of low cost Part 15 systems"
R.W. Simpson - RF Design - December 1990

/21/ "Performance of DPSK with convolutional encoding on time varying fading channels"
S.Y. Mui, J.W. Modestino - IEEE Trans. on Communications, vol COM-25 n° 10 - October 1977

/22/ "Bandwith efficient coding for fading channels : code construction and performance analysis"
C. Schlegel, D.J. Costello - IEEE J. on Selected Areas in Communications, vol 7 n° 9 - Dec 1989

/23/ "Modeling and performance evaluation of mobile VHF radio channels employing FSK, DPSK, QPSK and 8-ary PSK as modulation scheme"
F. Swarts, H.C. Ferreira - IEEE Global Telecoms Conference Globecom'91 - Dec 1991

/24/ "A satellite paging system for land mobile users"
I.E. Casewell, J.C. Ferebee, M. Tomlinson - IEE Fourth International Conference on Satellite systems for Mobile Communications and Navigation - October 1988

/25/ "Low complexity concatenated coding schemes"
A. Brine, P.G. Farrel, R.A. Harris - International Journal of Satellite Communications, vol 7 pp 209/217 - 1989

FIGURES

figure 1 : Mesures de températures d'antenne pour terminaux S80 dans la bande 137-138 MHz

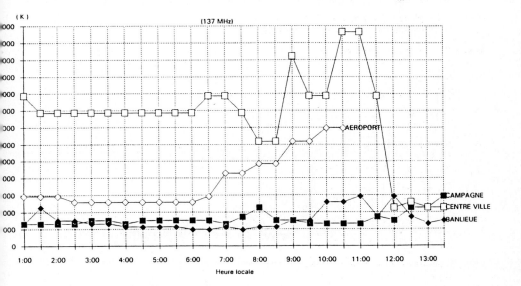

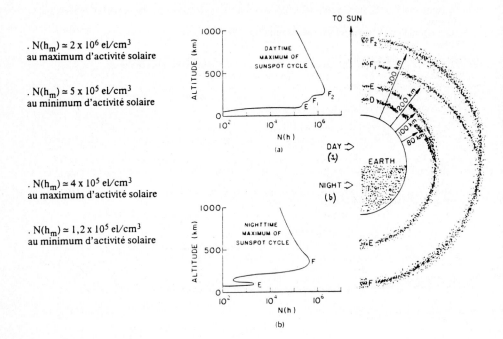

. $N(h_m) \simeq 2 \times 10^6$ el/cm^3
au maximum d'activité solaire

. $N(h_m) \simeq 5 \times 10^5$ el/cm^3
au minimum d'activité solaire

. $N(h_m) \simeq 4 \times 10^5$ el/cm^3
au maximum d'activité solaire

. $N(h_m) \simeq 1,2 \times 10^5$ el/cm^3
au minimum d'activité solaire

figure 3 : Réponse impulsionnelle du canal mesurée en ville à Paris (extrait de /13/)

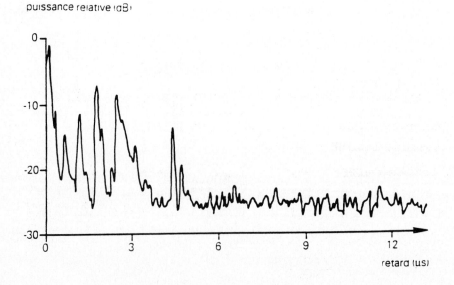

<u>figure 4</u> : Schémas synoptiques des trois scénarii principaux A, B et C

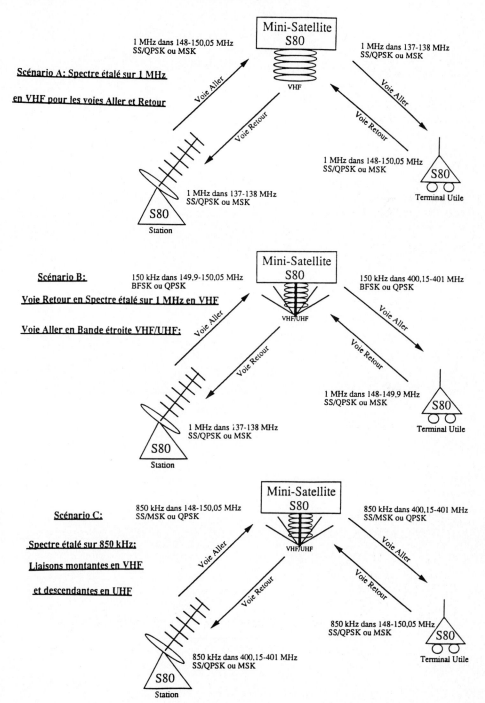

99

SESSION II

MOYENS DE LANCEMENT

LAUNCH SERVICES

Les petits lanceurs

(Projets actuels et futurs dans le monde)

W.G. NAUMANN, ESA

Résumé

L'intérêt pour l'utilisation de satellites de taille modeste s'accroît. Ces satellites ont besoin d'un service de lancement fourni à l'aide de "petits" lanceurs capables de lancer entre 100 kg et 1000 kg sur une orbite polaire de 1000 km d'altitude.

Une vingtaine de projets existe actuellement, les uns ayant déjà atteint le stade opérationnel, les autres étant en cours de développement ou encore à l'étude.

Chaque lanceur a ses particularités et contraintes. Sur le plan technique, les petits lanceurs posent peu de problèmes ; la plupart des projets fait d'ailleurs appel à des éléments existants ou au moins à des technologies maîtrisées. Les particularités de la base de lancement disponible ou choisie peuvent par contre constituer un handicap pour un certain nombre de projets, de même que des aspects politiques. La condition fondamentale cependant pour la viabilité d'un projet est l'obtention du financement et de commandes.

Les petits lanceurs disponibles sans difficultés et à des prix intéressants sont encore rares.

1. Introduction

L'utilisation de petits satellites pour toutes sortes de missions trouve depuis 2 ans environ de plus en plus d'intéressés. Initiée notamment par les militaires à travers les études sur les "Lightsats" de la DARPA, des programmes STEP et RESERVE de l'USAF, l'utilisation de petits satellites a été adoptée par la NASA (Projets COMET et SMEX) et connaît un véritable boom depuis la présentation du projet Iridium par Motorola qui suscite des projets concurrents, d'autant plus que la conférence mondiale des radiocommunications de 1992 (WARC 92) a enlevé des contraintes relatives à l'allocation de fréquences aux systèmes de communication mobiles.

En plus de ces missions essentiellement militaires ou commerciales, la communauté scientifique, pour qui les performances des lanceurs lourds se sont trop éloignées de leurs besoins, revendique des moyens légers et moins coûteux pour la réalisation de ses missions et, enfin, pour bon nombre de pays l'utilisation de petits satellites est le moyen qui leur permet d'entreprendre des programmes spatiaux nationaux indépendants.

Sans que l'on puisse parler de l'existence d'un véritable marché, les projets surgissant côté des satellites provoquent des projets complémentaires côté des lanceurs.

On peut aujourd'hui en lister une bonne vingtaine (Tableau 1). Il est difficile d'établir une liste exhaustive et à jour, la situation évoluant rapidement. Pour la présentation sommaire qui suit, les lanceurs ont été groupés selon leur état d'avancement. On s'est limité aux lanceurs capables de lancer entre 100 kg et 1000 kg sur une orbite polaire de 1000 km d'altitude, performance qui devrait satisfaire les besoins des missions réalisées à l'aide de "petits" satellites.

2. Petits lanceurs opérationnels

2.1.   Shavit (Israel Space Agency)

Le lanceur Shavit, construit par Israeli Aircraft Industries, a lancé les satellites israéliens Offeq-1 (1988) et Offeq-2 (1990) ; le lancement d'Offeq-3 est prévu pour 1993. A partir de sa base Palmachim AFB il n'est lancé que vers l'ouest, au dessus de la Méditerranée afin d'éviter que des débris de lanceur ne tombent sur du territoire arabe. En 1990, Israeli Aircraft Industries et Delta Research, Huntsville ont formé un groupe appelé SLV Vector, Inc. et proposé un lanceur dérivé du Shavit pour le programme COMET de la NASA mais la proposition n'a pas été retenue. Ce lanceur aurait besoin d'une autre base de lancement pour devenir exploitable.

2.2.   Pegasus (Orbital Sciences Corp.)

Pegasus est actuellement la seule entreprise d'un développement nouveau moyennant des investissements privés qui a réussi à atteindre un état opérationnel et à obtenir un nombre significatif de contrats et options.

Pegasus, un lanceur ailé à trois étages lancé d'un B52, a été développé sous forme d'un joint venture par OSC et Hercules (boosters et coiffe) à partir de 1987. En 1988 OSC a reçu son premier contrat, de la DARPA, couvrant 1 lancement et 5 options. Depuis, OSC a obtenu 10 autres contrats fermes plus 34 options de l'USAF et 9 de la NASA. Pegasus a été lancé deux fois à ce jour ; lors du 2ème lancement le satellite a été placé sur une mauvaise orbite.

OSC a récemment acheté un Lockheed L-1011 Tristar en vue du remplacement des lancements avec le B52. Les essais en vol du L-1011 sont prévus pour 1993 après adaptation de l'appareil.

OSC étudie un certain nombre de possibilités pour augmenter la performance du lanceur - Pegasus 2 à 4 étages (env. 800 kg en 185 km) et Pegasus 3 avec des nouveaux moteurs solides (env. 1300 kg en 185 km) - afin de suivre l'évolution des masses des petits satellites (en particulier Iridium).

2.3. Scout (G-1) (LTV)

Le Scout dans toutes ses versions a effectué depuis 1960 env. 115 missions. C'est le petit lanceur par excellence. Sa performance dans sa version actuelle est de 125 kg en orbite polaire de 1000 km. Il n'en reste actuellement que 3 exemplaires, tous affectés à des missions DOD ou NASA. La continuation du service par le LTV Missiles and Electonics Group déprendra des commandes qui seront enregistrées.

2.4. M-3S-II (ISAS)

C'est actuellement le dernier lanceur et le plus performant de la série des lanceurs M produits par Nissan pour l'ISAS. La politique du Gouvernement japonais contraint l'ISAS au développement de lanceurs à propergol solide et un diamètre des coiffes de 1,4m. Le M-3S-II n'est pas destiné à la commercialisation.

2.5. Cosmos (Glavkosmos)

Avec un actif de plus de 380 missions depuis son début en 1964 Cosmos est un des vétérans parmi les lanceurs et aujourd'hui le plus petit des lanceurs russes en service. Malgré des limitations concernant l'azimut de lancement il semble pouvoir placer env. 900 kg sur une orbite polaire de 1000 km. Le Cosmos fait partie de la gamme de lanceurs offerts par Glavkosmos, mais malgré cela très peu d'informations sont disponibles sur ce lanceur.

2.6. CZ-2C (China Great Wall Industry Corporation)

Comme le Cosmos c'est un lanceur bi-étages utilisant le couple N_2O_4/UDMH. Malgré les contraintes de tir, il dispose d'une performance importante et offre un grand volume aux charges utiles. Le lanceur est offert par CGWIC sur le marché commercial (il lancera par exemple le satellite suédois Freja en 1992) mais il tombe actuellement sous la limitation à 9 du nombre de lancements chinois de satellites occidentaux jusqu'à 1994 (accord USA/Chine).

3. Petits lanceurs en développement

3.1. Conestoga (EER/SSI)

Conestoga est un autre projet financé par des capitaux privés. Space Services Inc., maintenant une division de EER, a commencé le développement en 1981. La conception est basée sur l'utilisation des Castor 4B et Star 48B de Thiokol. Plusieurs versions avec un nombre variable de Castors 4B utilisés permet d'obtenir une plage de performance entre 80 et 260 kg en orbite 1000 km/90°. Un vol suborbital a été effectué à partir de Matagorda I. en 1982. Conestoga peut être lancé par une installation mobile. EER a été retenu pour la fourniture des services de lancement pour le programme COMET, sponsorisé par la NASA. COMET est une capsule récupérable offerte par Westinghouse comme entreprise commerciale pour des missions expérimentales. Le contrat de la NASA couvre 3 lancements (1993, 94, 95) et 2 options (96, 97).

3.2. ASLV (ISRO)

Le développement de l'ASLV est financé par le gouvernement indien et dirigé par l'ISRO. Les 2 premiers lancements (1987 et 1988) des 4 lancements approuvés n'ont pas réussi. Le lanceur est essentiellement destiné aux lancements des satellites indiens SROSS mais la tentative d'une commercialisation ultérieure ne peut pas être exclue.

3.3. VLS (IAE/CTA - Brésil)

Le Brésil dispose avec Alcantara d'une base de lancement presque idéale, mais le développement de son lanceur avance difficilement. Le Brésil cherche de l'aide auprès des pays qui disposent de l'expérience et de moyens dans ce domaine. Un aboutissement du programme est difficile à prévoir.

L'excellente situation d'Alcantara a attiré l'attention de China Great Wall Ind. Corp. et de Glavkosmos.

3.4. Scout 2 (ISA/BPD/LTV)

Depuis 1988, BPD associé à LTV étudie et propose le développement d'un Scout 2 composé de 2 propulseurs à poudre dérivés des PAP AR4 et du Scout G-1 avec un 4ème étage dérivé du Mage 2. Le lanceur serait essentiellement lancé depuis la plate-forme San Marco, mais également de Vandenburg ou de Wallops. La performance en orbite polaire de 1000 km serait de 220 kg. Une version avec 4 propulseurs d'appoint portant cette performance à 450 kg est à l'étude. L'aboutissement du programme ne semble pas encore complètement assuré. Un autre projet - San Marco Scout - purement italien est à l'étude.

3.5. CZ-1D (China Great Wall)

Ce lanceur est supposé être prêt à la commercialisation à un prix qui serait de l'ordre de 10 M$. Mais le lanceur ne sera produit qu'en cas de demande. Il est également soumis à l'accord USA/Chine (9 lancements jusqu'à 1994). Etant donné les contraintes de tir, la performance du CZ-1D en orbite polaire est relativement modeste.

3.6. Taurus (OSC)

OSC a été retenu en 1989 par la DARPA pour un contrat de 11 M$ ayant comme objet le développement d'un petit lanceur standard. Le lanceur devrait pouvoir être lancé 72h après la demande à partir d'une installation complètement mobile et rapidement déployable. Le contrat demandait un lancement de démonstration de VAFB en 1991 (maintenant prévu en 1992) et contient des options pour 4 autres lancements d'une valeur de 60 M$. Taurus est composé de 4 étages à propergols solides dont le premier étage est dérivé de l'ICBM Peacekeeper (Thiokol), les autres 3 étages provenant de Pegasus (Hercules). Du point de vue performance, Taurus peut se comparer à COSMOS et CZ-2C tout en étant nettement plus léger. En revanche le diamètre du volume offert aux charges utiles est avec 1,3m nettement inférieur à ceux des concurrents (2,2m et 3m respectivement). OCS espère pouvoir offrir des lancements commerciaux à env. 16 M$ et avec 18 mois de préavis seulement.

3.7.   M-5 (ISAS)

Le M-5 est développé par Nissan dans le cadre du programme spatial japonais sous la responsabilité de l'ISAS et destiné en premier lieu à servir aux missions nationales. M-5 est constitué d'étages à poudre comme tous les lanceurs M de l'ISAS, mais le premier lanceur qui n'est plus limité à un diamètre de 1,4m (autorisation donnée par le Gouvernement en 1990). Un premier lancement est planifié pour 1995. Une tentative de commercialisation de ce lanceur ne semble plus complètement exclue bien qu'elle ne soit pas évidente au prix estimé de l'ordre de 40 M$ et avec les contraintes saisonnières bien connues qui pèsent sur la cadence de lancement des lanceurs japonais (2 périodes par an). Pour contourner ces contraintes, ISAS et Nissan ont d'ailleurs commencé des études sur une version ailée à 3 étages lancée comme Pegasus à partir d'un avion (B-747 ou C-5 ou A-225).

3.8.   Aquila (American Rocket Comp.)

American Rocket Comp. (AMROC) entreprend depuis 1985 à l'aide d'investisseurs privés le développement de lanceurs basé sur l'utilisation de la technologie hybride (LOX ou N_2O/HTPB). Après plusieurs séries d'essais au sol réussies, le premier essai en vol en 1989 a échoué. AMROC espère maintenant pouvoir offrir le lanceur à 4 étages Aquila vers 1995.

3.9.   PSLV (ISRO)

Le développement du lanceur à 4 étages (2 solides, 2 liquides) avec 6 propulseurs d'appoint s'inscrit dans le programme spatial du Gouvernement indien. Commencé en 1987 le développement devrait aboutir en 1992 par le lancement du satellite IRS-1E en orbite polaire, type d'orbite pour laquelle le lanceur est spécialement conçu. Avec sa masse au décollage de 275 to le lanceur ne figure que parmi les petits lanceurs à cause de sa performance modeste (~ 900 kg en 1000 km polaire) qui résulte des contraintes sévères sur l'azimut de tir. Sans contraintes sa performance serait 60% plus élevée. ISRO planifie 1 lancement par an pendant les prochaines années. Il n'est actuellement pas connu de tentatives de commercialisation.

4.   Petits lanceurs en projet

4.1.   Small orbiter (Royal Ordnance Corp.)

Royal Ordnance Corp. a entamé le développement d'un petit lanceur basé sur les moteurs à poudre du Skylark et du Stonechat. La performance même de la version la plus puissante parait très modeste. Peu d'informations sont disponibles sur ce projet.

4.2.   Liberty 1 (Pacific American Launch Systems Inc.)

La "Pac Am" a été créé en 1982 dans le but de développer un service de lancement commercial pour des petites charges utiles. Le lanceur étudié est le seul connu à faire appel à la technologie cryotechnique. Le lanceur proposé à 2 étages et d'une masse au décollage de 30 to devrait pouvoir injecter env. 1 to en orbite basse ; sa performance en orbite polaire de 1000 km n'est pas connue. L'utilisation de la base de lancement "Palima Point" à Hawaii, proposée par les autorités locales de Hawaii mais non réalisé et incertaine, a été envisagée pour ce projet. Le prix de lancement annoncé est de 5 M$, mais l'aboutissement dépend de l'obtention d'un financement et de la réalisation de la base de lancement.

4.3.   ALV (Australian Launch Vehicles Pty. Ltd.)

ALV a été créé en 1988 pour le développement d'une capacité modeste de lancement. Le financement par le Gouvernement de 2 lancements est attendu. Les lancements seraient effectués à partir de Woomera et plus tard de Cape York. Les situations du Liberty 1 et du ALV sont similaires.

4.4.   Astra B1 (E-Prime Aerospace)

Comme pour beaucoup de projets privés, les informations sont également rares sur ce lanceur Astra B1. Tous les moteurs (solides) du lanceur seraient fournis par Thiokol, le corps étant dérivé du Peacekeeper.

4.5.   LittLEO (General Technology Systems Ltd.)

La proposition du LittLEO résulte de l'étude d'un groupe d'industriels européens (GTS, BAe, Royal Ordnance, Saab, MBB) en collaboration avec le Gouvernement de la Norvège en vue de l'utilisation de la station Andøya pour les lancements. Le lanceur de 4 étages qui fait également appel aux moteurs de Thiokol (Castor IVA et Star 48) aurait une performance d'environ 300 kg en orbite polaire de 1000 km. La difficulté à laquelle est confrontée cette entreprise est également l'obtention du financement.

4.6.   J1 (Mitsubishi/Nissan)

Les industriels impliqués dans le développement du H2 (Mitsubishi/Nissan) et la production du M-3SII (Nissan) proposent le développement d'un petit lanceur pour le marché commercial. Il utiliserait un propulseur d'appoint du H2 comme premier étage complété du 2ème et 3ème étage du M-3SII. Les promoteurs affichent une performance de 1000 kg en orbite basse de 250 km, prévoient une disponibilité en 1995/96 et estiment le prix de lancement à 29 à 35 M$. La NASDA semble favorable à ce projet mais ne dispose pas encore d'un financement approuvé.

4.7. DLA-P (CNES)

Le CNES, qui est le maître d'oeuvre du développement du lanceur européen Ariane 5, propose le développement, moyennant un financement gouvernemental, d'un lanceur d'une capacité de 1000 kg en orbite polaire de 1000 km et disponible vers 1998. Il serait constitué de 2 étages à poudre de 85 to et 30 to respectivement et d'un 3ème étage liquide de 5 to, dérivé de l'étage supérieur d'Ariane 5. Le lancement se ferait de Kourou bien entendu.

6. Conclusions

Malgré le nombre et la variété impressionnants de projets, l'utilisateur qui cherche à mettre en orbite un satellite ou une série de satellites trouvera après une analyse critique que les moyens sûrs et disponibles sans difficultés majeures et à des prix intéressants sont encore rares. On peut retenir le Pegasus de OSC qui a réussi à s'installer grâce à des contrats gouvernementaux mais on notera aussi que ce lanceur n'a effectué jusqu'ici qu'un vol réussi et un réussi à moitié ; il n'a donc pas encore atteint le stade de la maturité. Pour les charges utiles plus lourdes il existent effectivement CZ-2C et Cosmos, deux lanceurs opérationnels et même offerts à des prix intéressants pour l'utilisateur par China Great Wall Ind. et Glavkosmos. Le lancement du satellite suédois Freja par un CZ-2C est un exemple qui prouve que ce lanceur offre une possibilité réelle. Cependant, l'utilisation de ces deux lanceurs est mal reçue par les gouvernements et concurrents occidentaux puisque les prix (bas) offerts résultent des conditions économiques très différentes de celles des économies occidentales. Ainsi le nombre de lancements "occidentaux" par les Chinois est-il limité à 9 jusqu'en 1994 et les lancements par les Russes sont souvent empêchés par le refus de la licence d'exportation du satellite (exception récente : INMARSAT 3 pour lancement par PROTON).

Parmi les lanceurs en développement, le Conestoga d'EER, qui a été retenu pour le programme COMET, et le TAURUS de OSC, qui peut s'appuyer sur des contrats gouvernementaux semblent avoir une chance de devenir opérationnels bientôt et d'attirer des clients. L'entrée en service de l'Aquila n'est pas prévue avant 1995 et AMROC ne semble pas encore avoir vaincu la méfiance des sponsors et des clients vis-à-vis de sa nouvelle technologie hybride. Le CZ-1D souffre du même handicap que le CZ-2C. Les autres projets n'ont pas encore atteint un stade qui permettrait de bâtir des programmes sur leur utilisation.

La réalisation des lanceurs J1 et DLA-P dépendra des décisions des Gouvernements concernés; pour ce qui concerne l'ensemble des autres projets industriels, il est difficile de prévoir leur avenir.

L'utilisateur trouve et trouvera donc des moyens pour lancer des charges utiles dites petites. Ce qu'il ne trouve pas (encore ?) c'est le moyen de lancement réellement bon marché, abstraction faite de l'exploitation de la filière chinoise ou russe.

Une proposition qui parait de plus en plus souvent maintenant vise la reconversion des missiles balistiques en lanceurs commerciaux (les SS18, SS20 russes ou Minuteman américains par exemple). Techniquement possible, l'idée fait peur aux Gouvernements et à l'industrie aérospatiale car, si réalisée, l'inondation du marché des lanceurs risque de ruiner une grande partie de l'industrie spatiale établie.

Références :

(1)   Interavia Space Directory 1991-92

(2)   World Guide to Commercial Launch Vehicles by Franck Sietzen Jr., Pasha Publications, Arlington, USA 1991

(3)   International Reference Guide to Space Launch Systems by Steven J. Isakowitz, Ed. 1991, Publié par AIAA Washington, USA

(4)   ESA Launch Vehicle Catalogue, Ed. 1991

(5)   Dossiers de Programme, DLA-S et DLA-P, CNES 1992 (document non public)

Désignation	Origine	Etat d'avt.	Masse au décollage to	Performance H_circ km	Performance Incl. deg	Performance Masse kg	Vol cyl. C/U Ø m	Vol cyl. C/U haut. m	Base de lancement	Limitation azimut de tir	Nbre étages	Re-marque
Small Orbiter (LV4)	UK (Royal Ordnance Corp.)	E	?	? / 1000	? / 90	150 / ?	?	?	?	?	4P	
Shavit	Israel (ISA)	O	?(20)	555 / 1000	90 / 90	(150)) / (100))	~1,2	?	Palmachim AFB	vers ouest	3P	
Pegasus	USA (OSC)	O	19	555 / 1000	90 / 90	240 / 120	1	1,5	DFRF ou VAFB	0 - 360°	3P	
Conestoga II	USA (EER)	D (1992)	?(20)	555 / 1000	90 / 90	270 / (80)	1,45	2,10	Mobile Matagorda Isl. ou Wallops FF	vers sud ou est	3P	3 Castor + 1 Star
Scout (G-1)	USA (LTV)	O	22	555 / 1000	90 / 90	167 / 125	0,8	1,2	VAFB Wallops FF San Marco	i: 76° - 146° 38/41°;50/52 2,9° - 38°	4P	
Liberty 1	Pacific American Launch Systems Inc.	E	30	LEO / 1000	/ 90	1000 / ?	2(?)	?	Palima Point, Hawaii	entre est et sud	2 L	cryot.
ASLV	Inde (ISRO)	D (1992)	39	400 / 1000	47 / 90	150 / ?	0,8	1,2	SHAR Center (Sriharikota)	140°	5P	
ALV	Australie (ALV Pty. Ltd.)	E	47	? / 1000	? / 90	200 / ?	(1,4)	?	Woomera et Cape York	vers sud ou est	2(?)P + 2B	
VLS	Brésil (CTA/IAE)	D (?)	51	555 / 1000	90 / 90	180 / (60)	1	1,2	Alcantara	(-10 - 100°)	4P	

Tableau 1/1 : Petits lanceurs

111

Désignation	Origine	Etat d'avt.	Masse au décollage to	Performance H_circ km	Performance Incl. deg	Performance Masse kg	Vol cyl. C/U φ m	Vol cyl. C/U haut. m	Base de lancement	Limitation azimut de tir	Nbre étages	Remarque
Scout 2-2	Italie/ USA	D (1993)	52	555 1000	90 90	(310) (220)	1	1,2	Voir Scout (G-1)	Voir Scout (G-1)	4P +2B	
ASTRA B1	E PRIME Aerospace Corp.	E	?	LEO		680	?		CCAFS	? (57° - 112°)	4P	
M-3S II	Japon (ISAS)	O	62	555 1000	90 90	310 0	1,4	2	Kagoshima Space Center	90° - 160°	3P + 2B	4ème ét. en option
Conestoga III	USA (EER)	E/D	?(65)	555 1000	90 90	650 (180)	1,45	2,10	Voir C.II	Voir C.II	4P	5 Castor + 1 Star
LittLEO	G.B. (GTS)	E	67	600 1000	SSO SSO	500 (300)	?	?	Europe (?)	?	4P	
Scout 2-4	Italie/USA	E	(78)	555 1000	90 90	(650) (450)	1	1,2	voir Scout (G-1)	voir Scout (G-1)	4P + 4B	
CZ-1D	Chine (CGWIC)	D (1992)	80	300	70	550[1] 740[2]	1,5 1,0	1 2	Jiuquan Sat.L.C.	57° - 70°	2L 1P	[1] 3 axes [2] spinné
Taurus	USA (OSC)	D (1992)	82	555 1000	90 90	1000 840	1,3	2,4	CCAFS VAFB	57° - 112° 185° - 270°	4P	
Conestoga IV	USA (EER)	E/D	?(90)	555 1000	90 90	840 (260)	1,45	2,10	Voir C.II	Voir C.II	4P	7 Castor + 1 Star
J1	Japon (MHI)	E	~ 100	250 500 1000	? 90 90	1000 690 ?	1,4	2	Tanegashima Space Center	85°-135°	3P	

Tableau 1/2 ; Petits lanceurs

Désignation	Origine	Etat d'avt.	Masse au décollage to	Performance H_circ km	Incl. deg	Masse kg	Vol cyl. C/U φ m	haut. m	Base de lancement	Limitation azimut de tir	Nbre étages	Remarque
Cosmos	CEI (Glavk.)	O	120	400 / 1000	(74) / (74)	~1200 / (~900)	2,2	1,8	Plesetsk + Kapustin Yar	? (10° - 90°) ? (100°)	2L	N_2O_4/ UDMH
M-5	JAPON (ISAS)	D (1995)	130	185 / 1000	90 / 90	1300 / ?	2,2	3,3	Kagoshima Space Center	90° - 160°	3P	
Aquila	USA (AMROC)	D (1995)	(131)	550 / 1000	90 / 90	1000 / 880	1,6 / 1	0,6 / 1,9	VAFB	(180° - 270°)	4	Hybride LOX/ HTPB
DLA-P	France (CNES)	E	140	500 / 1000	90 / 90	1150 / 1000	2,6	3	Kourou	-10,5°-91,5°	3 (2P+ 1L)	
CZ-2C	Chine (CGWIC)	O	190	550 / 1000	SSO / SSO	1100 / ?(700)	3	2	Jiuquan Sat.L.C.	57° - 70°	2L	N_2O_4/ UDMH
PSLV	Inde (ISRO)	D (1993)	275	900 / 1000	SSO / SSO	1000 / ?(900)	(3)	?	SHAR Center (Sriharikota)	140°	2P 2L +6B	

Tableau 1/3 : Petits lanceurs

Désignation (Performance 1000 km pol.)	Opérateur	Opér. depuis	Nb de lancem. (~ fin 91)	Taux succes. %	Manifest 92	Manifest 93	Manifest 94	Prix Lancement	Prix au kg 1000 km polaire	Remarques
Shavit (100 kg ?)	Israel Space Agency Tel Aviv, Israel	1988	2	100	-	1	-	22 M$	0,22 M$	Contraintes sévères de lancement. Non disponible sur le marché
Pegasus 120 kg	Orbital Sciences Corp. Fairfax, Va. USA	1990	2	100	3	3	1	7-12 M$	0,06-0,1 M$	Lancement aéroporté ; plusieurs sites de lancement possibles
SCOUT (G-1) 125 kg	Ling Temco Vought (LTV) Miss. & Electr. Group, Dallas, Tx, USA	1979	15	100	1	2	?	10-12 M$	0,08-0,1 M$	Il n'en reste que 3, affectés à des missions DOD ou NASA
M-3S-II (0 kg)	ISAS Kanagawa, Japon	1971	6	100	-	1	-	31 M$	0,1M$ 555km (0kg→1000km)	Non commercialisé
Cosmos (900 kg ?)	Glavkosmos Moscou, CEI	1964	389	97,9	?	?	?	?	?	2 échecs en 1991
CZ - 2C (700 kg ?)	China Great Wall Industry Corp. Beijing, RPC	1975	12	100	2	-	1	~ 20 M$	0,03 M$ (?)	Limitation par Accord USA-RPC

Tableau 2 : Petits lanceurs opérationnels

Désignation (Performance 1000 km pol.)	Source de financement	Contractant principal	Période de dév.	IOC prévue	Remarques
Conestoga II,III,IV (80) à (260)	Capitaux privés US	Space Services Inc., Houston (Div. de EER Systems Corp.)	1981 1992	ouvert	Basé sur l'utilisation des Castor 4B et Star 48B comme dernier étage (Thiokol) ; vol sub-orbital de démonstration en 1982.
ASLV (0 ?)	Inde, Gouvernement, ISRO	ISRO, Vikram Sarabhai Space Center, Trivandrum	1973 -1993	1994	Dérivé du SLV-3. 4 lancements approuvés ; 2 échecs jusqu'ici (1987,1988) 2 lancements restent à faire. Commercialisation ?
VLS (60)	Bresil, Gouvernem. IAE/CTA	Avibras Industria Aerospacial SA, Sao José dos Campos	1975 -1994(?)	?	Basé sur la technologie des FS SONDA I à IV. Manque de financement ; cherche de l'aide auprès d'autres pays. Base de lancement (Alcantara) très bien placée.
Scout 2 (220)	Italie, Gouvernement, ISA	BPD (avec LTV)	1988 -1994(?)	1994(?)	Basé sur le Scout G-1 ; 2 boosters dérivés des PAP AR4, 4ème étage dérivé du Mage 2.
CZ-1D (200 ??)	Chine, RP Gouvernement, Min. of Astronautics	CGWIC et Beijing Wan Yuan Industry Corp.	1985(?) -1991	?	Prêt à la commercialisation. Lancement prévu seulement en cas de demande. Soumis à l'accord USA/Chine (9 lancements jusqu'en 1994).
Taurus (840)	USA, Gouvernement DARPA	OSC (Space Data Corp., Pheonix)	1989 -1992	1993(?)	Lancement de démonstration prévu en 1992. Peut être lancé à partir d'une installation mobile (tout sur remorques).
M-5 ?	Japon, Gouvernement, ISAS	Nissan Motor Co., Tokyo	1989 -1995	1996(?)	Programme décidé et financé. Commercialisation non exclue.
Aquila (880)	Capitaux privés US	American Rocket Company (Amroc) Camarillo, Cal.	1985 -1995	1996	Technologie hybride (LOX ou N_2O/HTPB). Plusieurs séries d'essais au sol effectuées. Echec du premier essai en vol en 1989.
PSLV (900)	Inde, Gouvernement, ISRO	Vikram Sarabhai Space Center	1987 -1992	1993	Combinaison d'étages solides(2) et d'étages liquides (2)+ 6 prop. d'appoint solides (2è étage équipé du moteur VIKAS).

Tableau 3 : Petits lanceurs en développement

Désignation (Performance 1000 km pol.)	Proposé par	Financement envisagé	IOC prop.	Remarques
Small Orbiter (LV4) (?)	Royal Ordnance Corp. Bucking-hamshire, R.U.	Investissment par l'entreprise (?)	1992(?)	Basé sur le moteur à propergol solide "Stonechat".
Liberty 1 (?)	Pacific American Launch Systems Inc. Menlo Park, Cal.	Capitaux privés ou contrat gouvernemental	J+ 2ans	2 étages, tous LOX/LH. pressurés ; MAD 30 to ; 1 to en LEO de Palimas Point, Hawaii, pour 5 M$. Le projet attend son financement.
ALV (?)	Australian Launch Vehicles Pty. Ltd., Australie	Financement gouvernemental + investissement pr. (?)	?	Financement gouvern. pour 2 essais en vol attendu ; situation inconnue
ASTRA B1 (?)	E-Prime Aerospace Corp. Titusville, Fla.	Investissemnet par l'entreprise (?)	?	Les moteurs à propergol solide seraient fournis par Thiokol Situation d'avancement inconnue
LittLEO (300?)	Gen. Tech. Systems Ltd avec BAe, MBB, Saah, et la Norvège	Privé et/ou gouvernemental	1992(?)	Basé sur Castor 4A et Star 48 ; lancé de Andøya en Norvège. Situation d'avancement inconnue.
Scout 2-4 (450)	BPD Difesa & Spazio Colleferro	Financement gouvernemental	1995	Version avec 4 propulseurs d'appoint
J1 (450?)	Nissan Motor Co. et Mitsubishi Heavy Ind.	?	1996	Propulseurs d'appoint du H2 + 2ème et 3ème étage du M-3SII
DLA-P (1000)	CNES	Financement gouvernemental	1998	P85 + P30 + L5

Tableau 4 : Petits lanceurs en projet

Endroit Désignation	Etat Autorité	Coordonnées Lat./Long.	Azimut de tir	Remarques
Plesetsk	CEI Min. Défense	62,8° N 40,1° E	(10°-90°?)	Opérationnel. Plus de 1300 lancements. Inclinaisons habituelles : 66°,74°,83°. Dog-leg nécessaire pour ≥ 90°.
Kapustin Yar	CEI Min. Défense	48,4° N 45,8° E	(100° ± ??)	Opérationnel (depuis 1947). Plus de 85 lancements. Inclinaison habituelle : 51°. Utilisé rarement maintenant.
Jiuquan JSLC	RP Chine CSLTCG	40,6° N 99,9° E	(sud-est)	Opérationnel. Limité aux tirs vers sud-est. Inclinaisons habituelles : 57°-70°. Dog-leg pour ≥ 90°.
Kagoshima K. Space Centre	Japon ISAS	31,2° N 131,1° E	90° - 160°	Opérationnel. Inclinaisons nominales : 31°-85°. Lancements autorisés en janv.févr. et août/sept. seulement.
Tanegashima T. Space Centre	Japon NASDA	30,2° N 131,0° E	85° - 135°	Opérationnel. Inclinaisons nominales : 28°-70° ; dog-leg pour plus. Restrictions saisonnières pour J1 ?
Palmachim AFB	Israel Forces de l'air	31,9° N 34,7° E	Départ rétrograde	Base militaire au sud de Tel Aviv. Inclinaison nominale de 143°. Deux lancements : Offeq 1 et 2 (1988 et 1990).
Sriharikota SHAR	Inde ISRO	13,7° N 80,2° E	≤ 140°	Opérationnel. Contrainte sévère sur l'azimut de tir.
Kourou CSG	France CNES	5,2° N 52,8° O	-10,5° - 91,5°	Opérationnel. Plus de 50 lancements. Inclinaisons 4°-100°. Pas de contraintes saisonnières. Accès facile.
Alcantara	Brésil (CTA/IAE ?)	2,3° S 44,4° O	(similaire à Kourou)	Certaines installations existent. Prévue pour le lancement du VLS. La Chine et la CEI intéressées.
Kenya San Marco PF	Italie Gouvernement	2,9° S 40,3° E	82° - 130°	Plate-forme maritime. Bien placé pour lancements équatoriaux (i : 2,9° - 38°).

Tableau 5/1 : Bases de lancement pour petits lanceurs

Endroit Désignation	État Autorité	Coordonnées Lat./Long.	Azimut de tir	Remarques
Cape Canaveral ESMC/CCAFS	USA USAF	28,5° N 81,0° O		Opérationnel. Plus de 420 lancements. Pour lancements en orbites équatoriales.
Vandenburg WSMC/VAFB	USA USAF	34,4° N 120,4° O	164° - 287+	Opérationnel. Plus de 490 lancements. Pour lancements en orbites polaires.
Edwards DFRF	USA NASA	35,0° N 118,0° O	0 - 360°	Décollage porteur (B52) Pegasus.
Wallops I. WFF	USA NASA	37,8° N 75,5° O	85° - 109° 126° - 129°	Opérationnel. Utilisé par EER pour Conestoga
Matagorda I.	USA (militaire)	28,2° N 96,4° O	Vers le sud	Champs d'exercice pour tirs d'artillerie et de bombardement. Utilisé par EER pour Conestoga.
Hawaii Palima Pt.	USA a. d.	19,2° N 155,5° O	Entre est et sud	Au sud de Hawaii. Projet commercial destiné au lancements commerciaux.
Andøya A. Rocket Range	Norvège NSC	69,2° N 16,0° E	Vers le nord	Adapté pour lancements en orbites polaires. Envisagé pour le projet LittLEO.
Woomera	Australie	31,1° S 136,8° E		Pourrait être utilisé pour premiers lancements ALV
Cape York Spaceport	Australie a.d.	12,3° S 143,0° E		A l'étude. Investissement incertain. Envisagé pour le projet ALV (et Zenit).

Tableau 5/2 : Bases de lancement pour petits lanceurs

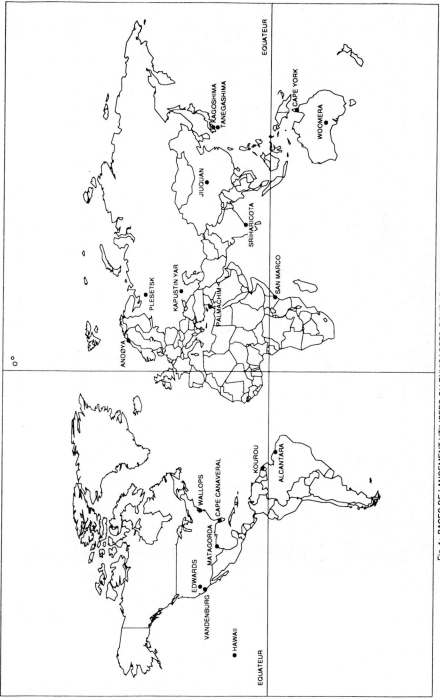

Fig. 1: BASES DE LANCEMENT UTILISEES OU ENVISAGEES POUR LE LANCEMENT DE "PETITS LANCEURS"

119

SMALL SATELLITE CONSTELLATION DEPLOYMENT STRATEGIES

Giuseppe Rondinelli and Enrico Masci

TELESPAZIO S.p.a. - Via Tiburtina 965 - 00156 Roma, Italy

ABSTRACT

In view of the business opportunities offered by small satellites, a large number of firms are developing systems with different constellations applicable to commercial use.
For all these communications systems the deployment strategy and the associate launcher selection play a strategic role being related to the investment plan and to revenues.
Two types of launchers can be envisaged for small satellites: small launchers or conventional launchers.
Foreseeing the market growth new small launchers are planned and their programs are at different stages of development.
The conventional launchers can accomodate small satellites in cluster or in piggyback mode. The piggyback mode is suitable only for single launch or for implementation of constellations with a limited number of satellites. To implement constellations with a large number of satellites it is necessary to adopt a cluster mode launch to inject them directly into the final orbit.
This paper shows some optimization criterias for deployment policies of small satellite constellations; after a brief review of planned system from an orbital point of view, it deals with a series of tradeoff considerations between: launchers/orbits type, launcher capability/constellations implementation, launcher/launch base selection, launcher availability/constellation deployment time, launch strategy/orbit and constellation requirements.

1. INTRODUCTION

The need for communications is increasing throughout the World, the trend is to go towards a final solution represented by a Global Personal Communications System.
The possible applications range is wide, from the emergency, search and rescue, business connection for travellers to the more simple personal communications requirements.
These systems are complementary to the cellular network, were it is developed, and integrate the existing service in region were the population density or the local political or economical situation dont'allow an expansion of the terrestrial communications services.
In this context, considering these new perspectives, a large number of firms are developing systems offering services that use different satellite constellations.
The principal characteristics of the proposed systems are two: the adoption of Low Earth Orbit and the use of Small Satellites.

The selection of a Low Earth Orbit is highlighted by a great number of constraints as: service, coverage requirements, temporal availability, spacecraft power requirements.

SYSTEM	ORBIT & Altitude	INCL.	PERIOD	ORBITAL PLANES	SAT. PER PLANE	TOTAL SAT.	SERVICES	ESTIMATED COSTS US $
ORBCOMM	Circular 970 Km	50° 90°	104.47 min.	3 2	6 1	18 2	Two way data comm. Geolocation	283 Millions
GONETS	Circular 1390 Km	83°	113.56 min.	6	6	36	Data and Messaging in store and forw. comm.	N.A.
LEOCOM	Circular 780 Km	90°	100.44 min.	4	6	24	Two-way data comm. Store and forw. comm.	180 Millions
LEOSAT	Circular 970 Km	40°	104.47 min.	3	6	18	Two-way data comm.	21 Millions
STARSYS	Circular 1300 Km	60°	111.59 min.	4	6	24	Position reporting Messaging comm.	300 Millions
ODISSEY	Circular 10371 Km	55°	359.53 min.	3	4	12	Voice and data comm. Geolocation	1.3 Billions
IRIDIUM	Circular 765 Km	90°	100.13 min.	7	11	77	Voice and data comm.	2.5 Billions
ELLIPSO 1	Elliptic 576/1439 Km	63.4°	105.25 min.	2	3	6	Voice and data comm. Geolocation	214 Millions
ELLIPSO 2	Elliptic 426/2900 Km	63.4°	119.57 min.	2	9	18	Voice and data comm. Geolocation	
ARIES	Circular 1018 Km	90°	105.5 min.	4	12	48	Voice and data comm. Positioning	292 Millions
GLOBALSTAR	Circular 1389 Km	52°	113.53 min.	8	3	24	Voice and data comm. Geolocation	657 Mill. (24 sat) 830 Mill. (48 sat)

TABLE 1 – COMMUNICATIONS SYSTEM CHARACTERISTICS

As regards the use of small satellites, the existing technology offers the possibility of providing on board communications payloads composed of several trasponders and, at the same time, the opportunity to reduce investment costs necessary for the systems implementation.
Therefore there are also other proposed systems that foresee the use of a constellation, these are for example high value services such as environmental data relay or dedicated data trasmission services.
It is also possible to build and launch small colocated geostationary satellites allowing a gradual implementation of multisat/multitransponder system. The principal benefits of such a system are : only one orbital slot and only a single frequency plan can be requested, the system can begin to operate in a very short

time , it is possible to recondition the whole program on the basis of Return Of Investments.

2. THE LAUNCHER ROLE

For all the above mentioned communications systems the deployment strategy plays a strategic role, being related to the investment plan and to revenues, which become significant only when a significant number of satellites is in orbit and a suitable market penetration is achieved.
In this strategic planning key factors are: the launcher selection, the launch cost and the launch service availability and completeness. Two types of launchers can be envisaged for small satellites: small launchers or conventional launchers.

LAUNCHER	PAYLOAD (Kg)			REL. %	TOTAL LAUN.	PROC. LEAD TIME Months	LAUNCH RATE CAPAB. per Year	LAUNCH COST Mil. US$	MAX COST/Kg Polar Orbit US K$	STATUS	FIRM
	Polar Orbit 200 Km	Equat. Orbit 200 Km	GTO								
Scout	210	270	---	98	93	24-36	5-6	10-12	57	Operational	LTV
Scout II	390	510	---	--	--	24-36	5-6	15	38.5	Development	LTV-BPB
Taurus I	1200	1630	---	--	--	--	--	15	12.5	Development	OSC
Taurus IA	1800	2450	---	--	--	--	--	18	10	Development	OSC
Pegasus	360	450	---	100	1	12	12	7-12	33.4	Operational	OSC
Aquila 21	1400	1900	---	--	--	--	--	--	--	Development	AMROC
Littleo	720	980	---	--	--	--	--	--	--	Planning	GTSL *
H1	1400	---	1100	100	7	12	1	90	64.3	Operational	Mits.H.I.
Kosmos	900	---	---	98	377	--	28	--	--	Operational	CSI **
Burlak	750	1020	---	--	--	--	--	6	8	Development	CSI

* General Technology System Limited
** CSI Ministry of Defense, CSI Accademy of Sciences, GlavKosmos

TABLE 2 – SMALL LAUNCHER CHARACTERISTICS

3. SMALL LAUNCHERS

By using a Launcher of this class it is possible to inject one or more small satellites up to a total of 2000 Kg in a circular Low Earth Orbit.
At present the existing small launchers are the American SCOUT G1 and PEGASUS, the Russian KOSMOS and the Japanese H-1. Foreseeing prevision of the market growth new launchers are planned and their programs are at different stages of development. Examples of these are the American AQUILA and TAURUS, the Italian S.MARCO SCOUT, the European LITTLEO and the Russian BURLAK whose performances are

shown together the characteristics of existing small launcher in table 2.
In particular as it can be seen the cost per Kg on orbit is higher respect to a corresponding cost for an heavy launcher but if this phenomena is evident for the oldest launchers as Scout and H1 as regard the new launchers generation it can be noted a reduced cost and a potential trend of further reduction as in the case of the Pegasus and its improved version Taurus.

LAUNCHER	PAYLOAD (Kg)			REL. %	TOTAL LAUN.	PROC. LEAD TIME Months	LAUNCH RATE CAPAB. per Year	LAUNCH COST Mil. US$	MAX COST/Kg Polar Orbit US K$	STATUS	FIRM
	Polar Orbit 200 Km	Equat. Orbit 200 Km	GTO								
Ariane 40	3500	4600	1900	100	1	29	8	80-100	28.6	Operational	Arianespace
Ariane 44L	7500	9500	3770	75	4	29	10	100-140	18.7	Operational	Arianespace
Atlas I	4200	5800	2340	100	1	36	4	59-80	19	Operational	General Dy.
Atlas IIa	6100	8000	2900	--	--	36	4	80-90	15	Development	General Dy.
Delta 6925	2800	3800	1450	100	14	--	10	45-50	18	Operational	McDonnel D.
Delta 7925	3500	4700	1850	100	1	--	10	45-50	14.3	Operational	McDonnel D.
Titan II	3400	4200	1800	100	2	30	3	43	13	Operational	Martin Mar.
Titan IV	15000	17800	8500	100	3	33	10	154	10.3	Operational	Martin Mar.
Proton	17000	---	5500	92	75	18-24	13	35-70	4.2	Operational	CSI *
Soyuz	6800	---	--	98	875	--	45	15	2.2	Operational	CSI
Molniya	6300	---	--	95	258	--	16	15	2.4	Operational	CSI
H2	6500	---	4000	--	--	24	4	100-120	18.5	Development	Mits. H. I.
Long March 3	3800	---	1400	85	7	--	2	32-50	13.2	Operational	CGWIC **

* CSI Ministry of Defense, CSI Accademy of Sciences, GlavKosmos
** China Great Wall Industry Corporation

TABLE 3 – CONVENTIONAL LAUNCHER CHARACTERISTICS

4. CONVENTIONAL LAUNCHERS

The conventional launchers can accomodate small satellites in cluster or in piggyback mode.
The piggyback mode requires additional constraints on the satellite in order to make compatible the interfaces with the main passenger or with the possible support platform, as in the case of ASAP for Ariane. It is suitable only for single launch or for implementation of constellations with a limited number of satellites, maximum 2 or 3. In fact the probability of having different launches of the primary passenger on the desidered orbit is very low, the same occuring for the launch frequency.

Thus, for implementing constellations with a large number of satellites it is necessary to adopt a cluster mode launch.

Many projects are running in this field by different firms; the European ARIANE and the American TITAN and DELTA are being equipped with special adapters for cluster launch, having the great advantage of being able to inject up to 12 satellites of the Mini-sat class directly in the final orbit, saving fuel mass and reducing the launch cost and satellite complexity.

Table 3 summarizes the characteristics and the performances of the principal Launchers on the market together with their launch cost and cost per Kg on polar orbit.

5. DEPLOYMENT STRATEGY KEY FACTORS

The flux diagram in table 4 represents a logical-analytical technique for the optimal selection of a deployment sequence. The inputs considered for the constellation are : orbital parameters for each orbit, number and location of the satellites in each orbit plane. A second set of inputs consists of mass, volume and size of the dry payload with the relative interfaces.

Politics

The launchers selection for a generic mission involves some economic-political considerations that have to be investigated before proceeding to the technical-economic analysis. An example of these are bad relationships between governments or companies that produce launchers and manage launch bases. Another example could be the economic competition upon world scale between companies that implies restrictions on export licence or technology transfer.

Launcher/Spacecraft envelope fitting

The ability of a specific launch vehicle to accomodate the payload mass and volume is one of the most important issue in selecting a launch opportunity. The payload capacity of a vehicle generally refers to all hardware above the launch vehicle interface, excluding the payload fairing. It includes all the hardware needed to adapt the satellites to the booster, pyroptechnic devices, any customer-supplied propulsion units required for precision orbit injection and/or post-release orbital plane changes together with spin or de-spin payload platform as required. The vehicle payload weight capacity is dependent on the desired orbit (semi-major axis and inclination) as well as the latitude of the launch site. The payload weight capacity should also include a weight margin of 15-25% for payload weight growth and the other vehicle weight/performance uncertainties. Each launch vehicle provides one or more payload fairing options, that impose stringent limits on the payload volume and on the design of booster adapter structures, and significantly affect the weight requirement for the booster adapter, particulary in the case of multiple-satellite launches. For some vehicles special payload fairings can be designed to accomodate oversized payloads reducing in general the payload weight capability of vehicle and increasing the non-recurring development costs.

Costs

In the tables 2 and 3 are presented the some launch costs. It is important to note that in order to obtain a significant value, the cost per kg launched in orbit must be considered.

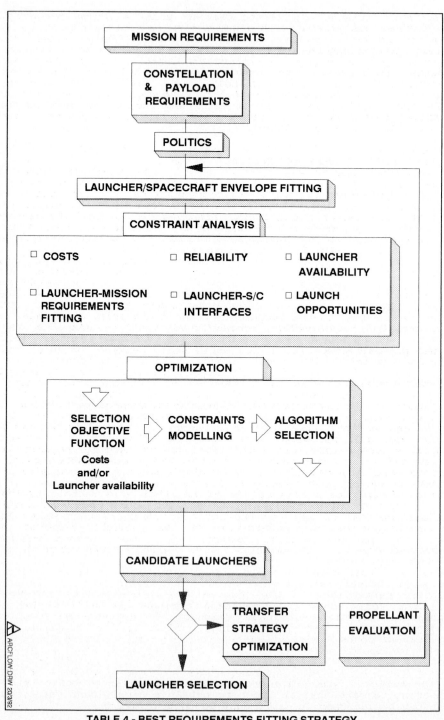

MISSION REQUIREMENTS

CONSTELLATION & PAYLOAD REQUIREMENTS

POLITICS

LAUNCHER/SPACECRAFT ENVELOPE FITTING

CONSTRAINT ANALYSIS

☐ COSTS   ☐ RELIABILITY   ☐ LAUNCHER AVAILABILITY

☐ LAUNCHER-MISSION REQUIREMENTS FITTING   ☐ LAUNCHER-S/C INTERFACES   ☐ LAUNCH OPPORTUNITIES

OPTIMIZATION

SELECTION OBJECTIVE FUNCTION
Costs and/or Launcher availability

CONSTRAINTS MODELLING

ALGORITHM SELECTION

CANDIDATE LAUNCHERS

TRANSFER STRATEGY OPTIMIZATION

PROPELLANT EVALUATION

LAUNCHER SELECTION

ARCFLOW DRW 20/3/92

TABLE 4 - BEST REQUIREMENTS FITTING STRATEGY

The cost of launch services generally plays the leading role in the overall system budget; for the considered missions the launch costs can vary between $15,000 per kg of payload for a secondary launch opportunity, to $100,000 per kilogram for dedicated launches. For this reason, the launch strategy not only strongly depends upon the mission objectives, but helps to define the mission constraints and objectives. Cost considerations therefore would lead to choose a reduced number of larger launch vehicles for implementing the operational constellation. This consideration may be outweighed, however, by the increased program risk associated with a potential launch failure.

Reliability

Two are the factors that have to be considered in terms of reliability : performance and schedule. Over the years the typical launch vehicle reliability has improved from 0.85 to around 0.95. For mature launch systems reliability is the ratio of successful launches to total attemps. Determination of reliability can be difficult or impossible for relatively new or untested launch systems. Reliability assesments for new or nearly new vehicles which are based on modifications to existing designs or are comprised of proven subsystems are more precise than for vehicles of totally new design. The ability of the launch systems supplier to meet the defined launch schedule is also an important consideration. Schedule delay can result from either overcommitment, manifesting more launches than either the production facilities or launch site facilities can accomodate, or from program delays due to retrofits, modifications, etc.

Launch opportunities

Three different types of launch opportunities are considered: secondary payload launches, shared launches and dedicated launches. Secondary payload launches are those in which space may be available on a vehicle carrying a primary payload to an orbit which is acceptable to the analysed mission. For these opportunities both orbit and launch schedule are dictated by the primary payload mission. Secondary payload is made available subject to both available space and compatibility with the primary payload. No launch delays or orbit changes to accommodate the secondary payload are generally permitted. These opportunities are available on larger boost vehicles such as Ariane, Atlas, Delta, titan and Proton. Secondary launches offer by far the lowest cost to orbit, but may adversely impact mission scheduling and compromise system performance due to non-optimum launch schedules and final orbits. As an example of the performances of the secondary launches, in table 5 the Ariane launches are presented , it can be seen that the launch opportunities in LEO orbit have been rare and not uniformly distributed.

Year	79	80	81	81	83	84	85	86	87	88	89	90	91
Total Launches	1	1	2	1	2	4	4	3	2	7	7	6	5
Launches on GTO	1	1	2	1	2	4	4	2	2	7	7	5	4
Launches on LEO	0	0	0	0	0	0	0	1	0	0	0	1	1

TABLE 5 – ARIANE PERFORMED LAUNCHES

Shared launch opportunities are those the payload shares a launch vehicle with another payload. Their primary advantage is the ability to share launch costs when the launcher capacity exceeds the needs of a single payload.

Dedicated launch opportunities are the most expensive launch option, but allow the maximum flexibility for final orbits achievements and mission schedule.

Launcher/Mission Requirements fitting

The launch site locations and allowable launch azimuth restrict the available orbital inclinations which can be achieved by direct ascent (see table 6). The one-site and downrange facilities may impose unacceptable restrictions in some cases. When is considered the possibility of an orbit transfer using spacecraft engine, then the launcher final orbit goes away from initial conditions and new constraints must be considered.

LAUNCH SITE	LAT. (deg).(min)	LONG. (deg).(min)	INCL. RANGE (deg)	LAUNCHERS
Kourou (FRA-ESA)	05.32 N	52.46 W	5.2 - 100.5	Ariane Littleo
C.Canaveral (USA)	28.30 N	80.33 W	29.0 - 57.0	Atlas Delta Titan Taurus
Vandenberg (USA)	34.36 N	120.36 W	56.0 - 104.0	Delta Titan Taurus Scout
Wallops (USA)	37.51 N	75.28 W	38.0 - 51.5	Taurus Scout
S.Marco (ITA)	02.56 S	40.12 E	3.0 - 38.5	Scout
Baikonour (CSI)	45.54 N	63.18 E	51.5 - 72.0	Proton Soyuz Molnya Cosmos Burlak
Plesetsk (CSI)	62.48 N	40.24 E	63.0 - 83.0	Soyuz Molnya Cosmos Burlak
Kasputin Y. (CSI)	48.24 N	45.48 E	48.5 - 51.0	Cosmos Burlak
Tanegashima (JAP)	30.24 N	130.59 E	31.0 - 85.0	H and M-Vehicle
Andoya (NOR)	63.30 N	15.70 E	69.0 - 90.0	Littleo
Xichang (CHI)	28.06 N	102.18 E	27.5 - 31.1	Long-March

TABLE 6 - LAUNCH SITES

In case of either a secondary or a shared launch, the final orbit may not be the optimum orbit to provide the needed services defined. Each of these factors have also to be analyzed in terms of mission objectives impact, the results of this analysis incorporated into the launch selection process. Launch vehicle injection errors must also be examined.

Launcher/Spacecraft interfaces

During the powered ascent phase and stage and payload separation phases the launch vehicle subjects the payload to severe environmental stress. These stress have not to exceed the design limits of the spacecraft and booster adpter considering adequate safety margins. Moreover, the main characteristics of the electrics and mechanics interfaces between launcher and spacecraft must also be evaluated.

Launcher Availability

In considering this aspect it is necessary to know the launch base alternatives and launcher avaibility, considering the planned launches. This constraint is very important in allowing to characterize the temporal launch sequence, which can be used like objective function to be minimized (e.g. emergency breakdown missions, military missions, etc). Usually the launcher availability depends also on ground support, accessibility of the launch site, and launch support personnel.

6. DEPLOYMENT STRATEGIES OPTIMIZATION

Once defined the constraints for each launcher, it is necessary to choose the objective function. If cost savings considerations prevail the choise will be to minimize the costs/Kg in orbit, if viceversa the time saving factor prevails, the choise will be to minimize the time requests for the launches. In case both these factors have to be optimized, it is possible to use a multi-objective function.
The optimality notion has to be dropped for multiobjective problems because a solution which minimizes one objective will not, in general, minimizes the other objectives.
The constraints of analytic modelling have to be discuss for each case in the sphere of the coupling between satellite and launcher.
On the basis of considerations developed three analytic forms are possibles (table 7). The objective functions are respectively costs function $c(x)$, launchers avaibility time $t(x)$, both of them $z(x)$. The $g(x)$ functions are m and represent the equality constraints. The $h(x)$ functions are p and represent the disequality constraints. The x vector has n components and provides the independent variables.

1°		2°		3°	
min $c(x)$	$c: R^n \rightarrow R$	min $t(x)$	$t: R^n \rightarrow R$	min $Z(x)$	$Z: R^n \rightarrow R^2$
$g(x)=0$	$g: R^n \rightarrow R^m$	$g(x)=0$	$g: R^n \rightarrow R^m$	$g(x)=0$	$g: R^n \rightarrow R^m$
$h(x)\leq0$	$h: R^n \rightarrow R^p$	$h(x)\leq0$	$h: R^n \rightarrow R^p$	$h(x)\leq0$	$h: R^n \rightarrow R^p$
				$Z(x)= \begin{vmatrix} c(x) \\ t(x) \end{vmatrix}$	

TABLE 7 - OPTIMIZATION MODELS

Among all the optimizations algorhythms the selection falls on two methods, the sequencial penalty functions method (SPF) and the sequencial increased lagrangian functions method (SILF). The SPF method implementing is the simplest even if it is subjected to hill condition for small values of the penalty coefficient. This algorhythm can be used when high numeric precision is not required. The SILF method is less subjected to hill condition phenomena and moreover it consents a high speed of convergence.

Considering a parking orbit different from the final orbit, an orbital transfer maneuver has to be foreseen but still achieving some advantage. In fact satellite mass and volume (propellant, tank, engines, etc.) increase but it is possible to inject on parking orbit a greater payload or to use a less expensive launcher.

It is important to underline that a strategy with a transfer increases mission overall risk, even if takes into account redundant systems.

Therefore the logical flow, taking into account a new launcher or a new sequence of launchers, is repeated unless economic-political considerations. The objective functions will take note of a trend, for example a decreasing of the costs/Kg in final orbit, and when a trend change is detected the optimun solution has been achieved.

Since a final check between the candidates launchers and the optimal solution will be performed in terms of risk, cost, and reliability, in order to increase these parameters safety margins, this implies the accceptance of a suboptimal solution.

7. CONCLUSIONS

To select an optimal strategy for small satellite constellation deployment it is necessary to focus the attention on two primary objective functions: cost/kg on orbit and time of deployment.

Considering all the factors involved in the process, a mixed technique performed both logically and analytically allows to minimize the selected objective functions.

REFERENCES

[1] **G. Rondinelli, F. Graziani**: " Orbit acquisition and control for small satellites in inclined eccentric orbits", Space Dynamics Toulouse, November 89, Cepadeus-Editions Toulouse pag. 195-202.

[2] **F. Ananasso, G. Rondinelli, P. Palmucci, B. Pavesi**: "Small Satellite Applications: A New Perspective in Satellite Communications", The 14th International Communication Satellite Sistems Conference and Exhibit, Washington Dc, March 1992.

[3] **S.J.Isakowitz** : "International Reference Guide to Space Launch Systems", AIAA 1991 Edition.

[4] "Micro satellite Feasibility study", Telespazio MFS/SYS-230/I2, 1991.

[5] "Commercial Space Services Rended by GLAVKOSMOS of the USSR", GLAVKOSMOS, Moscow, 1990.

[6] "Launch Vehicle Catalogue", ESA, December 1990.

[7] **E.Masci**: " Low Thrust Orbital Tranfer Optimization " Doctorate Thesis , University of Roma 'La Sapienza', February 1991.

DELTA LAUNCH VEHICLE
ACCOMMODATIONS FOR SMALL SATELLITES

K. R. Knox

Delta Launch Vehicle Division
McDonnell Douglas Space Systems Company
Huntington Beach, Calif. 92647

ABSTRACT

The small satellite market has suffered from the lack of availability of a low-cost and responsive transport to orbit. The emergence of new small launchers is helping to satisfy this need with dedicated launches at more affordable cost. The Delta launch vehicle also offers significant benefits to the small satellite community by comanifesting several satellites on a dedicated launch. The cost effectiveness for the constellation deployment of similar satellites is evident when compared to individual launches with dedicated launchers. This study also examines the possibility of comanifesting small satellites of different sizes and masses into low Earth orbits. The comanifesting possibilities are enhanced with Delta's range of performance capabilities, choice in launch site and restart capability which satisfies a wide range of orbit altitudes and inclinations. The conclusion suggests Delta offers significant advantages to the individual satellite.

INTRODUCTION

The reemergence of small satellites has been motivated by several forces. Technology improvements in data management and power systems are allowing respectable capabilities in small-class payloads. The current plans for worldwide communication systems by small satellite constellations are an excellent example of the advances that are now leading to economic viability. The needs of the scientific community have not been totally satisfied with the launch transport options that have been available. The small satellite has frequently compromised its orbit parameter and flight duration; has been subjected to costly safety compliance requirements and has yearned for affordable and responsive transport service. The desire to be a single operator of a specifically tailored design, rather than participate (and compromise) in a shared project, has also aided the growth in small satellites. But the most powerful motivation of all is the reality of the budgeting process, where low-cost projects have a better chance of surviving than big ticket items. The emergence of new small launchers has been a direct result of these unsatisfied needs. The Delta launch vehicle has been and continues to be a responsive and affordable choice for microsatellites as complementary (secondary) payloads* The feasibility of the Delta vehicle to comanifest several small satellites in a multiple payload mission has been studied with the results provided herein.

DISCUSSION

The Delta II vehicle (Figure 1) for multiple low Earth orbit (LEO) payloads is generally a two-stage configuration with nine strapon thrust augmentation solid motors and a 10-ft-diameter fairing (Model 7920-10). The Delta second stage's ability to perform multiple restarts is particularly attractive for deployment of multiple payloads. Smaller payload fairings of 8- and 9.5-ft diameter are also available. Vehicle configurations of either six or three strapon solids, in addition to the standard nine solid configuration, have been studied; these offer possible launch service cost savings after the development effort has been absorbed. Delta is launched from three launch pads that are in current operation. Two are located on the east coast at Cape Canaveral Air Force Station (CCAFS), and one located on the west coast at Vandenberg Air Force Base (VAFB). The launch sites (Figure 2) offer availability to any orbit inclination and capacity to satisfy responsive launch demands. The CCAFS launch site recently performed 12 launches in 12 months. The performance capabilities for the Model 7920-10 vehicle to a 400-nmi circular orbit, as well as the six and three solid version, for polar and eastward inclinations are presented in Table 1.

Multiple payload configurations on Delta have previously concentrated on packaging similar payloads for a constellation deployment mission. Generally the per payload launch service cost on Delta for multiple satellite deployment is lower than individual deployment on available dedicated launchers. An example of a packaging concept for 46-in.-diameter payloads is shown in Figure 3. This common support and deployment system concept can be configured to accommodate three to eight payloads and has a heritage from previous Delta missions that required multiple satellite deployment .

J.M. Garvey, Delta II Secondary Payload Opportunities, MDC H5769, August 1990.

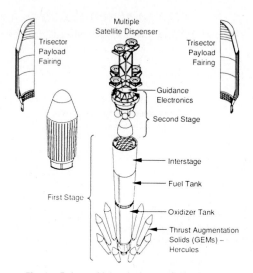

Fig. 1 – Delta multiple mission configuration

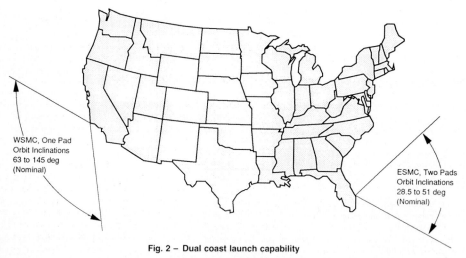

Fig. 2 – Dual coast launch capability

Table 1 – Delta lift capability to 400-nmi circular orbit

Vehicle configuration	Polar (i = 90 deg)	Eastward (i = 28.5 deg)
Nine solids	7240 lb	9600 lb
Six solids	5430 lb	7420 lb
Three solids	3780 lb	5450 lb

A new multiple payload feasibility study examined the concept of comanifesting a variety of small payload sizes and weights into a single Delta mission. This study began with the selection of a 400-nmi circular orbit as a baseline case. This altitude appears to be representative of a typical mission for a majority of current small satellite plans. At this altitude, the lift capabilities and fairing envelope of current and planned domestic launch vehicles were used to define a generic set of candidate payloads to be comanifested. Additionally, a Lifesat envelope and weight of 3300 lb was included as a middle-sized candidate to also be considered for comanifesting. The mass and shapes of these four generic type payloads are presented on Table 2.

132

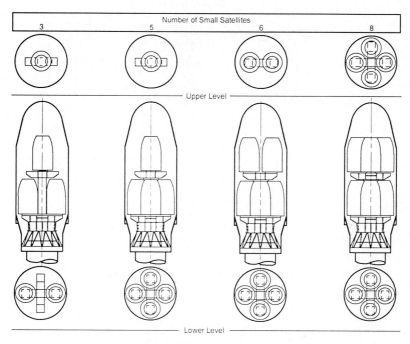

Fig. 3 – Constellation packaging concepts

Table 2 – Characteristics of four generic small payloads

Payload type	Mass (lb)	Dimensions (in.)
A	400	46 dia x 36 height
B	1100	48 dia x 96 height
C	2000	48 dia x 120 height
D (Lifesat)	3300	Conical

The second step in the study was to develop a matrix of possible comanifests using the four generic payloads and the Delta lift capabilities of Table 1. The vehicle performance capability was reduced by 10% to provide allowance for a payload mounting and dispensing structural system. A volume criteria was also applied which assumed a 75% packaging efficiency of the cylindrical portion of the 10-ft-diameter fairing. The volume criteria resulted in a maximum payload volume of 590 cu ft for each option. Another constraint allowed only a maximum of eight payloads to be manifested because the burden of gathering more than eight different payloads for a single launch seemed unrealistic. The resulting possible combinations in this matrix is 53 options (Table 3). As an example, option code E1 in Table 3 comanifests two Type D payloads with two Type A payloads.

The third step of the study was to screen this matrix using nonviable duplications and packaging feasibility as the screening criteria. Four nonviable options (E12, E18, W13, and W23) were eliminated by observation that the manifests duplicated a three-solid and probably lower cost option. Packaging layouts of the options were performed to evaluate feasibility. Eight additional options were eliminated (shaded entries of Table 4) as nonfeasible from a packaging viewpoint. Sketches of packaging concepts for the remaining viable options are shown in Figures 3 and 4. The remaining 41 options also contain manifests that are duplicates when comparing the east coast and west coast. These duplicates are retained for completeness and annotated with "Dup". When accounting for these duplications, the 41 options actually contain 32 unique arrangements.

The study also examined comanifesting the generic small satellites with a 2000-lb payload destined for a geosynchronous (GEO) orbit. The 2000-lb payload would require a Star 37FM-type third stage for the proper geosynchronous transfer orbit (GTO). Only an east coast launch site and the nine solid vehicle configuration were considered. The excess performance capability of this mission that is available for small comanifested satellites depends on the mission trajectory profile. One mission profile would have the second stage placing the entire payload into an

Table 3 – Comanifest option matrix

Vehicle	Code	Type D (3300 lb)	Type C (2000 lb)	Type B (1100 lb)	Type A (400 lb)	Total wt (lb)	Margin (lb)	Total volume (cu ft)
		Quantity per satellite type						
ESMC-LEO								
7920	E1	2			2	7400	1249	581
	E2	1	2	1		8400	249	608
	E3	1	1	1	2	7200	1449	551
	E4	1		1	5	6400	2249	530
	E5		4		1	8400	249	537
	E6		3	1	2	7900	749	547
	E7		2	3		7300	1349	553
	E8		2	2	1	6600	2049	487
	E9		1	4		6400	2249	528
	E10			5	1	5900	2749	537
	E11			4	4	6000	2649	541
	E12				8	3200	5449	277
7620	E13	2				6600	6	512
	E14	1		1	1	6400	206	482
	E15		3		1	6400	206	412
	E16		2	2	1	6600	6	487
	E17		2		6	6400	206	459
	E18				8	3200	3406	277
7320	E19	1		1	1	4800	-57	391
	E20		2		2	4800	-57	321
	E21		1	1	4	4700	43	365
	E22			2	6	4600	143	409
	E23				8	3200	1543	277
WSMC-LEO								
7920	W1	2				6600	-75	512
	W2	1	1	1		6400	125	482
	W3	1		3		6600	-75	558
	W4	1		2	2	6300	225	526
	W5		3		1	6400	125	412
	W6		2	2	1	6600	-75	487
	W7		2	1	3	6300	225	456
	W8		2		6	6400	125	459
	W9		1	4		6400	125	528
	W10		1	3	3	6500	25	531
	W11			5	1	5900	625	537
	W12			4	4	6000	525	541
	W13				8	3200	3325	277
7620	W14	1		1	1	4800	87	391
	W15	1			3	4500	387	360
	W16		2		2	4800	87	321
	W17		1	2	1	4600	287	361
	W18		1	1	4	4700	187	365
	W19		1		7	4800	87	368
	W20			4	1	4800	87	437
	W21			3	4	4900	-13	440
	W22			2	6	4600	287	409
	W23				8	3200	1687	277
7320	W24	1				3300	102	256
	W25		1	1		3100	302	226
	W26		1		3	3200	202	230
	W27			3		3300	102	302
	W28			2	3	3400	2	305
	W29			1	6	3500	-98	308
	W30				8	3200	202	277

approximate 1100-nmi circular orbit. The third stage and payload would be separated and small satellite deployment operations would begin. This profile results in about 1700 lb of excess performance capability to the approximate 1100-nmi orbit. A second mission profile would have the second stage with the entire payload placed in a 400-nmi circular

Table 4 – Screened option matrix

Vehicle	Code	Quantity per satellite				Percent of launch mass per each statellite			
		Type D (3300 lb)	Type C (2000 lb)	Type B (1100 lb)	Type A (400 lb)	Type D	Type C	Type B	Type A
ESMC-LEO									
7920	E1	2			2	45%	0%	0%	5%
	E2	1	2	1		39%	24%	0%	0%
	E3	1	1	1	2	46%	28%	15%	6%
	E4	1		1	5	52%	31%	17%	6%
	E5		4		1	0%	24%	0%	5%
	~~E6~~		~~3~~	~~1~~	~~2~~	~~0%~~	~~25%~~	~~14%~~	~~5%~~
	E7		2	3		0%	27%	15%	0%
	E8		2	2	1	0%	29%	16%	6%
	~~E9~~		~~1~~	~~4~~		~~0%~~	~~31%~~	~~17%~~	~~0%~~
	E10			5	1	0%	0%	19%	7%
	~~E11~~			~~4~~	~~4~~	~~0%~~	~~0%~~	~~18%~~	~~7%~~
7620	E13	2				50%	0%	0%	0%
	E14	1	1	1		52%	31%	17%	0%
	E15		3		1	0%	31%	0%	6%
	E16		2	2	1	0%	30%	17%	6%
	E17		2		6	0%	31%	0%	6%
7320	E19	1		1	1	69%	0%	23%	8%
	E20		2		2	0%	42%	0%	8%
	E21		1	1	4	0%	43%	23%	9%
	E22			2	6	0%	0%	24%	9%
	E23				8	0%	0%	0%	13%
WSMC-LEO									
7920	W1	2 (DUP)				50%	0%	0%	0%
	W2	1 (DUP)	1	1		52%	3%	17%	0%
	W3	1		3		50%	0%	17%	0%
	W4	1		2	2	52%	0%	17%	6%
	W5	(DUP)	3		1	0%	31%	0%	6%
	W6	(DUP)	2	2	1	0%	30%	17%	6%
	~~W7~~		~~2~~	~~1~~	~~3~~	~~0%~~	~~32%~~	~~17%~~	~~6%~~
	W8	(DUP)	2		6	0%	31%	0%	6%
	~~W9~~	~~(DUP)~~	~~1~~	~~4~~		~~0%~~	~~31%~~	~~17%~~	~~0%~~
	~~W10~~		~~1~~	~~3~~	~~3~~	~~0%~~	~~31%~~	~~17%~~	~~6%~~
	~~W11~~	~~(DUP)~~		~~5~~	~~1~~	~~0%~~	~~0%~~	~~19%~~	~~7%~~
	~~W12~~	~~(DUP)~~		~~4~~	~~4~~	~~0%~~	~~0%~~	~~18%~~	~~67%~~
7620	W14	1 (DUP)		1	1	69%	0%	23%	8%
	W15	1			3	73%	0%	0%	9%
	W16	(DUP)	2		2	0%	42%	0%	8%
	W17		1	2	1	0%	43%	24%	9%
	W18		1	1	4	0%	43%	23%	9%
	W19		1		7	0%	42%	0%	8%
	W20			4	1	0%	0%	23%	8%
	W21			3	4	0%	0%	22%	8%
	W22	(DUP)		2	6	0%	0%	24%	9%
7320	W24	1				100%	0%	0%	0%
	W25		1	1		0%	65%	35%	0%
	W26		1		3	0%	63%	0%	13%
	W27			3		0%	0%	33%	0%
	W28			2	3	0%	0%	32%	12%
	W29			1	6	0%	0%	31%	11%
	W30	(DUP)			8	0%	0%	0%	13%

Note: Strike-through entries indicate nonviable options

orbit. The comanifested small satellites would then be deployed, and the second stage would be restarted to achieve the 1100-nmi orbit for third stage and geosynchronous payload deployment. The second profile would result in about 3000 lb of excess capability at the 400-nmi orbit. The matrix of possible comanifesting options of 3000 lb of generic small

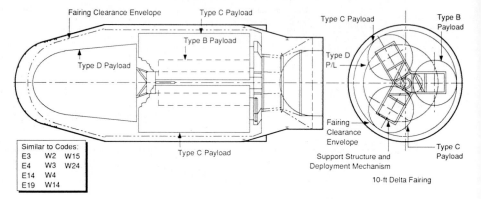

Similar to Codes:
E3   W2   W15
E4   W3   W24
E14 W4
E19 W14

10-ft Delta Fairing

Fig. 4 – Option code E2 (1 D, 2 C, 1 B) packaging concept

satellites with the 2000-lb geosynchronous payload has six options (Table 5). Figures 5 and 6 show two of the packaging options and also show alternate structural support concepts of a center-post concept and support using a fixed segment of the fairing. Only one of these options (H4) will fit within a standard 10-ft-diameter fairing due to the length of the third stage/2000-lb geosynchronous payload package (Figure 7). The remaining options will fit within a studied version of a 10-ft-diameter fairing that contains a 5-ft extension in the cylindrical section.

Table 5 – 2000-lb GEO comanifested with LEO satellite options

Code	Type D (3300 lb)	Type C (2000 lb)	Type B (1100 lb)	Type A (400 lb)	Total wt (lb)	Margin (lb)
	Quantity per satellite type					
H1	1				3300	-300
H2		1	1		3100	-100
H3		1		2	2800	200
H4		3			3300	-300
H5			1	4	2700	300
H6				6	2400	600

Comanifesting of small satellites on a dedicated Delta launch appears both technically and economically feasible for a variety of missions. Similar satellites in constellations can also be launched more cost effectively than using dedicated single launchers. Several packaging concepts for comanifesting a variety of generic payloads have potentially attractive cost benefits for the individual programs. A common support and deployment concept for both the constellation and

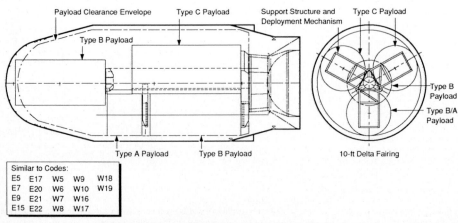

Similar to Codes:
E5   E17 W5   W9   W18
E7   E20 W6   W10 W19
E9   E21 W7   W16
E15 E22 W8   W17

10-ft Delta Fairing

Fig. 5 – Option code E16 (2 C, 2 B, 1 A) packaging concept

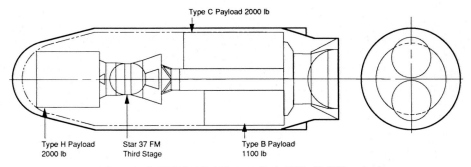

Fig. 6 – Option code H2 (1 E, 1 C, 1 B) comanifests GEO with LEO payloads

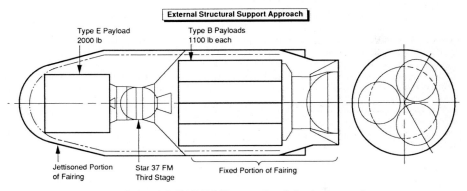

Fig. 7 – Option code H4 (1 E, 3 B) uses external structural support

variety of generic payloads appears possible. The launch of a combination of GEO and LEO payloads is possible, but has less appeal if a new fairing development is required.

The concepts presented offer benefits over other alternatives. Problems associated with complementary (secondary) payloads of compromised orbit parameters and liability concerns by the primary payload are greatly reduced. Added cost associated with safety compliance and the responsiveness in manifesting onboard a manned transport system are also reduced. The potential launch services cost savings of comanifesting on a Delta as compared to a dedicated single launcher also appear to be attractive. Delta offers an enviable launch success and launch rate record which provides confidence in the launch service selection for small satellites.

The Delta second stage's ability to restart allows the payloads to be placed in different orbits. Figure 8 presents an example orbit insertion for Option Code W12 (four 1100- lb spacecraft and four 400-lb spacecraft). This example places the four 1100-lb spacecraft into a 400-nmi, 90-deg inclined circular orbit. The second stage is restarted and circularized at 600 nmi where two of the 400-lb spacecraft are deployed. The second stage is restarted again and cicularized at 800 nmi where the remaining two 400-lb spacecraft are deployed. A second example (not shown) performs a plane change maneuver for Option Code W13 (eight 400-lb spacecraft). This example deploys four of the spacecraft in a 400-nmi, 98.4-deg inclined (sun synchronous) circular orbit. The second stage is restarted twice to deploy the remaining four spacecraft in a 500-nmi, 90-deg inclined circular orbit. Also note that phase changes within a constant altitude are also possible by developing slightly elliptical transfer orbits. Thus, phase changes, altitude changes, and inclination changes are all achievable. These examples show the flexibility and versatility of the restartable second stage to design a mission scenario that satisfies a varying set of payload requirements.

The viability of this approach requires a programmatic solution to the problems associated with the gathering of several different payloads for a specific mission. A manifest integration task is required to group interested payloads into a specific mission with similar orbit parameters. The mission success can be enhanced by the availability of standby payloads to maintain a full manifest in the event a selected payload becomes unavailable for any reason. Ordering and payment for launch services is probably outside the capability of the individual small satellite provider. A mission director agency could be established to serve as the focal point, as well as the mission integrator, between the small satellite and the launch

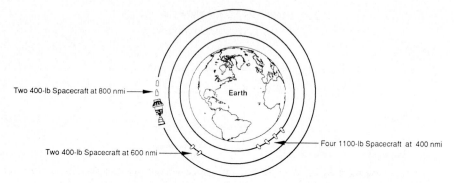

Fig. 8 – Eight spacecraft are deployed into three different orbits

service providers. Another programmatic issue is the development cost of new launcher hardware. This development could also be managed by a single agency and be borne over several missions, if a common support and delivery system can be developed.

SUMMARY

Comanifesting small satellites on the Delta launch vehicle offers several benefits. First, the variety of vehicle configurations (number of strapon solid motors and fairing diameter options) and launch sites allows more flexibility in accommodating desired physical shapes and mission orbit parameters. Second, the individual satellite launch service cost will be significantly less than a dedicated single launcher. Third, the long and successful launch record of the Delta program provides the added confidence in achieving a successful program.

LES DERIVES LEGERS D'ARIANE 5

JM ASTORG

Centre National d'Etudes Spatiales (CNES)
Direction des Lanceurs, EVRY (FRANCE)

RESUME

Les dérivés légers d'ARIANE 5 sont aujourd'hui étudiés pour compléter la gamme des services de lancement du lanceur ARIANE 5 vis-à-vis des satellites héliosynchrones (dérivé S), et des petits satellites (dérivé P). Le dérivé P est un lanceur de trois étages (deux à poudre et un étage terminal liquide réallumable) capable de placer sur une orbite polaire circulaire à 1000 km, un satellite de 1000 kg, ou deux de 450 kg. Il est principalement dérivé des propulseurs à poudre et du dernier étage d'ARIANE 5. Le volume offert aux satellites est particulièrement important, puisque le diamètre maximal interne est 2.8 m, et la hauteur de la coiffe de 6 m environ. Les dérivés légers seront lancés depuis la base de lancement ARIANE en Guyane, et utiliseront toutes les installations liées à ARIANE 5, avec cependant un batiment de préparation spécifique pour une bonne souplesse opérationnelle. Le premier vol du dérivé P est prévu en 1998.

ABSTRACT

The ARIANE 5 light Derivatives are studied in order to complete ARIANE 5 launch services with regard to medium-size sun-synchronous spacecrafts (S derivative) and small satellites (P derivative). The P derivative is a three stages launcher with two solid-propellant motors, and a bi-propellant upper stage. It is capable to put 1 ton on a 1000 km circular polar orbit, or two 450 kg spacecrafts on th same orbit. The light derivatives are mainly derived from ARIANE 5 solid-propellant booster and upper stage. The payload volume is particulary large (2.8 m internal maximal diameter, 6 m height). The light derivatives will be launched from the ARIANE spaceport in Guyana, they will use all ARIANE 5 facilities for payload preparation and launch operation, with a specific building for launcher integration. The P derivative first flight is scheduled in 1998.

1. INTRODUCTION

Les lanceurs de la famille ARIANE n'ont cessé d'augmenter leur performance: en 1980, ARIANE 1 effectuait son premier vol, et avait une performance de 1850 kg en orbite de transfert géostationnaire (GTO). Dans la foulée, ARIANE 2 et 3 étaient développés, ce qui a permis d'accroitre cette performance jusqu'à 2580 kg, et de réaliser des lancements doubles. ARIANE 4 a suivi ARIANE 3, avec toujours le même objectif: suivre la croissance des masses de satellites de communication en offrant un lanceur versatile, dont la performance pouvait varier entre 1900 et 4200 kg. Aujourd'hui, ARIANE 5 est en développement, et effectuera son premier vol en 1995: sa capacité en GTO est 5900 kg en lancement double, et son coût sera inférieur de 10% à celui d'ARIANE 4.

ARIANE a suivi et même anticipé, le marché des satellites de communications géosynchrones dont la masse n'a cessé d'augmenter. On peut d'ailleurs prévoir que cette tendance se poursuivra au début du siècle prochain, à en juger par les plates-formes à l'étude actuellement chez les constructeurs de satellites.

Une filière a donc été construite d'ARIANE 1 à ARIANE 4, en réutilisant les principaux éléments du lanceur, en particulier les moteurs. Il est donc naturel de prévoir le même avenir à ARIANE 5, qui est un lanceur complétement nouveau.

En ce qui concerne les petits satellites, ils ont avec ARIANE 4 des opportunités de lancement grâce à ASAP (Auxiliary Structure for Auxiliary Payload), qui est une plate forme placée autour de la case à équipement, sous le satellite principal, comme on peut le voir sur la figure 1. Elle peut recevoir jusqu'à 200 kg lorsque le lanceur est surpuissant par rapport à la masse du satellite principal, mais la masse de chaque satellite doit être inférieure à 50 kg.

Elle a déjà été utilisée notamment lors des vols héliosynchrones d'ARIANE 4.

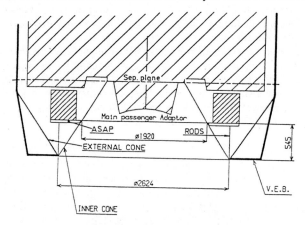

Fig. 1: Plateforme ASAP pour le lancement de petits satellites avec ARIANE 4

Cependant, cette possibilité a ses limites: d'abord en masse de satellite, puis en nombre de vols (ceux où ARIANE 4 est surpuissant, c'est-à-dire principalement les missions héliosynchrones, et elles sont assez rares). Dans une situation où le marché des petits satellites devrait de développer, en cadence de lancement, mais aussi avec des satellites dont la masse va croître, il est nécessaire de prévoir d'autres solutions: c'est l'objet des dérivés légers ARIANE 5.

Ainsi, contrairement aux dérivés d'ARIANE 1, les dérivés d'ARIANE 5 pourraient être moins puissants que le lanceur de base, mais il s'agit toujours de s'adapter à un marché prometteur: celui des petits satellites, et par la même occasion celui des satellites héliosynchrones.

La démarche que nous avons suivi consiste donc à dériver un lanceur d'ARIANE 5, en lui donnant deux missions: l'une adaptée pour les petits satellites, et l'autre pour les satellites héliosynchrones de taille moyenne, dont le nombre devrait augmenter vers la fin du siècle. Ces deux classes de satellites sont très différentes en masse, mais peuvent correspondre à deux versions de lanceur proches. La première est appelée dérivé S (comme SSO), et la deuxième dérivé P (comme petit lanceur).

Partant d'éléments d'ARIANE 5, cette démarche a bien entendu l'avantage d'utiliser un lanceur dont les composants principaux, et en particulier les moteurs auront fait leur preuves sur ARIANE 5. De plus, toute une logistique mise en place pour ARIANE 5 peut être aussi utilisée.

On décrit ici plus en détail la version P adaptée pour le lancement des petits satellites.

2. DESCRIPTION GENERALE

2.1 Configuration du lanceur

Les **idées directrices** ayant conduit à la définition choisie sont les suivantes:

    - parmi les éléments d'ARIANE 5, seuls les propulseurs à poudre donnent une base adéquate pour des dérivés légers, l'étage principal cryotechnique d'ARIANE 5 étant trop puissant,

    - la technologie de propulsion à poudre doit être utilisée au maximum dans le cadre des Dérivés légers d'ARIANE 5, pour des raisons de coûts de lancement (facilité de mise en oeuvre par rapport à la propulsion liquide),

    - la réutilisation des propulseurs d'ARIANE 5 offre l'avantage particulièrement intéressant de bénéficier d'une infrastructure industrielle existante qui sera opérationnelle au moment de la phase de développement et de production des Dérivés légers d'ARIANE5,

    - un étage terminal à liquide et réallumable est nécessaire, à la fois pour assurer une bonne précision d'injection, et pour pouvoir effectuer des réallumages.

La configuration générale du dérivé P est donnée sur la figure 2.

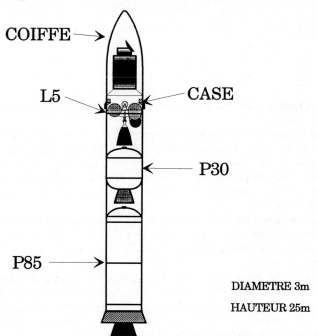

Fig 2: configuration générale dérivé P

Il s'agit d'un lanceur à 3 étages:

        - le premier étage **P85** est dérivé des propulseurs à poudre d'ARIANE 5: il en réutilise en particulier des éléments de structure métallique, et le même propergol (85 tonnes de chargement). Sa tuyère est de même principe que celle des propulseurs d'ARIANE 5 (orientable avec butée flexible),

        - le deuxième étage **P30** utilise lui aussi un moteur à propergol solide, de même composition que celui des propulseurs d'ARIANE 5 (chargement de 30 tonnes), mais sa structure est bobinée avec des fibres de carbone, pour réduire la masse de l'étage,

        - le troisième et dernier étage **L5** fonctionne avec des ergols liquides (MMH et N_2O_4): il est équipé du même moteur que le deuxième étage d'ARIANE 5 (27 kN de poussée), mais n'emporte que 5 tonnes d'ergols au lieu de 9.7 tonnes sur ARIANE 5.

Compte tenu des dimensions souhaitées, la coiffe du dérivé P est nouvelle: elle a un diamètre de 3.1 m extérieur, et une hauteur (7 m) qui permet de faire des lancements doubles grâce à une structure porteuse interne.

Les équipements électriques sont les mêmes que ceux utilisés sur ARIANE 5.

Le dérivé S (adapté pour les charges utiles inférieures à 4 tonnes sur orbite héliosynchrone), est obtenu par l'ajout d'un propulseur à poudre d'ARIANE 5, en temps que premier étage, et par le remplacement de la coiffe du dérivé P par la coiffe longue d'ARIANE 4.
La masse au décollage du dérivé P est d'environ 140 tonnes, sa hauteur 25 m, et son diamètre 3 m.

2.2 Séquence de vol

Le vol s'effectue de la façon suivante (voir fig. 3):
L'ordre d'allumage du P85 étant donné, le lanceur quitte sa table de lancement avec une accélération au décollage d'environ 4,5 m/s2. Après environ 10 s de vol, le lanceur bascule, et la phase de vol à incidence nulle commence. La durée de fonctionnement du P85 est d'environ 2 minutes.
 Le P85 est largué après détection de sa queue de poussée: le lanceur a alors atteint une altitude d'environ 38 km, et l'étage à poudre P30 est à son tour allumé. C'est le début de la phase de guidage.
Sa durée de fonctionnement est aussi de deux minutes. Après extinction du P30, l'étage L5 est allumé et permet d'obtenir la vitesse de satellisation requise. Sa durée de fonctionnement est d'environ 10 minutes.
La coiffe est larguée quand le flux thermique est inférieur à 1135 W/m2, c'est-à-dire peu après le début du vol du L5.
Après extinction de l'étage L5, le composite satellite/lanceur se trouve injecté sur une orbite intermédiaire de bas périgée (par exemple 200 km), et poursuit une phase balistique pendant environ une demie-orbite. A l'apogée, le moteur du L5 est réallumé, et l'orbite finale est atteinte par circularisation. Cette procédure avec une phase balistique intermédiaire, a l'avantage d'accroître la performance par rapport à une injection directe.
La phase finale du vol est constituée par l'injection du satellite après une série de manoeuvres effectuées grâce au Système de Contrôle d'Attitude (SCA) du lanceur.

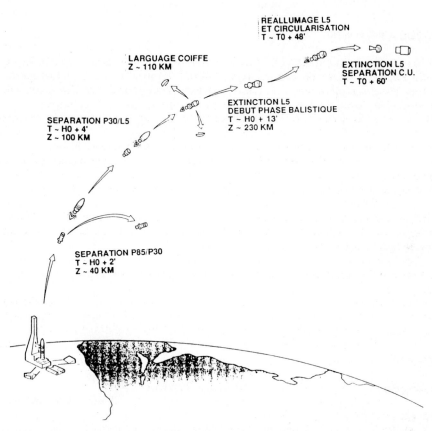

Fig. 3: Séquence de vol du dérivé P.

Les figures 5 et 6 montrent l'évolution de la pression dynamique et de l'accélération au cours du vol (celle-ci ne dépasse pas 6g).

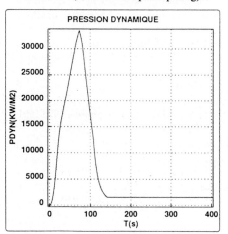
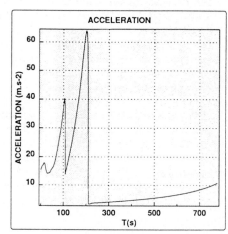

Fig. 5 et 6: Evolution de la pression dynamique et de l'accélération au cours du vol

143

2.3 base de lancement

La base de lancement d'ARIANE en Guyane française présente de nombreux avantages de par sa situation et ses nombreux équipements. Elle est en particulier aussi bien adaptée pour les lancements vers des orbites équatoriales, que fortement inclinées. Par ailleurs, certains éléments du lanceurs sont produits en Guyane, par exemple le propergol de l'étage P85.

Elle est dotée de batiments et d'équipes opérationnelles pour la préparation des charges utiles.

De par sa conception, la zone de lancement d'ARIANE 5 se prête bien au lancement de dérivés de ce lanceur. En effet, elle est très dépouillée car la plupart des opérations s'effectuent avant le transfert vers cette zone.

Il est donc tout à fait possible de l'utiliser pour les dérivés légers sans que les campagnes de lancement d'ARIANE 5 et des dérivés légers n'interfèrent. Un batiment spécifique est cependant nécessaire pour l'intégration du lanceur, ce qui permet d'assurer une bonne souplesse opérationnelle à l'ensemble, car chaque lanceur est préparé dans un batiment séparé, seule la zone de lancement étant commune.

Les satellites sont préparés dans l'Ensemble de Préparation des Charges Utiles (EPCU), et peuvent y être installés dans la coiffe avant l' intégration de toute la partie haute sur le lanceur.

2.4 Programme de développement

Tâches de développement

Le développement des Dérivés légers d'ARIANE 5 comporte:
    - le développement et la qualification au sol des éléments constitutifs des lanceurs dérivé S et dérivé P,
    - le développement et la qualification des moyens de lancement et des moyens logistiques,
    - la réalisation des études et essais système simultanés sur les deux versions de lanceur, et la qualification en vol du système avec le lancement du dérivé P.

Les principaux éléments à développer sont la tuyère et le chargement du P85, la structure et le chargement du P30, les réservoirs et la structure du L5, les différentes structures interétages et enfin la coiffe du dérivé P.

Le vol de qualification aura lieu dans la version dérivé P puisque c'est elle qui concentre toute les nouveautés par rapport à ARIANE 5.

Planning de développement

Le développement a été évalué à 4 ans et demi, ce qui conduit à un vol courant 1998, si la décision de programme a lieu fin 1993.

3. LES SERVICES DE LANCEMENT DU DERIVE P

3.1 Performance

Lancement simple

La performance spécifiée du dérivé P est **1000 kg sur l'orbite 1000 km circulaire inclinée à 90°**. La figure 6 donne les abaques de performance en fonction de l'orbite circulaire considérée, et pour un lancement simple.
Pour une orbite équatoriale circulaire à 1000 km, la performance est 1450 kg.

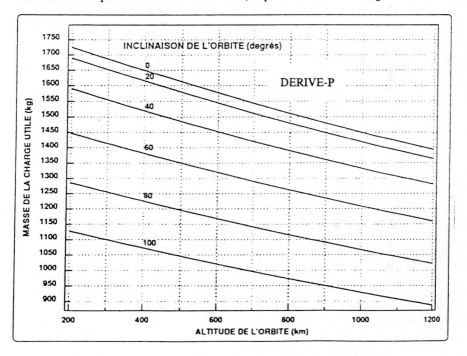

Fig. 6: abaque de performance dérivé P en lancement simple.

Lancement double

Le dérivé P a la capacité de réaliser des lancements doubles compte tenu de sa performance, et grâce à une structure porteuse interne. Cette possibilité trouve tout son intérêt pour la réduction des coûts de lancement.
Pour une orbite circulaire à 1000 km, inclinée à 90°, le dérivé P peut lancer deux satellites de 450 kg.
Par ailleurs, l'étage L5 étant réallumable, le dérivé P peut placer les deux satellites sur des orbites légèrement différentes soit en inclinaison, soit en apogée ou périgée. La figure 7 illustre cette possibilité pour le changement d'inclinaison, en donnant la changement

d'inclinaison que peut réaliser l'étage L5 pour l'un des deux satellites, en fonction de la masse des satellites (on suppose pour simplifierla masse des deux satellites identique). Plus cette masse est élevée, moins la performance du lanceur permet de changement d'inclinaison.

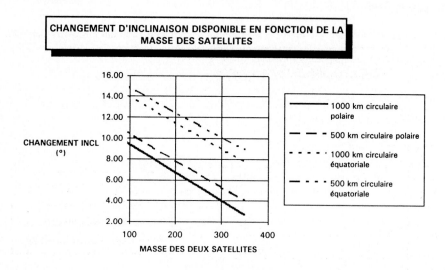

Fig. 7: changement d'inclinaison disponible en lancement double dérivé P

A tître d'exemple, pour une orbite circulaire polaire à 1000 km, et pour deux satellites de 200 kg, un satellite peut être placé sur une orbite inclinée à 90°, et l'autre inclinée à 83.5°. Il est aussi possible de placer les deux satellites dans un même plan , mais avec des apogées ou périgées différents. La figure 9 donne un exemple de cette possibilité, en considérant deux satellites de masse identiques, dont l'un est placé sur une orbite circulaire, et l'autre sur une orbite elliptique de perigée egal au rayon de l'orbite du premier satellite, comme indiqué sur la figure 8.

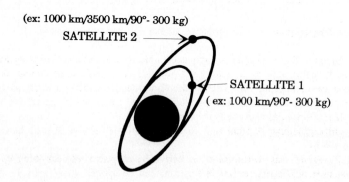

Fig. 8: possibilité de lancement double avec orbites de même plan

La figure 9 donne, pour quatre orbites, et en fonction de la masse des deux satellites, l'apogée que l'on peut atteindre pour le deuxième satellite. Par exemple, deux satellites de 400 kg peuvent être placés l'un sur 1000 km circulaire polaire, et l'autre 1000 km/1700 km polaire.

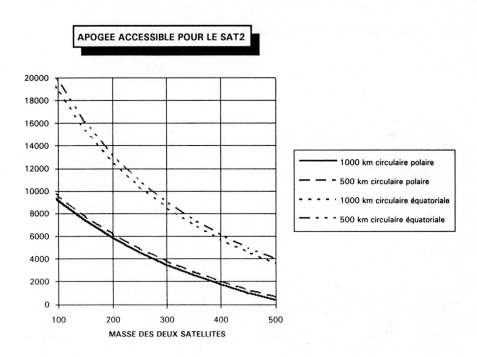

Fig. 9: changement de l'apogée d'un des satellites

3.2 Précision d'injection

Les dérivés légers utilisant les mêmes équipements électriques qu'ARIANE 5, et un étage terminal avec le même moteur, la précision d'injection sera aussi bonne que sur ARIANE 5, c'est-à-dire avec une erreur inférieure à 0.04° sur l'inclinaison et à 4 km sur le demi-grand axe.

3.3 Volume disponible pour la charge utile

Le volume disponible sous coiffe pour la charge utile est représenté sur la figure 10, en configuration lancement double et simple.

Le diamètre maximal utile est 2.8 m sur une hauteur de 2.5 m environ: cela constitue un volume particulièrement important pour des satellites d'une tonne, ce qui peut conduire à une simplification du satellite, par exemple à l'utilisation d'antennes non déployables.

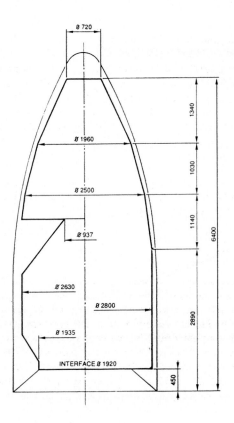

Fig. 10: volumes disponibles sous coiffe pour le dérivé P

3.4 Environnement du vol

Sur le plan thermique et acoustique, l'environnement en vol devrait être assez proche de celui d'ARIANE 5. Les charges mécaniques seront un peu plus élevées, à cause de l'accélération quasi-statique, qui restera cependant inférieure à 6 g.

3.5 Fiabilité

La fiabilité spécifiée pour les dérivés légers est la même que pour ARIANE 5, c'est-à-dire une probabilité de réussite de la mission plus grande que 0.985. En fait, la fiabilité calculée est supérieure à cette valeur grâce à l'utilisation de propulseurs à poudre.
Il est à noter que tous les éléments critiques pour le vol auront fait leurs preuves sur ARIANE 5.

3.6 Souplesse opérationnelle

Le concept même du dérivé P a été choisi de façon à offrir un véhicule souple de mise en oeuvre, condition primordiale pour le lancement de petits satellites. L'utilisation de propulseurs à poudre permet de réduire les durées de campagne, et la séparation des zones d'intégration des dérivés légers et d'ARIANE 5 donne toute la souplesse souhaitée, tout en offrant aux responsables des charges utiles les mêmes services que pour ARIANE 5.

3.7 Coût du service de lancement

L'utilisation de matériel de vol non spécifique, c'est-à-dire produits pour d'autres véhicules de lancement, l'amortissement des frais fixes d'opération sur différents lanceurs permettra d'obtenir un coût de lancement bas et compétitif.

4. CONCLUSION

Les dérivés légers compléteront les services de lancement d'ARIANE 5 à partir de 1998 avec deux lanceurs bien adaptés pour les satellites héliosynchrones (dérivé S) et les petits satellites (dérivé P). La démarche suivie est classique: elle consiste à dériver d'un lanceur existant (ARIANE 5), une famille de lanceurs qui constitue une panoplie adaptée au marché. Les avantages sont nombreux: le coût de développement est réduit, et l'on tire le maximum bénéfice des investissements considérables qui ont été faits pour ARIANE 5. De plus, les lanceurs dérivés bénéficient de technologies éprouvées, et la même qualité de service peut être offerte aux différentes classes de satellites, avec toute la souplesse opérationnelle voulue.

NEXT LAUNCH SYSTEM

BY PROF. C.OIKNINE

ISRAEL AIRCRAFT INDUSTRIES LTD
ELECTRONIC DIVISION

1. Introduction

Israel Aircraft Industries (IAI) is proposing the NEXT launch system to provide a low cost launch service capability for small satellites. The NEXT launch system is an adaptation of the existing IAI developed Shavit-I launcher vehicle system and a substantial amount of hardware and software of NEXT has been flight proven in the Shavit-I program.

Two successful launches were performed by the Shavit-I launcher on September 19,1988 and on April 3,1990.

The proposed NEXT launch system includes all supplies, facilities, personnel and services necessary to design, develop, produce test integrate and launch the vehicle, and place the designated payload into the required orbit.

2. NEXT Technical Description

The NEXT (see figure 1) is composed of three propulsion stages using solid rocket motors and one upper propulsion module using a bi-propellant thruster. Two identical solid rocket motors (with exception of the expansion ratio of the nozzles) are proposed in the first two stages.

The total length of the regular version is about 20m and its launch weight is about 30 ton. The first stage has a three axis control system using four air-vanes and four jet-vanes. The jet-vanes are used only during the first seconds of the flight. The second and the third stage are guided and controlled in pitch and yaw by a Liquid Injection Thrust Vector Control (LITVC).

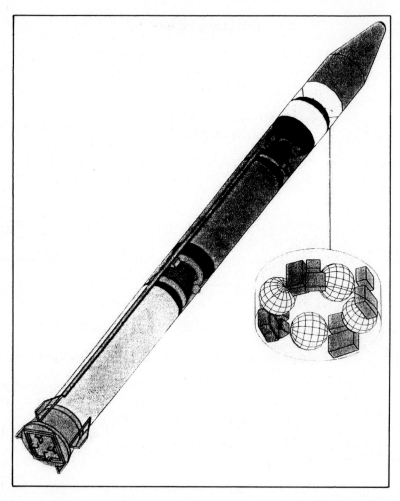

Figure 1. <u>NEXT Launcher</u>

Flight experience indicates that a roll control is unnecessary for the second stage.

The bi-propellant module (BPM) has a double function of propulsion and of attitude control. Before third stage ignition, the attitude control is assured by the BPM. After separation of the third stage and until injection, the BPM can give an impulse velocity at the perigee orbit and gives an additional velocity impulse at apogee in order to get a circular orbit. The BPM allows a maximum benefit of the three solid motors energy, an accurate adjustment of the injection requirements and a good degree of flexibility to reach the payload mass and orbit requirement.

The three rocket-motor casings are wound from graphite fiber in an epoxy resin matrix and are an essential part of the structure. Their interstages are built of aluminum skin and stiffeners. The BPM structure is based on graphite epoxy composite. The different stages are joined by external clamps and the flight staging is carried out by activating pyrotechnical bolts.

The system avionics is composed of two identical and independent systems in order to achieve redundancy; the avionic units of each of the avionic systems are interconnected by a MIL-STD-1553B dual redundant communication bus. Every avionic system has its own pyrotechnical system which is redundant by itself.

The navigation system includes three low cost strapdown platforms (SDP.U), an Inertial Navigation Unit (IN.U), and a GPS as receiver unit. The SDP.U provides the guidance and control system with the data needed to the navigation and to the control. The gimbaled platform (IN.U) is located in stage-II and used for initial alignment and for accurate navigation during the two first stages. The GPS Unit is located in Stage-IV and takes over the IN.U role after the second and third staging.

The NEXT is assembled horizontally and then transported erected and launched by the same LET transporter.

3. Flight Control

The flight control components of NEXT and the guidance and control algorithms are based on Shavit-I's flight control system.

3.1 Mission Profile

Figure 2 illustrates the sequence of events of a NEXT typical mission in its ascent phase. After the burn-out of the third motor, there is a short coasting phase followed by a bi-propellant thrusting. The velocity impulse given by the BPM allows an accurate adjustment of the injection velocity. Such adjustment is required in order to get proper injection into circular or elliptical orbits.

A mission which requires injection into a high circular orbit is managed as follows. A transfer orbit is accomplished with the above bi-propellant impulse, forming an ellipse whose apogee is at the height of the required circular orbit. A second bi-propellant impulse, executed at this apogee, injects the spacecraft into the circular orbit.

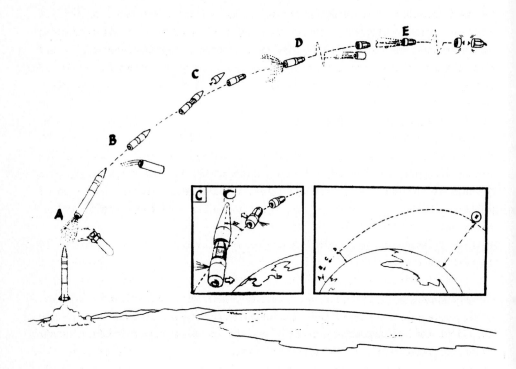

Figure 2. NEXT Typical Mission Profile

3.2 Flight Control and Staging

The first stage is controlled by four air-vanes and four jet-vanes having a maximum deflection angle of twenty degrees. After some seconds of flight, the jet-vanes are jettisoned.

The second and the third stages are controlled in pitch and yaw by an LITVC system.
The bi-propellant module (BPM) includes a main axial motor and an Attitude Control System (ACS) in pitch, yaw and roll composed of several 20N bi-propellant thrusters.

154

The configuration of the staging joints is uniform. Two bulkheads with trapezoid shaped teeth, connected together by external V-shaped clamp. The clamp is released by pyrotechnic activation, to enable the staging event.

The NEXT lift-off is obtained by simultaneously igniting the first motor and releasing the base clamp.   The I/II staging is also accomplished by simultaneously igniting the second motor and releasing the clamp which holds the two stages together. The II/III staging is obtained at high altitude using the BPM to separate the third stage from the second stage. Staging of the BPM from the third stage is similar to the II/III staging. However, calibrated springs are employed for fairing removal and staging the spacecraft from the

3.3 Guidance and Control (G&C)

The NEXT G&C is based on implicit guidance and on digital control. The nominal trajectory is shaped during design, and the flight path angle is commanded as a function of time. The flight consists of four stages, each of which is divided into phases. The criteria to switch from one phase to another are based either on time or on physical values.

The guidance and control of the first three stages is derived from the Shavit-I G&C. After lift-off, the NEXT is kept vertical until its velocity reaches a minimum value. Then, a transition turn is commanded by the guidance computer. After   seconds of flight, the jet-vanes are jettisoned. A few seconds before the first motor's nominal burn-out time, the guidance is overridden and the control command cancels the angles of attack, allowing a safe staging. The staging is carried out when the longitudinal acceleration reaches a definite value.

After the second motor ignition, an acceleration feedback is employed in the control loop in order to reduce the LITVC fuel consumption at high dynamic pressure. Then, the guidance law continues to command the flight path angle to maintain the gravity turn. After second motor burn-out, a coasting phase is carried out, until the aerodynamic effects are negligible. This phase allows the third stage to start in safe conditions. During this phase the control of the NEXT angular motion is attained by the BPM.

The third stage is divided into two phases. During the first phase, the BPM orients the stage in a predetermined orientation for fairing jettison and then it orients the stage prior to motor ignition. The second phase begins with the motor ignition. The guidance system commands the trajectory angle to obtain zero flight path angle at orbit injection.

The fourth stage G&C laws calculate and perform the ΔV impulses needed to meet the mission requirements. There are two possible ΔV impulses: the first is executed near perigee, just after third stage engine burn-out, and the second one at apogee.

* The first ΔV enables taking into account the differences between the actual velocity at third motor burn-out, and the velocity needed in order to get into the required elliptic orbit.
* The second ΔV enables to get into the nominal circular orbit as required.

4. NEXT System and Launch Services

The NEXT launch system incorporates modern flight proven components and has three major elements; The launcher vehicle, the launcher erector transporter (LET) and the launch operations support equipment housed in a van.

The NEXT vehicle consists of a three stage solid rocket motor booster with a liquid bi-propellant system at the upper stage. The avionics system has a dual redundant architecture with two identical and independent avionics system. Each avionics system is interconnected by a MIL-STD-1553B dual redundant communication bus, which provides a second layer of redundancy for the system. NEXT navigation system is based on three strapdown platforms (SDP.U), and an inertial navigation unit (IN.U).

A PCM airborne data collection system collects, encodes and transmits data to the ground. Telemetry data sources include environmental conditions sensors, in-flight events, status parameters and 1553B traffic. The PCM stream is transmitted through a   transmitter to the receiver

Two redundant range safety systems are provided to enable flight termination from the ground by the test range safety officer to minimize the risk of the launch vehicle or its parts falling in a prohibited area.

The reusable elements of the launch system are operated and maintained as part of the launch operations. The launch operation services shall include the procedures necessary for launching payloads to orbit.

The New Approach for Launch Service Operation

IAI will provide launch services for small satellites in an extremely competitive market, using a central vehicle production assembly and test facility together with an operation center that will support the customers.

This facility will deliver fully-integrated flight-certified NEXT launch vehicles to the integration area at the launch site. At the integration site, full functional tests are performed to verify no damage during transportation. The Payload is integrated and tested and the LET loaded with NEXT and the payload are transported to the launch pad together with the launch control shelter and the telemetry antennas.

The launch pad can be any suitable reinforced concrete pad to support LET and NEXT. After connecting the control shelter to the LET the telemetry antennas, and test range communications, a short integration test is performed, NEXT is erected by LET and the system is ready for countdown.

The proposed operation together with NEXT's modern proven technologies present a quantum leap over existing traditional operations and technologies.

Low Cost Launch Services

The NEXT launch vehicle is a growth version of the flight demonstrated Shavit-I vehicle which launched Israel's satellites. Most of the subsystems are therefore flight proven and are Non-Developed Items.

Another key factor in reducing launch service cost is having very effective simple operations. Typical time at the launch site will be about a week, which reduces a typical mission cost including launch site services, range test equipment and full launch into orbit significantly.

Reliable Launch Vehicle

The design philosophy stresses high reliability through the use of proven and matured technology together with wide design margins and redundancy of critical components such as guidance and navigation units.

Operational Simplicity

The NEXT launch systems present a dramatic reduction of launch system complexity. The launch vehicle arrives at the launch site on the LET fully tested and flight certified.

Launch site activities are limited to payload/fourth stage integration and encapsulation in the payload fairing, liquid propellant fueling and prelaunch tests. This approach of a self-contained launch system not only reduces the cost and improves the reliability of the system but assures system availability independent on any other launch site services or test range equipment.

Performance

Accurate orbit injection, is one of the key characteristics of NEXT. Most low earth orbit missions require the sattelite to be placed in either a circular or elliptical orbit at a sufficient altitude to avoid excessive orbit decay.

While direct insertion into an elliptical orbit can be effectively accomplished with a three stage solid booster (Shavit-I, Pegasus), it is highly inefficient to place a satellite into circular orbit above about 300 Km with only three thrust increments. To obtain reasonable propulsion efficiency it is necessary to place the satellite into a transfer orbit with a perigee of between 150 and 185 Km and then raise the orbit with appropriate velocity increments added at perigee and apogee to shape the orbit.

The need to accommodate various orbit shapes and insertion accuracies and given inclination angles requires a restartable upper stage propulsion system. NEXT with its fourth stage bi-propellant module and with its sophisticated and accurate guidance will provide injection into a variety of required orbits.

Orbital accuracy for NEXT missions is affected mainly by the navigation system errors.

Typical accuracies are estimated as:
* ±0.1 deg for the inclination
* ±30 Km for the altitude of the final circular orbit.

For a typical elliptical orbit [220 x 750 Km] the accuracies in the perigee and apogee altitude are respectively estimated as ±3 Km and ±40 Km.

In a degraded mode, if an INU failure occurs during the powered flight, injection in orbit can still be achieved with a lower precision. In all cases inclination precision will be better than 0.3°.

Circular and elliptical orbit performance are shown typically for VAFB (Vandenberg Air-Force Base) and CCAFS (Cape Canaveral Air-Force Station) (figure 4). In all cases, the insertion into a circular orbit at an altitude higher than the injection altitude is obtained after executing two V pulses by the BPM. The mode of insertion gives better performance than direct ascent insertion. However, for low altitude orbits direct insertion can be used and the performance is shown in figure 4.

The maximum acceleration of the NEXT launcher which is about 2g at launch remains always below 8.5g.

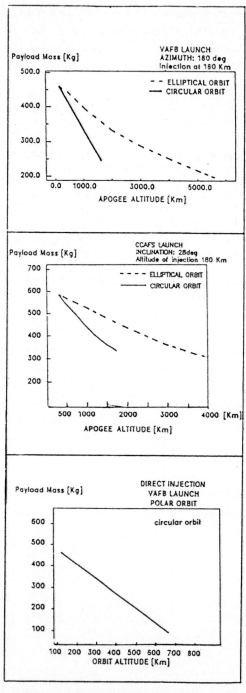

Figure 4. NEXT Circular and Elliptical Orbit Performance

SYNTHESE DE LA SESSION
MOYENS DE LANCEMENT

Ce symposium a bien montré que le marché des petits satellites, en pleine effervescence, est un marché très dispersé : orbites demandées très variées, masses de 50 à 1000 kg, lancements par grappes ou lancements dédiés, etc. Le seul consensus existant concerne le prix du service de lancement qui doit être le plus faible possible.

La seule classification que l'on peut faire au sein de ce marché permet de regrouper, d'une part, les petits satellites ou systèmes de petits satellites à vocation opérationnelle ou commerciale, qui ont des exigences précises concernant le lancement (orbite visée, date de lancement en particulier), et qui sont prêts à payer pour ce service, et, d'autre part, les satellites qui sont prêts à amender leurs exigences pour bénéficier d'un coût de lancement marginal (Piggy back).

Seule la première catégorie pour justifier et rentabiliser l'existence de lanceurs dédiés aux petits satellites, qui ne sont pas forcément des « petits » lanceurs. Inversement, seule la commercialisation effective des petits lanceurs existants et le développement de nouveaux lanceurs permettra d'ordonner ce marché et de créer des standards, comme ASAP l'a fait pour le Piggy back.

SYNTHESIS OF THE SESSION
LAUNCH SERVICES

This symposium has clearly shown that the small satellite market, in a turmoil of excitement, is very dispersed: a wide variety of orbits requested, masses from 50 to 1000 kg, launches in clusters or dedicated launches, etc. The only agreement that exists concerns the price of the launch service; it should be as low as possible.

The only classification that can be applied to this market groups together, on the one hand, small satellites or systems of small satellites for operational or commercial purposes which have precise requirements concerning the launch (target orbit and launch date in particular) and are prepared to pay for this service and, on the other hand, satellites that are ready to adjust their demands in order to obtain a marginal launch cost (piggy back).

Only the first category can justify the existence of launchers dedicated to small satellites (which are not necessarily "small" launchers) and make them financially viable. Conversely, only effective commercialisation of the existing small launchers and the development of new launch vehicles will bring some order to this market and allow standards to be set as ASAP has done for piggy back launches.

SESSION III

SCIENCES DE L'UNIVERS

SPACE SCIENCES

SMALL MISSIONS FOR SPACE SCIENCE

H. OLTHOF, ESTEC, NOORDWIJK, THE NETHERLANDS

Following the recommendations of the ESA Science Programme Review Panel (SPRT) chaired by Prof. Klaus Pinkau the Executive initiated the analysis of the interest in small missions within the European scientific community.

The following actions were taken:

a)   A Call for Ideas for small missions was widely distributed and resulted in 52 responses addressing various aspects of Solar System, Astronomical as well as Earth oriented research. The scientific content was screened by the Space Science Advisory Committee and was considered satisfactory to highly satisfactory.

b)   The Executive organised a workshop on "Design Approaches and Development Philosophies of Small Satellites", which clarified the small satellite concept and their implementation.

c)   The Executive undertook a technical assessment of two examples of small satellites:

> SOLID - solar diameter measurement
> CUBE - UV Cosmic background survey.

The results of the actions undertaken by the ESA Executive were discussed at a meeting of the Science Programme Committee (SPC) in May 1992 and let to the following conclusions:

1.   ESA should continue fostering small satellite programmes in the ESA Member States.

2.   ESA should pursue opportunities of cooperation with the Member States by offering limited support to be decided on a case-by-case basis.

Strategy for a Small Satellite Program and a
Proposal for a First Mission

N. Pailer[1], G. Hampel[1,] E. Bachor[1], G. Lippner[1], and H. Kunow[2]

[1]Deutsche Aerospace, Dornier, Friedrichshafen
[2]Universität Kiel

Abstract

As a complementary element to the relatively big and complex satellites
there is a world-wide trend to small and ingenious missions. Dornier was
in particular interested in two aspects:

- introduce an new concept for a program of Small Satellites based
  on a Modular Bus Unit System

- to prove the idea of a small complement, called ULYSSES
  Reference Mission URM, to the big interplanetary mission ULYSSES

Aspects of the Modular Bus System are high flexibility of central
systems, like Data Handling and AOCS, timely implementation of Ground
Station requirements, application of a Flight Spare Philosophy, and no
hard requirements but minimum requirements to start with. Assuming
frequent launch possibilities a "production line philosophy" could be
applied for basic units or components.

The original idea within the former ISPM (International Solar Polar
Mission) program was the simultaneous investigation of both solar poles
with two solar probes (one from ESA one from NASA). But in 1981 NASA
cancelled its contribution for cost reasons. Therefore it remained only
a single-point measurement of the European ULYSSES solar probe in the
heliosphere which has a very complex structure with a high degree of
temporal and spatial variability.

For this reason the small satellite URM, carrying the five main ULYSSES
instruments on board, is supposed to compensate partly for the cancelled
USA spacecraft by performing scientific baseline measurements. Therefore
the main scientific objectives of URM are identical with the primary
objectives of ULYSSES. The mission will be performed on a highly
eccentrical orbit with an apogee outside of the magnetosphere. These
in-ecliptic reference measurements above the Earth's magnetosphere are
of high scientific interest as well as of practical use: forecasting
geomagnetic storms which may otherwise harm expensive equipment in
particular in northern countries. URM could serve as a testbed for a
future "solar weather forecast" service beeing of use for long-line
communications, high flying planes and for manned space missions (space
station, lunar base, manned mission to Mars, etc.).

A Feasibility Study was performed during an international Satellite
Design Workshop for students at Dornier with support from ESA, DARA,
Fokker, and Kayser Threde.

As URM supports an interplanetary space probe it is thought to be a
typical example for a small scientific satellite. The paper will give an
overview of the URM idea.

1. Introduction

It all started more than 30 years ago with a silvery sphere of about 50
cm in diameter. Ever since SPUTNIK 1, satellites have been getting
bigger, more complex, and more expensive.

Today, Europe is - at least in the field of Space Science - strongly
participating in "big" science projects with a number of large and
medium-sized missions in order to be at the forefront of space science.

"In addition there should still remain room for simple but ingenious
missions both to cover as yet unexplored areas and to keep pace with the
shifting needs of science. A programme composed solely of large missions
would be in danger of loosing its scientific vigour." ("Space Science
Horizon 2000", ESA).

Unfortunately, the small but ingenious missions which are of particular interest for this paper have not been specifically defined. However a "Call for Ideas for Small Missions" by ESA resulted in quite a number of typical proposals:

o Astronomy   11 responses

o Planetary   12 responses

o Space Plasma   12 responses

o Solar Physics   7 responses

With new launch opportunities and launcher systems becoming available, the interest in small space missions will further increase. A trend to smaller and less complex missions is also seen world-wide.

While big projects suffer mainly from long development time small missions allow returning space projects to human scale, where the creativity and spirit that propelled our space programme in its first decade can reinvigorate it in its fourth decade.

Today's small satellites are of fundamentally different origin and character than the small satellites of the 60's and 70's. Several factors have contributed to the emergence of this new "small and smart" satellite systems. Today they have greater capacities for communication, observation, and scientific exploration than their predecessors, in part because they exploit microelectronic and micromechanical technologies that were not available in the earlier years of space endeavors. Advances led to the declining cost of memory and increased processing speed and new approaches. Small satellites have now a level of affordability and flexibility that makes them attractive to a much larger and more diverse customer base.

2. Characteristics of a Small Satellite Programme

Before starting a new programme element the typical characteristics have to be discussed first. "Small" does neither mean only "low weigth" nor necessarily "cheap". It means more "ingenious, smart, quick, compact":

o applications of advanced technologies: characterised by capabilities, performance, and processes, which have - compared to conventional technologies as already used - significantly improved; e. g. technological revolution and not evolution. The advances can be provided in the following fields: mass, performance complexity, power lifetime, manufacturing, volume, operations etc.

o mass and size fit low-cost launchers, like PEGASUS

o short duration of two to three years typically for Phase C/D to permit more frequent missions:

- reduce number of subsystem contractor
- small but interdisciplinary teams
- reduce amount of documentation by "hands-on" supervision
- close ties between user, agency and prime contractor
- more use of performance goals instead of hard requirements

o overall programme cost low to medium

o high performance and low cost to be achieved by intelligent use of experience and modern technology

2.1 Requirements for a "Small Satellite Bus"

A "bus" does not mean a complete system to put some payloads on. It is considered as a system which can be integrated on the basis of available components with only minor modifications necessary; the structure may be considered as an exception. This approach is new for space science missions but was the basis in the field of sounding rocket experiments: standardised components were brought together under minor modifications only.

This new approach is called "Modular Bus Unit System". Its design is optimised for simple modifications (e.g. exchange of electronic components) and a production line philosophy should be applied to basic units.

```
┌─────────────────┐
│ Satellite Bus│
├─────────────────┘
│
├─ system configuration has to consider a full range
│  of application rather than a mission specific design
│
├─ structure is mission specific
│
├─ slowly spinning spacecraft
│  (covers most applications)
│  or 3axis stabilised
├─ pointing <1 degree
│
├─ total mass about 200 - 300 kg
│
├─ launchers: PEGASUS-class, ARIANE piggy-back
│
├─ orbit: LEO and GTO
│
├─ lifetime: 1 - 2 years
│
└─ short turnaround time
```

```
  ┌─────────┐
  │ Strategy │
  ├─────────┘
  │
  │
  ├─  design is e.g. for AR (inside the adapter)
  │   but with respect to PEGASUS rqts
  │
  ├─  basic structure consists of the launch adapter and a
  │   single platform for independent mounting of instruments and S/S
  │
  ├─  high degree of modularity for central systems
  │
  ├─  procure peripheral equipment as standard items
  │
  ├─  incorporate Ground Operations Rqts as early as possible
  │
  └─  use Protoflight Model Philosophy without Flight Spare Units
```

2.2 The Modular Bus Unit System

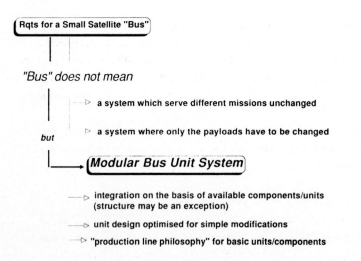

172

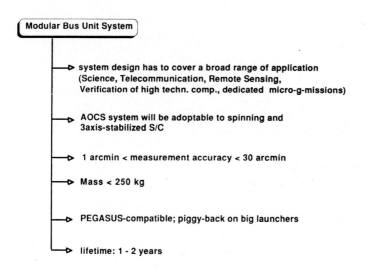

Modular Bus Unit System

- ➤ system design has to cover a broad range of application (Science, Telecommunication, Remote Sensing, Verification of high techn. comp., dedicated micro-g-missions)

- ➤ AOCS system will be adoptable to spinning and 3axis-stabilized S/C

- ➤ 1 arcmin < measurement accuracy < 30 arcmin

- ➤ Mass < 250 kg

- ➤ PEGASUS-compatible; piggy-back on big launchers

- ➤ lifetime: 1 - 2 years

3. URM Mission

3.1 The Idea behind

The original idea of ISPM (International Solar Polar Mission) programme was to study the two poles of the Sun simultaneously with two probes. When NASA left the programme in 1981, ULYSSES remained the only probe to study the very complex heliosphere with its many temporal and spatial interactions. Fig. 1 shows the ULYSSES trajectory above the solar poles.

All attempts to try to compensate for the loss of the American probe failed because of the high cost involved. The Ulysses Reference Mission (URM) could be an interesting alternative.

As there is no chance left to launch a second probe, which would fly on a route similar to that of ULYSSES, but to the opposite solar pole, a cost-saving alternative is being studied. This is the URM idea, which could make parallel measurements to ULYSSES' flights over the poles on a highly eccentric orbit in the ecliptic (apogäum outside the Earth's magnetosphere).

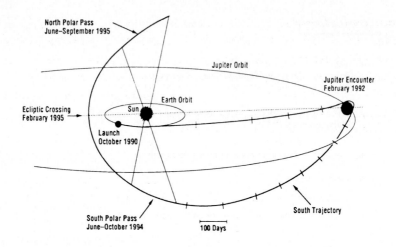

Fig. 1: Typical ULYSSES trajectory to Jupiter and back to the solar poles

3.2 Mission Objectives

The artist illustration in Fig. 2 shows the various phenomena observable by ULYSSES. As URM is supposed to serve as reference mission in the ecliptic it will allow for a "stereoscopic" view of the heliosphere and therefore will enhance these aspects. Direct measurements of URM will be related to items No 3, 5, 6, 7, 9, and 10.

Additionally to the scientific reasoning of the URM there are certain possibilities for some practical application of solar wind particle informations. It is known that charged solar wind particles hitting the Earth's magnetosphere can produce severe damage to expensive equipment in particular in northern countries like USA, Canada, and Scandinavia.

Power plants respectively power distribution companies, for example, suffer from spikes in their power lines induced by distortions of the Earth's magnetic field. That causes damage to transformers and sometimes their blowing up. The replacement is expensive and time-consuming. Additional service could be provided to everybody exposed to radiation: high flying planes, satellites, manned space missions etc. The next geomagnetic storm season is around 1994.

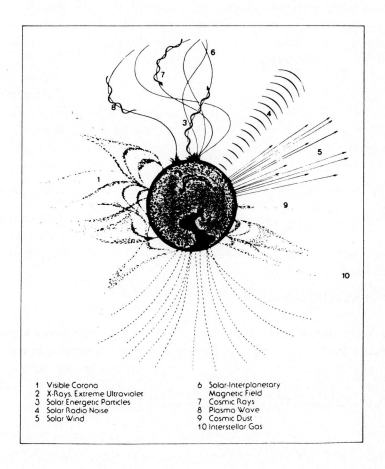

1 Visible Corona
2 X-Rays, Extreme Ultraviolet
3 Solar Energetic Particles
4 Solar Radio Noise
5 Solar Wind
6 Solar-Interplanetary Magnetic Field
7 Cosmic Rays
8 Plasma Wave
9 Cosmic Dust
10 Interstellar Gas

Fig. 2: Artist illustration of various phenomena observable and partly enhanced by URM. Direct measurements of URM will be related to items No 3, 5, 6, 7, 9, and 10

3.2.1 Model Payload for URM (Overview)

The URM is designed to use experimental H/W which is identical to the experiments onboard the ULYSSES S/C. The backup units are available as flight units for URM, the H/W is tested and space-proven.

Experiment	Principal Invest.	Scientific Obj.	Remarks
COSPIN (SIM)	H. Kunow University Kiel	cosmic rays and solar particles	- intensity - energy - composition - distribution
TAUS (BAM-I)	H. Rosenbauer MPAe, Lindau	solar wind ions	- density - velocity - direction
ANGAS (KEP-3)	H. Rosenbauer MPAe, Lindau	neutral interstellar gas	- density - bulk velocity - temperature
MAGNET (HED)	A. Balogh Imp. College, London	magnetic fields	

The DUST experiment from the MUSES S/C - not included in the table above is foreseen to replace the big ULYSSES dust sensor.

4. Concept Alternatives

ESA as well as the different national space agencies are discussing Small Scientific Mission Programmes. The most promising philosophy is not yet established. Therefore the URM idea follows three different approaches:

4.1 Make optimum Use of available H/W

Since ULYSSES was successfully launched in Oct. 1990 the flight spare
H/W of the ULYSSES programmme can be made available by ESA for further
use. The URM mission, planned to carry five of the main ULYSSES flight
spare instruments on board, could be built with about 80% of available
H/W. Certainly, some functions would be oversized. In case of a low-cost
Russian launcher (e. g. MOLNIYA or COSMOS) this would still be the most
cost-effective approach.

The spacecraft will consist of a relatively simple spinning platform and
a cylindrically shaped solar array. Three booms are foreseen to carry
the magnetic field experiment. The total mass of the spacecraft will be
between 120 - 130 kg.

4.2 Adapt the ULYSSES S/S to the direct Needs of URM

The cylindrical part of the configuration shown in Fig. 3 houses the
spacecraft equipment platform. The conical part indicates possibilities
to increase solar array surface and/or the P/L volume and therefore some
growth potential respectively flexibility. The bus is complemented by
three booms to be deployed carrying the sensors for the magnetic field
experiment. The total mass of the spacecraft is about 100 kg.

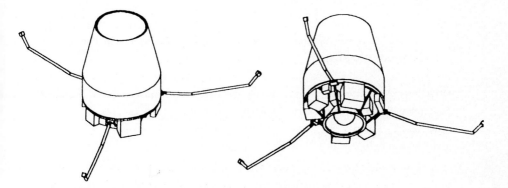

Fig. 3: One of the three optional configurations for URM

This configuration is taylored to be launched on a SCOUT-II launch vehicle. The mass and volume contraints require a different solution: The ULYSSES H/W is used in the form of modules resp. PCB's, (Printed Circuit Boards) which are selected in accordance with the needs of the system, without redundancy, and repackaged in one of the original housings. For the OBDH this means that instead of the 3 units CIU, RIU and RCIU (Remote Control I/F Unit) only one nonredundant OBDH unit inside the RIU housing is created. The same is done with the power units PCU and PDU. The PCU (Power Control Unit) contains both power regulation PCB's and power switches. The power switching PCBs will be complemented with identical size PCBs from PDU to form a combined power control and distribution unit.

In the AOCS electronics the redundant processing electronics are housed in separate boxes. A single AOCE unit contains already all interfaces and functions to connect to the OBDH, sun sensors and cold gas actuators. Some unused functions like cat bed heaters switching or the conscan processor will remain. With the above concept, a system can be built, which has proven hi-rel technology, known and verified performance and interfaces with a minimum penalty of carrying along functions, which are not needed. A considerable part of the existing documentation like integration procedures and I/F verification procedures can be utilized.

This configuration was subject to the Satellite Design Workshop held at Dornier in April 1991 (Proceedings are available).

4.3 Establish a New System of adaptable Components as Basis for a
      Future Programme

While using "leftover" flight qualified hardware from previous projects is cost-effective, specifically when also the payload is from the same spacecraft, its use is limited in the long run. The two main drawbacks are:

178

- limited supply of existing hardware
- advances in technology are not utilized.

Therefore, a third option to support the future small satellite programs is proposed. Independant from the development status of "periphery" equipment like RF units, star, earth or sun sensors, actuators, power control and distribution electronics, there is a definite potential to capitalize on the recent technology advances in the areas data handling, altitude and orbit control and navigation electronics. To be attractive for a wide variety of small satellite missions this system must be broken down into modules, which are needed on all spacecraft but in different quantities and arrangements:

- control processing

- command processing and distribution for on-off, serial load and time tagged commands

- data acquisition for analog and digital data

- telemetry formating

- control of onboard mass memory for data storage and retrieve (for downlink)

- timing and synchronisation signals

- event datation

- adaptable processor memory capacity for AOCS closed loop control algorithms

- S/W up- and download capability

Not all of the above facilities are required for the URM, i.e. the mass memory control, but most likely needed in other applications.

The modularity of the system must be such that a development model with commercial grade parts can be assembled in a very early stage of a spacecraft program.

High data rates and tight real time requirements for attitude control functions should be dealt with separate adaptions to avoid an overdesign for the majority of users.

With the savings in mass, power and volume a URM spacecraft can be realized in the 70 to 80 kg range.

SMALL SATELLITE MISSIONS TO LONG-PERIOD COMETS

by

Ettore Perozzi° and Eduard M. Pittich*

° Telespazio, Via Tiburtina 965, 00156 Roma (Italy)
* Astronomical Institute, Slovak Academy of Sciences,
    842 28 Bratislava (Czech and Slovak)

Abstract

Long-period comets (those with period of revolution greater than 200 years) are probably the best preserved primitive bodies of the solar system. They are "new" comets in two respects: it is their first apparition in historical times and it is possibly their very first passage close to the Sun. As a consequence their surface material has not been altered by the physical processes following the oneset of cometary activity. Planning a space mission toward a long-period comet poses a challenging problem as to the fact that the target object is known only at the time of its discovery, a mere few months before its perihelion passage. The possibility of actually sending a mission to a long-period comet is reviewed in the light of small satellites and launchers technology.

Introduction

In the last decade there has been a major interest towards the realization of missions to minor bodies, and specifically comets. These objects became a major goal for space exploration when it was recognized that they are original remnants of the early phase of solar system formation. This interest has been confirmed by the Primitive Bodies cornerstone set within the long-term plan of the European Space Agency, and by the many cometary missions sent by several space agencies in the last few years. The close view of the nucleus of comet P/Halley is the most spectacular result of this politics.

Up to now there are three comets which have been (or soon will be) visited by space missions: P/Giacobini-Zinner (ICE, in 1985), P/Halley (GIOTTO, VEGA, and SAKIGAKE in 1986) and P/Grigg-Skjellerup (GIOTTO, 10 july 1992). The fact that all of them are short-period comets can be explained on the basis of simple mission analysis considerations (e.g. see Yeomans 1985). Short-period comets are defined as those with period of revolution less than 200 years: we know more than 150 objects and the majority of them have been observed more than only once. From a strictly mission-planning point of view this means that it has been possible to determine the orbit of the comet using observations covering a rather long time span, often extending to several returns and that the physical characteristics of the comets are known in advance. Both arguments are crucial, since a conventional space mission requires to know several years in advance the position and the characteristics of its target. Furthermore, if the orbital and physical characteristics of a comet are well known, the chances for recovering the comet are higher. In their investigations on the dynamical evolution of the whole short-period comets population, Carusi et.al (1985) and Belyaev et.al (1986) have ordered the sample considering the number and epoch of cometary apparitions and have computed an empirical "quality class" (ranging from 1 to 5) which gives an idea on the goodness of the orbit reconstruction together with the effect of nongravitational forces on orbit prediction. In table 1 is reported data relative to the three short-period comets visited so far.

Catalogue Number	Name	Number of Apparitions	Quality Class
1	HALLEY	30	4
24	GIACOBINI-ZINNER	12	5
29	GRIGG-SKJELLERUP	16	5

In the case of long-period comets, none of the above information is available. In this class of comets are included those objects which have period of revolution greater than 200 years, thus grouping together comets which did not have enough time to be observed more than once in historical times (long-period) as well as those entering for the very first time the inner solar system from the Oort cloud in nearly hyperbolic orbits (the so-called "new" comets). We observed to this time more than 650 such new comets (long-period and hyperbolic), on average 3-4 new comets per year, in the period 1987-1989 being 12-15 per year. The limited time span during which the surface of the comet has been active guarantees an high scientific interest for a space mission. On the other hand, the comet is "new" also with respect to mission planning because no prediction can be done on the spatial location and timing of its appearance. This implies that only a limited time is allowed to actually prepare the mission: from the comet discovery at least some months of observations must be performed in order to determine a reliable orbit; the flight time needed to reach the comet in a favourable encounter configuration must be also included. In particular this last constraint cannot be fulfilled by means of conventional missions, while it seems less problematic in the light of the recent developments in small satellites and launchers technology.

Mission Opportunities

The feasibility of a space mission to a long-period comet has been extensively discussed by L.Kresak and E.M.Pittich in 1984. In what follows, we have summarized the major points outlined in that paper:

- apparitions of long-period comets are rare and unpredictable;

- long period comets have large orbital eccentricities and random inclinations so that encounters can only happen close to their nodes which, in turn, may fall at large heliocentric distances;

- the relative geometry Earth-Comet-Spacecraft at encounter may result not satisfactory;

- two or three months of astrometric observations are needed in order to establish that the comet is a long-period one;

- there is a limited time span between discovery of the comet and launch, and this implies constraints also on the flight time;

- no major planets swingby can be planned, and only in few cases terrestrial planets may help.

As it can be seen, the constraints listed above can be divided into two groups: those imposed by the dynamical characteristics of long-period comet orbits (high-inclination, high-eccentricity), and those depending only on the present status of our space technology (limited delta-V, long lead times for mission planning).
As concerning the purely dynamical problem, Kresak and Pittich have found that, taking into account long period comets discovery rates and geometrical considerations (nodes too distant are disregarded), it can be estimated a frequency of one mission opportunity per year within values of the geocentric excess speed between 5 and 10 km/sec and flight times less than one year.

The problem is then to assess the practical feasibility of the mission. The major difficulty appears to be the limited time at disposal to organize and launch an interplanetary mission. An improvement of the techniques of faint comet detection (e.g. from space orbiting satellites such as IRAS or ISO) might help to increase the time span from comet discovery to launch, but there are a number of difficulties to realize an ambitious program such as space-based surveys of the sky. The availability of small satellites and launchers seems a more straightforward way of solving the problem.

There are some advantages due to the peculiar characteristics of the target: a mission to a long period comet has never been done before, while repeated missions, even with few experiments on board, may bring information to study the long-period comet population as a whole. Science payload can be then kept to a minimum without losing the high scientific return of the mission. As a reference, each individual GIOTTO experiment weighted a few kilograms, its CCD camera being the heaviest with 13.5 kg (Reinhard 1987). Taking into account that a powerful third stage must also be provided in order to inject the spacecraft into interplanetary space at a relatively high excess velocity, a reasonable estimate for a satisfactory science payload is about 50 kg.

A narrower choice applies to the launcher. Because of the afore mentioned time constraints of the mission, the possibility of being carried as a secondary payload from a conventional launcher is excluded (e.g. Ariane). In this respect, small launchers are best fitting the peculiar characteristics of the mission and it appears that carriers like Scout and Pegasus may already provide good opportunities (Feustel-Buechl and Pfeffer 1989).

Conclusions

Long-period and "new" comets are offering a unique opportunity for probing the almost unaltered composition of planetesimals in the solar nebula. The peculiar dynamical characteristics of a mission towards these comets poses severe constraints to actually realize such missions. In particular the long waiting time for the comet to appear and the limited time span from discovery to launch, leave no chance of planning a conventional space mission. Interplanetary missions with small satellites have been shown to be feasible at the present technological state of the art (Jones 1992), while the development of small launchers, lowering the cost and the complexity of launch operations, may solve the major difficulties posed by a mission to a long-period comet. With this assumptions it has been possible to show that small satellite missions to long-period comets become now feasible and that these comets are the only objects of the Solar System that cannot be reached at present by any other means.

References

Belyaev N.A., Kresak L., Pittich E.M. and Pushkarev A.N. 1986: "Catatlogue of Short-Period Comets", Bratislava.

Carusi A., Kresak L., Perozzi E. and Valsecchi G.B., 1985: "Long-Term Evolution of Short-Period Comets" Adam Hilger ltd, Bristol and Boston.

Feustel-Buechl J. and Pfeffer H.A., 1989: "Flight Opportunities for Small Payloads". ESA bull. 60, 34.

Kresak L. and Pittich E.M., 1984: "Opportunities of Ballistic Missions to Long-Period Comets". Bull. Astron. Inst. Czechosl. 35, 363.

Jones R.M., 1992: "Small Spacecraft For Planetary Exploration" This book.

Reinhard R., 1987: "The Giotto Mission to Halley's Comet". In 'Exploration of Halley's Comet', M.Grewing, F.Praderie, R.Reinhard eds, 949.

Yeomans D.K., 1985: "The Selection of Comets for Future Space Missions". In 'Dynamics of Comets', A.Carusi and G.B.Valsecchi eds.

SMALL SPACECRAFT FOR PLANETARY EXPLORATION

ROSS M. JONES
JET PROPULSION LABORATORY
CALIFORNIA INSTITUTE OF TECHNOLOGY
4800 OAK GROVE DRIVE
PASADENA, CA., 91109

ABSTRACT

There is need for lower cost, more frequent planetary science missions to compliment the "once a decade" large multi-disciplinary missions. The Solar System Exploration Division of NASA's Office of Space Science and Applications has initiated a program of planetary missions using small spacecraft. This program is called Discovery. This paper will summarize conceptual designs of small spacecraft (100 to 500 kg) for potential Discovery missions to near Earth asteroids. Another class of spacecraft that could be used for Discovery missions are called microspacecraft. Microspacecraft would be compatible with small launch vehicles such as Pegasus. The term "microspacecraft" is used here for spacecraft concepts whose mass is about 10 kg. This paper will also summarize a study of a microspacecraft for a mission to near Earth asteroids.

INTRODUCTION

The purpose of this paper is to summarize some of the Jet Propulsion Laboratory's work in small spacecraft for planetary missions. In this paper, spacecraft will be placed into 3 different categories depending upon their dry (without propellant) mass. For the purpose of definition, standard, small and microspacecraft are defined to have a dry mass of approximately 1000, 100 and 10 kg respectively.

The Jet Propulsion Laboratory (JPL) has been involved in small spacecraft since the start of the "space age". JPL's first spacecraft in 1958, Explorer 1, had a mass of only about 5 kg. The trend since Explorer 1 has been to larger spacecraft as launch vehicle capability increased. This trend is clearly presented in figure 1. Figure 1 presents the dry mass of all planetary spacecraft launched by NASA versus their date of launch. Figure 1 includes the early Pioneer planetary spacecraft; the series of Mariner spacecraft designed and built by JPL, Voyager, Galileo, and the most recent of the Mariners CRAF and Cassini that are presently being designed at JPL. Figure 1 also includes the recently launched Magellan and soon to be launched Mars Observer spacecraft both designed and built by JPL contractors Martin Marietta and General Electric respectively.

There are two clear trends shown in figure 1 i.e., the dry mass of planetary spacecraft has increased by over a factor of ten and the launch frequency has dramatically decreased with time. Certainly, there are many factors responsible for these two trends. One factor is that as spacecraft grow in mass (and inevitably capability and complexity) their cost also grows. Even though the ratio of cost to capability may go down, the absolute cost of the spacecraft goes up and has gone up faster than the financial resources available to support such programs. The situation of more costly spacecraft programs and a relatively fixed amount of resources leads to less frequent programs.

One obvious approach to counter this situation is to plan and carry out less costly programs, which is precisely the purpose of the Discovery program.

DISCOVERY

During fiscal year 1990, the Solar System Exploration Division (SSED) within NASA's Office of Space Science Applications (OSSA) initiated a study of a series of small missions for planetary exploration modelled somewhat on the long established Explorer program and the recently established Earth Probes programs within OSSA. This new initiative of SSED is called "Discovery". The Discovery program is meant to be "small" primarily in a financial sense where the total program cost for one Discovery mission is to be less than $150M.

The program objectives of Discovery are as follows: 1) to provide science investigations at the small, low cost end of the mission spectrum, 2) to allow for rapid responses to new emerging science opportunities, 3) to provide the opportunities for conducting collaborative/cooperative ventures with other agencies, foreign and/or domestic, 4) to give increased opportunities to young researchers in the field of planetary science and 5) to provide a programmatic vehicle for trying and testing new technologies at acceptable risk levels.

In order to set reasonable bounds on the missions to be considered within Discovery and to be consistent with the programmatic realities of securing a place in the OSSA Strategic Plan, the following constraints and/or guidelines have been established: 1) Discovery mission costs shall be limited to less than $150 million, 2) Discovery missions shall be conducted as a series of small, low cost missions which draw from the common designs, common experiences, hardware/software inheritances, etc. to form a program. Missions in this program would be flown between 1996 and 2006, 3) Discovery missions are being restrained to Delta class or preferably smaller launch vehicles, 4) science investigations shall be basic and focused on addressing the most fundamental questions and 5) congressional approval for a Discovery mission will be sought on an individual basis independent of any other Discovery missions.

Consistent with the objectives and the constraints, the scope of the Discovery Program is necessarily limited relative to past planetary exploration missions. Thus, the small missions to be considered have modest performance requirements in all categories. Specific missions to be considered include the near Earth bodies (asteroids and/or comets), the moon, Venus, and Mars as possible targets.

In support of the Discovery Program, JPL performed a conceptual spacecraft system design for both a near Earth asteroid flyby and a rendezvous mission.

Discovery Asteroid Flyby

For the flyby study the selected target was the large near Earth asteroid, Eros. The missions was constrained to the Pegasus launch vehicle. There were two minimum science requirements. First, obtain at least 2 images that have at least 100,000 pixels filled by Eros with a resolution of 30 m or better per pixel. Second, obtain images with a resolution of 300 m per pixel or better at approximately 30 minute intervals for the five hours proceeding closest approach and the 5 hours following closest approach.

A conceptual design of a camera was created for this study. The characteristics of the optics of this camera were as follows: 1) 1 meter focal length, 2) 12 milli-radian field of view and 3) an effective F number of 10. The camera used a 1024 by 1024 CCD array with 12E-6 meter pixels. The camera concept had a shutter time of 2.5E-3 sec and a readout rate of 2.0E+5 bits per second. The physical characteristics of the camera were as follows: 1) 3.5 kg, 2) 8 watts and 3) sized to be a cube 7 inches on a side.

The nominal launch date was chosen to be 5/28/95. Pegasus would deliver the spacecraft to a 200 km circular orbit. An upper stage was required to inject the flight system onto a flyby trajectory with Eros. The nominal arrival date was 3/14/96.

The spacecraft conceptual design used the science and mission requirements discussed above and the following derived spacecraft requirements. The spacecraft and its upper stage shall be consistent with the injection performance of Pegasus to a 200 km orbit (400 kg) and the injection energy requirement of 1.89 $(km/sec)^2$. The injected mass allocation was about 75 kg. The spacecraft lifetime shall be at least 1.0 year. The spacecraft shall have on-board failure protection algorithms for potential system failures, that can, if enabled place the spacecraft in a safe configuration for at least 7 days without ground intervention.

The spacecraft shall be capable of providing about 130 m/sec of delta V for all post launch manuevers. The spacecraft shall be capable of executing all manuevers in any inertial direction.

The spacecraft shall be capable of simultaneous X band radio metric tracking, telemetry and commanding and shall be compatible with the NASA/JPL Deep Space Tracking Network. The spacecraft shall be generally consistent with the recommendations of the Consultative Committee for Space Data Systems (CCSDS).

The resulting spacecraft conceptual design was compatible with Pegasus and was injected to Eros with a Star 24C solid rocket motor. The spacecraft was spinning at all times at about 10 rpm except for the injection when it was spun up to about 100 rpm. The spacecraft was configured as an oblate disk with a diameter of about 1 meter. Figure 2 presents the spacecraft configuration. The structure was aluminum. The post injection delta V requirements (150 m/sec) were met by a mono-propellant subsystem. The spacecraft was powered by body mounted solar cells and a battery. Attitude control references were the Sun and the star, Canopus. The computer for the spacecraft was a 1750A micro-processor. All data was stored in a solid state memory. All communications with Earth were supported by an X band subsystem. The objective of this study was to assess the first order feasibility of using Pegasus to launch a mission to the near Earth asteroid, Eros in May of 1995 with a total program development cost of less than $150M. The primary issues were technical and cost feasibility. To first order, technical feasibility was demonstrated and the estimated program cost was well below the goal.

Discovery Asteroid Rendezvous

For the rendezvous study the selected target was the near Earth asteroid, Anteros. The mission was allowed to use a Delta launch vehicle. The science requirements were to image the entire surface of the asteroid at a resolution of at least 6 meters per pixel and obtain IR and elemental composition information.

The following instruments were the payload for the rendezvous mission: 1) a visible wavelength camera, 2) an IR point spectrometer and 3) a gamma ray spectrometer. The camera had a 154 milliradian field of view with f/2, 80 mm optics, a 6 color filter wheel and a 1024 by 1024 micrometer CCD detector. The IR spectrometer had a 100 milliradian field of view and covered 0.8 to 2.5 micrometer spectral region. The gamma ray spectrometer had a wide field of view. Only the IR instrument required cooling. The mass and power requirements of the camera, the IR spectrometer and the gamma ray spectrometer were 4.5 kg and 8 W; 4.5 kg and 4 W and 18 kg and 12 W respectively. The nominal launch date was chosen to be May 20, 1997. The Delta 7925 would inject the spacecraft directly onto a trajectory with Anteros. The nominal arrival date was July 8, 1998.

The spacecraft requirements were the same as for the flyby spacecraft presented previously except for the following items: 1) the injection energy of 40 $(km/sec)^2$ from the Delta limits the spacecraft injected mass to about 570 kg, 2) the spacecraft lifetime needed to be at least 3.0 years. 3) the post launch delta V requirement was 1200 m/sec and 4) the spacecraft was required to be capable of performing the manuevers in orbit around the asteroid to a precision of 0.001 m/sec or better.

Figure 3 presents the external and internal views of the resulting conceptual design of the Discovery rendezvous spacecraft, respectively. Power is provided by a body-mounted, silicon solar array this is designed to allow a very wide range of sun angles. Command and data handling functions are centralized in a computer and mass data storage capability is in excess of 0.1 Gbit. Telecommunications are all X-band, include a 3 W RF power amplifier, and utilize body-mounted antennas. There is one high-gain antenna and three low-gain antennas which allow commandability at any spacecraft orientation. The spacecraft is fully spin stabilized during cruise and then switches over to momentum bias operation after rendezvous. This is accomplished by despinning the spacecraft up a single momentum wheel instead. In both cases, the boresight of the high-gain antenna is aligned with the momentum vector and thus allows continuous HGA communications when Earth-pointing is selected. In the momentum bias mode, continuous nadir pointing of the instruments is available simultaneously as long as an orbit about the target body is selected that has its normal pointed at Earth. Fine sun sensors and the science [and star] camera provide necessary spacecraft attitude information; no gyros are required. Propulsion is provided with a simple monopropellant hydrazine system with a capacity of 348 kg of usable propellant. The spacecraft was designed to be fully redundant in all the usual components.

ASTEROID INVESTIGATION WITH MICROSPACECRAFT

This section presents the results of the conceptual design of a microspacecraft intended for investigation of near Earth asteroids. Technology for microspacecraft is primarily coming from two agencies within the US Department of Defense i.e., the Defense Advanced Research Projects Agency (DARPA) and the Strategic Defense Initiative Organization (SDIO). The purpose of the AIM (Asteroid Investigation with Microspacecraft) conceptual design effort was to develop a microspacecraft system concept which would demonstrate the feasibility and advantages of using microspacecraft for science missions. Only technology that had its fundamental performance parameters demonstrated was used in this study.

The mission chosen for this conceptual study is a flyby of a near Earth asteroid. This selection is an attempt to make the mission significant from a science viewpoint, while limiting the demand the mission will place on the flight system and launch vehicle. Near Earth asteroids have only been examined through ground based telescopes. Closer examination would produce data which would

bring new insight to many aspects of planetary science, making
missions to these bodies very attractive.

Science requirements can be modest for a near Earth asteroid
mission. A small, body mounted camera with color filters is an
adequate payload. Color images at resolutions of 10-20 meters
per pixel can reveal a great deal about the surface features,
composition, and overall dimensions and volume of the target.
Images taken over the relatively short time period of a flyby may
also reveal information about the spin axis and rate of a body if
the spin rate is rapid enough.

At the start of this study it was decided to use the Pegasus
launch vehicle and attempt to launch 3 microspacecraft to 3
different near Earth asteroids with a single launch vehicle.
Considerable work in the past year has established a large data
base of near Earth asteroid flyby trajectories with the following
characteristics: 1) post injection delta-V requirement of less
than 200 m/s, 2) injection energies less than $_4$ km^2/sec^2, 3) Sun
range of 1.2 AU or less and 4) Earth-spacecraft range of 1.6 AU
or less at any time during the mission. While specific targets
and a launch date have not yet been identified, there is no doubt
that such targets exist.

Performance of the Pegasus to the 200 km circular park orbit is
452 kg. A solid rocket motor (SRM) was selected to provide the
spacecraft with the 3400 m/s required to obtain the injection
energy of 4 km^2/sec^2 from the 200 km park orbit. Since the
spacecraft was to be designed with 3-axis attitude control, an
SRM with a thrust vector control (TVC) nozzle controlled by the
microspacecraft would allow a non-spinning injection.
It was assumed for this study that an injection stage very
similar to the STAR 17A from Morton-Thiokol could be developed
with a TVC nozzle. After launch by the Pegasus into the park
orbit, each SRM/microspacecraft pair separates from the launch
vehicle one at a time. The SRM is fired to place the
microspacecraft on its asteroid flyby trajectory. An injection
correction maneuver is performed by the microspacecraft
immediately after SRM burnout and separation. Staging in this
way allows each spacecraft to be injected onto a different
trajectory from a common park orbit and launch vehicle.

The spacecraft concept for this mission weighs only 25 kg and
could be displayed on a table-top. Its overall dimensions are
0.4 x 0.5 x 0.6 meters. It includes a Ka-band telecommunications
subsystem capable of downlinking over 300 bps to a 70 m station
from 1.6 AU. The power subsystem has a lithium based secondary
battery and a body-mounted multi-bandgap solar array which
produces up to 55 Watts of power at a solar range of 1.2 AU. The
3-axis attitude control subsystem includes reaction wheels, the
Quartz Rate Sensor micro IMU, and a miniature star camera with a
pointing accuracy of 0.01° which can update the inertial
reference in 50 msec. The data and command subsystem features an
RH-32 central computer capable of 20 Mips to control all

spacecraft functions, and a solid state memory with 1 Gbit capacity. Structure is largely graphite epoxy with aluminum in areas where thermal conductivity is critical. The 200 m/s hydrazine propulsion subsystem has a carbon fiber wound tank and six thrusters weighing only 45 g each. Mini louvers and distributed heaters regulate the internal temperatures of the spacecraft. Imaging science is taken with a six color F/10, 1 m focal length, Cassegrain camera with a 1024 x 1024 CCD array. Figure 4 presents a summary of the AIM microspacecraft concept.

The spacecraft is configured as a hexagonal cylinder with solar cells on its six vertical faces. Apertures are cut out of these faces for the imaging camera, sun sensor, Ka-band antenna, and thrusters. The star camera looks out the recessed top face, which houses louver boxes to regulate thermal dissipation to space. The bottom face is devoted to the shunt radiator and the solid rocket motor interface structure which surrounds the centrally located propellant tank. Inside the volume bounded by the solar array, the louver boxes, the shunt radiator, and the tank are three internal bays separated by vertical shear plates. Inside these bays are the subsystem components. Figures 6 and 7 show external and internal views of the spacecraft. Components are arranged in the bays to meet field of view requirements, proximity requirements, and thermal constraints. Bay 1 houses all of the telecommunication components. Bay 2 houses the computer, reaction wheels, and the star camera. Bay 3 houses the power box, shunt regulator, and battery, the camera, and the IMU.

SUMMARY

There are two clear trends when one looks at the launch frequency and size of planetary spacecraft since about 1958. The dry mass of planetary spacecraft has increased by over a factor of ten and the launch frequency has dramatically decreased with time. It is clear that there is a need for smaller, faster more frequent planetary science missions. NASA SSED has started the Discovery program to address smaller, faster missions for planetary exploration. This paper summarized two small spacecraft concepts for potential Discovery asteroid flyby and rendezvous missions. This paper also discussed a concept for a microspacecraft which could be launched by Pegasus and perform asteroid flyby missions. The microspacecraft is based upon advanced technology primarily developed by the United State's Department of Defense and other government agencies.

ACKNOWLEDGEMENT

The research described in this paper was carried out by the Jet Propulsion Laboratory, California Institute of Technology, under a contract with the National Aeronautics and Space Administration.

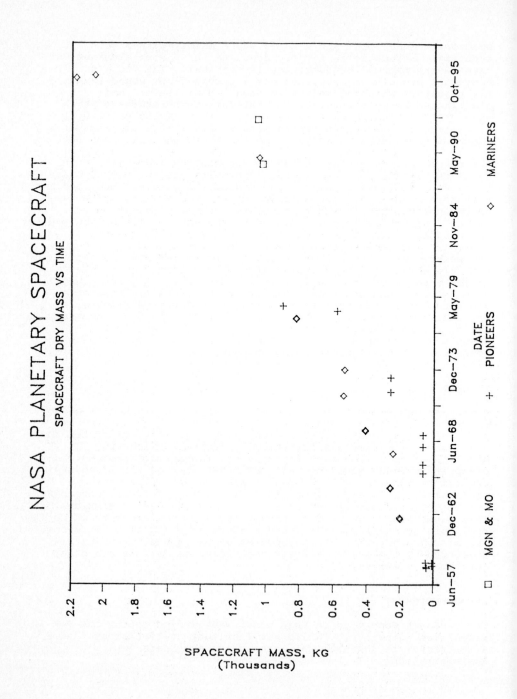

Fig. 1   Dry Mass of NASA Planetary Spacecraft vs. Time.

JPL DISCOVERY FLYBY SPACECRAFT

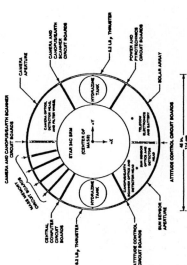
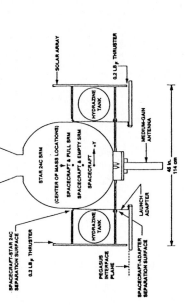

SCIENCE PAYLOAD (BODY MOUNTED): CAMERA
(FOR SINGLE STRING VERSION)
POWER SOURCE: BODY-MOUNTED SILICON SOLAR ARRAY
ENERGY STORAGE: NICKEL-CADMIUM BATTERY
CENTRAL COMPUTER: GVSC 1750A WITH 0.5 GBIT STORAGE
TELECOM: ALL X-BAND; 2 FOV MGA & 1 LGA; 3 W RF POWER
ATTITUDE CONTROL: ALL SPIN; SUN & STAR(OR EARTH)REF.
PROPULSION: HYDRAZINE (7 KG USABLE)
STRUCTURE: CYLINDRICAL
           (AL SHEET METAL & AL HONEYCOMB)

TOTAL WET MASS: 77 KG
LAUNCH VEHICLE: PEGASUS

SPECIAL FEATURES:
CONTINUOUS MGA COMMUNICATIONS AVAILABLE
NO ARTICULATED STRUCTURES
   LARGE SUN-S/C-EARTH ANGLE ACCEPTABILITY
   ELECTRONIC TARGET CLOCK ANGLE TRACKING
NO DEPLOYED STRUCTURES
NO GYROS

Fig. 2   Discovery Asteroid flyby spacecraft.

193

JPL DISCOVERY RENDEZVOUS SPACECRAFT

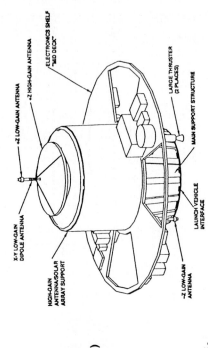

SCIENCE PAYLOAD (BODY MOUNTED):
  CAMERA
  IR POINT SPECTROMETER
  GAMMA-RAY SPECTROMETER
POWER SOURCE: BODY-MOUNTED SILICON SOLAR ARRAY
CENTRAL COMPUTER: WITH >0.1 GBIT STORAGE
TELECOM: ALL X-BAND; HGA & 3 LGAs; 3 W RF POWER
ATTITUDE CONTROL: SPIN/MOMENTUM BIAS
PROPULSION: MONOPROP. HYDRAZINE (348 KG USABLE)
TOTAL DRY MASS: 237 KG
LAUNCH VEHICLE: DELTA 7925

SPECIAL FEATURES:
  CONTINUOUS HGA COMMUNICATIONS AVAILABLE (AT≥1.1 AU)
  CONTINUOUS COMMANDABILITY IN ANY S/C ORIENTATION
  CONTINUOUS INST.NADIR POINTING AVAILABLE (AT≥1.1 AU)
  LARGE SUN-S/C-EARTH ANGLE ACCEPTABILITY
  HIGH REDUNDANCY (INCLUDING CAMERA)
  NO DEPLOYED STRUCTURES
  NO ARTICULATED STRUCTURES
  NO GYROS

Fig. 3   Discovery Asteroid rendezvous spacecraft.

194

AIM MICROSPACECRAFT CONCEPT

MASS BUDGET (kgj)	
Telecom	2.05
Power	2.48
ACS	2.64
Command & Data	1.67
Structure	3.69
Propulsion	1.52
Thermal	1.49
Imaging Camera	2.00
Subtotal (with 30% cont.)	22.80
Monopropellant	2.45
Total Wet S/C	25.25
Injection SRM	111.65
Total (x3)	410.70
L/V Adapter	16.50
Mass to LEO	427.20
L/V to LEO	452.00
L/V Margin	24.80

POWER BUDGET	(W)
Transponder	5.0
IMU	3.5
Reaction Wheels	15.0
Computer	2.0
Heaters	1.0
Imaging Camera	4.0
Subtotal	30.5
Losses (25%)	7.6
Subtotal with Losses	38.1
20% Cont.	7.6
Total	45.7

* Power shown is for encounter (worst case demand)

* Worst case power generation is 46 W at 1.2 AU.

PERFORMANCE

POINTING KNOWLEDGE	0.1° (0.01° at star camera calibration)
DOWNLINK DATA RATE	315 bps; 70 m; 1.6 AU 68 bps; 34 m; 1.6 AU
DATA STORAGE	1 Gbit
DELTA-V CAPABILITY	200 m/s
HEIGHT 0.6 m	MAX DIAMETER 0.5 m

Fig. 4   AIM asteroid flyby microspacecraft.

BRIDGE - Un petit satellite scientifique pour la géodésie

Bénédicte ESCUDIER	-	Sup'Aéro
Michel BOUSQUET	-	Sup'Aéro
François BARLIER	-	GRGS
Georges BALMINO	-	GRGS
Maryline RANC	-	THARSYS
Reinhold BERTRAND	-	Université de Stuttgart

Introduction

Cet article présente une synthèse des résultats obtenus lors des premières études d'une mission scientifique réalisée par un petit satellite embarquant en orbite basse le système de localisation par effet Doppler "DORIS ". Cette mission consiste principalement en l'amélioration de la connaissance du champ de gravité terrestre et de l'atmosphère. Après avoir détaillé les objectifs de cette mission et les caractéristiques de la charge utile, les choix préliminaires des orbites envisagées sont justifiés. L'article présente enfin les principaux bilans du système et différentes architectures pour le satellite.

1 - OBJECTIFS SCIENTIFIQUES

1.1 - Etude du champ de gravité terrestre

Le champ de gravité terrestre peut se développer en harmoniques sphériques auxquels on associe une résolution spatiale ou longueur d'onde. La détermination des longueurs d'onde s'obtient à partir de l'analyse de l'orbite des satellites artificiels. La résolution spatiale du champ est liée à l'altitude du satellite, et est d'autant meilleure que celle-ci est basse. Par ailleurs la qualité de la restitution de la trajectoire se dégrade d'autant plus que l'altitude de l'orbite du satellite est basse. La précision des modèles de champ de gravité est donc moins bonne pour les courtes longueurs d'onde.

Le sytème DORIS (Détermination d'Orbite et Radiopositionnement Intégré par Satellite) permet la détermination précise des orbites. DORIS a été embarqué sur le satellite SPOT 2 dont l'orbite est circulaire et d'altitude 800 km. Les mesures obtenues ont été introduites dans le modèle du champ de gravité GRIM 4 développé par le Groupe de Recherche en Géodésie Spatiale (GRGS) à Toulouse, et le Deutsches Geodätisches Forschung Institut (DGFI) à Munich. Il en a résulté une meilleure connaissance du potentiel terrestre qui apparait en comparant différents géoïdes dont certains intègrent les données altimétriques donnant actuellement les meilleurs résultats au-dessus des océans.

L'amélioration du modèle permet un progrès sensible dans la détermination des orbites (évaluation des résidus) des satellites, dont a profité en particulier le satellite SPOT 2 (Tableau 1). Les amplitudes des perturbations de la trajectoire de ce satellite ont pu être calculées jusqu'à des degrés et ordres de 50 en notant cependant des lacunes importantes dans l'information.

	GEM T2	GRIM 4	GRIM 4 Doris
Lageos	9.2 cm	8.0 cm	5.7 cm
Starlette	15.0 cm	12.0 cm	12.0 cm
Spot 2	5.0 mm/s	7.9 mm/s	1.8 mm/s
Nova 1	7.1 mm/s	6.2 mm/s	4.7 mm/s

Tableau 1 : Comparaisons des résidus pour diffrents modèles et orbites

En revanche, la plupart des lacunes disparaissent lorsque l'on considère par simulation une altitude d'orbite de 400 km. Sur la Figure 1 a été portée de plus l'amplitude des perturbations sur les mesures elles-mêmes ; compte tenu de la sensibilité du système de mesure (0.3 mm/s), la figure confirme l'existence d'informations disponibles jusqu'à des degrés et ordres de 80. Un autre exemple est donné sur la Figure 2 pour une orbite excentrique (périgée : 242 km, apogée : 1200 km), où apparaissent des résonances marquées et l'existence d'information significative jusqu'à des degrés et ordres de 90.
Ces résultats de simulation montrent l'intérêt d'embarquer l'instrument DORIS sur un satellite en orbite basse ou excentrique : c'est l'objectif du projet de satellite BRIDGE qui établit un pont entre les connaissances obtenues avec les satellites SPOT, TOPEX/POSEIDON et les résultats escomptés avec un satellite spécialisé tel qu'ARISTOTELES.

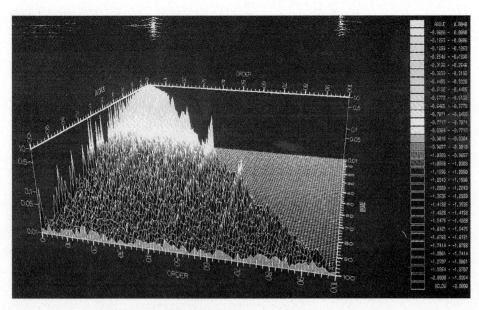

**Figure 1 : amplitude des perturbations sur les mesures
(orbite circulaire 400 km)**

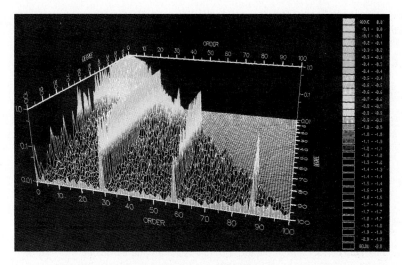

**Figure 2 : amplitude des perturbations sur les mesures
(orbite elliptique 240/1200 km)**

1.2 - Etude de l'ionosphère

L'expérience DORIS/SPOT2 montre que l'on peut cartographier à l'échelle globale l'état de l'ionosphère en terme de contenu électronique intégré à l'heure locale de passage du satellite [ESC-89].Les autres moyens de mesure permettent un suivi de l'ionosphère dans le temps sur des zones géographiques limitées par les stations au sol. La résolution du modèle est de l'ordre de 10° en latitude et de 90° en longitude.

Les missions DORIS/SPOT2, DORIS/SPOT3, DORIS/SPOT4 permettront un suivi de l'évolution de l'ionosphère sur une longue période à l'heure locale de SPOT.

La mission TOPEX/POSEIDON permettra un balayage des différentes heures locales avec une répétitivité de 4 mois environ.

Plusieurs configurations sont envisageables :

- BRIDGE est placé sur une orbite circulaire à la même heure locale que SPOT ou qu'un autre satellite porteur de DORIS sur une orbite d'altitude plus élevée ; les mesures comparées à celles du satellite haut permettront d'avoir une mesure de la structure verticale de l'ionosphère (l'altitude maximum d'ionisation est comprise généralement entre 300 et 450 km).

Si l'orbite choisie pour BRIDGE est excentrique, l'apport sera plus riche puisque l'on disposera alors d'un balayage de la limite supérieure du domaine exploré.

- BRIDGE est placé sur une orbite circulaire d'heure locale différente des autres satellites porteur de DORIS ; l'apport est alors la mesure à une heure locale non couverte par les systèmes existants, le défaut étant que seule la partie basse de l'ionosphère est explorée (ce qui est aussi une limitation des ionosondes).

Dans le cas d'une orbite excentrique, des études statistiques sur la structure de l'ionosphère pourraient être effectuées.

1.3 - Etude des variations de la densité de la thermosphère

Un facteur important dans l'amélioration de la précision de la trajectographie d'un satellite est une meilleure prise en compte des forces non gravitationnelles dont l'évaluation nécessite en particulier la connaissance d'un modèle de la thermosphère terrestre.

L'analyse de la trajectoire d'un satellite équipé de l'instrument DORIS peut fournir des informations utiles à la détermination de la densité totale de la thermosphère.

Par ailleurs, l'installation à bord d'un satellite en orbite basse de microaccéléromètres pourrait permettre de dissocier les effets des forces d'origine gravitationnelle et non gravitationnelle. La meilleure qualité de la trajectographie en résultant permettrait d'affiner les modèles de champ de gravité et de thermosphère.

En particulier de très nombreuses données de densité totale plus précises et mieux distribuées dans le temps, l'espace, et les conditions variées d'activité solaire et géomagnétique pourraient être utilisées pour d'améliorer les modèles semi-empiriques de thermosphère existants.

2 - LE SYSTEME DORIS

2.1 - Principe

Le système est basé sur la mesure du décalage Doppler de signaux radioélectriques émis par des balises au sol et reçus à bord du satellite lorsque celui-ci est en visibilité de ces balises.

Un récepteur installé à bord d'un satellite effectue des mesures de déclage Doppler sur deux fréquences émises respectivement à 2036.25 MHz et à 401.25 MHz par des balises appelées balises d'orbitographie, dont la position est préalablement connue. La mesure sur la deuxième fréquence sert à l'élimination de l'erreur relative à la propagation ionosphérique. Un traitement mathématique de ces mesures, associé à une modélisation des forces agissant sur le satellite, essentiellement l'attraction gravitationnelle terrestre, permet de restituer la trajectoire précise du satellite. Dans un second temps, le système peut, par des mesures similaires, servir à localiser des balises placées dans des régions soumises à des déformations notables. Ces balises sont les balises de localisation.

2.2 - Description

Le système DORIS est principalement constitué d'un récepteur embarqué sur satellite, de balises d'orbitographie nécessaires pour établir l'orbite du satellite, de balises de localisation mises à la disposition des utilisateurs selon leurs besoins, et d'une balise maîtresse chargée d'assurer la liaison entre le sol et le satellite (Figure 3). Un service est chargé de déployer les balises, d'entretenir le système et d'élaborer les programmes de travail, de traiter les informations et de les rediffuser aux utilisateurs.

La partie embarquée sur le satellite comprend :

- Un récepteur ou MVR (Mesure de Vitesse Radiale), d'un poids de 17 kg et d'une consommation de 20 W, principalement constitué de deux récepteurs 401.25 et 2036.25 MHz (385X280X210 mm).

- Un oscillateur ultrastable à quartz dont la précision est de $5 \ 10^{-13}$ sur des durées de 10 à 100 secondes.

- Une antenne omnidirectionnelle.

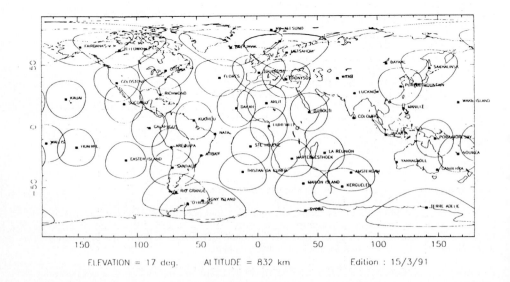

Figure 3 : Organisation du sytème DORIS

2.3 - Traitement des mesures

Lors d'un passage en visibilité d'une balise, le récepteur DORIS mesure le décalage Doppler des ondes émises par comptage du nombre de cycle à l'intérieur d'un intervalle de temps parfaitement défini. Cette mesure représente la variation de distance satellite-balise pendant une durée de l'ordre de 9 secondes et est appelée par simplification "vitesse radiale". Ce sont ces mesures qui entrent dans les calculs d'orbite et de localisation de balise.

3 - ANALYSE DE MISSION

Le choix de l'orbite étant un élément clé de l'analyse de mission. Il est influencé par une multitude de facteurs plus ou moins contraignants tels que:
- durée de vie du satellite sur son orbite : la durée minimale demandée

par les scientifiques est d'environ 6 mois de vie opérationnelle,
- inclinaison quasi polaire : le satellite balaie alors régulièrement tout le géoïde ce qui assure une répartition globale des mesures,
- accessibilité des orbites avec les lanceurs envisageables,
- fenêtres de visibilité du satellite par une station sol à Toulouse,
- contraintes imposées par l'instrument DORIS,
- contraintes de conception de la plateforme.

Une étude effectuée à SupAéro [HAV-91] a examiné des orbites circulaires et elliptiques entre 200 et 1500 km d'altitude susceptibles de répondre à la mission. Les différents paramètres et leur impact sur la mission et le système ont été étudiés pour retenir finalement trois orbites de base.

3.1- Durée de vie sur l'orbite
A partir de la durée de vie opérationnelle de 6 mois minimum, des orbites permettant d'obtenir une durée de vie supérieure à 300 jours pour tenir compte les incertitudes de l'activité solaire et pour assurer une marge opérationnelle ont été recherchées. Plusieurs méthodes de prévision de durée de vie ont été appliquées :
- méthode de Kendrick [WER-78], qui donne une estimation du cas le plus défavorable avec une erreur de l'ordre de 50%,
- intégration numérique de la trajectoire du satellite sur son orbite.
Les résultats sont présentés dans le Tableau 2. Il montre également les altitudes de l'orbite dégradée au bout de 300 jours.

Orbite initiale [kmxkm]	Méthode de Kendrick [jours]	Intégration numérique [jours]	Altitudes après 300 jours [kmxkm]
200 x 1250	117	180	-
250 x 1000	208	293	-
250 x 1250	293	458	231 x 788
275 x 750	152	242	-
275 x 1000	339	477	254 x 661
275 x 1250	439	>500	265 x 980
275 x 1500	659	>500	269 x 1260
300 x 500	99	130	-
300 x 750	229	356	257 x 439
300 x 1250	644	>500	294 x 1081
400 x 400	109	198	-
400 x 500	250	412	336 x 398
400 x 1250	2711	>500	398 x 1217

Tableau 2 : Durée de vie et dégradation de l'orbite

Pour obtenir la durée de vie orbitale de 300 jours, il faut que le périgée soit supérieur à 250 km pour des orbites elliptiques. Pour les orbites circulaires, l'altitude initiale doit être supérieure à 400 km. De plus on remarque une évolution importante d'orbite au bout de 300 jours à cause de la traînée atmosphérique. Il paraît donc difficile de maintenir une certaine forme ou orientation d'orbite (par exemple une orbite héliosynchrone) pendant toute la durée de vie opérationnelle.

3.2 - Inclinaison et orientation de l'orbite

Pour pouvoir comparer les mesures obtenues avec les mesures SPOT, mais aussi en prenant en compte les contraintes de conception du système et de la plateforme (par exemple éclairage des panneaux solaires), une orbite initiale héliosynchrone pourrait représenter une option attractive. Dans ce cas l'inclinaison serait fixée pour un demi grand axe et une excentricité donnés. Comme les simulations ont montré une dégradation relativement modeste de l'heure locale de l'orbite (Figure 4) avec environ 70 minutes au bout de 300 jours sur orbite, une orbite héliosynchrone paraît envisageable. Mais il faut aussi prendre en compte le fait qu'une injection héliosynchrone demande une bonne précision d'injection, ce qui pose des problèmes pour des petits lanceurs tels que Pegasus [MOS-89].

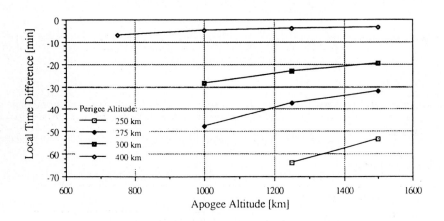

Figure 4 : Différences en heure locale après 300 jours en orbite

3.3 - Lancement

Une possibilité très intéressante financièrement est l'utilisation du lanceur Ariane/ASAP (Ariane Structure for Auxiliary Payloads). Ceci impose une contrainte importante sur la masse totale du satellite (<50 kg) mais aussi une limitation des orbites possibles. L'orbite finale pour les lancements ASAP est soit l'orbite de transfert géostationnaire (GTO), soit l'orbite héliosynchrone circulaire d'altitude voisine de 800 km. Comme le balayage des altitudes basses est au centre d'intérêt de la mission BRIDGE, cette option impliquerait d'attendre la diminution naturelle de l'altitude d'orbite ; ce temps d'attente dépasserait 10 ans, ce qui n'est pas acceptable.

La solution la plus adaptée est donc un lancement spécifique avec un système comme Pegasus. Ceci permettrait de choisir l'orbite selon les exigences de la mission et également d'augmenter la masse totale de la plateforme et d'ajouter éventuellement d'autres charges utiles.

3.4 - Visibilités du satellite

Comme toutes les orbites intéressantes sont quasi polaires, les fenêtres de visibilités se répètent régulièrement et avec une durée suffisante pour transmettre les télémesures de l'instrument et pour charger les télécommandes.

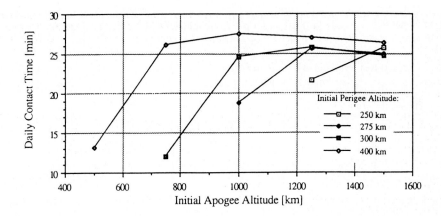

Figure 5: Temps moyen de visibilité par jour (fin de mission)

La Figure 5 résume les temps de liaison moyens pendant une séquence de 4 jours à la fin de la mission. Elle considère une station sol à Toulouse, et différents types d'orbites héliosynchrones.
La durée moyenne de liaison par jour sera donc de 12 minutes dans le pire des cas ce qui exigerait une cadence de données de l'ordre de 10 kbits/s pour transmettre toutes les télémesures d'une journée.

3.5 - Contraintes imposées par la charge utile

Le système DORIS fonctionne en orbite basse jusqu'à une altitude de 200 km avec des limites techniques de l'instrument concernant la vitesse radiale du satellite par rapport à une balise sol (< 11 km/s) et l'accélération Doppler sur le signal de mesure (< 1600 Hz/s).

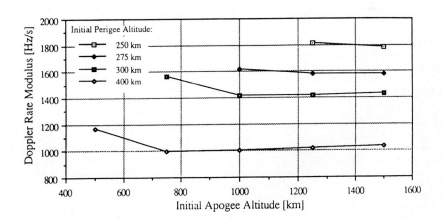

Figure 6: Accélération Doppler maximale (fin de la mission)

203

La Figure 6 résume les accélérations Doppler pour la fréquence supérieure de la porteuse DORIS (2036,25 MHz) à la fin de la mission. La limite technique de l'instrument est atteinte pour une orbite avec une altitude initiale du périgée de 275 km.

3.6 - Contraintes système de la plateforme

Les contraintes de conception de la plateforme pour le choix d'orbite concernent surtout les éclipses et le frottement atmosphérique.

Avec une orbite héliosynchrone il serait possible avec un certain choix de l'heure locale, d'éviter toute éclipse sur la durée de vie opérationnelle du satellite. Ceci permettrait une économie de masse importante au niveau du sous-système alimentation électrique. Mais cette option imposerait des exigences supplémentaires sur la fenêtre de lancement et comme exposé dans les paragraphes précédents, la précision d'injection d'orbite avec un petit lanceur pourrait empêcher une constellation d'orbite optimisée. Les études et prédimensionnements de la plateforme ont donc été effectués pour le cas le plus défavorable d'éclipse avec un taux d'éclipse pouvant atteindre 41,2 % [HAV-91].

Comme la mission exige un fonctionnement de la plateforme en orbite très basse, le fort couple de frottement atmosphérique représente un effet perturbateur important de l'attitude de la plateforme (le système de contrôle d'attitude doit garantir un pointage de l'antenne DORIS de +/- 5° entre l'axe géométrique de l'antenne et le nadir). Les études de préconception dont quelques résultats sont exposés ci dessous traitent les cas d'une plateforme stabilisée de manière passive (gradient de gravité) ou active (roue d'inertie).

3.7- Résumé

Le choix d'orbite est influencé par une multitude de facteurs et de contraintes. Une étude paramétrique a permis de préciser l'enveloppe des orbites susceptibles de répondre à la mission et de retenir finalement trois orbites de base:
(1) une orbite circulaire à 450 km altitude
(2) une orbite elliptique 300x600 km
(3) une orbite elliptique 275x1250 km
Les trois orbites ont une inclinaison d'environ 98° pour assurer l'héliosynchronisme. Elles remplissent les exigences mentionnées au début et ont servi comme scénario de base pour les études de conception et de prédimensionnement.

4 - PREDIMENSIONNEMENT DE LA PLATEFORME

Les études de conception de la plateforme [BER-91] ont considéré plusieurs configurations correspondant à différents types d'architecture et différents principes de stabilisation dont une plateforme stabilisée par gradient de gravité avec des magnétocoupleurs (Figure 7). Avec les dimensions 450x450x600 mm³ elle pourrait être lancée par un système tel qu'ASAP, si le passager principal permet une augmentation en hauteur du microsatellite.

L'antenne est embarquée dans une position fixe sur le plateau inférieur (pointé vers le nadir). Le plateau supérieur porte le mât de gradient de gravité. Les boîtiers électroniques de la charge utile et des sous-systèmes sont fixées sur les deux plateaux.

Cette plate forme dispose d'un générateur solaire avec des cellules AsGa fournissant une puissance maximale de 46 W. Une batterie de 65 Wh permet un fonctionnement permanent de la charge utile sous les conditions les plus défavorables (solstice d'été et taux d'éclipse 42,2%).

Un calculateur centralisé gère l'ensemble des sous-sytèmes et la charge utile: Il stocke les données scientifiques générées en permanence par DORIS et les transmet pendant les visibilités à la station sol. A partir des données d'attitude mesurées (magnétomètre et senseurs solaires), il contrôle également de manière autonome l'attitude du satellite en commandant les magnétocoupleurs.

La bande de fréquence pour la télécommunication est la bande S. Une puissance émettrice de 3,3 W suffit pour assurer la transmission de toutes les télémesures avec un taux d'erreur de 10^{-5}. Le Tableau 3 illustre les bilans de liaison pour la liaison montante et descendante.

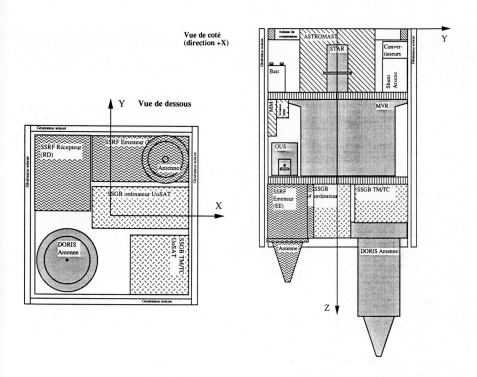

Figure 7 : Plateforme BRIDGE stabilisée par gradient de gravité

	Liaison montante (500 bps)	Liaison descendante (10000 bps)
Rapport de l'énergie par bit à la densité spectrale de bruit: Effet du filtre: + 2 dB	11,5 dB	11,5 dB
Débit binaire:	27,0 dB Hz	40,0 dB Hz
Pertes en espace libre: orbite à 450 km alt., site 10°	163,2 dB	163,2 dB
Pertes additionnelles: atmosphère: 0,2 dB; précipitations: 0,1 dB; Pertes à l'emission: 1 dB; dépointage: 9 dB	10,5 dB	10,5 dB
Facteur de qualité de la station réceptrice:	$-28,0$ dB K^{-1} Antenne omni. G=1; T=584 K	$-0,87$ dB K^{-1} Antenne circulaire, diamètre 1m; G=25 dB, T=398 K
Constante de Boltzman:	$-228,6$ dB W $Hz^{-1}K^{-1}$	$-228,6$ dB W $Hz^{-1}K^{-1}$
Marge:	2,0 dB	2,0 dB
PIRE:	**13,6 dB W**	**-0,53 dB W**
PDC: (Rendement FET 27%)	0,27 W	3,3 W

Tableau 3 : Bilans de liaison

Une première étude de préconception [BER-91] a démontré la faisabilité d'une telle plateforme pour des orbites circulaires avec une masse totale de 55 kg (c.f. Figure 8). D'autres études approfondies au niveau de la structure du satellite [LLO-91] ont montré qu'une réduction de masse au dessous la limite ASAP de 50 kg semble réalisable. Mais la précision de pointage de l'antenne à la fin de vie du satellite reste un paramètre sensible.

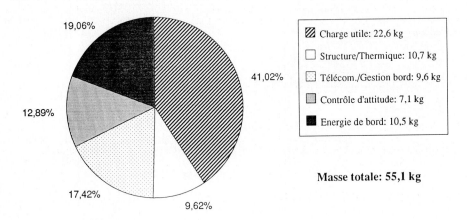

Charge utile: 22,6 kg

Structure/Thermique: 10,7 kg

Télécom./Gestion bord: 9,6 kg

Contrôle d'attitude: 7,1 kg

Energie de bord: 10,5 kg

Masse totale: 55,1 kg

Figure 8 : Bilan de masse

Si les orbites elliptiques sont envisagées, la stabilisation par gradient de gravité devient difficile à mettre en oeuvre. Les études correspondantes ont donc considéré une stabilisation d'attitude par roue d'inertie [JUN-91]. Des magnétocoupleurs assurent l'acquisition de l'attitude après la séparation du lanceur et réalisent les manoeuvres de désaturation. Cette étude a également examiné les possibilités d'une plateforme adaptée au lanceur Pegasus. La Figure 9 illustre ce type d'architecture avec une antenne repliable pour le lancement.

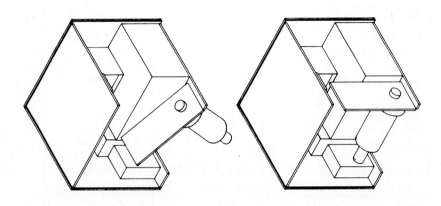

Figure 9 : Plateforme BRIDGE stabilisée par roue d'inertie (configuration Pegasus ; illustration du déploiement de l'antenne Doris)

5 - CONCLUSION

Les résultats obtenus montrent la faisabilité de la mission envisagée. L'utilisation d'une plateforme "microsatellite" permet d'envisager la réalisation de la mission dans des délais de développement courts et à faible coût. Après cette première étude de mission réalisée en collaboration entre Sup'Aéro, des étudiants de différentes universités européennes, des laboratoires de recherche et un industriel, le développement de ce petit satellite, au delà de son intérêt scientifique, serait un excellent support de formation aux techniques spatiales par l'implication d'étudiants dans la réalisation et l'exploitation d'un projet spatial.

REFERENCES BIBLIOGRAPHIQUES

[BER-91]   BERTRAND R. *Etudes sur une plateforme de micro-satellite pour des missions scientifiques*, Projet de fin d'études, ENSAE/Institut für Raumfahrtsysteme Universität Stuttgart, Toulouse/Stuttgart, IRS 91-S-15, 1991.

[ESC-89]   ESCUDIER P. et PICAUD N. *Utilisation des mesures Doris pour la modélisation l'ionosphère*, Rapport CNES 1991

[HAV-91]   HAVEMMAN M. *Mission Analysis of BRIDGE: Orbit Proposal for a Small Scientific Satellite*, Projet de fin d'études, ENSAE/Institut für Raumflugtechnik und Reaktortechnik TU Braunschweig, Toulouse/Braunschweig, 1991.

[JUN-91]   JUNG M. *Etudes du contrôle de la stabilité d'un microsatellite lors de missions scientifiques*, Projet de fin d'études, ENSAE/TU München, Toulouse/München, 1991.

[MOS-91]   Mosier M. et Harris G. *Payload Interface Guide for the Pegasus Air-Launched Space Booster*, 3rd AIAA/USU Conference on Small Satellites, Logan, USA, 1989.

[SIV-91]   Sivillà Llobet S. *Définition de la structure d'un petit satellite pour l'étude du champ de gravité et l'ionosphère,* Projet d'études, ENSAE, Toulouse, 1991.

[WER-78]   Wertz J. R. et al. *Spacecraft Attitude Determination and Control,* Kluwer Academic Publishers, London, 1978.

COSMIC DUST AND SPACE DEBRIS MEASUREMENTS ON BOARD THE SMALL SATELLITES **HITEN** AND **BREM-SAT**

H. Iglseder

ZARM, Center of Applied Space Technology and Microgravity, Univ. Bremen, Germany

ABSTRACT

On 24 January 1990, ISAS (The Institute of Space and Astronautical Science) launched a space engineering satellite HITEN from Kagoshima Space Center, Japan (JKSC). The HITEN primary mission goals are to verify technologies and techniques required for lunar and planetary missions in the near future. A short introduction of the MUSES-A mission objectives is given. Beside the technology demonstration a small scientific experiment related with the detection and the measurement of mass, velocity and crude flight direction of micrometeoroide particles with a miniaturized dust detector (MDC) has been performed. After a short introduction describing the experiment setup and the measuring principle the results of the two years of operation of the MDC on board HITEN are discussed. From these cosmic dust particle measurements preliminary results are derived, which show the cosmic dust flux versus time, particle velocity and mass. The spatial, the directional distribution, and first considerations of the orbital flight velocities of the measured particles will be presented. Results of all MUSES-A mission phases in the geomagnetic tail region of the Earth, in the vicinity of the moon and the Lagrangian points (L4 and L5 fly-by) are discussed.

Future measurements with the MDC on board the university micro-satellite BREM-SAT, which will be launched in a GAS-CAP container by the Space Shuttle during the German D-2 Mission in February 1993, are described and predicted Space Debris impact rates of MDC-BREM-SAT will be presented. Finally, the advantages to perform scientific experiments by means of small satellite missions will be demonstrated.

Fig. 1a: HITEN spacecraft at launch

Fig. 1b: BREM-SAT with GAS-Ejection System

I. INTRODUCTION

The MUSES-A - HITEN primary mission goals are to verify technologies and techniques required for lunar an planetary missions in the near future. These include:

(1)   Orbit control utilizing gravity assist lunar swingbys as a precursor for the ISAS's GEOTAIL spacecraf one of the planned fleet of ISTP (International Solar Terrestrial Physics) missions.
(2)   Insertion of a sub-satellite "Hagoromo" into lunar orbit.
(3)   Optical navigation experiments for the first time on a spin-stabilized spacecraft.
(4)   Tests of a fault tolerant onboard computer and packet telemetry experiments.
(5)   Cis-lunar aerobrake demonstrations.
(6)   Detection and measurement of mass and velocity of micro-meteoroide particles with the Munich Du Counter MDC.

The Munich Dust Counter (MDC) is a scientific space experiment on board the HITEN Satellite of the MUSE! A mission of the Institute of Space and Astronautical Science (ISAS) of Japan and the university satelli BREM-SAT of ZARM. It has been developed by the Chair for Astronautics of the Technical University Muni (TUM) of Germany with support by the European Space Research and Technology Centre (ESTEC) of ESA, t the German Federal Ministry for Research and Technology and the German industry. The MDC has bee designed to determine mass and velocity of cosmic dust particles by measuring the impact charges generated t high velocity impacts of dust particles on a gold target. The mass of the MDC Flight Unit is 605 g, the pow consumption is 1.8 W. The actual sensor area is 10 cm x 10 cm, the field of view is 148 deg. Details of th instrument are given by Igenbergs et al. [1].

The MUSES-A spacecraft is the 13th scientific satellite developed by ISAS. It is a spin stabilized spacecra with a diameter of 1.4 m, a height of 0.8 m and a mass of 197 kg. The MDC is installed on the main instrume platform behind an aperture of 12 cm x 12 cm in the solar cell panel. As the MDC is mounted on the perimet of the spinning spacecraft, it scans the ecliptic plane within one revolution of the satellite. The spin period 3 seconds. The spin axis of the spacecraft is perpendicular to the ecliptic plane.

The Satellite HITEN was launched from the Kagoshima Space Center, Japan into a highly-elliptical orbit arour the earth with perigees between some thousand and 100000 km, and apogees between 300000 an 1.53 million km, see figure 2a and 2b.

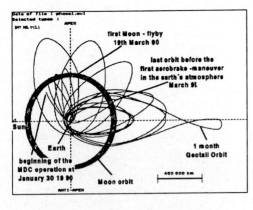

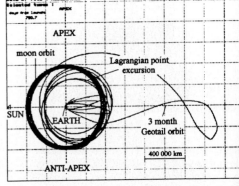

Fig. 2a: MUSES-A orbit first phase   Fig. 2b: MUSES-A orbit - second phase

sub-satellite was inserted into an orbit around the moon and a total of 11 lunar swing-bys has been carried out during the two year mission. The second phase ended in February 1992 with an insertion of HITEN around the moon. This was carried out successfully and the investigation of moon's dust environment has started since 15th of February 1992. A description of the MUSES-A mission is given by Igenbergs et al. [2] and Uesugi [3].

II. MEASUREMENT PRINCIPLE AND SIGNAL TYPES

The MDC experiment, see Fig. 3a, measures the electrical charges generated by high velocity impacts of small masses on a gold surface. The setup consists of a target and two charge collector plates which are biased by negative and positive voltages. The impact plasma is separated into positive ions on the negative collector and electrons and negative ions on the positive collector. The charges are measured by two independent channels incorporating charge sensitive amplifiers, connected to the collectors and analog-to-digital-converters. The signals from the A/D converters are collected in a digital memory and the experiment is controlled by a central microprocessor. The traces of up to 24 impact signals are stored and transmitted by the Satellite HITEN to the Tsuda Space Station and from there to Munich and to ZARM for data analysis. During the two years of operation 348 events (203 in the first and 145 in the second year) were evaluated. During the evaluation of the charge signals, amplitude and risetime are determined. Using the procedure described by Iglseder [4] [5], mass and velocity of the impacted dust particle can be derived from these parameters using the following formulae:

$$\pm Q/m = c_r * v^b$$

$$t = c_g * v^d$$

with: m particle mass; v particle velocity; Q maximum charge; t signal risetime; c_r, c_g, b, d calibration constants.

There are two signals measured for one particle impact, the ion and the electron signal. These give two values for particle mass and velocity, from these an average value can be calculated. The signals measured so far and shown in Fig. 2 were classified from Iglseder [6] into eight types.

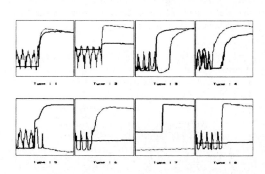

Fig. 3a: MDC - Cosmic Dust Counter   Fig. 3b: Signal types encountered by the MDC experiment

Signals of type 1 to 4 show the typical shape expected for dust particle impacts. Black lines are indicating the electron channel EC- and the grey lines the ion channel IC-signals. While type 1 is just perfect, the type 2 signals have some noise on the EC. Type 3 signals show a remarkable delay on the IC while type 4 show a delay on the EC. Type 5 signals show only a signal on the EC, type 6 only a signal on the IC. All these effects are due to certain impact locations inside the sensor and could be verified during the calibration of the instrument [7]. Type 7 signals have a very fast burst on the EC, type 8 a very fast burst on the IC. These signals are supposed to be noise and not due to particle impacts.

211

During the calibration of the experiment the associated measurement errors have been determined. Calibration has been done using iron particles. Assuming a similar dependence for real dust particles, the measured velocity is accurate within 0.65 to 1.47 of the actual velocity, and the measured mass is accurate within 0.33 to 2.70 of the actual particle mass. Here the inaccuracy of the velocity is included as the particle velocity is needed for the calculation of the particle mass.

III. OVERVIEW OF COSMIC DUST PARTICLE OBSERVATIONS

The nominal operation of the MDC experiment started on March 3, 1990, after 4 weeks of initial tests and optimization of the experiment software. During the two years of operation, until the 15th of February 1992, a total of 348 impacts have been recorded.

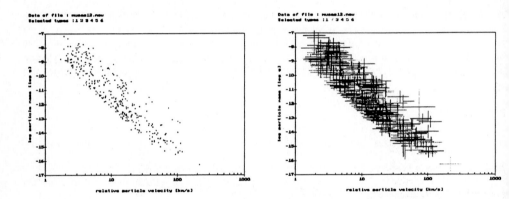

Fig. 3a & 3b: Cosmic dust particles as measured by the MDC from March 3, 1990 until February 15, 1992, (Fig. 3b with associated error bars)

In Fig. 3a all data are shown in mass/velocity diagram together with the sensitivity range of the MDC. In Fig. 3b the same measurements are shown, together with the error bars for the velocity and the mass values. Particle velocities from 1.8 km/s up to 200 km/s and particle masses between 10^{-7}g and 10^{-17}g were determined.

IV. COSMIC DUST PARTICLE FLUX

Fig. 4 gives the the impact rates of cosmic dust particles as recorded by the MDC during two years of operation which started 38 days after launch. The average of slightly more than 0.5 impacts per day, is indicated in the graph by a dotted line. It corresponds to an overall flux of 2.2 to $5.5*10^{-4}$ m^{-2}s^{-1}, taking into account the sensor area of 100 cm^2, and measured in the mass range of 10^{-17} to 10^{-7} g, as given in Fig. 3a.

The data of Fig. 4a indicates enormous variations of the impact rates by four to five orders of magnitudes.

This observed behaviour is an indication for a nonhomogeneous dust flux which is composed by random particles, groups and swarms, as found with previous experiments, Hoffman et al. [8] and Fechtig et al. [9].

In Fig. 4b, the particle flux for masses greater than 10^{-16}g versus the distance from earth is shown. An increasing particle flux rate by about a factor ten near the Earth was measured.

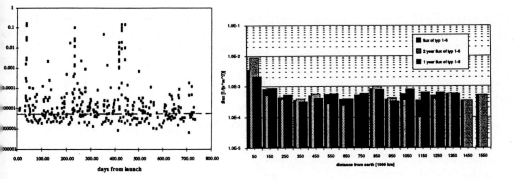

Fig. 4a: Impact rate of dust particles   Fig. 4b: Cumulative particle flux versus distance from Earth

n Fig. 5a and 5b the determined heliocentric particle velocity versus the particle mass for impact types 1 to 4 and 5 to 6 are shown. Particle velocities of more than 200 km/s have been encountered, but most of the observed article velocities at 1AU are around 30 km/s.

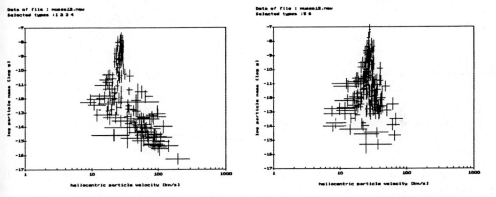

Fig 5a & 5b: Heliocentric particle velocity versus particle mass, types 1 to 4 and types 5 to 6

V. DIRECTIONAL DISTRIBUTION OF COSMIC DUST PARTICLES

As the field of view of the MDC is 148 deg., in ecliptic and about 74 deg in north/south direction, the nformation about the particle flight direction for a single measurement is only accurate to that numbers. But by dding many measurements, which have been obtained by scanning the ecliptic plane on a spinning spacecraft, ome information about the directional distribution of the cosmic dust particles can be obtained. The graph in ig. 6 gives the number of particles measurements observed from the different directions from apex, sun, anti-pex and anti-sun. The measurements have been arranged according to the particle velocity in logarithic scale. Here it can be seen that the fast dust particles, having velocities of more than 40 km/s, are encountered most •ften from the inner solar system. On the other hand rather slow dust particles, with velocities of less than • km/s, are coming most often from the apex direction.

213

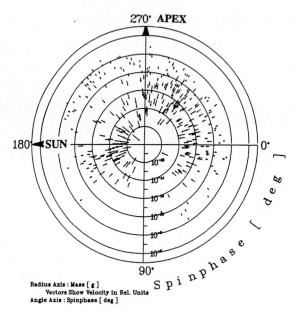

Fig. 6: Directional distribution of cosmic dust particles as observed by the MDC

It seems that particles having masses greater than 10^{-10} g are coming more frequently from approximately the apex direction, while particles with masses less than 10^{-14} g are more frequently coming from the sun direction.

Fig. 6 give an indication for two populations of dust particles: The apex-particles, as described by Grün and Zook [10], coming roughly from the apex direction, having greater masses and low velocities (relative to the earth system). These might by "overtaken" by the satellite while spiralling down towards the sun. On the other hand the beta-meteoroids, Zook and Berg [11], come from the inner solar system, having small masses and hyperbolic orbits. These may be accelerated outwards by interaction with the radiation pressure.

VI. SUMMARY OF THE ACHIEVED RESULTS

Determination of the mass-, velocity- and angular distribution of cosmic dust particles and beta-meteoroids in the Earth-moon system.

Detection of pro- and retrograde beta-meteoroids in the solar system.

Accurate measurements of the cumulative particle flux of cosmic dust particles and beta-meteoroids.

Evidence of different cosmic dust particles like apex-particles, beta-meteoroids and particles with high inclinations.

Evidence of swarms, groups and random particles. Enormous variations of the instantaneous fluxes and impact rates of micrometeoroids.

No significant indications for dust clouds near the Lagrangian-points L4 and L5 (Kordylewsky-clouds).

Indications of the existence of interstellar particles.

VII. SPACE DEBRIS MEASUREMENTS ON BREM-SAT

Since the beginning of the Space Age in 1957 an extraordinary number of man-made objects have been injected into orbits around the Earth. Figure 7a shows a snapshot of all catalogued space objects in low Earth orbits on 1 January 1987, [15,16,17]. Besides the man-made objects in space, there is also the natural environment of extra-terrestrial particles, the meteoroids. They range in size from macromolecules to kilometersized bodies. Masses as low as 10^{-16} g near Earth have been measured. The particle flux of extra-terrestrial particles and spacecraft debris in low Earth orbits (LEO) is given in 7b, [14]. It shows a clear dominance of the debris in the picogram range, whereas the fluxes are comparable in the microgram range.

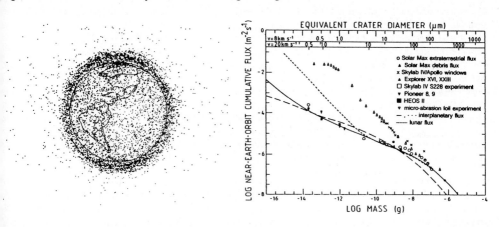

Fig. 7a: Snapshot of all catalogued space objects in LEO   Fig. 7b: Particle-flux of cosmic dust and space debris

Debris such as fragments from accidental explosions of rocket stages, paint chips and spent pieces of solid rocket motor propellant could be hazardous to the health of low orbiting satellites. The main questions to be answered in this case are: has the amount of dust particles increased since the beginning of space flight and how large is the proportion of "man-made" debris. The scientific objective of the space debris experiment is to study the growth of dust flux in low Earth orbits from altitudes of 300 km down to 150 km. Particles with masses between 10^{-7} g and 10^{-16}g and velocities of 1 to 200 km/s can be measured. The maximum lifetime of the satellite will be two months. First results of the predictions to determine the impact rates are shown in Fig. 8.

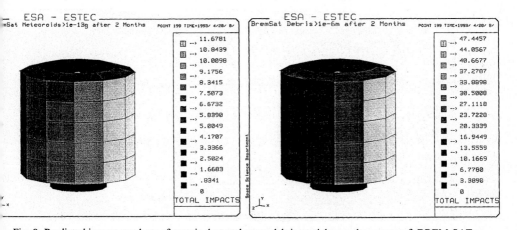

Fig. 8: Predicted impact numbers of cosmic dust and space debris particles on the spacecraft BREM-SAT

Results from the MDC experiment will be compared with results from previous dust experiments which operate in LEO like LDEF. The mass sensitivity and the effective sensor area are similar to the dust detectors on board the Pioneer 8, HEOS-2 and Hiten [13] spacecraft. Phenomena to be investigated in detail will include:

Interplanetary dust flux measurements by the Pioneer 8 and 9 spacecraft revealed a highly anisotropic dust flux which was attributed to a stream of small beta-meteoroids [11] leaving the solar system on hyperboli trajectories due to the action of radiation pressure. Bigger particles were encountered mostly from the ape direction of spacecraft motion indicating that they move on low-angular momentum orbits.

The second scientific objective is a technological one. First of all the limitations of mass, space and powe available for the experiment MDC on the spacecraft BREM-SAT was very challenging. Therefore the fina design was a compromise between the requirements of the measurement principle and especially the spac available. Finally everything which is absolutely necessary for the measurement principle could be achieved, e.g two charge sensitive amplifiers, a high voltage generator for collector bias voltages and also a microprocesso system to control the experiment. But it was not possible to incorporate e.g. additional charge sensitiv amplifiers for an entrance grid. One major problem associated with sensitive measurements in space is the nois encontered there. To handle this, the experiment was designed to store and transmit to ground the whole charg signals rather than to perform an on board evaluation of amplitude and risetime, giving the opportunity to inspec the complete signal shape on the ground. By this charge signals generated by dust impacts can be clearl distinguished from noise signals. Additionally, valuable informations also about the noise environment for thi kind of experiments in space can be obtained.

Received telemetry data are processed by the Quick Look Software for the MDC developed by TUM/ZARM and both ion and electron channel charge data of each impact are displayed in analog curves with digital data o the position, attitude and spin phase of the spacecraft at the time of impact. The commands required for th operation of the MDC experiment, such as uploading software into MDC RAM, are sent from BREM-SAT Operation Center (BSOC) at ESTRAC GROUND STATION on canary island.

By measuring dust particles in low earth orbits, interesting information about the mass, velocity and the fligh direction of the cosmic dust and man made space debris striking the spacecraft can be obtained. Additionally nev technological insights in the developement of space experiments will be gathered. Within a cooperation betweei ZARM and the Institute of Space Technology at the Technical University of Munich the space experimen Munich Dust Counter was developed and manufactured within one and a half year from start of the project unti integration on the satellite BREM-SAT. The project will managed by ZARM and funded by the Federal Ministr for Research and Technology of Germany. It will supported by DARA, ESTEC, the Max-Planck-Institut fü Kernphysik, Heidelberg and DASA.

VIII. RECOMMENDATIONS

Start the project with clear defined specifications and interfaces!!

Work with a small team of experts, minimize the team size

Reduce the documentation, keep short and perfect

Combine technological and scientific aims

Optimize the costs and use the advantage of the standardization

Plan prompt projects, duration 2 to 3 years

Collaborate with center of excellences, guarantor for a fast success

IX. REFERENCES

[1] Igenbergs E., Hüdepohl A., Uesugi K., Hayashi T., Svedhem H. Iglseder H., Koller G., Glasmachers A., Grün E., Schwehm G., Mizutani H., Yamamoto T., Fujimura A., Ishii N., Araki H., Yamakoshi K., Nogami K. (1990) *"The Munich Dust Counter - A Cosmic Dust Experiment on Board of the MUSES-A Mission of Japan"*; In *"Origin and Evolution of Interplanetary Dust"* (eds. A.C. Levasseur-Regourd and H. Hasegawa), Kluwer Tokyo, 45-48, 1991

[2] Igenbergs E., Hüdepohl A., Uesugi K., Hayashi T., Svedhem H. Iglseder H., Koller G., Glasmachers A., Grün E., Schwehm G., Mizutani H., Yamamoto T., Fujimura A., Ishii N., Araki H., Yamakoshi K., Nogami K.; *"The Present Status of the Munich Dust Counter Experiment on Board of the HITEN Spacecraft"*; In *"Origin and Evolution of Interplanetary Dust"* (eds. A.C. Levasseur-Regourd and H. Hasegawa), Kluwer Tokyo, 1991

[3] Uesugi K., Matsuo H., Kawaguchi J. and Hayashi T.; *"Japanese First Double Lunar Swingby Mission HITEN"*; 41st Congress of the IAF, Dresden, 6-12 October 1990

[4] Iglseder H.; "Ladungsemission beim Hochgeschwindigkeitseinschlag". Dissertation, TU-München, 1986

[5] Iglseder H., Igenbergs E.; *"Measured Charge Generation by Small Mass Impact at Velocities Between 1 and 45 km/s"*; Int. J. Impact Engineering, Vol 5, pp381-388, San Antonio, 1987

[6] Iglseder H.; *"Catalogue of MDC-Muses-A Micrometeorite Impacts"*; Scientific Report, ZARM University of Bremen, July 1991 & June 1992

[7] Münzenmayer R.; *"Kalibrierung des Weltraumexperiments MUNICH DUST COUNTER"*, Diplomarbeit RT-DA 90/12; Chair of Astronautics; Technical University of Munich; 1990

[8] Hoffmann H.-J., Fechtig H., Grün E., and Kissel J.;*"Temporal Fluctuations and Anisotropy of the Micrometeoroid Flux in the Earth-Moon System Measured by HEOS-2"*. Planet. Space Sci. 23, 981; 1975

[9] Fechtig H., Grün E. and Morfill G.; *"Micrometeoroids within Ten Earth Radii"*; Planet. Space Sci., Vol. 27; pp. 511-531; 1979

[10] Grün E. and Zook H. A., *"Dynamics of Micrometeoroids in the Inner Solar System"*; In *Solid Particles in the Solar System;* (I. Halliday and B. A. McIntosh, Eds.) pp. 293-298; Reidel. Dordrecht. 1980

[11] Zook H. A. and Berg O. E.; *"A Source for Hyperbolic Cosmic Dust Particles"*; Planet. Space Sci. Vol. 23, pp. 183-203; 1975

[12] Grün E. , Zook H. A., Fechtig H. and Giese R.H., *"Collisional Balance of the Meteoritic Complex"*; Icarus 62, pp. 244-272, 1985..

[13] Hüdepohl A., *"Entwicklung und Bau eines Weltraum-Experiments an Bord der japanischen Mond-Mission MUSES-A zur Messung kleiner Staubteilchen im Erde-Mond-Bereich"*. Zwischenberichte, Lehrstuhl für Raumfahrttechnik, Technische Universität München, 1988, 1989, 1990.

[14] McDonnell J.A.M., *"Microparticle Studies by Space Instrumentation"*, Cosmic Dust, Wiley, Chichester, S.337 (1978).

[15] Authors, *"Space Debris"* The Report of the ESA Space Debris Working Group, ESA-SP-1109 (1988).

[16] Rex D., *"European Investigations on Orbital Debris"* , Adv. Space Res. Vol. 10, No. 3-4, pp. (3)347-(3)358, (1990).

[17] Authors, *"Report on Orbital Debris"* Interagency Group (Space), National Security Council, Washington, D.C. (1989).

SYNMOD: A LOW-RESOURCE, LOW-COST MEANS OF MONITORING THE NEAR-EARTH SPACE DEBRIS ENVIRONMENT

by
J. DERRAL MULHOLLAND

Institute for Space Science & Technology (Gainesville FL, USA & Magagnosc, France)
and
Observatoire de la Côte d'Azur-CERGA (Nice, France)

ABSTRACT

Synoptic Monitoring of Orbital Debris (SYNMOD) is a concept that envisions a network of satellites equipped with high time-resolution orbital debris impact detectors based on those of the LDEF Interplanetary Dust Experiment (IDE). The ideal network consists of such devices orbiting at a wide variety of altitudes and inclinations, with continuous temporal coverage. Such data will revolutionize debris modelling and prediction, which IDE has decisively shown to be inadequate. Modest downlink telemetry requirements permit rapid evaluation of the local debris environment at each spacecraft and, by simultaneous analysis of the data from the entire network, of the global debris environment. No other system provides such information, which opens the long-range possibility of designing reactive systems capable of extending spacecraft instrumentation lifetimes by a significant factor. The option of installing the detectors on the solar panel backsides insures that the system can be adapted in a uniform way to a large variety of spacecraft, large *and* small, without impacting their primary functions. The concept is all the more attractive in that it can be implemented at relatively low cost and with extremely low demands on spacecraft resources.

Current debris predictions are based on isotropic circular-orbit models. IDE provided the first-ever mapping of the angular distribution of small particulates in the near-Earth environment over an extended time interval and at high time resolution. That environment was shown for the first time, and contrary to all predictions, to be extremely non-isotropic and time-variant. Most of the orbital debris is contained in clouds sometimes exceeding 2000 km in extent, in which the particle density can exceed the long-term background mean by nearly four orders of magnitude. Some of those clouds are in eccentric orbits. Knowledge of such an environment can only be had by continual monitoring on a global network. SYNMOD is proposed as the basis for such monitoring.

1. INTRODUCTION: The problem of orbital debris

Orbital debris represents an inescapable hazard for all space activities. The spatio-temporal results from the LDEF Interplanetary Dust Experiment (IDE) suggest that such debris already constitutes by far (>80%) the major part of the dust environment at 500 km altitude[1], but both the spatial distribution and especially the temporal variation are too poorly known. The U. S. Congress Office of Technology Assessment has concluded that uncontrolled growth of space operations, including by the private sector, could eventually impose severe limitations on both manned and unmanned missions[2]. Other responsible official bodies have also addressed this issue[3-6]. ESA has recently launched a major modelling program for both large and small particles in near-Earth space. Similar efforts have been underway for several years at NASA/JSC and elsewhere, but the brutal fact is that there is simply not an adequate base of real data. The issue is not just the possibility of catastrophic collisions, but also the problems of erosive damage to instruments and other functional systems and the even more subtle degradation of the observing environment[7]. This will likely be a critical problem for space surveillance systems, and for Space Station Freedom and other long-duration spacecraft, but it is or should be a matter for concern for nearly all users of space. More accurate predictive models and real-time damage control protocols are urgently needed, and this requires both more comprehensive data in space and time and more sophisticated analysis techniques. Little directional or temporal data exist. Occasional sampling of the debris environment will not suffice, and untimed sampling is <u>inadequate</u> to modelling needs that are sensitive to the spatio-temporal structure of that environment.

1.1. Recent discoveries about the orbital debris small-particle environment

One of the principal sources of new information on the low-Earth orbit (LEO) small-particle environment is the identification and characterization of orbital debris events recorded by the LDEF Interplanetary Dust Experiment (IDE). This work is in progress, involving efforts at the ISST Space Astronomy Laboratory (Gainesville, Florida USA), ISST-Europe (Grasse/Magagnosc, France), and various collaborating laboratories. IDE was conceived as a scientific experiment, with the primary goal of exploring the natural cosmic dust environment in near-Earth space, providing directional data with time resolution of a few seconds for impacts in the submicron to 100μ range. Among the first results has been a confirmation of the phenomenon of beta meteoroids[1], possible due to the directionality and high time resolution of the IDE instrumentation. These same characteristics, however, show clearly that already in 1984, the small-scale particulate environment at 500 km altitude was dominated by manmade debris, which is very non-isotropic and time-variant[8]. It is perhaps not an exaggeration to claim that these data have already revolutionized our ideas on the debris environment by showing the importance of anisotropy and time variation, largely neglected in current debris models. Our results illustrate the power of such data, which we believe to be unmatched by any other current observing method. Many debris clouds have been identified as recurring events whose spatial extent and evolution can be studied with these data. LDEF's collision with one such cloud encompassed within 2 minutes' time nearly 1% of all the hits recorded by IDE over its 348 days of activity[9]; during those 2 minutes, the areal flux per time resolution unit rose nearly 4 orders of magnitude above the long-term average on the ram face. This marked the onset of an orbital event sequence involving at least 25 encounters with the same orbital debris cloud on near-successive orbits of the spacecraft. Since all impacts occurred on the South and East panels, the debris were evidently in a high-inclination orbit, going northbound at its common node with the LDEF orbit. Perhaps the most noteworthy aspect of the IDE results, however, is that the time coordinate permits one to see that the near-Earth particulate environment is enormously "clumpier" than previous data sets or models based on untimed accumulations predict[10]. Some of the clouds extend for more than 2000 km, 5% of the orbital circumference. And even yearly averages are variable in a surprising way[11]. It is only with a much larger body of directional, high time-resolution data such as these that one can make real progress towards a good understanding of the structure, dynamics, and evolution of the orbital debris environment.

Another implication of the IDE data is that fine-scale debris particles can have serious consequences even beyond the possibility of scouring of optical, heat transfer, or other delicate surfaces. The problem is forward scattering of sunlight. Forward scattering is the reason why a dirty windshield is most bothersome to the driver when he is facing directly into the Sun; for micron-size particles, it is the most efficient reflective mode. We predict that, when a targeting surveillance system encounters a debris cloud at a time when it is obliged to look sunward, there will be several minutes of confusion during which a "friend-or-foe" recognition system will not be reliable[12]. This suggests that it would be useful to be able to recognize these events by non-optical means and, if possible, to predict them.

As an outgrowth of this work, IDE investigators have developed a program for low-resource **synoptic monitoring of orbital debris (SYNMOD)** to be applied to a large variety of Earth-orbiting spacecraft. An impact detector system for hypervelocity particulates is proposed for the general class of solar-powered artificial Earth satellites. This system will detect and record the location and the exact time of impact of orbital debris particles and micrometeoroids of sizes from 0.1 to several 100 μm, covering a mass range of over 10 orders of magnitude. A second-generation version could extend the upper range to several mm, into the radar-observable domain. It is suggested that this instrument would be more appropriately considered as a new element of the spacecraft system, rather than as a scientific experiment package.

2. THE SYNMOD CONCEPT

The LDEF data provide a good starting point, but a detailed, long-term evolutionary model for orbital debris will require a database that combines: 1) higher counting rates, for better statistics; 2) longer time periods, to measure seasonal variations and to assure the separation of debris clouds from meteor streams; 3) different orbital altitudes and inclinations, to map the radial and global distribution of debris; and --- perhaps most important --- 4) simultaneous measurements from several satellites, allowing one to follow the dispersion and decay of debris clouds. High time-resolution is necessary due to the extreme clumpiness of the debris environment, shown by LDEF/IDE data. We advocate a project of **low-resource Synoptic Monitoring of Orbital Debris (SYNMOD)** to provide such a database. The central idea is that active detectors of IDE type be mounted systematically on the backsides of the solar panels, as well as other locations of known directionality, on satellites launched for whatever purpose. We also propose that SYNMOD units be considered <u>system</u> elements to be included on as many satellites as practicable. This paper addresses both the central issues and some of the practical aspects of this idea.

The SYNMOD instrument is designed to provide high time-resolution records of impact events of particulates in the size range from 0.1 μm to several hundreds of microns. Detector packages are to be mounted in symmetrically opposed pairs on the back sides of the solar panel structures, as well as elsewhere on the spacecraft when possible. They are modified versions of the IDE packages flown with great success on LDEF. The solar panel mountings will be much lighter, because the panel structure itself provides the mechanical support lacking on LDEF. The basic detector element is a metal-oxide-silicon (MOS) capacitor operated under voltage. An impact of energy higher than a particular threshhold triggers a discharge whose time is recorded. The sensitivity of the detector is a function of the dielectric thickness. For the SYNMOD program, we propose to group wafers of five sensitivity levels on each detector panel. The system requires limited on-board data storage in which to accumulate impact data, environmental parameters, and "housekeeping" items between periodic data dumps via downlink telemetry. The already-high temporal resolution of LDEF will be improved upon, to better investigate debris burst structure and evolution. The primary objective of SYNMOD does not require retrieval; nonetheless, this is desirable when possible, to allow testing of the engineering systems and sampling of impactor source residues.

Most space measurements of the particulate environment in low Earth orbit have been conceived for studying dust of cosmic origin, not manmade contaminants. Little directional or temporal data exist. Acquiring such a database is not just another "scientific" experiment, but an urgent matter of surveillance, monitoring, and modelling of an environmental problem that poses considerable economic impact and physical hazard. The proposed program will provide such a database. The central idea is that active detectors of the IDE type be mounted systematically on the backsides of the solar panels of satellites launched for whatever purpose. That location has the signal advantages of providing considerable area and known directionality. Such accommodation will not provide the complete six-directional coverage as on LDEF, but the facts that the directions will be precisely known at all times and that other spacecraft may well be carrying the same equipment at complementary altitudes and orbital inclinations will still provide a spatio-temporal database presently unmatched by any other technique. This can be accomplished without compromising the basic function of the solar panels. No special vehicle is necessary; SYNMOD can "piggyback" on any spacecraft that can provide enough collection area. The IDE-type detectors, described below, are sensitive to particles in the submicron to submillimeter size range. The range could be extended to the millimeter range by modifying the existing design or by using it in conjunction with another existing detector, based on polarized thin-film polyvinylidene fluoride (PVDF)[13]. Such a modification is under study for possible application to later missions.

Even a single multi-month flight in a similar orbit to LDEF's would provide a useful validation of the IDE results, ten years later, and it would greatly increase the available database. But that does not suffice. To really know what the environment is and where it is going, what is needed is a serious four-dimensional database, covering both angular and radial space, plus continuously in time from some initial epoch. After one or more proof-of-principle flights, we propose the establishment of a network of SYNMOD monitors. There should be at least two at any given altitude, in different orbit inclinations, to sample the entire spherical space. Several altitudes should be monitored, from LEO to geosynchronous, to sample the entire radial space. An occasional elliptic orbit would be interesting, especially if it traversed the zone 800-1500 km, where we know there is a lot of garbage circulating. The network should be replenished as participating satellites die, although there is no need for identical orbits. Such a network would eliminate all guesswork about the current state of the debris environment.

2.1. Expected technological results

The immediate goal of the SYNMOD program is the acquisition of as extensive a database as possible of impact events whose directions are known approximately and whose epochs are known precisely, so that they can then be analyzed for information on the spatio-temporal distribution, density, and evolution of the manmade contamination of the near-Earth space environment. Such information is vital to all spacecraft operations and to the design both of spacecraft components and of payload instrumentation. The means of acquiring these data consists of well-proven devices and techniques. The data provided by this instrument are unique in the combination of particle size, temporal resolution, and directionality that they possess. The techniques for their analysis have either already been developed, or are in the process of being so developed for the IDE analysis.

It is evident that effective use of such observations in modelling either the orbital debris environment or the natural particulate population requires that one have a means of separating the two. We believe that work presently in progress at ISST --- the use of kinematic constraints on the directionality of impacting particles and the compilation of a morphological catalogue of the IDE data --- will provide the tools that will permit this[14]. It is already clear that a large fraction of the LDEF impacts occur in "orbital sequences", where the spacecraft passed through a given cloud on several consecutive orbits. These are clearly debris events, involving intersections of LDEF's orbit with particulate clouds that often are 1000 km or larger. The fact that they persist holds open the possible analysis of dispersion and orbital evolution. The morphology within an event may permit one to estimate the age of the cloud and the type of source, whether it is a member of a sequence or not. Indeed, in some circumstances, it will be possible to identify the source of some debris clouds. JPL radar experiments suggest that such clouds contain potentially destructive bodies as well as dust[15].

The acquisition of a significant body of SYNMOD data from even a single spacecraft will augment the now-available database of these unique spatio-temporal data, covering another time window, permitting a direct evaluation of the evolution of the debris accumulation during the preceding decade, in a size range that carries significant operational hazards but is unobservable with current groundbased techniques. If the SYNMOD instrument is accepted on a variety of spacecraft, then we can make a major contribution to the eventual achievement of a global and valid spatio-temporal model of the manmade orbital debris environment, a goal that is far from our grasp today and which is of the utmost importance for the future of space exploitation.

On perhaps a longer time scale, but certainly not of lesser importance, the SYNMOD network would permit the development of mitigation techniques that could provide both a dramatic increase in the functional lifetimes of a large class of spacecraft instruments, and a significant amelioration of the surveillance confusion problem. Presuming that the IDE discovery of large debris clouds is validated by future SYNMOD carriers, one could begin equipping instruments at risk with means of either closing or swinging away from the closure velocity vector on a warning signal. How would that warning signal be generated? There are at least two conceivable scenarios: 1) The network detectors could have tracked the cloud well enough to predict an approximate orbit, and standard calculations would then predict its intersections with any spacecraft, or 2) The target spacecraft could itself carry a mini-SYNMOD unit, and the onboard computer programmed to recognize cloud encounters and determine the time interval between them. The latter method would, of course, require that the target suffer at least two sandblasts before reacting, but better two than 25!

3. THE SYNMOD INSTRUMENT

3.1. Proposed experimental methods and techniques:

The proposed SYNMOD measurement concept is based on a relatively simple device, consisting of a parallel-plate capacitor with one plate exposed to the environment of space. The inner plate is voltage-biased through a high resistance. When a hypervelocity particle impacts the detector, a signal is obtained from this plate. Afterwards, the detector automatically reverts to the original bias conditions and is able to detect subsequent impacts. The MTS and LDEF missions have shown that these devices will operate reliably in the space environment. Additional calibration tests, beyond the qualification tests run for MTS and LDEF, are planned as part of the SYNMOD program.

The capacitor-type micrometeoroid impact detector, developed by Prof. J. J. Wortman of the North Carolina State University, is a product of metal-oxide-silicon (MOS) technology that is widely known for its rôle in the manufacture of field-effect transistors and integrated circuits. The detector is a circular wafer of low-resistivity, p-type (boron-doped) silicon that forms the inner electrode of the capacitor. A layer of silicon dioxide is grown on the wafer by thermal oxidation, to form the dielectric of the capacitor. An aluminum coating is then connected to a printed circuit board with gold leads, which are themselves bonded by thermocompression to each electrode.

Detectors of different sensitivities are obtained by means of different thicknesses of the SiO_2 dielectric. Two sensitivities have been used in past spacecraft applications. The more sensitive of the two has a dielectric thickness of 0.4-μm, a capacitance of 0.165 μf, and a threshhold specific impact energy density parameter $dv^2 = 2.81$ m^3s^{-2}. The less sensitive has a 1.0-μm dielectric thickness, a capacitance of 0.070 μf, and dv^2 twice that of the other. Prof. Wortman can produce other thicknesses, and we propose to add devices with 0.1, 0.2 and 2.0 μm dielectric thickness to the flight ensemble.

Both the 0.4-μm and the 1.0-μm units have been shown to function properly as hypervelocity microparticle impact detectors over a wide range of temperature. When the detector is impacted by a projectile, a signal is obtained that is strongly dependent on the bias voltage. The device exhibits a self-clearing feature; the discharge stops automatically when the voltage across the capacitor has been reduced to somewhere below 20 V. The energy of the discharge vaporizes a tiny fraction of the aluminum electrode in a circular area centered at the impact site. Once a discharge has occurred, the vaporized area is no longer sensitive to impacts, but the probability of this causing lost observations is almost nil. The vaporization terminates the shorted condition and permits re-establishment of normal bias voltage after a dead time of a few tens of milliseconds. There also, the effect on possible loss of observations is essentially nil. Transient power consumption due to impact shortout is dependent on the dielectric thickness, but of the order of 1 mW; if the entire IDE detector complex had shorted simultaneously, the power drain would have been < 0.3 W. The non-discharge power consumption of a detector is only its stable current leakage rate: for the 1 m^2 "strawman" instrument, < 1 mW. A more detailed discussion of detector characteristics is given in reference 16.

The MOS device by itself is only a capacitor, not a detector. To constitute a detector, the capacitor must be wedded to the electronic data collection system, which is accomplished by attaching the electrodes to a simple electronic chip that itself connects to a multiplexer system integrated on the substrate to which the MOS wafer is mounted. Such an approach constitutes a clear advantage over the 1970-era technology used on LDEF. The detector is the fundamental element of the instrument, but it is unreasonable to consider it as a viable unit in and of itself. The viable operational module is a multi-element array of detectors, to assure a large enough detection surface area to have a particle flux sufficiently large to provide good statistics, and to assure that any given catastrophic impact will not compromise the overall effectiveness of the system. These arrays can, in principle, be distributed in a totally arbitrary fashion. The "strawman" module is twenty 102-mm wafers, equivalent to eighty 51-mm wafers as on LDEF, with a practical minimum 5-wafer group of one each of the different sensitivities. Any geometric arrangement is possible, and each application will be considered separately, in concert with the spacecraft designers.

The SYNMOD data system is very simple and has already flown on the NASA Meteoroid Technology Satellite (Explorer 46) and LDEF in a more primitive form. The communication channel and protocol is a single multidrop network, with a single controlling node for any number of detector groups. A typical group might consist of eight 100-mm CMOS wafers, each with several detector segments. The connection between the individual detectors and the spacecraft data handling system (DHS) is accomplished by four elements: Each detector connects through a protective chip to a multiplexer circuit that services several detectors. Each group feeds to its own line driver, or local group controller, which latches the events registered on its associated detectors and clocks them serially onto the common data bus lines when polled by the central logic-control-interface module, where the synchronization data are added. This buffer is accessed by the computer interface. Only a portion of the SYNMOD Logic Interface Package (SLIP) is spacecraft-specific. When any given detector issues an impact signal, it is communicated to the memory buffer, which stores the tick count from the SYNMOD instrument clock and the detector identification. Periodically, the spacecraft clock stores the SYNMOD clock synchronization data to the buffer and triggers a detector interrogation sequence that determines the status of each detector and, if and only if that status has changed since the last interrogation, transmits the detector identification and the tick count to the memory buffer. After the interrogation sequence, the buffer is dumped to the DHS for later downlink transmission.

3.2. Instrument Heritage

The detector was developed by Prof. J. J. Wortman and calibrated by Mr. Philip C. Kassel, for flight on NASA's Explorer 46 spacecraft, which flew a successful mission in 1974, establishing the existence of submicron-sized particles in meteor streams[17]. Prof. S. Fred Singer then directed and brought to fruition the Interplanetary Dust Experiment (IDE) on the NASA Long Duration Exposure Facility (LDEF), with detectors fabricated by Wortman . This mission was launched in 1984 and was to have lasted for 9 months. External circumstances dictated that the craft remain in orbit until January 1990, for a duration of 5.7 years. Post-flight testing showed that, while the battery powering the 0.4 μm detectors had discharged, due to the power drain associated with the large number of impacts suffered over a period more than 9 times longer than the nominal mission, the less-sensitive 1.0 μm detectors were still under power and functional. The 0.4-μm detectors showed a slow monotonic attrition, presumably from massive local particle fluxes, but at the end of a year, some 90% were still functional.

3.3. Proposed emplacement of detectors

The SYNMOD concept requires that the detectors be mounted in a coherent fashion on numerous spacecraft, with the constraint that they be mounted with a known normal direction. Many spacecraft are not stabilized to some specific direction, but they have one component that is so stabilized, and it is the **same** for nearly all solar-powered spacecraft --- the solar panels nearly always point toward the Sun. Even for those spacecraft whose solar panels are not always pointed directly sunward, their directions are accurately known at all times. The heart of the SYNMOD idea is the combination of known direction and precise timing.

There is nothing "magic" about the antisolar direction, but it provides a commonality that maximizes the number of available spacecraft with large surface availability and permits a uniform analysis protocol. We propose, therefore, that our "instrument" be mounted on the backsides of a spacecraft's solar panels. The idea of mounting monitoring devices in that location is not revolutionary; thermal sensors and a variety of other instruments are already allocated a small part of that space. Indeed, like those other panel-mounted devices, we propose that our SYNMOD arrays be considered as a part of the spacecraft system, rather than as a scientific or technological experiment. Solar panel engineers at several establishments have given us no reason to doubt the feasibility of the concept.

One of the advantages of these detectors is that they provide an almost infinite flexibility of installation. One can use as many or as few as available space will allow, and the results will still be useful in some measure, although there obviously is a practical minimum controlled by the ambient particle flux. They can be put in many possible geometric arrangements, as densely packed or as dispersed as one prefers. Our baseline proposal is a configuration that will approach our "strawman" instrument of about 1 m^2 of detection area. One-tenth of that is probably a practical minimum.

We must address the question of how to supply power to the detectors and how to get the signals back. The wings are articulated to permit deployment from the launch position. Detector communication must be done in a way that presents no hazard of fouling these articulations. In addition, most solar generators must rotate to track the Sun, presenting a "BAPTA" (or ""SADA") problem. Each detector must be accessed by wire leads, and one obviously cannot run hundreds of wires across the joints, nor add hundreds of commutator rings on the axles. The solution is to associate each detector or small grouping of detectors with a multiplexer circuit etched directly onto the mounting substrate. These feed to a parallel communications line that connects all of the arrays on a given wing with a small "state machine" mounted in the spacecraft body. In this fashion, it will only be necessary to run 4 wires (8 if one wants redundancy against lines broken by direct impacts) across panel articulations. There are several wire harness designs that can accomplish this task without interfering with the articulations, and we will work with the engineers to adopt that which seems most acceptable to them. This should not be a problem. Another obvious question is that of the mass that must be borne by the panel structure. The specific mass of a solar panel structure is on the order of 1 kg/m^2. The solar cells add about the same amount. The MOS detectors and the substrate on which they are mounted will add about 2 kg/m^2 on the surface covered, a small fraction of the total structural mass of the panels affected. The SYNMOD instrument should also be benign from the standpoint of the thermal and electromagnetic environment.

While we believe that the solar panel emplacement is practical without adverse effect on the primary function of those panels, and that it provides advantages both in available surface area and in uniformity of data analysis protocol, we do not exclude other locations where a useful amount of area might be available. This is especially true if, *in addition to* solar wing locations, one could have at least one detector group on each of two orthogonal faces, for this would greatly enhance the directional separability in the data analysis process. Accommodation elsewhere on a spacecraft *in place of* solar wing emplacement is indicated when there are qualification concerns for solar array assemblies, as with the Eureca spacecraft. This implies less available detector area and is therefore unpreferred, but we take the view that *any* useful area is better than none. We define "useful area" as that which would at least detect the more important debris clouds but no finer detail; we estimate that this level is the equivalent of two 8-detector groups. The SYNMOD Team is ready to consider all alternatives and is experienced in accommodation studies of scientific payloads on many missions.

3.4. Expected performance and spacecraft resources required

We anticipate that the *average* detection rate for hypervelocity impacts will be on the order of 50-75 per day for a strawman system distributed in multiple directions. The temporal distribution will be extremely non-uniform, however, due to the fact that orbital debris is generated episodically. Over intervals of a few minutes, the count rate can exceed 10 per second per square meter in the ram direction. The detector status interrogation, to be performed about every 30 min, requires a cycle time of about 0.1 sec. We ask for a synchronization resolution from the spacecraft clock of at worst 1 sec, with 0.5 sec desired. It is this synchronization resolution that establishes the basic accuracy of the measurements.

SYNMOD is a truly low-resource instrument. There is no duty cycle for this instrument. It runs continuously throughout the mission, with neither need nor possibility of command intervention. We identify the following needs for the strawman instrument configuration (1 m² active area):
- command and data uplink: none.
- telemetry downlink: < 250 Kbits/day.
- power: normal operations 1 watt, max load < 1.3 watt
- mass: < 5 kg, independent of spacecraft-dependent support structures (unneeded on solar wings)
- mounting and alignment requirements: none
- thermal control: none
- volume: each group: ≥ 250 x 250 x 3 mm and ≤ 800 x 1000 x 3 mm (or equivalent area)
              electronics   50 x 50 x 150 mm anywhere on or in the spacecraft

4. CURRENT STATUS OF SYNMOD FLIGHT PROSPECTS AND FUTURE PLANS

The germ of the SYNMOD concept was planted in mid-1990, and the first attempts at developing it had only just begun when the Eureca-2 flight opportunity was announced later that year. A major effort was undertaken to use the Eureca-2 mission as a forcing function to define the outlines. That effort was successful to the extent that SYNMOD is adopted as part of the "strawman" payload for both engineering accommodation and costing studies for Eureca-2 and Eureca-3. As of this writing, the formal payload decisions for Eureca-2 are not yet made, but every indication is that SYNMOD has a very good chance of being selected for that 1995 launch. This will be a very important step from at least four standpoints: 1) It will be the first major new body of high time-resolution data on orbital debris impacts in LEO since mid-1985; 2) The Eureca orbit is very similar to that of LDEF, so it will provide both a validation and an update of the LDEF observations; 3) The retrieval of Eureca, as with LDEF, will provide an important opportunity for post-flight engineering evaluation of system component design and fabrication, preliminary to a full-scale network deployment; and 4) a significant part of the preliminary engineering applicable to all future flights will have been done, thus reducing the unit cost for follow-on missions.

While Eureca-2 is presently the only active flight project for which SYNMOD is a candidate, it is also being proposed for the payload of PECOS, a not yet authorized U. S. Department of Defense satellite project on which orbital debris observations are likely to constitute a major secondary mission. In addition, discussions are underway with respect to other potential carriers, both civil and military, from several different political entities. We welcome contacts from any and all with future plans for satellites large or small that might be interested in participating in an eventual SYNMOD environmental monitoring network, either as a member of the prime network, or simply with a local self-protection mitigation system.

5. ACKNOWLEDGEMENTS

Many people have contributed to the development of this project and to its progression towards flight status. The original concept to place detectors on the solar generator wings, which launched the SYNMOD idea, came from S. F. Singer (ISST), while J. P. Oliver (ISST & U. Florida, USA) conceived the real-time mitigation idea, as well as recognizing the forward-scattering problem. Other co-investigators and collaborators in various aspects of the project include D. Atkinson (POD Assoc., USA), F. Barlier (OCA-CERGA, France), E. Grün (MPIK, Germany), P. C. Kassel (NASA/LaRC, USA), A. Mamode & F. Nouel (CNES, France), J.-C. Mandeville (ONERA-CERT, France), J. A. M. McDonnell & T. J. Stevenson (U. Kent at Canterbury, UK), J. E. McKisson & J. L. Weinberg (ISST, USA), and J. J. Wortman (N. Carolina St. U., USA). We have also profited from advice, help and suggestions from J. Auternaud, P. Kamoun & L. Pelenc (Aérospatiale, France), G. Barrette (CSTC, USA), B. Edgar (Aerospace Corp, USA), H. Fechtig & E. Jessberger (MPIK, Germany), W. Flury (ESA/ESOC, Germany), W. H. Kinard (NASA/LaRC), Col. S. Harrison (Nat'l Space Council, USA), P. Haskins (ISST, USA), R. Rubio & S. Stallings (AFOTEC, USA). Special mention must go to G. Tomaschek (ESA/ESTEC, Netherlands) for his diligent efforts trying to assure that SYNMOD be manifested on Eureca-2.

6. REFERENCES

1. S. F. Singer, J. E. Stanley, *et al.*, "First Spatio-Temporal Results from the LDEF Interplanetary Dust Experiment", in <u>Advances in Space Research</u> **11**, Pergamon, London, pp. (12)115-122, 1991.
2. "Orbiting Debris: A Space Environmental Problem -- Background Paper", U. S. Congress Office of Technology Assessment, Washington, 1990.
3. "Space Debris", SP-1109, European Space Agency, Paris, 1988.
4. R. C. Reynolds & A. E. Potter Jr, "Orbital Debris Research at NASA Johnson Space Center", Tech. Memo. 102155, Nat'l Aeronautics & Space Administration, Houston, 1989.
5. "Report on Orbital Debris", National Security Council, Washington, 1989.
6. "Space Program: Space Debris a Potential Threat to Space Station and Shuttle", U. S. General Accounting Office, Washington, 1990.
7. J. L. Weinberg, presented at Space Shuttle Experiment and Environment Workshop, Henniker NH, August 1984; also "Optical Observations from the Space Shuttle", in <u>Advances in Space Research</u> **7**, Pergamon, London, 203-205, 1987.
8. J. D. Mulholland, "The Orbital Debris Environment is Extremely Non-Isotropic and Time-Variant", Orbital Debris Monitor **4**, N° 3, 1991.
9. J. D. Mulholland & J. L. Weinberg, "IDE Identifies Orbital Cloud", LDEF Spacecraft Environmental Effects Newsletter **2**, N° 1, 15 Mar 1991.
10. J. D. Mulholland, J. P. Oliver, *et al.*, "LDEF Interplanetary Dust Experiment: A High Time-Resolution Snapshot of the Near-Earth Particulate Environment", Proceedings *Hypervelocity Impacts in Space*, U. Kent Canterbury, in press, 1992.
11. J. D. Mulholland, C. G. Simon, *et al.*, "Long-Term Particle Flux Variability Indicated by Comparison of Interplanetary Dust Experiment (IDE) Timed Impacts for LDEF's First Year in Orbit with Impact Data for the Entire 5.75-year Orbital Lifetime", submitted for 2nd LDEF Science Conference, San Diego, 1992.
12. J. P. Oliver, "Effects of low earth orbit (LEO) debris clouds on star trackers and other optical devices", ISST Tech. Brief TB92/03/05A, 1992
13. J. A. Simpson & A. J. Tuzzolino, "Cosmic Dust Investigations. II. Instruments for measurement of particle trajectory, velocity and mass", Nucl. Instr. & Methods in Phys. Res. **A279**, 625-639, 1989.
14. J. D. Mulholland, S. F. Singer, *et al.*, "IDE Spatio-Temporal Impact Fluxes and High Time-Resolution Studies of Multi-Impact Events and Long-Lived Debris Clouds", in Proceedings *1st LDEF Science Conference*, National Aeronautics & Space Administration, in press 1992.

15. R. M. Goldstein & L. W. Randolph, "Observations of space debris at Goldstone", in Proceedings *Radars and Lidars in Earth and Planetary Sciences* (eds. T. D. Guyenne & J. J. Hunt), European Space Agency, Noordwijk, 1991.

16. P. C. Kassel, "Characteristics of Capacitor-type Micrometeoroid Flux Detectors When Impacted with Simulated Micrometeoroids", U. S. National Aeronautics & Space Administration, Washington, TN D-7359, 1973.

17. S. F. Singer & J. E. Stanley, "Submicron Particles in Meteor Streams", in *Solid Particles in the Solar System*, (eds. I. Halliday & B. A. McIntosh), Reidel, Dordrecht, pp. 329-332, 1980.

ROLE AND DEVELOPMENT OF SMALL SATELLITE MISSIONS IN SPACE PLASMA PHYSICS

A. Valenzuela

Max-Planck-Institut fuer extraterrestrische Physik
8046 Garching b. Muenchen, Germany

1. INTRODUCTION

At the beginning of the space era, all space programs were small. In 1957, Sputnik 1 was successfully launched by the Soviet Union ushering in the era of space research. In 1958 the Explorer 1 was launched by the United States making measurements of the Earth's upper atmosphere which indicated the presence of energetic particles and magnetic fields.

During the next several years series of small research satellites from the USSR - Sputnik, Luna and Kosmos - and from the USA - Explorer and Pioneer - expanded our knowledge of "space" at increasing distances from the Earth.

Orbits of the first satellites were nearly circular, just above the atmosphere. As the launch capability increased, satellites were sent far from the Earth in highly elliptical orbits. In 1958 Pioneer 1 reached 70.000 km apogee, Luna 1 escaped earth orbit after passing close to the moon in 1960 and the planets Venus and Mars were reached in the mid 1960's by USA Pioneers and the Soviet Venera and Mars series.

A "Space Mission Statistics" (Table 1) gives the number and percentage of launches in different categories. There have been approximately 270 scientific satellites launched or 9 % of all launches. Of these scientific satellites, 178 or 67 % have investigated the earth's magnetosphere including large observatories. Within the small magnetospheric class are 137 satellites or 77 % of all magnetospheric missions and 51 % of all scientific satellites.

In Table 2 the "Small Magnetospheric Satellites" are tabulated by "Nation". 95 % of the small magnetospheric missions have been under the direction of the USA, the USSR, Europe and Japan. Of those, NASA directed 48 missions and ESRO/ESA 6 missions.

Since the beginning of the space era there has been a steady increase in the number of small magnetospheric satellites launched and in the mass of each satellite as shown in Figure 1 "Time History of Small Satellites for Magnetospheric Research". These increases in numbers and mass were probably keyed to the increases in launch capability.

In the mid to late 1960's larger spacecraft were needed to make many measurements simultaneously to obtain cause-and-effect relationships. Therefore, the launch rate of small satellites decreased.

Also in the 1970's with limited space budgets, more scientific disciplines began to make use of space for probes to other planets, for astrophysics, and solar telescopes and for earth observations. Therefore, during the 1970's and 1980's there have been fewer space missions dedicated to plasma physics.

In the period of 1985 to the present, the rate is significantly less than one launch per year for the international magnetospheric research community. The community feels that this rate is not sufficient to provide new data or to progress at a reasonable pace to the stage of understanding the magnetospheric system (Shawhan, 1990).

2. SPACE PLASMA PHYSICS

In the discipline of space plasma physics, the widening of the temporal gaps between successive satellite missions can be well demonstrated by examining the launches of the European Space Agency (Haerendel et al., 1988) (Fig. 2). Eight out of nine missions were launched in the ten years between October 1968 and July 1978. The last mission, GIOTTO, came after a delay of seven years. For the next mission, CLUSTER, it is necessary to wait for at least ten years (from the GIOTTO launch in July 1985). Or stated differently, whereas the first ten years of scientific satellite program of ESRO/ESA brought eight missions for the field of magnetospheric physics, there will be only two missions during the subsequent twenty years.

If the scientists working in space plasma physics in a typical ESA country had not had the opportunity of participating in various national or multinational missions, they would be starved for data, and for chances of pursuing their research with advanced instrumentation. This situation is more critical if related directly to the scientific groups of one institute. In Figure 3 (Haerendel, 1988) we see the MPE satellite experiments successfully flown for plasma physics and for astrophysics. Without the small satellite missions it wouldn't be possible to maintain these scientific disciplines and the corresponding re-juvenation of the scientific personnel at our institute.

Although there have been more than 100 missions to study the magnetosphere (Table 1), the research has not reached the level of sufficient understanding where global models can quantitatively predict effects; many processes and large-scale features require more detailed measurements, theory and simulations.

3. CHARACTERISTICS OF THE PLASMA PHYSICS SATELLITES

One of the goals identified for the small plasma physics satellite programs is to provide a basis for international cooperative programs. The international nature of magnetospheric research is reflected in Table 2. Missions have been deployed by more than 12 nations plus the ESA/ESRO consortium. Six international satellite missions in the field of plasma physics will be mentioned in this paper to demonstrate the feasibility of small and/or low-cost scientific satellite projects. Three missions from the past: FIREWHEEL, AMPTE/IRM and VIKING (Hultqvist, 1982) and three future ones: FREJA (Grahn, 1992), EQUATOR-S and IMPACT. It is important to mention that all of these missions were conceived as complementary to the programs of ESA or NASA and were always faced with strongly limited resources.

There is no unique recipe for a successful approach to low-cost satellites, but some of the principles applied in the past will likely turn out to be valid and successful in the future.

The FIREWHEEL satellite was not given a chance to demonstrate the soundness of its development approach which was derived from sounding rocket technology and experience, and built at MPE. The ARIANE 1 launcher failed at its second test launch on May 30, 1980. The financial loss was not too great. The main spacecraft with its four ejectable subsatellites were produced for the total cost of about 7 MDEM, including instrumentation, mission preparation and launch costs (see Tables 3-5).

The AMPTE (Active Magnetospheric Particle Tracer Explorer) was perhaps the best example of a very successful international mission. Three satellites were launched together on August 16, 1984, by a USA Delta rocket. The Ion Release Module (IRM) was provided by Germany, the United Kingdom Subsatellite (UKS) by the United Kingdom and the Charge Composition Explorer (CCE) by the USA.

AMPTE is also representative of innovative science investigations within small magnetospheric missions. The primary goal of the AMPTE mission (Table 3) was to investigate plasma expansion, entry into the magnetosphere and energization through diffusion processes through the release and tracing of lithium and barium ions. Figure 4 depicts the orbits of the IRM/UKS co-orbiting pair covering both the solar wind and the magnetospheric tail and the CCE within the equatorial ring current region. Ion tracer release are indicated in the solar wind just in front of the bow shock to study plasma entry into the magnetosphere, in the magnetosheath region to produce an artificial comet (Valenzuela et al., 1986) and in the magnetospheric tail to investigate plasma diffusion and energization processes (Acuna et al., 1985). This 9-month period of active chemical release investigations was unique in that theories of plasma transport which were developed from 25 years of exploration and discovery were tested using new innovative techniques. Besides these active experiments, AMPTE also returned the first measurements of the elemental and charge-particle population in the magnetosphere over a wide energy range. These measurements by the CCE confirmed the hypothesis that charged oxygen must be significant component of the ring current region, for example. Table 6 shows the AMPTE published papers per year, with an up-dated total of more than 470 papers.

The AMPTE-IRM was the first satellite built in a Max-Planck-Institut with industrial subcontractor and flown successfully. In Germany we profited substantially from the experience gained with FIREWHEEL. The costs of the spacecraft development, including all internal costs of the MPE, i.e. also salaries and overhead, amounted to 18 MDEM (Table 4). The costs figures for the two companion spacecraft UKS and CCE were similarly low.

Two new projects of similar nature have been conceived, EQUATOR-S (Germany, USA, Italy) and IMPACT (Scandinavian countries, Germany). EQUATOR-S (Figures 6-7) is being attempted with an extremely tight budget. The great number and complexity of instruments of the IMPACT project will not allow the adoption of exactly the same approach as applied for the earlier missions, but much of the experience gained with them will be transferred to this mission.

Tables 3-5 summarize scientific objectives of these missions, some of their technical and financial characteristics and the launch opportunities and costs.

4. DESIGN PRINCIPLES

As stated above, there is no unique system design philosophy which allows a low-cost approach, much depends on opportunities and special scientific/technical-/financial boundary conditions. Often the last, the financial limitations, are over-riding and enforce unconventional proceedings and compromises. However, there are some common elements.

4.1. Lessons Learned

At MPE where the FIREWHEEL and AMPTE/IRM spacecraft were built in-house, we found the following aspects of our approach to be essential:

- The mission should be led by the Principal Investigator (PI) who is motivated to make the project a success.
- The PI may also significantly determine the configuration of the hardware having authority over decisions concerning all trade offs between science, engineering, programmatic, and risks.
- The leading team must have scientific, technical and management skills.
- They must carefully establish the mission requirements to fulfill the scientific objectives early. Frequently those objectives are translated in requirements more stringent than necessary. This may cause the development cost to move into an area of exponential growth.
- The program must be accomplished with a strong commitment to, and in close association with, the scientific group served by the mission. This should include those scientists and engineers who are intimately acquainted with the

project and thus can most ably translate science requirements into engineering/hardware specifications and development.

- No strict separation of science and engineering. Participation of scientists in spacecraft team is required.

- All participants in the program have to have a clear understanding of, and commitment to, their role and obligations.

- Close communication between the program participants.

This enables the finding of scientific/technical compromises and solutions of unexpected problems at all stages of design and development without sacrificing the essential objectives. Other lessons learned are:

- Suppress "Nice-to-Have" Requirements. Keep things as simple as possible to do the job adequately.

- Start the project with clearly identified specifications.

- Define clean and simple interfaces.

- Design telemetry system to maximize scientific return rather than strict ease of handling.

- Identify sources of major cost impacts.

- Define alternative solutions.

- Adopt innovative engineering solutions.

- Constant examination and review of all programmatic elements.

- Accomplish quality assurance under strongly reduced documentation by taking all necessary practical steps and by continuous, open personal communication of the entire spacecraft team, and sharing of responsibility.

- Use of screened commercial components instead of space-qualified or MIL-components.

- Careful inspection and testing of all purchased material and components, in-house qualification of non-space-qualified items.

- Thorough and, where feasible, long-term testing of all subsystems and systems.

- Redundancy of all essential subsystems.

- Reliability and performance assurance of the mission should be achieved by relying on the skills of those designing and building the spacecraft systems rather than excessive reliance on documentation and reviews.

- Even when independent review is required, one must rely on the people who design, build and test the hardware, to create the confidence as well as a suitable system for mission success.

- No prime industrial contractor.

- High degree of freedom in technical decisions, in particular with respect to choice of the subcontractor or of procured hardware items, granted by supervising and funding agency.

- Try to perform work in institutions/companies sized such that the job challenges their capabilities and keeps their interest. These smaller projects generally receive more attention from management at smaller companies than at bigger ones.

- Develop software towards implementing system performance solutions as well as related test and mission scenarios and efficient data collection and analysis. This again requires close coordination between scientific and engineering personnel.

4.2 The "Resource Envelope" Concept

The resource envelope contained a total mass, power and data rate for the overall science payload. No margin was given for this envelope. It was an absolute, never-to-be-trespassed boundary! This principle generated a lot of ingenuity in the design and operation of the science payload and contributed to the very efficient mission and it gave a stability to the system design work which contributed to the low cost.

Of course, if one sets up such an absolute "envelope" one cannot cheat - System Engineering has to be quite open about the fact that there are margins, but explain that he keeps the margins in his own pocket to hand out to subsystems and payload if really serious problems turn up. This kind of "local self-government" requires mutual trust between scientists and system designers.

4.3. Adhere Strictly to Mission-Essential Requirements

Despite the hard trade-offs described above the project adhered strictly to mission-essential requirements, e.g.:

- The satellite was extremely electrostatically clean
- The data rate required by the scientists was strictly enforced.

5. BENEFITS

The most common benefits of these low-cost missions are:

- Promote "first class" science at moderate cost.
- Fill the temporal and thematic gaps in the major science programs of the great space agencies.
- Provide quick response to the space science community.
- Rationalize budgets by permitting continuity in a given research field and attached technological developments.
- Provide opportunities for international cooperation.
- Improve technology transfer from scientific institutions into industry.
- Enable innovation for best compromise solutions without sacrificing essential scientific objectives.
- Improve space technology education.
- Improve scientific-technical management under the low-cost aspect.
- Improve implementation of "best efforts" contracts with industry.
- Enable minimum documentation and reviews with high grade of reliability.

6. SUMMARY

The motivation for small satellite missions is to increase the number of opportunities to conceive, develop, launch and operate high-quality scientific satellite missions, and thus create additional events to fill the ever increasing temporal and thematic gaps in the major science programs of the great space agencies.

There is a spectrum of approaches to developing low-cost scientific satellites but the essential ones are:

- Scientific motivation in the project team led by the PI.
- Flexibility in responding to the available resources and limitations.
- Support and encouragement from the funding agency.
- Availability of a suitable low-cost launch opportunity. This may set essential design constraints.
- Integrated work between scientists and engineers.
- Formal procedures of quality assurance, i.e. documentation, have to be largely sacrificed.
- Practical steps of material and component inspection and testing have to be maintained to assure reliability.
- An overall reduction of reliability in comparison with the major missions of the space agencies has to be accepted.
- Innovative engineering solutions and cooperation with industry.

So far, our experiences have been very positive and the satellites including VIKING (Hultqvist, 1992), which were successfully launched, proved to be sufficiently reliable.

Because of the small number of events, we cannot generalize those experiences, but we derive from them much encouragement for the future.

REFERENCES

Acuna, M.H., G.W. Ousley, D. Bryant, and G. Paschmann, 1985; Editorial: AMPTE - Mission Overview, Geoscience and Remote Sensing, GE-23:175.

Haerendel, G., 1988; MPE Communication.

Haerendel, G., and S. Grahn, 1988; From Firewheel to Impact, The German/Swedish Approach to Plasma Physics Satellites. Presented by A. Valenzuela at the IAF-Congress 1988, Bangalore, India.

Hultqvist, B., 1992; The VIKING Programme, Proceedings ESA/ESTEC Workshop on Design Approaches and Development Philosphies of Small Satellites, March, 1992; ESTEC, Holland.

Grahn, S., 1992; The FREJA Project, Proceedings ESA/ESTEC Workshop on Design Approaches and Development and Philosophies of Small Satellites, March, 1992; ESTEC, Holland.

Shawhan, S.D., 1989; Role of Small Satellite Missions in Magnetospheric Research; 103-114; Ed.: B. Hultqvist and C.-G. Falthammar, Plenum Press, New York.

TRW Space Log 1957-1987, 1988; Thomson, T.D., ed., TRW Space and Technology Group, Redondo Beach, CA.

Valenzuela, A., G. Haerendel, H. Foppl, F. Melzner, H. Neuss, E. Rieger, J. Stocker, O. Bauer, H. Hofner, and J. Loidl. The AMPTE Artificial Comet Experiments, Nature, 320, 700-703, 1986.

INTERNATIONAL SYMPOSIUM - SMALL SATELLITES SYSTEMS AND SERVICES, ESA/CNES,

ARCACHON, FRANCE, JUNE 29 - JULY 3, 1992

TABLE 1

SPACE MISSION STATISTICS[*]

CATEGORIES	TOTAL NO.	PERCENTAGE
- SUCCESSFUL SPACE LAUNCHES 1957-1987 Worldwide	2979	
- SCIENTIFIC SATELLITES Terrestrial, Planetary, Solar Wind, Astrophysics. Not operational: NOAA, GOES, DMSP, METEOR	267	9 %
- MAGNETOSPHERIC SATELLITES Not observatories: OGO, Some Kosmos, Prognoz, ATS or OV	178	67 %
- SMALL MAGNETOSPHERIC SATELLITES Sputniks, Explorers, Elektrons, IMPs, Alouette/ISIS, ISAS-Series, Aries, Interkosmos, San Marco, Viking	137	77 %

(*) REF.: TRW SPACE LOG 1957-1987, 1988, VOL. 23.
            TRW SPACE & TECHNOLOGY GROUP, REDONDO BEACH, CA, USA

TABLE 2

SMALL MAGNETOSPHERIC SATELLITES BY NATION*

NATION	PARTIAL NO.	TOTAL NO.	PERCENTAGE
USA		68	50 %
- NASA	48		
- OTHER USA GOVERNMENT	20		
FORMER SOVIET UNION		28	20 %
EUROPE		26	19 %
- UK	7		
- ESRO/ESA	6		
- ITALY	5		
- FRANCE	4		
- GERMANY	3		
- SWEDEN	1		
JAPAN		8	6 %
CANADA		4	3 %
OTHER		3	2 %
- INDIA, RRC & CZECHOSLOVAKIA			

240

TABLE 3: SCIENTIFIC OBJECTIVES / HIGHLIGHTS(*)

FIREWHEEL   PLASMA INJECTION WITH MULTIPOINT DIAGNOSTICS IN DEEP MAGNETOSPHERE (LAUNCH FAILURE !)

AMPTE   ARTIFICIAL COMETS, DETAILED STUDIES OF THE STRUCTURE OF MAGNETOPAUSE AND BOW SHOCK, IONIC AND MOLECULAR COMPOSITION OF RING CURRENT AND PLASMA SHEET, INTERSTELLAR PICK-UP He^+

VIKING   GLOBAL AND LOCAL INVESTIGATION OF THE AURORAL OVAL AND, IN PARTICULAR, OF THE AURORAL ACCELERATION REGIONS, THE GENERATION OF VARIOUS TYPES OF ENERGETIC PARTICLE BEAMS, THE NATURE OF FIELD-ALIGNED POTENTIAL DROPS, ASSOCIATED PLASMA WAVES AND EXCITATION OF ELECTROMAGNETIC WAVES LIKE AURORAL KILOMETRIC RADIATION

FREJA   HITHERTO UNAVAILABLE HIGH RESOLUTION MEASUREMENTS OF PHENOMENA AND PROCESSES IN THE UPPER IONOSPHERE WITH EMPHASIS OF HIGH LATITUDES AND OF THE INTERACTION WITH THE HOT PLASMAS OF THE MAGNETOSPHERE

EQUATOR-S   HIGH RESOLUTION MEASUREMENTS IN THE EQUATORIAL MAGNETOSPHERE, COMPLEMENTING THE OTHER ISTP MISSIONS

IMPACT   STUDY OF AURORAL SOURCE REGIONS, PLASMA ACCELERATION PROCESSES, MICROTURBULENCE, WITH MULTIPOINT DIAGNOSTICS, STUDY OF PARTICLE AND WAVE EVOLUTION ALONG FIELD LINES, ACTIVE EXPERIMENTS, TRACER PARTICLES, AURORAL IMAGING; ALL WITH VERY HIGH TEMPORAL RESOLUTION

(*) HAERENDEL AND GRAHN, 1988

TABLE 4: SPACECRAFT CHARACTERISTICS (*)

MISSION	YEAR OF CONCEPTION	YEARS OF FABRICATION	LAUNCH	DRY MASS (KG)	POWER (WATT)	NO. OF EXP.	INTEGRATION AT	TOTAL COST OF S/C EXP. EXCLUDED	LIFE-TIME
FIREWHEEL 81 MAIN, 4 SUBSAT.)	1977	1977-1980	MAY 80 (FAILURE)	1010	BATTER-IES	19	MPE+3 OTHER SCIENTIFIC LABS	2 MDEM	LAUNCH FAILURE
AMPTE-IRM	1975-1980	1980-1984	AUG. 84	620	60	6	MPE	18 MDEM	2 YEARS
VIKING	1977-1980	1980-1983; 1985-1986;	FEB. 86	286	60	6	SAAB SPACE AB	80 MSEK	1.3 YEAI
FREJA	1987-1988	1988-1991	JULY 91	230	87	5	SWEDISH IND.	~8 MUSD	?
EQUATOR-S	1990-1991	1992-1994	SEPT. 94	170	60	6	MPE	~8 MDEM	2 YEARS
IMPACT (2 SAT.)	1985-1992	1993-1996	96/97	2X750	2X150	2X16	?	~40 MUSD	

(*) HAERENDEL AND GRAHN, 1988

TABLE 5: LAUNCH OPPORTUNITIES (*)

MISSION	LAUNCH VEHICLE	LAUNCH AGENCY	LAUNCH OPPORTUNITY	CONTRIBUTION TO LAUNCH COSTS
FIREWHEEL	ARIANE I	ESA	LO2 TEST LAUNCH	1.1 MDEM
AMPTE-IRM	DELTA 3294	NASA	3 SAT, STACK WITH NASA/UK (DEDICATED)	0.9 DEM (KICKMOTOR ONLY)
VIKING	ARIANE	ESA	PIGGYBACK WITH SPOT	15 MFF
FREJA	LONG MARCH 2	CHINA	PIGGYBACK WITH FSW-1	4.3 MUSD
EQUATOR-S	SAN MARCO SCOUT	ASI	DEDICATED	-
IMPACT	?	?	DEDICATED	?

(*) HAERENDEL AND GRAHN, 1988

TABLE 6

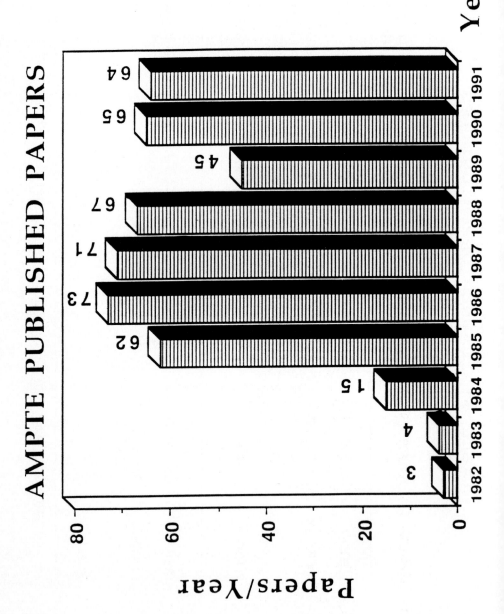

TABLE 7
List of Experiments and Instruments Installed in the IRM Satellite

No.	Item
1	DC-magnetometer sensor
2	DC-magnetometer electronics
3	DC-magnetometer filter
4	VLF magnetometer sensor
5	VLF magnetometer preamplifier
6	HF magnetometer sensor
7	HF magnetometer preamplifier
8	Iowa spectrum analyzer
9	E-field, preamplifier controller
10	Aerospace SFR-box
11	SULEICA sensor
11a	SULEICA HV-box
11b	SULEICA el. sensor
12	SULEICA electronics
13	MSIS sensor
14	MSIS electronics
15	3D plasma sensor
15a	RPA sensor
16	3D plasma electronics
17	Ba-canisters
18	Li-canisters
19	TM-TC-electronics (pyro, power control)
19a	TM-TC-electronics (micro-proc. etc.)
20	Coax relais box
21	Motorola transponder
22	Comrad receiver
22a	Comrad preamplifier + diplexer
22b	Elmada transmitter
23	Solar panels
24	Power battery I
24a	Power battery II
25	VHF ranging box
26	Torquer
27	Nutation dampers
28	Yo-Yo
29	PKM
31	Umbilical-, battery- and ordnance-plug
32	MPE control units
33	MPE HF spectrum analyzer
34	Radial TM-antenna
34a	Back up radial TM-antenna
35	On-axis TM-antenna
36	Sun sensor
37	Upper VHF transponder antenna
37a	Lower VHF transponder antenna
38	Power damper

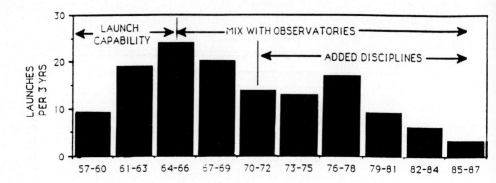

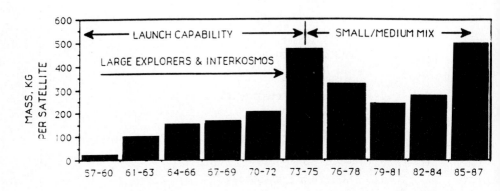

Fig. 1 : Time history of small satellites for
magnetospheric research
(Ref.: TRW Space Log 1957 - 1987, 1988)

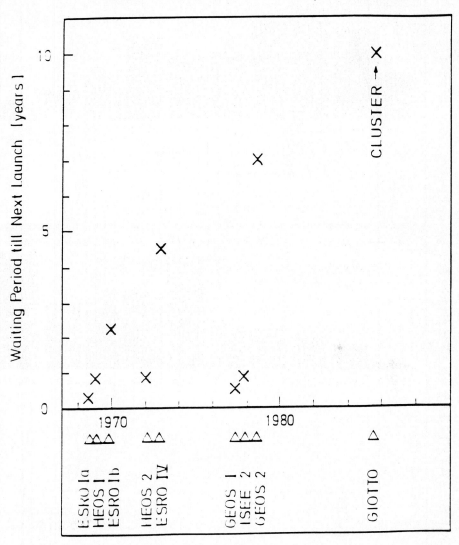

Fig. 2

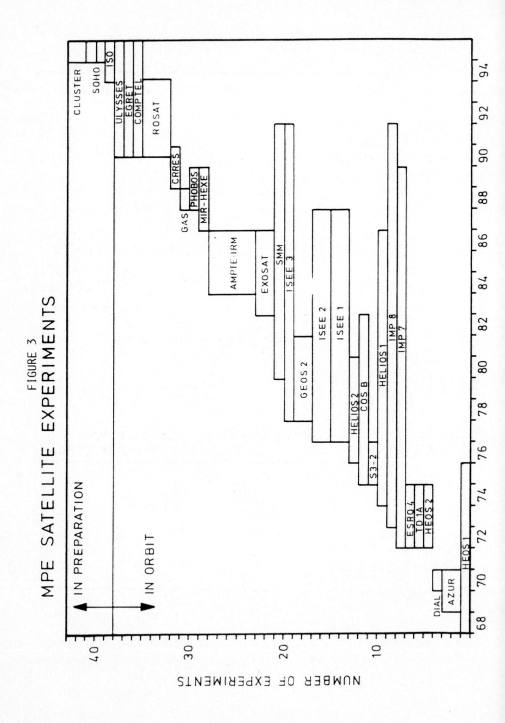

FIGURE 3

MPE SATELLITE EXPERIMENTS

FIGURE 4

AMPTE SATELLITE ORBITS AND CHEMICAL RELEASE LOCATIONS

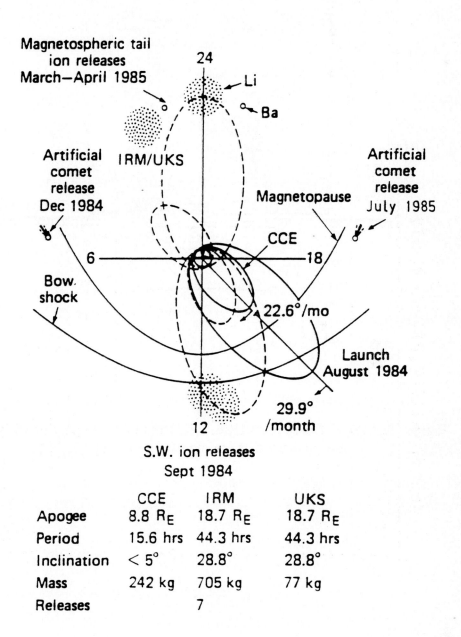

	CCE	IRM	UKS
Apogee	8.8 R_E	18.7 R_E	18.7 R_E
Period	15.6 hrs	44.3 hrs	44.3 hrs
Inclination	$< 5°$	28.8°	28.8°
Mass	242 kg	705 kg	77 kg
Releases		7	

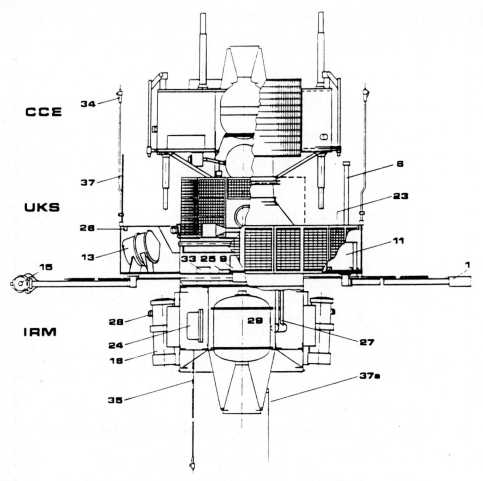

Fig. 5. The AMPTE Satellites IRM, UKS, and CCE in launch configuration (instruments are identified in Table 7).

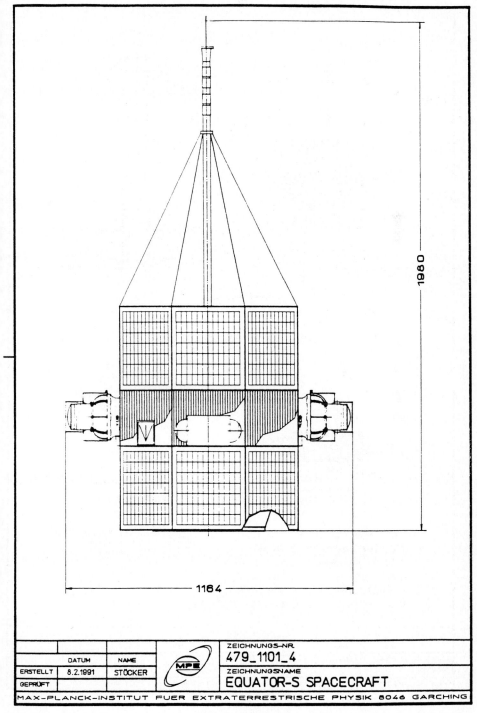

1980

1164

	DATUM	NAME
ERSTELLT	8.2.1991	STÖCKER
GEPRÜFT		

ZEICHNUNGS-NR.
479_1101_4

ZEICHNUNGSNAME
EQUATOR-S SPACECRAFT

MAX-PLANCK-INSTITUT FUER EXTRATERRESTRISCHE PHYSIK 8046 GARCHING

Fig. 6

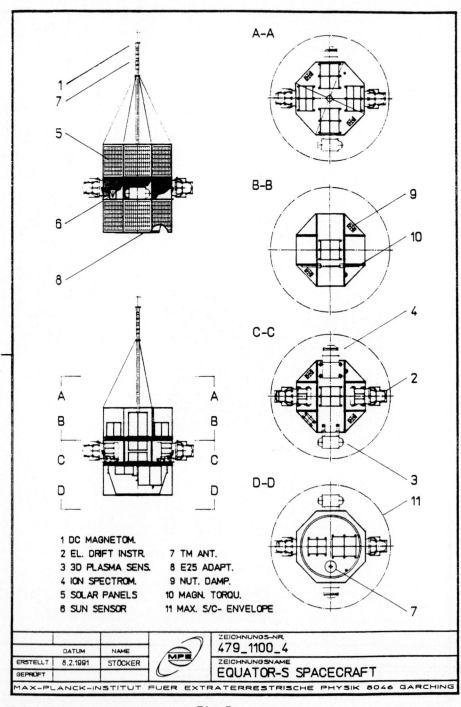

A-A

B-B

C-C

D-D

1 DC MAGNETOM.
2 EL. DRIFT INSTR.
3 3D PLASMA SENS.
4 ION SPECTROM.
5 SOLAR PANELS
6 SUN SENSOR

7 TM ANT.
8 E25 ADAPT.
9 NUT. DAMP.
10 MAGN. TORQU.
11 MAX. S/C- ENVELOPE

	DATUM	NAME
ERSTELLT	8.2.1991	STÖCKER
GEPRÜFT		

ZEICHNUNGS-NR.
479_1100_4

ZEICHNUNGSNAME
EQUATOR-S SPACECRAFT

MAX-PLANCK-INSTITUT FUER EXTRATERRESTRISCHE PHYSIK 8046 GARCHING

Fig. 7

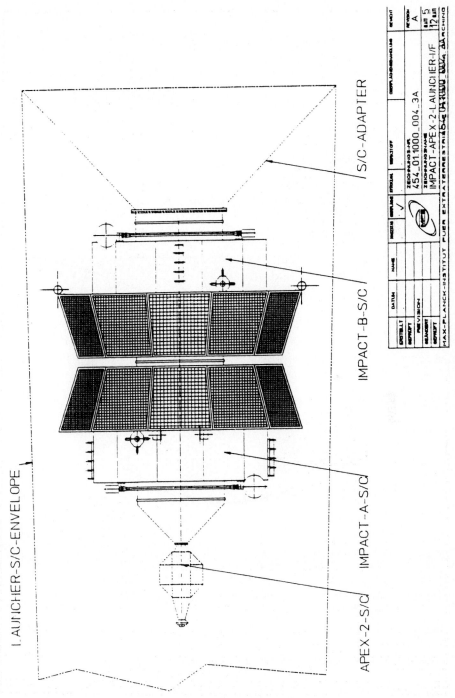

LAUNCHER-S/C-ENVELOPE

APEX-2-S/C   IMPACT-A-S/C   IMPACT-B-S/C   S/C-ADAPTER

FIGURE 8

				ZEICHNUNGS-NR	STÜCKLISTE	WERKSTOFF	CRSTL.LD-SHEBAMCELING	GEWICHT
ERSTELLT	DATUM	NAME	PRÜFER	✓	454_011000_004_3A			REVISION A
GEPRÜFT					ZEICHNUNGS-NAME			BLATT 5
	REVISION				IMPACT-APEX-2-LAUNCHER-I/F			12 un
GEÄNDERT								
GEPRÜFT								
MAX-PLANCK-INSTITUT FÜR EXTRATERRESTRISCHE PHYSIK 8046 GARCHING								

253

FIGURE 9

IMPACT FINAL ORBITS

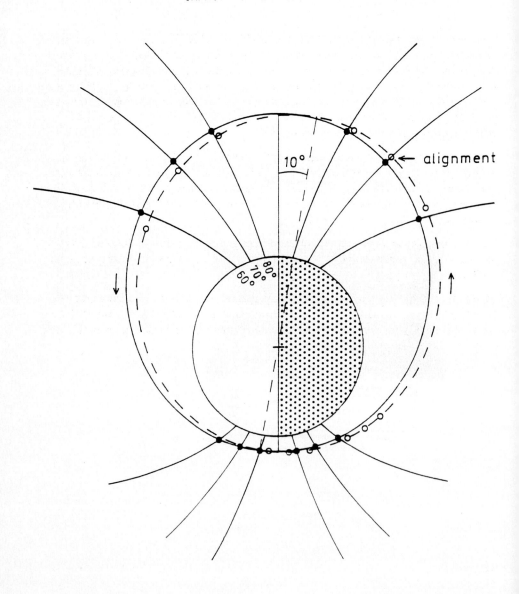

SYNTHESE DE LA SESSION
SCIENCES DE L'UNIVERS

Cette session fut marquée par la présentation de sujets fort intéressants, la variété des objectifs scientifiques traités et les avantages programmatiques indéniables que présentent les « petits satellites ». De ce point de vue, il faut dire que cette session a montré qu'il est possible de mener à bien des programmes scientifiques de « premier ordre » même avec de petits satellites. De nouvelles technologies et de nouveaux concepts opérationnels pourraient faire progresser la situation bien plus encore et rendre même possible la réalisation de missions dans l'espace interstellaire.

Les petits satellites utilisés pour les sciences spatiales présentent un intérêt particulier pour les petits pays, tirant avantage d'une exploitation faisant appel à un contractant principal et des collectivités d'usagers fidèles. Les petits satellites ayant déjà volé et les résultats scientifiques qu'ils ont permis d'obtenir donnent une bonne notion des conditions à remplir lorsque l'on utilise cette approche.

Il a également été souligné que les aspects pédagogiques des petits satellites ne devraient pas être sous-estimés, de façon à stimuler le développement et la stabilité de la collectivité d'usagers scientifiques.

Cependant, pour devenir une réalité, les nouvelles missions scientifiques nécessitent également des ressources financières. De nouvelles approches dans le domaine des initiatives économiques, également discutées au cours du symposium, pourraient sans aucun doute contribuer à résoudre les problèmes de budget.

Bref, « il suffit de se lancer ! ».

SYNTHESIS OF THE SESSION
SPACE SCIENCES

This session was highlighted by the presentation of very interesting topics, the variety of the scientific objectives covered, and some obvious programmatical advantages of "small satellites". In this respect it is fair to say, that this session has revealed evidence, that "first class science" can be done with small satellites too. New technologies and new operational concepts would enhance the situation even more and would make even deep space missions feasible.

Small space science satellites seem to be specifically attractive for smaller countries, gaining benefit from prime contractorship and dedicated user communities. Already flown, small, scientific satellites and the scientific results achieved with them, give a good understanding on the specifics to be respected with this approach.

It was also highlighted, that the educational aspects of small satellites should not be underestimated, stimulating the scientific user community, to make it probably grow and stable.

The new scientific missions have to be however accompanied by monetary resources too, to make them a reality. New entrepreneurial approaches, also discussed during the symposium, could certainly contribute to ease the budgetary stress.

So, in one word : "Let's just do it!".

SESSION IV

OBSERVATION DE LA TERRE

EARTH OBSERVATION

OBSERVATION DE LA TERRE A PARTIR DE MINISATELLITE

EARTH OBSERVATION FROM SMALL SATELLITES

PAR C. VIALET

MATRA MARCONI SPACE

RESUME :

• L'observation de la terre à partir de l'espace présente de nombreux avantages que de plus en plus d'utilisateurs veulent exploiter.

Chacun de ces utilisateurs a des besoins particuliers qui conduisent à des spécifications de missions très diverses. Pour satisfaire ces besoins il est possible, à partir d'un principe d'instrument, qualifié et d'une plate-forme standard, de réaliser à coût réduit et en un temps minimal un ou plusieurs minisatellites adaptés à l'application envisagée.

Les instruments de base sont dérivés d'instruments déjà développés pour d'autres satellites. Deux ou plusieurs de ces instruments peuvent être combinés pour former un ensemble adapté à une nouvelle mission.

La plate-forme MMS/FAIRCHILD a été conçue de façon modulaire pour s'adapter facilement à une grande variété de missions.

Le satellite ainsi conçu s'intègre parfaitement dans un schéma classique de lancement avec PEGASE ou TAURUS, ou tout autre lanceur équivalent, et d'utilisation de stations de réception SPOT/ERS/LANDSAT.

Après une présentation rapide des différents types de missions d'observation et de leur intérêt, la présentation portera sur leurs spécificités et montrera comment, à partir d'un type d'instrument et d'une plate-forme modulaire qui seront décrits, il est possible de concevoir un minisatellite ou une constellation de minisatellites capable de remplir deux missions type qui seront présentées.

EARTH OBSERVATION FROM SMALL SATELLITES

ABSTRACT :

• Earth observation from space has numerous interesting aspects that more and more users want to take advantage of.

Each of these users has particular needs which lead to a wide range of missions specifications. In order to fulfil these needs it is possible, from a qualified instrument principle and a standard small satellite platform, to build in a short time one or several low cost small satellites specifically designed for the planned mission.

The basic instruments are derived from already existing ones developed for other satellites. Several of these instruments can be combined to meet the requirements of a new mission.

The MMS/Fairchild small satellite multimission platform is of a modular design so that it is easily adaptable to a wide range of missions.

The corresponding satellite is compatible with the PEGASUS or TAURUS launcher, or any other equivalent one, and can use SPOT/ERS/LANDSAT ground stations.

After a rapid presentation of various types of earth observation missions and their potential application, the multimission platform and various instruments will be presented. Two small satellite missions will be derived and presented.

1. EARTH OBSERVATION MISSIONS

• Some of the main objectives of the on-going earth observation programs are the global environment monitoring and the earth (land and water) resources management. These programs concern either restricted geographical areas or the whole earth.

In both of these cases, small earth observation satellites can proved to be very useful :

- when the data provided by one or two operational satellites cannot fulfill completely the global mission with the minimal sampling requirements.

- when there are conflicts over specific areas or when fast processing is needed over a specific country.and of course, when the size of the payload is compatible with the mission (Synthetic Aperture Radars, for instance, are for the moment excluded).

• The altimetry satellite, described in this paper is a good example of the 1st case : the TOPEX/POSEIDON data should be completed by the data of 2 other satellites, in order to achieve the adequate temporal and spatial sampling for the ocean altimetry and to be able to modelize correctly the ocean currents.

• Several visible/near infrared high resolution missions derived from the same instrument concept can be envisaged to illustrate the second case :

- the instruments(imagers) enable a spatial resolution from 15 to 30 meters (up to 50 m), with a swath width of 60 to 100 km.

- Each instrument has a dedicated spectral band.

• The number of instrument(s), their resolution (radiometric and geometric), their off track or along track viewing capability depend on the applications as described hereunder :

a) Renewable resources :

The data can be complementary to low resolution data (to focus on details) or to high resolution data (as SPOT'S ones) to reduce the acquisition and processing delays for short duration phenomena.

The main possibilities are summarized in Table 1/1. They are characterized by their short delay of acquisition

b) Non Renewable resources (geology, pedology ...).

They only need a 4 times/year acquisition.

They can be monitored directly using narrow band (0,85 μm - 0,87 μm for the iron), spectrometers or through their effects on the vegetation ("stress"), the requirements are then the "same as for vegetation i.e. : 0.5 μm to 0.65 μm ; 0.65 μm to 0.7 μm.

c) Besides these 2 main applications, cartography and mapping are specific cases (sometimes complementary to the previous ones). Compared to cartography which requires only contour determination mapping needs stereography imaging which can be obtained by :

- across track depointing like for SPOT (with a few days between the 2 views of the pair)

- fore and aft pointing on the same track (with or without across track capability to reduce the acquisition delay)

The best single spectral band is 0.65 μm - 0.67 μm, but other bands offering a good geometrical quality can be suitable with a multi spectral capability and adequate processing being the best solution, the resolution should be in all cases as good as possible.

All these missions, as described in the following paragraphs, can be fulfilled by using simultaneously on the same platform one or several instruments with complementary characteristics.

2. - EARTH OBSERVATION MULTIMISSION PLATFORM

2.1. - GENERAL DESCRIPTION

The MMS/FAIRCHILD class II multimission platform has been designed to readily adapt to a broad range of missions on small satellites.

The launch mass capability from 100 kg to 300 kg can be extended to 500 kg. Such a wide range is compatible with many earth observation potential missions and with present and future small satellite launchers capabilities.

Key features of the bus design are :

- a structured system that accommodates the components configuration necessary to meet a variety of missions.

- standard set of attitude control sensors and torquer that are configured through control of the on-board computer to provide the required control mode, be it three axes stabilized or spin stabilized.

- a modular solar array panel with hinges that permit variations in solar array area and angle to the spacecraft. The power could be further increased by use of a solar array drive. The battery sizing could be increased to 20 Ah.

- a telemetry and command system which provides flexible formats, data storage, and pre-processing of data if required.

- a propulsion concept that permits increments of propulsion for orbit insertion and maintenance, with up to 30 kg ergols.

- sufficient margin in mass, power, telemetry, command and memory to accommodate payloads with expanded requirements.

- ability to accommodate payloads on the bus structure, in the propulsion area when not required or by adding a payload module.

- a spacecraft with a low level of dynamical disturbances that will ensure future experiment compatibility without special design accommodation.

- a baseline spacecraft that can be launched in several ways including the PEGASUS/TAURUS expendable launch vehicles.

Figure 2/1.:   presents an exploded view of a baseline class II multimission platform.

Table 2/1 :   summarizes the core characteristics and capability, to be used as a guide to planning future missions, the modular design of the platform is such that a wide range of other capabilities and characteristics can be obtained and tailored for a specific mission.

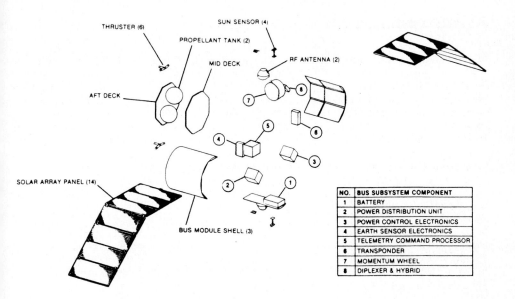

NO.	BUS SUBSYSTEM COMPONENT
1	BATTERY
2	POWER DISTRIBUTION UNIT
3	POWER CONTROL ELECTRONICS
4	EARTH SENSOR ELECTRONICS
5	TELEMETRY COMMAND PROCESSOR
6	TRANSPONDER
7	MOMENTUM WHEEL
8	DIPLEXER & HYBRID

FIGURE 2/1 : MMS–FAIRCHILD CLASS II SPACE VEHICLE PLATFORM

PARAMETER	CAPACITY	
– Allowable payload weight (includes payload module if used)	78 kg 135 kg	(750 KM CIRC) (200 x 1500 KM)
– Core weight	170 kg	
– Payload volume available	0.89 m3 Total	
– Available payload power (orbit average)	61 W	(For 750 KM CIRC Orbit 90° Incl)
– Battery capacity (total capacity of bus)	14 Ah	
– Bus voltage	28 ± 4 VDC	
– AOCS capability Pointing Knowledge Bias momentum (pitch axis) Pitch wheel control torque Magnetic torque (1 axis)	 .08 Deg .04 Deg ± 20 N.m.s .049 N.m .0005 N.m	
– Base plate thermal range (within bus or payload module)	10°C to 30°C	
– Data storage available	336 MBits	
– GSE	Set of elec. and mech. GSE for core	

TABLE 2. : CORE CAPABILITY TO SUPPORT PAYLOADS

2.2. DEVELOPMENT STATUS

The MMS/FAIRCHILD earth observation multimission platform, see Figure 2/2, development has reached a status of completion which authorizes the start of an application mission within a very short delay..

From details given on Table 2/2 it can be seen that the MMS/FAIRCHILD team takes the maximum advantage from the heritage of previous already operational satellites.

FAIRCHILD with the SMEX programme has developed modular core components for power, telemetry telecomand and structure which are three of the main standard subsystems of a platform.

MMS with SPOT and ERS has developed expertise in multimission platform concepts with an outstanding expertise in the fourth standard subsystm, attitude determination and control, this subsystem is of particular importance for several earth observation missions.

From their combined expertise, both companies can tailor the platform to a particular customer requirements with already existing and flight proven components for RF, thermal and propulsion subsystems.

MMS and FAIRCHILD engineers have access to the same powerful modern computer simulation tools. Feasibility studies can be carried out very quickly from already existing multimission modules. Then the programme can efficiently carry on until launch without interruption. Engineers in both companies trained to competitive low cost developments will be a key for success.

This experience combined with a complete set of qualified subsystem modules and components gives MMS/FAIRCHILD the capability to launch a new mission as early as 1996.

SUB-SYSTEM	PRIME	HERITAGE	PLANNED FLIGHT
STRUCTURE	FAIRCHILD	IN HOUSE DEVELOPMENT ALREADY QUALIFIED	1rst MISSION
TTC	FAIRCHILD	SMEX AND NASA/FAIRCHILD SPONSORSHIP	MID 92
RF	MMS/FAIRCHILD	STANDARD SPACE QUALIFIED S BAND EQUIPMENT	ALEADY FLOWN
POWER	FAIRCHILD	SMEX	MID 92
AOCS	MMS/FAIRCHILD	TOPEX POSEIDON AND MMS/FAIRCHILD SPONSORSHIP	MID 92
THERMAL	MMS/FAIRCHILD	STANDARD SPACE QUALIFIED EQUIPMENT	ALREADY FLOWN
PROPULSION	MMS	STANDARD SPACE QUALIFIED EQUIPMENT	ALREADY FLOWN
PLATFORM	MMS/FAIRCHILD	PREVIOUS SPACE PROGRAMS AND ON GOING INTERNAL AND AGENCIES SPONSORSHIP	1996 WITH 1993 K.O.

TABLE 2/2 : EARTH OBSERVATION MULTIMISSION PLATFORM DEVELOPMENT STATUS

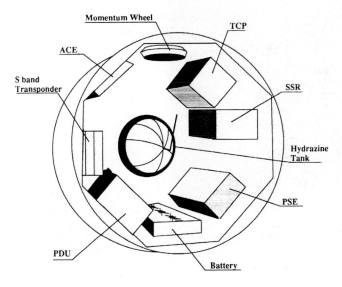

Momentum Wheel

TCP

ACE

S band
Transponder

SSR

Hydrazine
Tank

PSE

PDU

Battery

PDU: Power Distribution Unit

SSR: Soli State Recorder

PCE: Power Supply Electronic

ACE: Actuator Control Electronic

TCP: Telemetry & Command Processor

Figure 2.2 : MMS/FAIRCHILD multimission platform model and components layout

3. - EARTH OBSERVATION OPTICAL INSTRUMENTS

Following the success of the SPOT programme MMS is involved since 1983 in optical instruments for low earth orbit small satellites. Two types of lenses, 162 and 324 mm of focal length, have been developed for the Indian Remote Sensing (IRS) pushbroom cameras.

Dioptric lenses are very adequate for small satellites, they provide a high optical quality over a wide field of view and they are well adapted to the use of standard charge coupled devices detectors.

From the IRS basic lenses, the performances of which are summarised in Table 3/1, it is possible to derive earth observation instruments or combination of instruments for various wavelength in the visible and near infrared spectrum.

Since the successful launch of IRS several tenths of such lenses have been delivered, see figure 3/1, they have given images of very good quality and have proven very good stability of their performances.

. PARAMETERS		LISS-I REQUIR^T	LISS-II REQUIR^T
. Equivalent Focal Length (EFL)		162.2 ± .15 mm	324.4 ± 30 mm
. EFL tolerance for a set of 4 matched lenses		16 microns (10 as a goal)	32 microns (20 as a goal)
. Variation in EFL and Focal Distance with temperature		1 microns/°C	1 microns/°C
. Field of view		± 5 degrees	± 5 degrees
. F number		4.5	4.5
. Distortion %		.1 %	.1 %
. Variation in distortion for a set of 4 matched lenses		.01 %	.01 %
. Spectral filtering		See specific table 2	See specific table 2
. Veiling glare		2 %	2 %
. Minimum MTF over the entire image format (40 c/mm) spectral bands	B1	.70	.65
defined in table 2	B2	.70	.65
	B3	.70	.65
	B4	.70	.65
. Stability of optical axis after EV tests and during operation		1 micron	1 micron

FIGURE 3/1	**TABLE 3/1**
SET OF DIFFERENT LENSES	IRS LENSES PERFORMANCES

4. - EARTH OBSERVATION MICROWAVE INSTRUMENTS

In 1985, microwave radiometry activities started at MMS-F to complement the Instrumentation division expertise well known in optical technology. Among, the instruments manufactured in the microwave field, MMS had a large contribution to the ATSRM (Along Track Scanning Radiometer Microwave) developed for ERS 1.

This radiometer, illustrated in figure 4/1 includes a 0.6 m deployable antenna and two channels operating at 23.84 GHz and 36.5 GHz. The main objective of the corresponding mission is to provide integrated water vapour profile along subsatellite path.

MMS-F under CRPE prime contractorship, is responsible for the antenna with deployment mechanism, the radiometer electronics and the overall instrument integration. Its total weight is less than 30 kgs.

In order to enhance the information collected by the ATSRM radiometer, MMS-F studied a three channel radiometer for the french CNES (19 GHz, 22 GHz, 36.5 GHz) in view of an altimetry mission called ALTINET.

MMS-F in cooperation with Observatoire de MEUDON developed their own technology for the receiver front ends at microwaves and millemeter waves for future spaceborne applications like MHS (Microwave Humidity Sounder) and MIMR (Multifrequency Imaging Microwave Radiometer) between 6 GHz and 200 GHz.

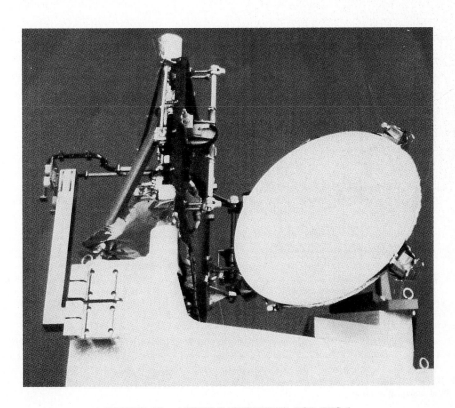

FIGURE 4/1 : ATSRM RADIOMETER FOR ERS 1

5. - GROUND SEGMENT

The Ground Segment must be commensurate in cost and complexity with the Space Segment and be compatible with a simple and efficient operational concept.

The traditional decomposition of the Ground Segment into a few major functional entities still applies, Figure 5/1 :

- Satellite Mission and Control Centre, which includes all facilities for monitoring and control housekeeping data processing, flight dynamics and mission planning
- Ground Stations, for telecommand transmission and housekeeping telemetry reception
- Ground Communications infrastructure
- Payload receiving stations, for reception of payload telemetry data
- Payload User Centre, which includes all facilities for payload data processing and user and interface

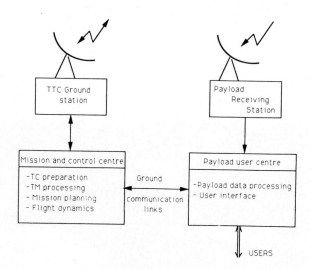

Figure 5/1 :   The ground segment functional configuration is identical to those of traditional satellites but the hardware software implementation are simplified to the maximum possible extent.

5.1. - MISSION & CONTROL CENTRE

The ground segment design has to remain simple and must be based on off the shelf hardware and software to the maximum possible extent. An example of ground station design is shown in Figure 5/2 which is based on a pair of industry standard 80386 microcomputer, a pair of TCP/IP interface boards to an Ethernet LAN, an S-band tracking antenna and associated communications equipment.

The design indicated displays a combination of the Payload data and housekeeping data, which can be done for missions which do not generate a bit rate exceeding typically 1 Mbps.

The S-band link is compatible with the S-Band networks of major Agencies (NASA, ESA, CNES, NOAA, NASDA) which can be connected to the Control Centre for maximum visibility during the critical early operations.

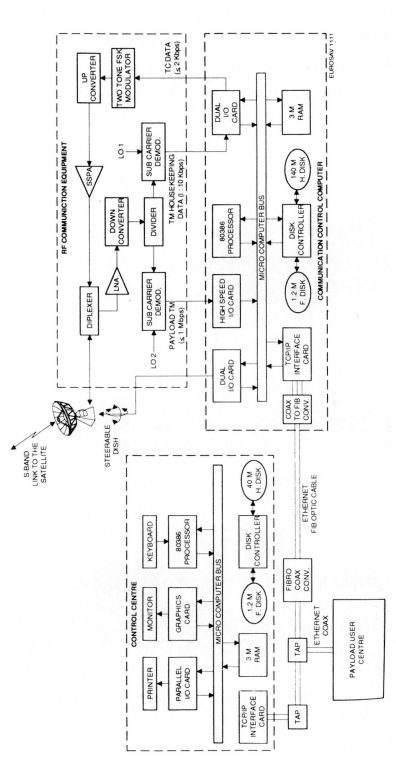

FIGURE 5/2 :   TYPICAL SMALL SATELLITE GROUND SEGMENT DESIGN BASED ON OFF THE SHELF HARDWARE

269

5.2. - PAYLOAD USER CENTRE

A payload user centre for small satellite missions will be either dedicated or will use the spare RF link and data processing capabilities of already existing ones.

The RF link is function of the data rate. If the data rate is very high, X band ground stations such as SPOT, ERS, LANDSAT Direct Receiving ones can be used, if it is low, as described previously S band ground stations can be used.

The data processing also is function of the data rate. For low data rate the data processing can be simple and performed by simple hardware and software tools. It the data rate is high the data processing capacity shall be large and for cost effectiveness, maximum compatibility with existing systems shall be a priority, only hardware and software tools are to be implemented.

FIGURE 5/3 shows the SPOT/ERS payload receiving station and user centre.

Figure 5/3 :   The SPOT/ERS payload receiving station at FUCINO can be use for small satellite earth observation mission. In the user centre only simple hardware and software modifications are to be implemented

270

6. - A SATELLITE FOR ALONG TRACK OPTICAL STEREO

A complete optical stereoscopic imaging system, able to produce accurate digital terrain model from a single orbit can be accomodated using the MMS-FSC class II platform

The overall system, depicted figure 6/1, is composed of the imaging satellite itself, a mission and control ground segment (S band station, control center and mission center), and an image ground segment (X band receiving station, processing center and interpretation means - figure 6/2).

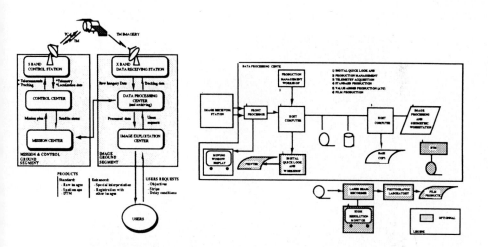

FIGURE 6/1 : OVERALL SYSTEM   FIGURE 6/2 : DATA PROCESSING CENTER

A baseline payload is a state-of-the-art push broom imaging instrument employing CCD linear arrays of detectors responding in the visible part of the spectrum.

Along track stereo is obtained with two optical heads pointing at 20° aft and fore, thus ensuring a base to height ratio of 0,7 for stereoscopy. Moreover, the relative accommodation of the two optical heads is optimized with respect to the considered range of latitudes targeted, and to the inclination of the operational orbit. This tuning allows to take into account the scroll of the ground under the spacecraft - due to the Earth rotation - during the acquisition of the stereoscopic couple.

Off track capability and in flight calibration are also provided.

The optical system consists in two identical refractive lenses mounted side by side on a common structure (figure 6/3). The 324 mm focal lenses are identical to those design and built by MMS for the IRS Indian satellite. The spectral band is optimized with regard to photometric performances, lens design (chromaticity) and thematic aspects. One CCD array with 4096 elements of 13 µm each is placed at the focal plane of each lens to achieve a total swath width of at least 60 km.

The in-flight calibration is performed by the sun illumination of the full aperture without complicating too much the design because of the small dimensions of the optics. The calibration system consists in a fixed diffusing halo screen.

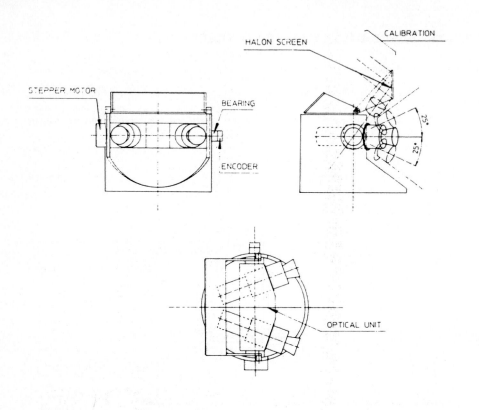

PARAMETER	VALUE
- Spatial resolution	15 to 25 m
- Field of view	+/- 3 to 5°
- Optical Head	2
- Along track stereo	+/- 20°
- Cross track capability	up to 25°
- Radiometric resolution	1%
- Modulation transfer function	20%
- Image bit rate	11 to 15 Mbit/s
- Mass budget	
with 2 lenses and off track	40 kg
without off track	30 kg
- Power budget	150 W (imaging)

FIGURE 6/3 : IMAGING INSTRUMENT AND ASSOCIATED PERFORMANCES

7. - A SATELLITE FOR ALTIMETRY

MISSION

Ocean altimetry from space, based on radar measurements, aims at determining the distance between the satellite and the ocean surface, see Figure 7/1.

This measurement allows to deduce the slope of the ocean surface, which is directly connected to the intensity of ocean currents.

Informations relative to wave height and speed of surface winds can also be obtained from altimetric measurements. Ocean altimetry is of interest for both military and civilian applications :

- Restitution of the mesoscale ocean circulation
- Knowledge of the Earth gravity field
- Monitoring of the general ocean circulation
- Contribution to climatology studies

The mesoscale ocean circulation restitution in the most contraining application in term of sampling requirements and calls for repetitive measurements to be made every 5 to 15 days with a spatial scale of 50 to 100 km. Moreover, the altimetric measurement must be performed with a precision of about 2 cm.

The above requirements can be met by a constellation of 3 small altimetry satellites flying at 800 km, based on the class II bus and taking advantage of the instrumentation experience acquired on the ERS 1 and TOPEX-POSEIDON programmes ;

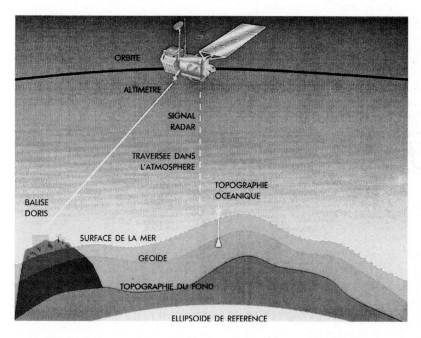

Figure 7/1 : the identical TOPEX/POSEIDON mission represents the culmination of the development of satellite altimetry over the past two decades. The satellite, jointly developed by CNES and Nasa is scheduled for launch by beginning of august 1992.

PAYLOAD

The payload, see Figure 7/2, is composed of :

-   the POSEIDON altimeter ;
-   a 3-frequency radiometer derived from the ERS-1 Along-Track Scanning Radiometer (ATSR) ;
-   the DORIS instrument

The radiometer and DORIS instrument are used to correct for the ionospheric and atmospheric effects which disturb the altimetric measurement.

Besides, DORIS allows to achieve the precise orbit determination accuracy required to exploit the altimetric measurements.

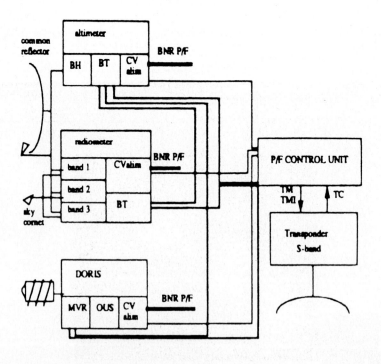

Figure 7/2 :   The payload is composed of a consistent set of instruments   benefiting form
the ERS-1 and TOPEX POSEIDON development and all contributing to the altimetric
performance

274

THE SATELLITE

The MMS/FAIRCHILD Class II bus is perfectly suited to the altimetry mission and payload requirements summarized in Table 7/1. The satellite lay-out is shown in Figure 7/3 which displays a three-module configuration :

- An aft propulsion module ;
- A central module which supports most of the bus subsystems ;
- A forward payload module with a deployable antenna shared by the radar altimeter and the radiometer.

The solar array appears in its fixed deployed configuration. In a stowed position, the satellite is compatible with a Taurus double launch.

Satellite budgets are given in Table 7/2.

	MASS	POWER
PAYLOAD	62 kg	110 W
PLATFORM	180 kg	60 W
ERGOLS (4 YEARS MISSION)	8 kg	-
TOTAL	250 kg	170 W

TABLE 7/1 :
SUMMARY OF MAIN MISSION AND
PAYLOAD REQUIREMENTS

ALTIMETRY	
Orbit	
Geometry	circular
Altitude	> 750 km
Phasing	+/- 1 km
Payload	
Altimeter	1
Radiometer	1
DORIS	1
P/L mass	62 kg
P/L power	
op	90 W
std-by	-
Data rate	2 kbps
Use	100%
Attitude control:	
roll	0,2°and0,015°/s
pitch	0,2°and0,015°/s
yaw	0,2°and0,015°/s

TABLE 7/2 :
SATELLITE BUDGETS

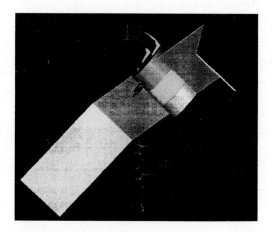

FIGURE 7/3 :
THE ALTIMETRY PAYLOAD CAN BE ACCOMMODATED
BY THE MMS/FAIRCHILD CLASS II BUS TO FORM A
SMALL SATELLITE OF ABOUT 250 KG COMPATIBLE
WITH A TAURUS DOUBLE LAUNCH.

8. - CONCLUSION

MMS and FAIRCHILD have combined their experience in space instrumentation and small satellite programmes to explore the potential offered by small satellites for Earth Observation applications.

The outcome of this work, which has been briefly presented in this paper, demonstrates that a variety of valuable Earth Observation missions can effectively be performed on the basis of existing instrument designs and on the basis of the MMS/FAIRCHILD class II bus.

Both optical and microwave instruments have been considered, selected for their modest mass and power requirements and for most of which MMS has a direct in-house expertise.

The MMS/FAIRCHILD class II bus is a multimission platform which is the workhorse of MMS/FAIRCHILD strategy on the emerging market of small satellites (150 to 500 kg) ; this bus benefits from the experience acquired by FAIRCHILD on the SMEX programmes and from the MMS experience on Earth Observation platforms in polar orbit : this bus already exists in a prototype form.

All the missions described can be realized whithin a short time frame and at a very low cost, enabling the deployment of a constellation of small satellites when required (e.g. for altimetry).

MMS and FAIRCHILD have been leading for now several years a consistent internal R&D programme to prepare themselves to become a major contender in the rapidly growing small satellites market.

Thanks to their multi-year investment effort, materialized by the existence of a small satellite multimission platform in prototype form, the so-called class II bus, and thanks to their experience in space instrumentation, MMS and FAIRCHILD are now confident that they can propose low cost small satellite missions which can complement more traditional satellites in a very valuable way.

Applications	Spectral bands typical	Spatial resolution	Swath width	Observation frequency	Accuracy (Location)	NOTES
AGRICULTURE Inventory Monitoring Control of croPs forecast	0.45- 0.5 mm 0.55 - 0.6 mm 0.65 - 0.7 mm 0.85 - 1 mm	20 to 30 m (Europe, Asia) 50 m (wide plantations)	100 km 200 km	7 to 21 days	256 levels 0.5 pixel	Acquisition delay and processing : < 4 to 7 days (Rapid access)
FORESTRY Inventory Tree height (Biomass) Damage assessment Forest management	0.52 - 0.58 mm 0.61 - 0.67 mm 0.8 - 1 mm (vegetal species)	15 to 20 m	100 to 200 km	10 to 30 days	256 levels (0.5 to 1 pixel)	Stereoscopic view needed for height and volume (short wavelength or panchromatic) -> 1/25000 scale
COASTAL AREAS & WATER POLLUTION Biological pollution phytoplancton	WATER COLOR 0.433 - 0.453 mm 0.510 - 0.530 mm 0.555 - 0.575 mm AEROSOL CORRECTION 0.745 - 0.759 mm 0.770 - 0.785 mm	Rivers and coastal areas 10 to 30 m	200 km	30 days	256 levels (1 pixel)	Aerosol diffusion correction
WATER RESOURCES (snow and ice) flood monitoring droughts ice/snow extent (topographic contours)	0.65 - 0.67 mm	10 to 30 m	200 km	7 to 30 days		Complementary to SAR data

TABLE 1/1 : TYPICAL RENEWABLE RESOURCES EARTH OBSERVATION APPLICATIONS AND RELATED CHARACTERISTICS

SMALL IMAGING SATELLITE
FOR EARTH OBSERVING SYSTEM ADJUNCT

Steven Kilston and Vera Kilston
Lockheed Palo Alto Research Laboratories*

Capt. Thomas F. Utsch
U. S. Air Force Space Systems Division+

ABSTRACT

As an adjunct to the Earth Observing System constellation of moderate-sized, long-life sensing platforms, a small multi-mission imaging satellite, which can efficiently complement and improve support to the data collection needs of experimenters, has been conceptually developed. The satellite's electro-optical sensing payload is designed to operate in many different data collection modes, to supply differing specific data needs at different times. Since the overall limiting factor to system performance is data downlink capacity, an operations mode allowing quick changes in the swath width, spatial resolution, and spectral bands being collected can optimize the system coverage for continuously varying data needs.

The system uses a 3-degree field-of-view camera, scanned in the cross-track direction (giving a maximum swath width, from a 700 km orbit, of over 1000 km) and up to 14 specific spectral bands (both panchromatic and finely-tuned), plus a tunable filter option, in visible and infrared wavelengths. A 45-cm aperture provides adequate resolution (5 to 10 m at 700 nm wavelength) and signal-to-noise ratio (for expected scene contrast levels). Proven technology is used to create a low-risk system design which includes low-disturbance reaction wheels, Si and HgCdTe detectors, commandable signal processing with data compression, and a reliable, high-efficiency thermal control system. Data would be delivered via the standard EOS transmission path.

The adjunct nature of the system allows experimenters to improve refresh periods for local areas where change comparison over short interval is desired. Deployment of the adjunct in an orbit such that its ground track followed a given EOS platform would allow virtually instantaneous data collection within an area of interest in multiple phenomenologies (e.g., synthetic aperture radar and electro-optical). The system would also be useful as an interim replacement in the event of lost EOS capability. The system is designed for short lifetime (3-5 years) to reduce unit cost and improve turnaround time of new technology into an operational system. The adjunct system funding can be adapted to tailor EOS budget profiles to meet varying funding availability. The system also could be used to support military data needs in event of a contingency military operation.

* Mail stop 97-10 / 201, 3251 Hanover St., Palo Alto, CA 94304-1191 USA
+ Mail stop SSD / XRF, P. O. Box 92960, Los Angeles, CA 90009 USA

1. INTRODUCTION

A small multi-mission electro-optical imaging satellite offers many advantages for improved remote-sensing data collection. Among these is its lower cost, a result primarily of its smaller size and economies due to multiple-unit production for many missions. Additional cost-effectiveness derives from on-orbit flexibility and commandability, for optimal and maximal system usage. This allows many operational modes, each including selectable scan rates to accomodate variations in intrinsic scene contrast, illumination, spectral bandwidth, and spatial resolution (pixel size). Rapid sensor pointability allows for repeated observations of a given location within single orbital passes. To conserve data stream sizes, readouts can be limited to appropriate choices of spectral bands, with coverage patterns or swath widths matched to scene locations of interest.

The basic concept for the Small Imaging Satellite (SIS) offers multi-spectral coverage in a wide range of resolutions. The SIS can fill an existing gap in spatial resolution (between 5 and 10 m), and can also acquire very-low-resolution sounding data with rapid coverage. It can provide multi-user, multi-mission support (even from LEO to GEO altitudes) with one basic design. Some additional advantages of this concept include system risk reduction compared to large satellites, due to a smaller cost for each launch; the rapid ground coverage and updates possible with a substantial constellation of satellites; and the ability to provide augmention and backup for many existing and planned satellite remote-sensing missions. Table 1 summarizes capabilities of the SIS to perform as an adjunct to EOS.

II.   BASIC EARTH OBSERVING SYSTEM (EOS) SATELLITE REQUIREMENTS

The need for accurate global climate change data to quantitatively measure whether climate change is occurring and what factors and substances are effecting the change is well established. Much of the data needed for the assessment is already being collected by operational space and ground monitoring systems. The EOS Program will greatly augment current data collection when deployed. Unfortunately, even with this massive data collection architecture, some environmental data needs will be neglected. As described in [1], most of the critical unmeasured data could be obtained by a smaller adjunct system. A smaller scale adjunct might even allow measurement of some of the needed environmental data before the complete EOS is deployed.

Use of small satellite adjunct platforms would also provide more flexibility to the EOS mission. If simultaneous measurements in many different phenomenologies were required, the adjunct observing platform (such as the Small Imaging Satellite) could be deployed to match the ground track of the main observing platforms to image the same areas in different wave bands from those of the main platform, or in a "tunable" fashion using the acousto-optical tunable filter (AOTF) on the SIS, and enhance temporal correlation of multiple phenomenologies (e.g. synthetic aperture radar and electro-optical).

TABLE 1:   Summary of Small Imaging Satellite Mission Performance

MISSION CATEGORY:	LOW-EARTH-ORBIT MISSIONS (LEO)	GEOSYNCHRONOUS MISSIONS (GEO)
Climate	Cloud Cover, Moisture Content Atmosphere, Sounding & Aerosols VIS & IR, 5 TO 25 m resol'n. Land and Sea Boundaries,Local Mapping, Snow and Ice, Agriculture, Visual & MWIR, 5 to 12 m res.	Cloud Cover-Global, Thermal Sounding Visual to LWIR bands 300 to 1200 m resol'n. Global Mapping Visible to LWIR 300 to 1200 m resol'n
Chemistry & Biological Processes	Ocean Cond and Produtivity, Mineral Ident., Pollution, Vegetation Condition Visual, 5 to 10 m resolution	
Orbit,Alt.; Range	705 km; 916 km	35800 km; 42000 km
Coverage	≤ 103° swath (1260 km), ≥ 4 s update; 0.75°-sq. starer, 0.25°-sq. tunable starer	20° diameter, 3° swaths 20 s revisit (2 s theater)
Scan rate, (°/s)	2 - 20 (data), 20 (slew)	8 (data), 10 (slew)
Wavebands (μm)	0.4-1.2 tunable, 0.5-0.8, 0.7-1.1, 1.0-1.3, 1.55-1.75, 3.55-3.93, 4.6-4.8, 8.5-9.0, 10.3-11.3, 11.5-12.5	0.5-0.9,3.55-3.93, 3.7-4.0, 4.2-4.3, 6.7-7.0, 9.6-9.7, 10.3-11.3, 11.5-12.5
Focal Plane Array: array size, detector material & (size, μm)	Panchromatic, f /7: 4123 x 56 Si CCD, (40) IR & Ocean Sensing, f/ 7: 3299 x 40 HgCdTe, (50) 1100 x 20 HgCdTe, (150) Land, etc., f/7: 3299 x 56 Si CCD, (50) Hi-Resolution Starer, f/15: 1024 x 1024 Si CCD, (40) AOTF array, f/10 393 x 393 Si CCD, (50)	Cloud Cover,Sounding, Land Surface Characterization, f/7: 3299 x 40 HgCdTe, (50) 4123 x 56 Si CCD, (40) 1100 x 20 HgCdTe , (150)

Based on the characteristics of data received from the main platform, the AOTF spectral transmission window would be modified to provide data on a specific environmental parameter thought to be critical to the observed data from the main observing platform. The SIS, being very easily tasked, could modify om command the collection configuration (spectral bands, spatial resolution, field of view) to serve specific niche data collections and serveing as a "workhorse" system supporting more efficient use of the more exquisite and finely-tuned main observing platforms.

Given that budgetary fluctuations exist and are unpredictable for all government programs, use of more or fewer small adjunct imaging systems can be useful in tailoring budget profiles to be consistent with funding availability at any given time and still ensure that the EOS would not suffer from data collection gaps. While not a replacement for an EOS platform, the SIS could ensure data continuity to maintain climate profiles and calibration of the data being collected.

Calibration is a large concern to EOS. The general technique for maintaining highly precise and accurate calibration over long time periods (15 years) requires overlap between successive platforms which measure the same parameters. The overlap also allows cross-checking of data between platforms to ensure data reliability. The SIS can assist this function by serving as the overlap measurement system between two successive main observing platforms in the event of an unavoidable gap. As an example, very high accuracy measurement of the sun's irradiance (0.1 percent calibration accuracy) is a key part of EOS. Use of secondary payloads on satellites of opportunity is the approach used by EOS to collect this data. While a cost-effective approach, use of secondary payloads introduces additional risk. An adjunct system like the SIS could be used for cross-checking with secondary solar irradiance payload instruments and ensure data continuity in event of unexpected failure of a host satellite.

Some climate-forcing parameters which can be measured with electro-optical imaging or sounding and provided by the SIS are: ozone (O_3) in the troposphere; water vapor; tropospheric aerosols, such as SO_2; spatial cloud pattern changes caused by emissions and pollution; and snow and vegetation cover.

As part of an international Mission to Planet Earth, the EOS is currently planning to field 17 instruments on a fleet of 6 different satellites. These all are to be flown in 3 copies each, with design, launch, and operational phases extending to 2017. Table 2 presents a summary of the currently planned concepts.

Having established how a small adjunct imaging system can complement the EOS main oberving platforms and what specific climate data needs to be collected, the balance of this paper is devoted to showing that a small imaging system can provide this data in sufficient quantity and accuracy to augment the EOS usefully.

III. CHARACTERISTICS OF THE SMALL IMAGING SATELLITE SENSOR

The overall design philosophy for SIS is to use proven technology for a low-risk system. The nominal design, based on the heritage of the RESERVES sensor (see [2]), has optics with a 45 cm aperture, giving a 3 degree field-of-view line scanner system, plus optional staring-operation focal planes (for imaging with higher spatial or spectral resolution). Figure 1 shows the optical layout and perspective. The design incorporates up to 14 spectral bands (visible-band to LWIR, both panchromatic and narrow) in a single integrated long scanning array (using Si and HgCdTe detectors), plus potential for a tunable filter (for hyperspectral measurements) in front of one of possibly two staring focal planes (with Si CCD arrays). Commandable signal processing options allow scene pre-filtering; together with use of optimal data compression, this keeps overall data downlink rates within reason, using the standard EOS transmission protocols. The system may include a learning/feature-detection capability based on advanced concepts in probabilistic neural network chips now available. A high-efficiency mechanical/radiative thermal control system can be expected to be reliable over the relatively short SIS lifetime.

TABLE 2: SUMMARY OF CURRENT EOS CONCEPTS WITH SMALL IMAGING
SATELLITE APPLICATIONS

EOS-AM-1	Instruments observe terrestrial surface: clouds, aerosols, radiation balance
	ASTER - ADVANCED SPACEBORNE THERMAL EMISSION AND REFLECTION RADIOMETER - images of land, water and clouds in 14 spectral bands within: 0.5-0.9, 1.6-2.5, and 8-12 microns - 60 km swath width - 15m-90m resolution
	CERES - CLOUDS AND EARTH'S RADIANT ENERGY SYSTEM - measures clouds and radiation flux - 3 spectral bands: 0.2-100, 0.2-3.5, and 6-25 microns - 21 km resolution
	MODIS-N - MODERATE RESOLUTION IMAGING SPECTROMETER-NADIR - measures surface biological and physical features - 36 spectral bands: 0.4-15.4 microns - 0.25-1.0 km resolution
	MISR - MULTI-ANGLE IMAGING SPECTRO-RADIOMETER - Cloud and surface angular reflectances, atmospheric opacities - 4 spectral bands: 0.44-0.86 microns - 1.9 km resolution
EOS-COLOR	Measures ocean biomass and productivity
EOS-AERO	Measures atmospheric aerosols
EOS-PM-1	Instruments measure clouds, precipitation, radiative balance, snow and ice, sea surface temperature, ocean productivity
	AIRS - ATMOSPHERIC INFRARED SOUNDER - ozone, temperature and humidity profiles, surface profiles - 3600 spectral channels: 0.4-1.7 and 3.4-15.4 microns
	CERES see above **MODIS-N**
EOS-ALT	Radar altimeter, 5.3 and 13.6 GHz Measures wave height, ocean circulation, wind speed, ice sheet mass
EOS-CHEM	Measures atmospheric chemicals and reaction products, ocean surface stress

The spacecraft bus will be a very low-cost design based on a standard small-satellite bus, with fairly high pointing-accuracy and low-disturbance reaction wheels.

Given the opportunities for EOS augmentation described in Section II and the multi-band flexibilty of the SIS to collect data in many spectral intervals, some of which are tunable on orbit with very high spectral resolution, a preliminary selection of SIS spectral bands is shown in Table 3. All of the major spectral channels for earth observation from near ultra-violet to 12.5 micron long wave thermal sensing are covered. The mode of operation of the system would be to vary the spectral bands being collected while varying the spatial resolution (using sub-pixel sampling or pixel aggregation to generate coarser resolution) and increasing or decreasing the swath width to remain within the limits of the data recording and storage system.

Table 4 presents a summary of representative signal-to-noise ratio calculations for the proposed SIS spectral bands, scan rates, and spatial resolutions. The spreadsheet uses scene and optics characteristics, sizes, and locations, combined with detector size and performance, scan rates or stare times, background phenomenology, and other relevant inputs, to determine single-pixel or time-delay-integrated signal-to-noise ratios. This can identify optics apertures and integration times required for each mission, to investigate potential designs for their effects on processing and satellite sizing. The attainable contrasts were adjusted to yield signal-to-noise ratios sufficient for accurate environmental measurements consistent with the accuracy of the EOS program. In general, low contrast levels are discernible with the proposed SIS designs, except when looking at dark surfaces, such as the ocean, in narrow spectral bands, where the photon counts are extremely low at the scan rate suitable for the other missions. Such missions can be run successfully by observing the very limited geographical regions where they are of interest, which allows greatly reduced scan rates.

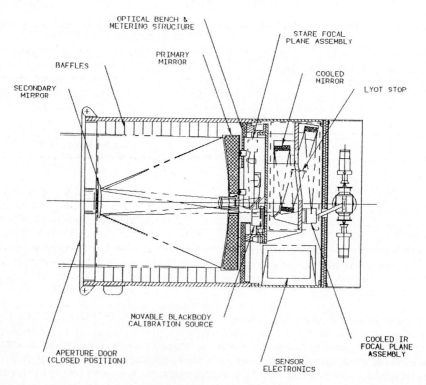

Figure 1: SIS Schematic

Table 3: Representative EOS Spectral Bands

BAND	WAVELENGTH(μm)	MISSION TYPES	PURPOSE
1	0.5 - 0.8	LAND SURFACE CHARACTERIZATION	HIGH-RESOLUTION IMAGING AND MAPPING
2	0.5 - 0.9	CLIMATE, LAND SURFACE CHARACTERIZATION	CLOUD COVER, LARGE-AREA MAPPING
3	0.4 - 1.2 tunable bands	BIOLOGICAL PROCESSES: HYPERSPECTRAL	OCEAN, BIOL., MINERALS, POLLUTION, ALBEDO, etc.
4	0.7 - 1.1	LAND SURFACE CHARACTERIZATION	SOIL MOISTURE, AGRIC., LAND/WATER BOUNDARY
5	1.0 - 1.3	LAND SURFACE CHARACTERIZATION	ICE AND SNOW DISCRIMINATION
6	1.55 - 1.75	CLIMATE	CLOUD AND SNOW DISCRIMINATION
7	3.55 - 3.93	CLIMATE	SEA SURFACE TEMPERATURE
8	3.7 - 4.0	CLIMATE	NIGHT CLOUD COVER
9	4.2 - 4.3	CLIMATE	CO_2 MEASUREMENT
10	6.7 - 7.0	CLIMATE	WATER VAPOR CONTENT
11	9.6 - 9.7	CLIMATE	OZONE MEASUREMENT
12	10.3 - 11.3	CLIMATE	TEMPERATURES
13	11.5 - 12.5	CLIMATE	WATER VAPOR CORRECT., TEMPERATURES

Table 5 presents an evaluation of the sizing and throughput of the entire focal plane array, needed for each mission, as well as implications for sensor dimensions, weight and power, and downlink data rate. Data compression factors have been chosen based upon current technology and data rate reductions attainable because data of interest may happen to appear only in subsets of the FOV or spectral bands. Continuous coverage swath sizes are calculated; although many platforms are needed for continuous coverage of the full earth from low-earth orbit (LEO), alternate operation can provide specific region coverages and revisit times.

IV. SMALL IMAGING SATELLITE SENSOR SUBSYSTEM DESIGN

The cross-section views of the sensor design in Figure 1 show three optical paths, which can operate at visual and infrared wavelengths. The slightly off-axis f/7 scanning optical path is relayed (re-imaging). This allows a cold-stop to minimize warm-optics noise hitting the focal plane, and helps greatly to reduce stray light.

TABLE 4: SIS Signal-to-Noise Ratio Analysis

MISSION · · · · · · · ->		Visual Hi-Res.	EOS Panch.	EOS Hyper.	EOS Albedo	EOS Land	EOS Clouds	EOS Temp.
MISSION VIEWING REQUIREMENTS								
MNW: Minimum Wavelength, μm		0.4	0.4	0.6	0.9	0.7	3.7	11.5
MXW: Maximum Wavelength, μm		0.8	0.8	0.605	0.92	1.1	4	12.5
RAD: Resolution/Accuracy Desired, m		5	15	250	30	30	30	120
PLN: Pixel X-scan Length at Nadir, m	F	4.18	8.95	7.83	7.83	11.19	11.19	34
PPA: Projected Pixel Area, sq. m.	F	17.45	80.15	61.36	61.36	125.23	125.23	1127
RAN: Observing Range at Nadir, km		705	705	705	705	705	705	705
TARGET & SCENE CHARACTERISTICS								
SCT: Scene Color Temperature, K		5900	5900	5900	5900	5900	300	300
TCT: Target Refl./Emit. Color Temp., K		5900	5900	5900	5900	5900	305	300.1
ETA: Effect. Target Refl./Emit. Area, sq. m.	F	17.45	80.15	61.36	61.36	125.23	125.23	1127.04
TPF: Fraction of Pixel Occupied by Target	F	1.00	1.00	1.00	1.00	1.00	1.00	1.00
ASE: Avg. Scene Emissivity or Reflectivity		0.2	0.2	0.2	0.2	0.2	1	1
TER: Target Emissivity or Reflectivity		0.22	0.22	0.22	0.22	0.22	1	1
IDF: Illumination Distance Factor (if sunlit)		2.2E-05	2.2E-05	2.2E-05	2.2E-05	2.2E-05	1	1
AIF: Atmosphere/Angle Illumination Factor		0.46	0.46	0.46	0.46	0.46	1	1
SFE: Spectral Feature Emission, W/sr		0	0	0	0	0	0	0
SRI: Scene Pixel Radiant Intensity, W/sr	F	349.64	1605.47	16.26	34.27	1477.65	20.77	1.0E+04
TRI: Target Pixel Radiant Intensity, W/sr	F	384.60	1766.02	17.88	37.70	1625.42	25.45	1.0E+04
TPC: TARGET PIXEL CONTRAST	F	10.0 %	10.0 %	10.0 %	10.0 %	10.0 %	22.6 %	0.1 %
SENSOR PROPERTIES								
APD: Aperture Diameter, m		0.45	0.45	0.45	0.45	0.45	0.45	0.45
f/#: Focal ratio		15.0	7.0	10.0	10.0	7.0	7.0	7.0
DIN: Detector length, μm		40.00	40.00	50.00	50.00	50.00	50.00	150.00
DCR: Detector width, μm		40.00	40.00	50.00	50.00	50.00	50.00	150.00
DAR: Detector Area, sq. cm.	F	1.6E-05	1.6E-05	2.5E-05	2.5E-05	2.5E-05	2.5E-05	2.2E-04
APA: Aperture Area, square cm	F	1590	1590	1590	1590	1590	1590	1590
OTR: Optical Transmission		0.7	0.7	0.3	0.3	0.7	0.7	0.7
QE: Quantum Efficiency		0.5	0.5	0.5	0.5	0.5	0.8	0.8
PJF: Photons/Joule, photons/s /W	F	3.0E+18	3.0E+18	3.0E+18	4.6E+18	4.5E+18	1.9E+19	6.0E+19
LDR: LOS Uncomp. Jitter/Drift Rate, μrad/s		100	100	100	100	100	100	100
JIT: LOS Jitter (1-dim.,1-sig.),μrad	F	0.10	0.00	3.50	1.00	0.00	0.05	0.14
GOB: Geometric Opt. Blur(Airy diam.),μrad		0	4	4	4	4	4	4
BLR: Blur Diameter(total,Airy eqvlt.),μrad	F	3.28	5.16	14.92	7.51	6.31	21.26	65.19
PXC: Pixel subtense cross-scan, μrad	F	5.93	12.70	11.11	11.11	15.87	15.87	47.62
PXI: Pixel subtense in-scan, μrad	F	5.93	12.70	11.11	11.11	15.87	15.87	47.62
BOD: Blur fraction on detector	F	1.000	1.000	0.919	1.000	1.000	0.920	0.911
SPD: Samples/Dwell		1	1	1	1	1	1	1
SCR: Scan Rate, °/s		stare	20.00	stare	stare	20.00	2.00	2.00
TIN: Integration Time, s	F	1.0E-03	3.6E-05	3.5E-02	1.0E-02	4.5E-03	4.5E-04	1.4E-03
SCE: Scene Electrons per readout	F	1.2E+05	2.0E+04	8.3E+04	7.5E+04	3.4E+04	3.3E+04	1.5E+08
SE: Signal Electrons per readout	F	11827	1976	7613	7535	3410	6812	1.8E+05
NOISE & PROCESSING PROPERTIES								
ABR: Avg. Bkgd.Radiance, W/sq.cm./sr/μm	F	5.0E-03	5.0E-03	5.3E-03	2.8E-03	2.9E-03	5.5E-05	9.0E-04
CLR: Clutter (1-sigma), W/sq.cm./sr/μm		0	0	0	0	0	0	0
BGF: Background Flux, photons/sq.cm./s	F	1.5E+13	6.8E+13	1.9E+11	6.0E+11	6.0E+13	3.6E+12	6.1E+14
CLF: Clutter Flux (1-sigma), ph./sq.cm./s	F	0	0	0	0	0	0	0
RoA: Detector Noise Factor		1.0E+06	1.0E+06	1.0E+06	1.0E+06	1.0E+06	1.0E+03	1.5E+02
TED: Detector Temperature		150	150	150	150	150	150	150
RON: RoA Noise, electrons/sample	F	36	7	264	141	10	953	12790
IEN: Internal Electron Noise		30	30	30	30	30	30	30
RE: Random Electron Noise	F	364	151	402	322	196	974	17687
CE: Clutter Electron Noise	F	0	0	0	0	0	0	0
TDI: Time Delay Integration Factor		1	28	1	1	28	10	5
SPF: Signal Processing Factor		1	1	1	1	1	1	1
SNR: TOTAL S/N RATIO	F	32.5	69.4	19.0	23.4	92.0	22.1	23.3
NEΔp; NEΔT: Refl.,%; Temp.,K	F	0.06%	0.03%	0.11%	0.09%	0.02%	0.226°K	0.004°K

TABLE 5: Small Imaging Satellite Sensor Parameters

MISSION - - - - - >		Hi-Res.	Panch.	Hyper.	Albedo	Land	Clouds	Temp.
CENTRAL WAVELENGTH, μm	L	0.60	0.60	0.60	0.91	0.90	3.85	12.00
ALTITUDE, km	L	705	705	705	705	705	705	705
RANGE, at maximum slant, km	F	916.5	916.5	916.5	916.5	916.5	916.5	916.5
DETECTOR FOOTPRINT (at nadir), m	F	4.18	8.95	7.83	7.83	11.19	11.19	33.57
DET. FOOTPRT. (in.-tr., at range), m	F	5.43	11.64	10.18	10.18	14.55	14.55	43.64
OPTICS APERTURE, cm	L	45	45	45	45	45	45	45
FOV LENGTH, °		0.35	3.00	0.25	0.25	3.00	3.00	3.00
FOV WIDTH, per band °	L	0.35	0.0407	0.25	0.25	0.0509	0.0182	0.0273
f / #	L	15	7	10	10	7	7	7
DIFFRACTION CIRCLE DIAM, μrad	F	3.3	3.3	3.3	4.9	4.9	20.9	65.1
DETECTOR IFOV, μrad	F	5.9	12.7	11.1	11.1	15.9	15.9	47.6
ARRAY LENGTH	F	1024	4123	393	393	3299	3299	1100
ARRAY WIDTH (TDI & STAGGER)	L	1024	56	393	393	56	20	10
NUMBER OF DETECTORS/ BAND	F	1048576	230903	154207	154207	184723	65972	10995
DETECTOR SIZE, μm	L	40	40	50	50	50	50	150
BACKGROUND, W/sq.cm./sr/μm	L	5.0E-03	5.0E-03	5.3E-03	2.8E-03	2.9E-03	5.5E-05	9.0E-04
DWELL TIME, μs	F	1.0E-03	3.6E+01	3.5E-02	1.0E-02	4.6E+01	4.6E+02	1.4E+03
SAMPLES PER DWELL	L	1	1	1	1	1	1	1
INTEGRATION TIME, μs	F	0.001	36.42	0.035	0.010	45.52	455.21	1365.62
MAXIMUM READOUTS/s/ BAND	F	1.0E+06	6.3E+09	1.5E+05	1.5E+05	4.1E+09	1.4E+08	8.1E+06
AVG. READOUTS / s (PER BAND)	F	1.7E+06	6.1E+09	3.5E+05	3.5E+05	3.9E+09	1.4E+08	7.8E+06
NUMBER OF BANDS / SPECTRAL REG.		1	1	4	3	1	2	2
DATA COMPRESSION FACTOR		4	4	4	4	4	4	4
DATA DOWN, MBPS	F	3	218	3	2	140	28	3
SPOT-TRANSIT LENGTH (in-track),km	F	4	37	3	3	37	37	37
GROUND(-TRACK) SPEED, km/s	F	6.76	6.76	6.76	6.76	6.76	6.76	6.76
SPOT-TRANSIT, or CYCLE TIME, s	F	0.6	5.4	0.4	0.4	5.4	5.4	5.4
SCAN TIME / CYCLE, s	F	1.0	5.2	1.0	1.0	5.2	5.2	5.2
SCAN RATE (BTH: whisk-broom), °/s	L	stare	20.00	stare	stare	20.00	2.00	2.00
SCAN LENGTH (Swath Width), °	F	0.35	103.14	0.25	0.25	103.14	10.31	10.31
SWATH WIDTH (contin.,cross-trk.),km	F	4.28	1269.05	3.08	3.08	1269.05	126.90	126.90
COVERAGE RATE/BAND, sq.km/s	F	18	8745	9	9	8745	875	875
SNR, at range	L	32.5	69.4	19.0	23.4	92.0	22.1	23.3
NEΔρ; NEΔT: Refl.,%; Temp.,K	L	0.06%	0.03%	0.11%	0.09%	0.02%	0.226°K	0.004°K

Figure 1 shows the narrow (0.3°) field-of-view dimension of the scanning optics; a view of the 3° field would show that the focal plane and relay mirrors are much longer in that dimension. The on-axis staring visual system includes a back end between the primary mirror and the relayed section of the scanning system. An on-axis Barlow-type lens assembly gives the optional staring path a high-resolution f/15 field-of-view (0.35° square); all other optical elements are reflective, for multi-wavelength use. The staring path includes a 45° fold mirror, which could easily be adapted to compensate for image motion or changes in focus. As the major optical elements are on-axis conic surfaces, manufacture of this system using highly lightweighted materials and structures should be straightforward.

The scanning focal plane array, with 10 fixed bands, is divided by a thermal isolator into an uncooled visual band section and a cooled (80 K) infrared band section. The large numbers of detectors in each pair of staggered-alignment rows are covered by filters necessary to define the spectral band for that row pair, with multi-color data received automatically as the rows all sweep across the scene. This wide-coverage FPA requires incorporation and careful alignment of many separate smaller line array sections, to comprise the entire long FPA. If so desired, early validation/experimental versions of the FPA can be flown with an even greater variety of spectral bands populating subsections of the array, to refine the choices of the most useful bands.

Signal processing development is crucial to success of the SIS sensor concept, due to its great influence on system weight and power. Ingenuity of design to make maximum use of state-of-the-art hardware is needed to handle heavy processing loads. A broad division of SIS sensor tasks into warning and mapping operations is useful to characterize objectives for the signal processing subsystem. For mapping in multiple spectral bands, huge quantities of data must be compressed and transmitted, so that high-fidelity images can be analyzed by equipment at ground stations. Processing for real-time or near-real-time data will require wide-band recorders or buffers. Special attention should be given to incorporating a re-programmable processing subsystem for sensor versatility and capability to perform multiple missions with a single satellite. Commanded by a ground station, changes in scene location, scan area and rate, and spectral bands observed could be made whenever situations demanded them.

Cooling required for the IR section of the FPA is provided by the mechanical cooler at the back end of the telescope; it consists of two Lucas coolers (minimizing vibrational disturbances) and the associated heat pipes. The cooling system also requires external radiators: one is sketched mounted on the telescope tube. For the sensor's hotter components, the mechanical coolers and processing electronics, a 0.25 m^2, 300 K surface will draw and expel 100 W of internal heat. A smaller cryogenic radiator (0.1 m^2) maintains the optical surfaces and structures at close to 160 K, dissipating their 3W of heat. A lightweight, rapid-readiness, FPA cooler with long storage life is needed for the SIS missions. In the temperature and cooling power regime of interest, the mechanical Stirling cycle cooler seems to be the optimum choice. It operates at a coefficient of operating power of approximately 100 W per W of cryocooling dissipation.

Reaction wheels are used in the SIS to minimize mechanical feedback to the satellite; current wheel concepts require no added power and less than 20% additional weight in the pointing and control subsystem. The two-gimbal scan system design gives a very wide field-of-regard. High resolution can be attained with a modestly stable line-of-sight (LOS), because the integration times are very short. Depending on orbit and mission, an absolute pointing system could be an option on the sensor or the satellite platform, using star or horizon sensors. Placements of gyros, as well as scan strategies with the LOS and mechanical subsystems, need clarification; apparent superiority of a whisk-broom scan direction and the possible need for image motion compensation should be decided. The mechanical envelope can be minimized with an expandable baffle structure. A good cross-gimbal wiring design is also needed.

Standby, average, and peak powers were estimated by summing subsystem contributions. Processor power is especially difficult to estimate at this stage, and will vary greatly with the missions and functions in operation. Continuing explorations of ways to perform processing functions at reduced power should be a high priority for the detailed design phase of the program. The power consumed by the payload varies from 120 W standby power to 370-600 W peak power for short duration. Total weight of the sensor payload is 112 kg. The total spacecraft weight is therefore 450 kg. Weight estimates assume a three to five year design life, with minimal redundancy, to reduce cost.

V. MILITARY CONTINGENCY OPERATION POTENTIAL

The main military applications possible with the SIS are: weather, cloud, ice, and snow measurements and locations; multi-spectral imaging and mapping of surface features; detection and tracking of vehicles and ships; warning of missile launches; and determination of ocean conditions. Arms control verification activities can be assisted by functional capabilities which serve the first three applications above.

Weather, cloud, ice, and snow measurements and locations, and determination of ocean conditions use the same spectral bands as those useful for EOS adjunct and backup missions. For military purposes, the precise location of surface and cloud features may be more critical than for EOS, so that higher resolution operation (with slower coverage) may be needed.

Multi-spectral imaging and mapping of surface features is possible with the SIS at much higher resolution than needed for EOS missions. For example, it can provide 5 to 10 m ground resolution (panchromatic band, at nadir, from an 705 km satellite altitude), with adequate signal-to-noise (S/N ≈ 32) for expected scene contrast levels (10%). Using the wide-angle, 3 degree field-of-view scanning array, 9 m resolution performance can be maintained over a continuous swath width greater than 1000 km. Vehicle and ship detection, while dependent on cloud-free lines of sight, is also possible with 5 to 10 meter ground resolution, and the IR bands provide detection capability at night. Incorporating well-studied SWIR and MWIR bands can give the SIS missile warning capabilities. The rapid coverage and quick revisits necessary for warning mission performance require a geostationary orbit.

A selection of bands appropriate for military use is listed in Table 6. These overlap considerably with the earth observation bands and can all be incorporated into a single SIS focal plane array, although the optional high-resolution visible-band focal plane will probably also be used for the above missions.

VI. CONCLUSIONS

A smaller flexible electro-optical system could serve as a useful adjunct to the EOS program. Providing improved revisit, area coverage, and calibration would be a useful complement to the main EOS observatories. An adjunct system also might be able to obtain critical environmental data earlier than the planned deployment of the EOS platforms. The adjunct also serves as a temporary back-up to EOS and can be used as a workhorse data collection system which can help to tailor sensing

Table 6: Military Mission Spectral Bands

BAND	WAVELENGTH, μm	MISSION TYPES	PURPOSE
1	0.45 - 1.0	VISUAL SURVEILLANCE, WEATHER	VISUAL MAPS (panchromic), DAYLIT CLOUDS
2	0.46 - 0.48	OCEANOGRAPHIC	BLUE - DEEP WATER DEPTH
3	0.50 - 0.52	OCEANOGRAPHIC	GREEN - OCEAN DEPTH
4	2.70 - 2.95	WARNING	MISSILE PLUME TRACKING
5	3.4 - 3.9	OCEANOGRAPHIC, WEATHER, IR SURVEILLANCE	SEA WAVES & TEMPERATURE, IR MAPPING, NIGHT CLOUDS
6	4.2 - 4.45	WARNING	MISSILE PLUME TRACKS, LATER STAGES
7	4.6 - 4.8	OCEANOGRAPHIC	LARGE SHIP DETECTION
8	8.5 - 9.0	IR SURVEILLANCE	LWIR MAPPING, TERRAIN, SHIP DETECTION
9	10.6 - 11.0	WEATHER	CLOUD HEIGHT, IR MAPPING
10	11.0 - 12.0	WEATHER	WATER VAPOR CORRECTION, LAND TEMPERATURE, IR MAPS

capabilities to available funding profiles.

This paper describes a small multi-spectral imaging sensor and satellite which can provide an adequate level of capability as an earth observation platform in obtaining multi-spectral images of the earth over wide swath widths. The system can contain 14 spectral bands from visible to long-wave infrared plus an acousto-optical tunable filter for further on-orbit tailoring of the spectral intervals collected. As a task-oriented system, the Small Imaging Satellite can be used to acquire various types of data with varying resolution and coverage area. The system can be operated in a dynamic fashion to respond to changing needs for data collection and to verify observations from the main platforms.

VI. REFERENCES

[1] Hansen, *et.al.*, "The Missing Data on Global Climate Change," **Issues in Science and Technology, Volume VII, Number 1,** fall 1990, pp. 62-69.

[2] "A Multi-Mission Sensor for the RESERVES Small Satellite Program", **SPIE Proceedings, Vol. 1495,** 1991; p.193.

MINI-SATELLITES ET ALTIMETRIE OCEANIQUE OPERATIONNELLE L'ADEQUATION

G. Bellaïche et JP. Aguttes

CENTRE NATIONAL d'ETUDES SPATIALES *

Abstract

This paper deals with the association of the concept of mini-satellites and oceanic altimetry missions.
First, it defines the most constraining missions requirements (mesoscale), and why mini-satellites constellation are quite adequate for such operationnal missions.
After describing the typical payload, the main mission-system compromises and the "economy" of the system, it presents the results of the satellite study.

Résumé

Ce papier traite de l'association du concept de mini-satellites et des missions d'altimétrie océanique.
Il donne tout d'abord le besoin des missions les plus contraignantes (méso-échelle), et montre la très bonne adéquation qui existe entre une constellation de mini-satellites et de telles missions opérationnelles.
Après avoir présenté la charge-utile type, les principaux compromis mission-système, et l'"économie" du système, il donne les résultats de l'étude satellite associée.

1.- ALTIMETRIE OCEANIQUE SPATIALE

1.1.- La mission

L'altimétrie océanique consiste en la caractérisation précise des diverses structures topographiques existant au sein des océans (ainsi que celles des glaces), et selon des échelles spatiales et temporelles variables suivant les objectifs.

Parmi toutes ces missions, celles qui nécessitent l'échantillonnage spatio-temporel le plus contraignant sont sans nul doute relatives aux phénomènes "méso-échelles", caractérisés par des échelles spatiales de 60 à 300 km, et des échelles temporelles de 10 à 30 jours.

Seul le satellite en orbite basse peut répondre au caractère global et répétitif de l'observation altimétrique; de plus, l'échantillonnage tel que celui imposé par les phénomènes méso-échelles, induit le besoin de plusieurs satellites en orbite simultanément; il faut donc ainsi penser un système spatial économiquement optimisé d'autant plus s'il s'agit de mettre en place un système opérationnel sur une durée typique de 12 ans.

1.2.- Les acquis

SEASAT a été le pionnier de l'altimétrie spatiale (1978), mais le satellite qui aura réellement consolidé ces objectifs et surtout permis le passage d'une phase initiale de "cueillette" d'informations (quelque peu aveugle), à une phase "finale" (à venir) de type opérationnel, est TOPEX-POSEIDON (lancé en 08/92), satellite franco-américain à caractère prioritairement scientifique.

Celui-ci aura tout d'abord permis la structuration et la consolidation, puis la validation en vol du traitement des données, à la fois dans le domaine bord (extraction de la hauteur altimétrique, corrections ionosphériques et troposphériques), mais aussi dans le domaine sol (modèles d'assimilation des données).

Il aura permis par ailleurs le soutien important de l'effort technologique en vue du développement d'un radar altimètre état solide pour l'instrument principal, et d'oscillateurs ultra-stables pour le système d'orbitographie précis.

C'est ainsi qu'arrivent maintenant à maturité la génération d'altimètre compact et robuste (en durée de vie) "POSEIDON", et le système d'orbitographie (et de positionnement) précis "DORIS", qui a par ailleurs fait ses premières armes sur SPOT2 (lancé en 01/92).

1.3.- Le futur

L'état de maturation tant au niveau de la maîtrise de la mesure qu'au niveau de la technologie instrumentale, permet d'envisager dès-à-présent des missions opérationnelles d'altimétrie océanographique, à l'aide de satellites en orbite basse.

Dans ce cadre-là, un certain nombre d'études se déroulent actuellement de par le monde, et nous présentons ici les résultats d'une étude inspirés de travaux menés par le CNES pour le compte de la DGA/DME française.

2.- ADEQUATION ENTRE ALTIMETRIE OPERATIONNELLE ET MINI-SATELLITES

2.1.- La constellation

Pour atteindre l'objectif méso-échelle, il suffit d'établir en vol une constellation de 3 satellites opérationnels (Cf § 3.5); ainsi il est possible de réaliser un échantillonnage sur traces montantes de 10 jours et 85 km, compatible avec le suivi des phénomènes recherchés, compte-tenu du sur-échantillonnage apporté par les traces descendantes.

2.2.- Cycle orbital et maintien de trace

L'approche mission classique pour extraire le signal méso-échelle consiste à utiliser des orbites répétitives avec un bon maintien de trace de l'ordre du km.

Dans un premier temps, l'accumulation de passages permet de restituer la Surface Moyenne Océanique (SMO) réputée stable, et qui pourra être retranchée lors de chaque passage utile afin d'isoler le signal méso-échelle; toutefois l'existence préalable de cette SMO (par exemple par une mission antérieure) peut éviter cette période initiale.

Il y a alors deux manières de parvenir à l'échantillonnage désiré, à l'aide d'une constellation de 3 satellites déphasés de 120° sur la même orbite :

- soit chaque satellite assure l'échantillonnage temporel par le choix d'un cycle orbital de 11 jours, le déphasage orbital des satellites, en multipliant les traces, assure alors l'échantillonnage spatial.

- soit chaque satellite assure le maillage spatial désiré avec un cycle temporel de 30 jours, le déphasage orbital des satellites leur permettant de se succéder sur une même trace avec un décalage de 10 jours.

Cette analyse conduit ainsi à la mise en évidence de l'intérêt et de la souplesse opérationnelle d'une constellation de satellites.

2.3.- La charge-utile

L'expérience acquise à ce jour sur ce type de mission conduit à la définition type de la charge-utile opérationnelle :

- un altimètre mono ou bi-fréquence réalisant la mesure de la distance satellite-surface de la mer instantanée avec une précision de 2 cm; l'option bi-fréquence permet d'obtenir directement la correction ionosphérique (phénomènes électriques); toutefois des modèles sophistiqués d'ionosphère permettent après traitements au sol, une correction de même qualité, et évitent le développement techniquement complexe de l'option bi-fréquence.

- un radiomètre tri-fréquence permettant la correction troposphérique (phénomènes physico-chimiques) par mesure du contenu en vapeur d'eau sur le trajet du signal altimètre, avec des performances radiométriques de sensibilité 0.3 K et de précision absolue 2.5 K.

- un système d'orbitographie précis permettant une restitution d'orbite de très grande précision : de l'ordre de 10 cm en radial après traitements sol.

Ainsi l'altimètre POSEIDON développé par ALCATEL ESPACE (F) est un radar altimètre bande Ku état solide (pas d'ATOP), mono-fréquence (13.65 GHz), compact (25 kg - 45 l), et relativement sobre (50 W consommés pour 3.2 W RF émis); on peut le considérer comme un instrument sur "étagère", son premier vol ayant lieu sur TOPEX-POSEIDON (08/92).

Quant au radiomètre nécessaire ici, il serait du même type que celui développé par MATRA (F) (et CRPE) pour ERS1, mais dans une version tri-fréquence (au lieu de bi pour ATSR-M), ceci afin d'obtenir la mesure de la colonne de vapeur d'eau subsatellite dans les 3 bandes principales (18.7, 21.3 et 36.5 GHz). Une étude de faisabilité a conduit aux caractéristiques suivantes : masse : 12 kg; volume : 7 l; consommation : 35 W; d'autres industriels possèdent aussi la compétence pour réaliser un tel type d'instrument, notamment ALCATEL-ESPACE en France.

A ces 2 instruments il faut associer une antenne unique à réflecteur quadri-fréquence : parabole hors d'axe Ø 850 mm; masse : 7 kg.

Enfin pour compléter cette charge-utile, le système d'orbitographie précis serait un récepteur DORIS bi-fréquence (2 GHz et 400 MHz), mesurant le décalage DOPPLER des signaux issus d'un réseau de balises sol réparties sur le globe (~ 45); réalisé par DASSAULT-ELECTRONIQUE, il est construit autour d'un Oscillateur Ultra Stable à 10 MHz développé par CEPE (F), et d'une antenne développée par STAREC (F); à noter que l'existence de ces 2 fréquences indispensables pour les corrections ionosphériques d'orbitographie, aide fortement les corrections ionosphériques de la mesure altimétrique; la génération actuelle de cet instrument (conçu il y a 8 ans !), a une masse totale (y compris l'antenne) de 25 kg pour un volume de 30 l et une consommation moyenne de 20 W; une nouvelle génération actuellement à l'étude doit permettre de ramener la masse à 15 kg et le volume à 20 l; le premier modèle vole depuis 01/90 sur SPOT2; le second sur TOPEX-POSEIDON (08/92); il volera à nouveau sur SPOT3 (mi-93), puis sur SPOT4 (lançable à partir de début 95), le tout dans sa version première génération que l'on peut considérer comme étant sur "étagère".

Ainsi l'ensemble constitué des 3 instruments, de toutes les antennes et d'un boîtier électronique de gestion des interfaces (10 kg, 15 l et 10 W) mène à une charge-utile de :
* masse : 80 kg
* volume : 100 l
* puissance : 120 W
et dont l'antenne principale a un diamètre de 850 mm.

Notons rapidement que le débit brut maximal pour l'ensemble des données charge-utile est de 1.7 kbits/s.

2.4.- Conclusion

Ainsi on voit apparaître une mission "self-consistant" qui peut être réalisée à l'aide d'une constellation de 3 satellites à coûts réduits en orbite basse, emportant une charge-utile optimisée de 80 kg; les satellites construits autour de cette charge-utile seront donc de la classe 200 kg : ce sont **des mini-satellites**.

3.- BESOINS MISSION ET CHOIX SYSTEME

3.1.- L'orbite

Compte-tenu de ce qui précède, le choix a été fait de la solution d'une constellation de 3 satellites dans le même plan orbital déphasé de 120° sur cette orbite, et dont le cycle de revisite est de 30 jours; ceci pour des raisons de gestion optimale de la constellation en mode dégradé (périodes à 2 satellites actifs).

Par ailleurs et pour des raisons de simplification du segment spatial (attitudes solaires constantes, perturbations d'orbite constantes, ...), il est choisi une orbite héliosynchrone.

La combinaison de ces 2 choix mène à un couple altitude/inclinaison lié; l'altitude nominale choisie est de 750 km (cycle 14+13/30), impliquant une inclinaison de 98.5° (orbite quasi-polaire).

Pour des raisons supplémentaires de simplification du segment bord, et du fait de l'indifférence de la mission à l'heure locale, il a été choisi 18h comme heure solaire locale au noeud ascendant; en effet, du fait d'un angle d'aspect solaire quasi-fixe, cette orbite présente un intérêt important tant au niveau de l'énergie bord par une simplification du GS (fixe), qu'au niveau de la stabilité thermique des équipements; de plus, cette orbite présente des avantages complémentaires comme la stabilité du plan orbital (variation d'inclinaison nulle), et même la possibilité d'avoir un mode survie héliocentrique "naturel".

Notons au passage que cette heure locale présente aussi l'intérêt d'une orbite sans éclipse pendant 75 % de l'année (à 750 km), et dont la durée, lorsqu'elles existent, est au maximum de 17 mn/orbite; c'est pourquoi le choix du noeud ascendant à 18h cale ces éclipses au-dessus du pôle sud et sur une période centrée autour du solstice d'été de l'hémisphère nord.

Enfin le maintien de trace requis par la mission est de ± 1.5 km à l'équateur.

3.2.- La zone de service

Le choix d'orbite permet du point de vue énergétique un fonctionnement global sans interruption, hormis pendant les éclipses.

Cette restriction est toutefois acceptable du point de vue mission car se situant au-dessus de la calotte polaire sud (zone d'intérêt faible).

Malgré ce choix, le faible débit de TM charge-utile associé à un réseau sol modeste ne contraint pas trop le poids relatif du stockage bord et du système de liaisons bord-sol; en effet, ce fonctionnement continu mène au besoin maximum d'une mémoire bord de 128 Mbits et un rythme de TM de 170 kbits/s pour 2 liaisons journalières.

Ainsi une zone de service globale et un fonctionnement continu peuvent être assurés, hormis pendant les éclipses.

3.3.- Moyens sol

Comme à l'accoutumée en Observation de la Terre, il faut ici séparer les stations sol de contrôle du satellite, et les stations de réception des données charge-utile.

Pour les premières, il sera utilisé le réseau classique de stations 2 GHz dont le CNES possède aujourd'hui 3 stations (et bientôt 4), réparties sur le globe.

Toutefois l'emport du système DORIS, donnant directement accès à la localisation SL, permet de réduire fortement l'utilisation de ce réseau au seul besoin TM/TC de servitudes; de plus le choix de l'heure locale 6h-18h se situe dans un "trou" de charge actuelle du réseau, puisque la plupart des satellites déjà clients sont calés à 10h30 ou 13h30.

Le centre de contrôle proprement dit sera spécifique à la mission; unique, il devra permettre le suivi et le contrôle de 3 voire 4 satellites en orbite (dont 1 éventuellement en veille orbitale); il devra notamment maintenir la "rigidité" de la constellation (position relative des 3 satellites dans le même plan orbital), ainsi que la trace au sol de cette constellation; il devra en outre réaliser les manoeuvres de mise à poste et de reconfiguration de la constellation (2, 3 ou 4 satellites en orbite).

Quant au réseau sol de réception des données, il pourra être unique; 2 liaisons de TM par jour sont alors suffisantes pour transmettre l'ensemble des données stockées à bord, via une liaison bande S (Cf § 4.6).

On notera pour mémoire que ces hypothèses de fonctionnement correspondent à une quantité d'informations égale à 600 Mbits reçus au sol par jour (pour la constellation).

3.4.- Le lanceur

Problème central des études sur les mini-satellites.

Si l'on dit qu'à ce jour le seul lanceur spécifique existant (devant encore confirmer sa qualification en vol !), est le lanceur aéroporté PEGASUS, on ne peut raisonnablement faire tout reposer sur cette seule opportunité.

En effet, pour un système opérationnel tel que celui-ci, qui doit vivre dans cette configuration typiquement 12 ans et par exemple au plus tôt à partir de 1998, quel sera le paysage des lanceurs dans environ 20 ans ?

Nul n'est capable de le dire !

C'est pourquoi une façon d'aborder le problème est de prendre comme contraintes de base (performances, volume, environnement) celles de PEGASUS, et de concevoir un satellite s'accommodant d'un lancement simple avec ce type de lanceur, mais aussi d'un lancement double (en satellite porteur) sur un lanceur de type TAURUS, et même d'un lancement triple (en grappe) avec un lanceur de type DLA-P (filière ARIANE).

Cette stratégie multi-lanceurs et multi-configurations permet de ne se lier aujourd'hui à aucune solution, et d'être suffisamment versatile pour s'adapter aux solutions qui émergeront ou évolueront à terme.

3.5.- La stratégie d'entretien de la constellation

Deux paramètres principaux pilotent cette stratégie :
- le lanceur avec sa capacité de lancement sa disponibilité et son coût.
- la "robustesse" du système, c'est-à-dire la tolérance de ce système à fonctionner en modes dégradés.

Pour analyser cette robustesse, il faut quantifier :

- le "service rendu", c'est-à-dire la qualité du service opérationnel en configurations nominale et dégradées.
- la "robustesse" du satellite lui-même, autrement dit son couple durée de vie/fiabilité.

C'est pourquoi il a été décidé d'analyser en détail (faisabilité technique et coûts), 2 filières de satellites :

- une filière dite "SL basic" sans redondances bord et à durée de vie modeste (typiquement 2 ans).
- une filière dite "SL consolidé" à robustesse élevée, avec redondances bord et durée de vie plus longue : 4 ans pour une fiabilité SL de 0.6.

De même il a été considéré 2 stratégies d'entretien :

- le renouvellement à date fixe des satellites (quel que soit leur état opérationnel).
- l'entretien de la constellation sur alerte.

Après évaluation du coût de ces 2 filières de satellites, l'économie du système complet passe par l'optimisation couplée de l'ensemble des paramètres ci-dessus.

S'il est possible de répondre à la question des coûts SL, il est beaucoup plus hasardeux de quantifier le service rendu; toutefois les premières analyses mission aboutissent au besoin d'une constellation minimale de 3 satellites actifs en mode nominal et de 2 en mode dégradé, mode ne devant pas abaisser le nombre moyen de SL actifs en deçà de 2.5 sur une année.

Enfin les simulations de l'économie du système ainsi constitué, montrent alors que la filière dite "consolidé", dont le coût unitaire SL est plus élevé que la filière dite "basic" (1.5 fois en coût récurrent), semble aboutir à un coût final après 12 ans d'exploitation plus faible que sa concurrente (Cf planche 1).

4.- DESCRIPTION DU SATELLITE

Notons tout d'abord que cette étude Satellite a été menée en collaboration avec AEROSPATIALE (F).

4.1.- Les options

Comme indiqué précedemment, il a été étudié 2 versions de satellite :

- une version dite "SL basic" (notée B dans la suite) sans redondance aucune (ni CU ni PF).

- une version dite "SL consolidé" (notée C) avec redondances au niveau CU et PF; ainsi compte-tenu de leur criticité respective vis-à-vis de de la dégradation de la mission en cas de défaillance, la CU est redondée de la façon suivante :
   * altimètre totalement redondé (redondance froide notée RF).
   * radiomètre partiellement redondé : seul le canal 21.3 GHz est doublé (RF).
   * DORIS non redondé.

Quant à la PF, elle est redondée de la façon suivante :
   * calculateur bord partiellement (redondance chaude notée RC)
   * certains équipements SCAO (RF) : le magnétomètre, l'électronique roue cinétique, l'électronique magnétomètre et magnétocoupleurs, et les tuyères.
   * l'électronique d'alimentation en énergie (RC) et la batterie (partiellement).
   * le transpondeur bande S (RF).

4.2.- Mécanique orbitale et sous-système de propulsion

Les premières analyses ayant conduit à un bilan de masse compris entre 220 (B) et 310 kg (C), et la capacité maximale de PEGASUS en injection directe sur l'orbite choisie étant de 200 kg environ, il s'est avéré nécessaire de rejoindre l'orbite finale via une phase de transfert sur une orbite 200-750 km, pour laquelle le lanceur actuel a une capacité de 330 kg environ.

Par ailleurs le besoin mission de maintien de trace imposant l'emport d'un sous-système de propulsion à hydrazine, celui-ci est dimensionné pour pouvoir aussi circulariser l'orbite (~ 20 kg).

Les différents postes contributeurs (circularisation, mise à poste, maintien de trace, veille orbitale, reconfiguration,...), mènent ainsi à un besoin total de 25 (B) à 32 kg (C), qui est satisfait par un réservoir unique de 40 l environ (capacité maximale 34 kg).

Ce sous-système est complété par 6 tuyères de 5 N, implantées sur les faces +X (vecteur vitesse), -X, et -Y du SL (2 par faces).

4.3.- Sous-système énergie bord

Celui-ci est architecturé autour d'un générateur solaire fixe de 2.3 m^2 à 2 ailes et équipé de cellules solaires AsGa, et d'une batteries de 24 (+2) éléments NiCd de 4 Ah délivrant une tension régulée de 28 V sous une profondeur de décharge de 40 % (peu d'éclipses).

Il peut délivrer en fin de vie 315 W de jour et 46 Wh en éclipse (pour un besoin de 35 Wh).

4.4.- Sous-système SCAO

Il est architecturé suivant un concept de stabilisation 3 axes par "moment cinétique embarqué", tout-à-fait adapté à l'heure locale choisie; il est bâti autour des équipements suivants (en version non redondée) :
- capteurs : 1 senseur terrestre + 2 senseurs solaires analogiques (grossiers) + 1 magnétomètre 3 axes.
- actuateurs : 1 roue cinétique (5 Nms) suivant l'axe tangage + 3 magnétocoupleurs.

Cette architecture "simple" permet ainsi de tenir les spécifications recherchées (Cf § 4.8).

4.5.- Gestion bord

Elle est architecturée autour de 2 boîtiers électroniques :
- une unité de gestion propre à la charge-utile, assurant notamment la fonction mémoire de masse de 128 Mbits.
- une unité de gestion bord de l'ensemble satellite (unité maître), assurant notamment l'interface TM/TC avec le transpondeur bord.

4.6.- Liaisons bord-sol (TM/TC)

Un seul transpondeur bande S (500 mW) est utilisé en 2 modes distincts exclusifs et programmables :
- un mode TM/TC de servitudes à environ 2 kbits/s 1 à 2 fois/jour/SL via le réseau 2 GHz.
- un mode TM Charge-Utile à 170 kbits/s 2 fois/jour/SL vers une seule station sol spécifique Ø 4 m.

4.7.- Sous-système mécanique et thermique

Ces 2 sous-systèmes ont bien-sûr été taillés "sur mesure" compte-tenu d'une part du volume alloué par le lanceur et d'autre part de la composition CU et équipements PF, ceci dans les 2 versions retenues (B et C).

Cela aboutit au niveau mécanique à un satellite de forme parallélépipédique à base hexagonale, antenne CU gerbée sur le coté (Cf planches 2 et 3).

Cette architecture et le pré-dimensionnement associé permettent alors le lancement multi-configurations et multi-lanceurs (Cf planches 4 à 6).

Quant au contrôle thermique il sera classiquement semi-actif (revêtements et réchauffeurs).

4.8.- Bilans

Toutes ces architectures conduisent aux bilans (comparés aux spécifications) présentés planche 0.

4.9.- Plan de développement

Un plan de développement a été établi et montre qu'il est possible de démarrer la mise en place de la constellation 4 ans après la décision de programme, ceci compte-tenu notamment du long délai d'approvisionnement des composants hyperfréquences de la CU (~ 2 ans), et du choix de réaliser un MIQ (EM) servant aussi de SL de référence sol.

Notons par ailleurs que la quasi-totalité des équipements PF ont été choisis sur "étagère" (sauf les cellules AsGa encore peu utilisées).

5.- CONCLUSION

On a ainsi montré que les mini-satellites étaient parfaitement adaptés aux missions opérationnelles d'altimétrie océanique.

De plus, les missions altimétriques les plus contraignantes au niveau échantillonnage (phénomènes méso-échelles), mettent encore plus en valeur la capacité des mini-satellites à voler en "flottille" et donc à permettre à tout moment un contrôle optimal de l'état du système, soit une optimisation dynamique de l'économie du programme.

Enfin l'étude satellite a montré la faisabilité de mini-satellites de 250 kg environ, lançables par PEGASUS, lanceur le plus contraignant aujourd'hui.

*   *   *

	Spécifications / Objectifs	Bilans (avec marges)
MASSE	Perfos PEGASUS1 : 330 kg	B : 204 kg C : 267 kg
PUISSANCE	/	B : 290 W C : 310 W
POINTAGE (R-T)	Contrôle : ± 0.45° Restitution : ± 0.21°	Contrôle : ± 0.36° Restitution : ± 0.15°
TM/TC	/	Servitudes : 2 kbits/s TMCU : 170 kbits/s (20 mn/jour/SL)
ERGOLS	Capacité Réservoir : 34 kg	B : 24 kg C : 32 kg
FIABILITE	B : ~ 0.5 à 2 ans C : 0.6 à 4 ans	B : 0.51 à 2 ans C : 0.62 à 4 ans

Planche 0

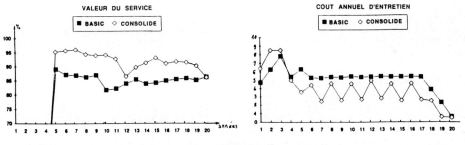

Planche 1

CONFIGURATION SATELLITE VERSION "CONSOLIDEE"

EN ORBITE

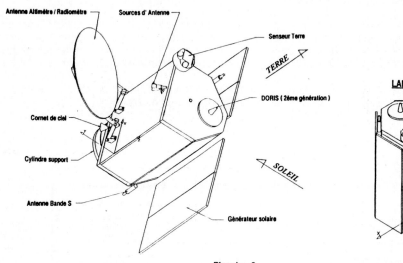

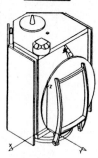

LANCEMENT

Planche 2

AMENAGEMENTS INTERNES

" BASIC "

" CONSOLIDEE "

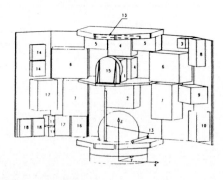

NOMENCLATURE DES EQUIPEMENTS			
CHARGE UTILE		**SCAO**	
1	UGCU	11	Magnetometre
2	DORIS boitier MVR	12	Electronique senseur solaire
3	DORIS boitier OUS	13	Magnetocoupleur (3)
4	RADIOMETRE boitier BH	14	Electron. magnetocoupleur
5	RADIOMETRE boitier TR	15	Roue cinétique
6	ALTIMETRE boitier BH	16	Electronique roue cinétique
7	ALTIMETRE boitier BI	**GESTION BORD**	
ALIMENTATION		17	Unité gestion bord
8	Regulateur	**COMMUNICATION**	
9	Boitier de distribution	18	Transpondeur bande S
10	Batterie		

Planche 3

300

CONFIGURATIONS SATELLITES

LANCEMENT SIMPLE PEGASUS

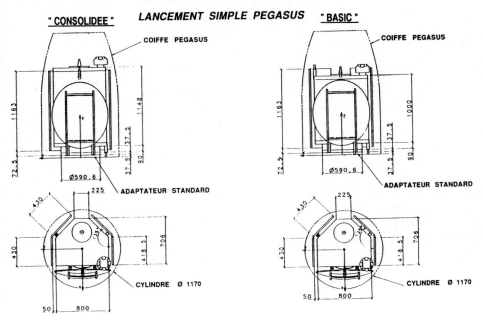

"CONSOLIDEE"

"BASIC"

COIFFE PEGASUS

ADAPTATEUR STANDARD

CYLINDRE Ø 1170

Planche 4

CONFIGURATION SATELLITE VERSION CONSOLIDEE
LANCEMENT DOUBLE TAURUS

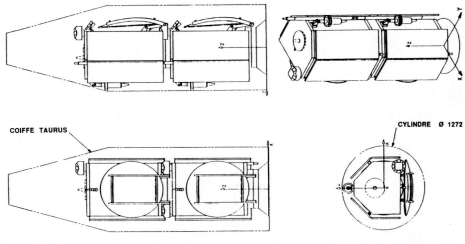

COIFFE TAURUS

CYLINDRE Ø 1272

Planche 5

CONFIGURATION DE LANCEMENT

301

CONFIGURATIONS SATELLITES / LANCEMENT TRIPLE DLA-P

(3 SATELLITES DE TYPE "CONSOLIDEE")

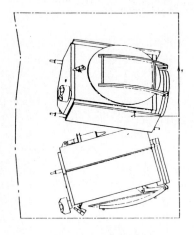

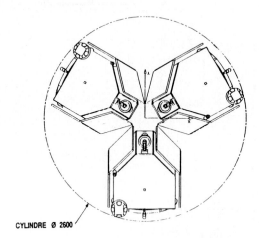

CYLINDRE Ø 2600

Planche 6

SYDONI

SYstème D'Observation Nocturne Intensifié

par

A. Colmon   M. Tissot   P. Turon

SODERN - Limeil-Brévannes

I.INTRODUCTION

La SODERN s'est spécialisée dans les équipements d'optronique spatiale. Son expérience acquise au cours des vingt dernières années lui confère une expertise reconnue dans les domaines des capteurs optiques de mesure d'attitude (capteurs de terre, capteurs solaires, viseurs d'étoiles) et les caméras d'observation des programmes SPOT et Hélios. Cette expérience lui permet de proposer de nouveaux instruments d'observation embarquables sur un petit satellite, tels que SYDONI. L'utilisation spatiale de la technique d'intensification d'image ouvre de nouvelles possibilités adaptées aux petites plate-formes.

II.L'IMAGERIE NOCTURNE

A.Avantages de l'imagerie nocturne

En l'absence de lumière solaire directe ou diffusée par l'atmosphère, l'imagerie reste possible dans le domaine infra-rouge à partir de 3,5 μm environ. Néanmoins les problèmes de mise en oeuvre sont très pénalisants : cryogénie à moins de 150 K, plans focaux très couteux, diffraction non négligeable pour les programmes à haute résolution.

Les techniques d'imagerie à bas niveau de lumière sont en comparaison très peu exigeantes et autorisent la prise de vue rapide dès qu'il subsiste un éclairement comparable à celui d'un quartier de lune. Une pupille de quelques centimètres et une caméra de l'ordre du décimètre cube sont alors intégrables sur un petit satellite pour une résolution au sol de quelques centaines de mètres depuis une orbite basse.

L'imagerie intensifiée peut fonctionner sur une grande partie de l'orbite. L'héliosynchronisme n'est pas nécessaire, la dynamique de signal accepté étant très importante. L'intérêt est d'ailleurs plus évident sur des orbites inclinées pour lesquelles le passage de la zone de crépuscule ne se fait pas à proximité des pôles, mais à des latitudes variées, correspondant à des régions intéressantes à observer.

Pour couvrir toute la dynamique d'éclairement possible en conservant un bon rapport signal à bruit, il est intéressant de coupler une caméra intensifiée et une caméra normale. L'encombrement et la masse de ces dispositifs est très faible quand on cherche des résolutions de l'ordre de la centaine de mètres. Il n'est donc pas pénalisant d'utiliser plusieurs caméras. Cela évite tout dispositif mobile (diaphragme réglable ou densité).

B.Ordres de grandeur photométriques

Pour fixer les idées, la nuit la plus sombre, loin de toute agglomération urbaine correspond à un éclairement de 10^{-3} lux, un quartier de lune à 10^{-2} lux, la pleine lune à 0,1 lux et la fin du crépuscule se situe vers 10 lux. La gamme d'éclairement visée, au niveau de la scène, s'étend de 10^{-2} lux à 10^4 lux.

Une optique très ouverte ($f/D = 1,4$) permet de transférer un niveau d'éclairement correct sur le plan focal : environ un dixième de l'éclairement de la scène, soit 10^{-3} lux dans le pire cas d'éclairement visé.

conditions	éclairement de la scène (lux)	éclairement sur le plan focal ($ph.s^{-1}.mm^{-2}$) à 550 nm
nuit étoilée	10^{-3}	3.10^5
quartier de lune	10^{-2}	3.10^6
pleine lune	0,1	3.10^7
crépuscule	10	3.10^9

C.Intensificateur

Il existe différents dispositifs intensificateurs. Dans les tubes de première génération, les électrons générés par la photocathode sont accélérés et focalisés par des électrodes pour être projetés sur un écran au phosphore. Un dispositif de couplage, généralement par fibres optiques, permet de lire l'image sur un CCD. Le défaut de ces tubes est que le gain est limité à quelques centaines et que l'image peut être légèrement déformée par la distorsion de l'optique électronique. La résolution est assez bonne. Les grandes photocathodes compensent leur mauvais rendement par une surface collectrice importante.

Les dispositifs de seconde génération utilisent des tubes dans lesquels est interposée une galette de micro-canaux, permettant un gain beaucoup plus élevé (quelques dizaines de milliers) au détriment de la résolution. La focalisation de proximité supprime les déformations de l'image. La galette de microcanaux permet de commander une obturation très rapide (jusqu'à quelques nano-secondes). La taille des galettes de micro-canaux ne permet pas encore d'obtenir des photocathodes aussi grandes qu'avec le principe de la première génération. Les modèles qui sont annoncés permettront d'ici quelques années de remplacer complètement les dispositifs de première génération.

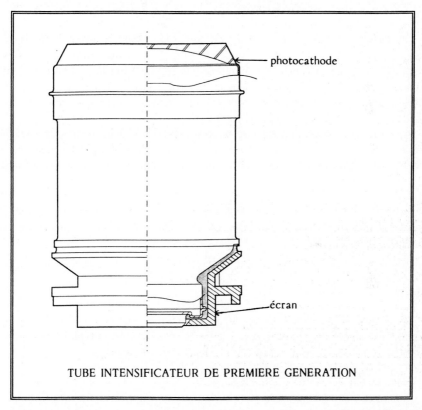

photocathode

écran

TUBE INTENSIFICATEUR DE PREMIERE GENERATION

Les intensificateurs de troisième génération se différencient des précédents par la photocathode qui est en arséniure de gallium. Le rendement quantique est alors amélioré. Il n'en existe pas encore de grande taille et leur durée de vie est plus limitée. Leur réponse spectrale étant étendue jusqu'à 850 nm offre d'autres possibilités d'observation.

Dans notre cas, le tube intensificateur de première génération offre actuellement le meilleur compromis sensibilité/résolution.

Une étude est en cours pour optimiser la technologie retenue pour la mission choisie. Les principaux facteurs sont :

- l'éclairement
- la durée de prise de vue
- la résolution
- le rapport signal à bruit nécessaire
- la fonction de transfert de modulation (FTM) exigée
- la bande spectrale d'observation.

La durée de vie de ces composants est de plusieurs milliers d'heures d'utilisation à bas niveau d'éclairement. Lorsque l'on ne les utilise pas, une faible tension de polarisation inverse suffit à stopper toute dégradation, quelque soit l'éclairement. Hors radiations, le vieillissement ne se produit que pendant la prise de vue. Il est donc possible de faire quelques centaines de milliers de prises de vue de moins de 10 secondes chacune.

Les prises de vue en plein soleil ne peuvent avoir lieu régulièrement sans précautions particulières (densité ou diaphragme). Un éblouissement accidentel pendant une prise de vue de nuit ou au crépuscule peut être évité en utilisant une mesure de l'éclairement incident pour couper la haute tension du tube.

La caméra non intensifiée doit avoir une optique assez fermée pour supporter sans éblouissement les scènes les plus lumineuses. Cela limite l'éclairement minimal à partir duquel elle est utilisable.

D.Rapport signal à bruit

Dans le cas d'un quartier de lune, minimum d'éclairement visé, on récupère 3.10^6 photons.s^{-1}.mm^{-2} autour de 550 nm, la bande spectrale de sensibilité maximale des photocathodes classiques. Les hypothèses de calcul sont les suivantes :

- photocathode de 40 mm de diamètre
- matrice : 500 * 500 pixels
- pixels de 20μm de côté
- diamètre du pixel ramené sur la photocathode : 50μm
- rendement de la photocathode : 0,1 électron/photon
- gain de l'écran : 100 photons/électron
- transmission de la fibre optique : 50%
- rendement quantique du CCD : 20%
- cadence de prise de vue : 15 Hz
- bruit de lecture du CCD : 100 électrons

Le flux incident est donc de 6000 photons par seconde et par pixel, soit 400 photons à la cadence de 15 images par seconde. Quarante électrons sont générés dans le tube, par la photocathode, donnant 4000 photons sur l'écran. 2000 arrivent sur le CCD et créent 400 électrons. Les quarante électrons issus de la photocathode sont à l'origine de 6 électrons de bruit ce qui, ramené sur le CCD, conduit à 60 électrons de bruit qui s'ajoutent aux cent électrons du bruit de lecture. Le rapport signal à bruit est ainsi voisin de trois.

Un CCD non intensifié et non aminci, ayant 40% de rendement, et des pixels de 20 μm de côté aurait à lire des paquets de 25 électrons à la cadence de 15 Hz : le rapport signal à bruit serait inférieur à 1.

Avec un signal plus important, le rapport signal à bruit s'améliore, mais est limité par le bruit de l'écran aux environs de 50. A ce niveau de signal, le CCD non intensifié fonctionne correctement et prend le relais. La transition a lieu aux environs de 100 lux. La figure suivante montre l'évolution du rapport signal à bruit en fonction de l'éclairement, pour les deux caméras. La courbe d'un CCD non intensifié avec une optique ouverte à F/1,4 montre l'apport du dispositif intensificateur.

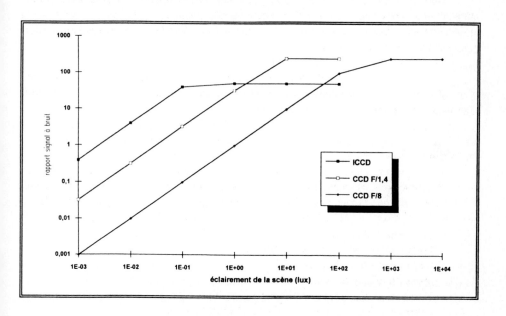

III.APPLICATIONS

Les applications possibles sont nombreuses. Elles couvrent tous les domaines où un suivi régulier est utile en évitant les heures pendant lesquelles un site n'est pas assez éclairé pour être photographié. Cette possibilité d'observation continue peut être utile soit pour augmenter la fréquence d'un suivi régulier, soit pour diminuer le préavis avant de pouvoir observer une scène particulière.

Il faut en contre-partie accepter une résolution dégradée par rapport à une prise de vue en plein soleil et un rapport signal sur bruit plus mauvais. La liste suivante, qui n'est pas exhaustive, fournit un aperçu des nombreux domaines d'application :

- météorologie
- catastrophes naturelles (tremblements de terre, inondations)
- feux de forêts
- éruptions volcaniques
- détection des nappes d'hydrocarbures sur les océans
- éclairage artificiel (villes, routes, aéroports,...)

IV.DESCRIPTION D'UNE MISSION PROBATOIRE

Nous proposons de vérifier les avantages de ce système de prise de vue sur une mission météorologique. Le suivi des phénomènes météorologiques tout au long de la journée est un complément intéressant des observations actuelles de Météosat. Les images obtenues étant de meilleure résolution, mais couvrant un champ plus faible, les applications sont tournées vers la météorologie locale.

Cette mission dont les besoins en performances sont modestes permet l'utilisation d'un micro-satellite et aboutit à un ensemble de coût réduit. On peut ainsi arriver à moindre risque à démontrer l'intérêt de l'observation intensifiée et la possibilité d'utiliser cette technique dans l'espace. La durée de vie nécessaire à cette démonstration est de deux ans.

L'utilisation opérationnelle du système décrit ci-dessous nécessiterait la mise en place d'un réseau de plusieurs micro-satellites pour assurer une fréquence de passage suffisante.

A.Performances de l'instrument

Les besoins actuels de la météorologie seraient satisfaits par une résolution de l'ordre de 600 mètres (la résolution actuelle de Météosat est d'environ 2,5 km). En utilisant pour la prise de vue une matrice de 500 x 500 pixels, on obtient des images représentant un terrain de 300 x 300 km.

La gamme des éclairements visés s'étend du crépuscule à un croissant de lune pour la caméra intensifiée et du crépuscule au plein jour pour la caméra normale.

La caméra non intensifiée doit être munie d'une optique assez fermée (F/8) pour restituer les scènes les plus lumineuses sans saturation. Sur les scènes les plus claires, le temps d'intégration est réduit jusqu'à 5 ms sans dégradation sensible de l'image due à la trainée pendant le vidage de la matrice. Cette caméra prend le relais de la caméra intensifiée à partir d'un éclairement de 100 lux pour trois raisons :

- son rapport signal à bruit devient supérieur
- le temps d'intégration du dispositif intensifié est déjà réduit à quelques dizaines de micro-secondes et nous sommes limités par la saturation
- utiliser un dispositif intensifié à ces niveaux d'éclairement réduit notablement leur durée de vie.

B.Caméras

Pour atteindre les objectifs de coût de la mission, nous envisageons d'adapter une caméra intensifiée existante. Le LEP (Laboratoire d'Electronique Philips) a développé plusieurs caméras intensifiées dont certaines sont adaptables à cette mission. Seule l'optique serait entièrement nouvelle.

La focale nécessaire est de 75 mm. Une optique ouverte à f/1,4 avec un champ de 21° est assez simple. La masse de l'ensemble de la caméra avec son optique peut être évaluée aux environs de 2 kg.

La caméra non intensifiée est encore plus petite. Les pixels étant plus petits, la focale est réduite à 25 mm. L'optique est moins ouverte. Sa masse est inférieure à 1 kg.

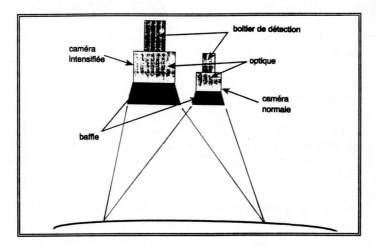

C.Contrôle d'attitude et d'orbite

Pour être certain de prendre l'image de la zone demandée, il suffit que l'erreur de pointage maximale se traduise par une erreur de localisation à la surface de la terre inférieure, par exemple, au quart du champ. Cela conduit, à 800 km d'altitude, à une précision d'attitude de l'ordre de 5°. Cette précision est accessible par gradient de gravité. Un couple est nécessaire pour retourner le satellite une fois en début de vie si il se stabilise avec les caméras regardant l'espace. C'est le rôle des boucles magnétiques. Le contrôle du lacet n'est pas nécessaire. Il suffit que la vitesse de rotation de SYDONI autour de l'axe de lacet reste inférieure à 2°/s.

Pour une application opérationnelle, l'inclinaison de l'orbite la plus favorable pour suivre la météorologie européenne est de 60°. La couverture s'étend alors jusqu'au sud de la Suède et de la Norvège et le temps d'observation de l'Europe est augmenté par rapport à une orbite quasi-polaire. L'orbite n'étant pas héliosynchrone, les conditions d'éclairement varient ce qui n'est pas gênant avec la dynamique des dispositifs intensifiés. La mission ne nécessitant pas de conserver cette trajectoire très précisément, aucun contrôle actif de l'orbite n'est nécessaire.

Pour ce type d'orbite, la figure suivante représente le pourcentage de l'orbite pendant lequel une transmission est possible. Pour une station en France métropolitaine cette durée est de quatre-vingt cinq secondes en moyenne par orbite. En pratique, la visibilité n'est possible que pour certaines orbites ; la durée d'un passage est de cinq minutes en moyenne.

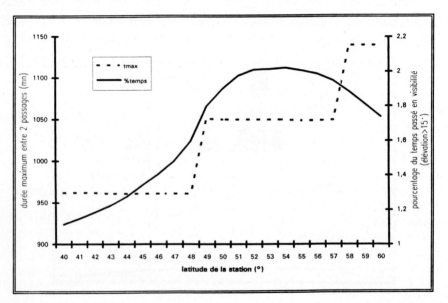

Pour des impératifs de coût, nous prévoyons le lancement du démonstrateur SYDONI sur la plate-forme ASAP d'Arianespace. L'orbite serait alors imposée par le satellite principal : le plus souvent une orbite polaire à 800 km d'altitude.

Le temps maximum s'écoulant entre deux passages successifs est de 11 orbites, soit environ 1050 minutes.

La date de prise de vue est élaborée au sol à partir des éphémérides et téléchargée au satellite. Cette contrainte pourrait être évitée sur un système opérationnel par l'utilisation d'un récepteur GPS embarqué. Une mesure d'horizon suffit pour connaître précisément l'attitude et choisir le meilleur moment de prise de vue.

D.Traitement du signal

La complexité limitée que nous désirons atteindre, et la puissance électrique disponible limitent le débit de télémesure. Une valeur de 20 kbits par seconde est accessible, ce qui permet de transmettre en moyenne 1,7 Mbit par orbite. Avec une efficacité de trame de 90%, on dispose de 1,5 Mbits de données utiles par orbite. Un algorithme de compression d'image moyen code un pixel sur 2 bits. Il est donc possible de transmettre trois images de 500 x 500 pixels par orbite, en moyenne.

L'amélioration du rapport signal sur bruit est possible en additionnant numériquement des images. Pour améliorer le rapport signal sur bruit de 3 à 10, il faut accumuler 10 images.

Le décalage, et éventuellement la rotation à apporter aux images pour les additionner peuvent être mesurés en reconnaissant des événements particuliers sur l'image comme des point brillants par exemple. Sur l'image suivante, les mêmes motifs sont recherchés au voisinage de leur position théorique pour déterminer la transformation nécessaire. Cette technique, moins couteuse que la corrélation en terme de puissance de calcul, se rapproche des techniques de visée stellaire maîtrisées par SODERN.

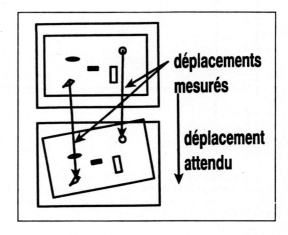

déplacements mesurés

déplacement attendu

La télémesure ne permettant pas de transmettre toutes ces images, le traitement doit être fait à bord. C'est à la portée des processeurs de signaux actuels. Il faut mémoriser à bord 10 images avant traitement. Si un pixel est numérisé sur 8 bits, la mémoire nécessaire est de 2,5 Mo. Deux méga-octets supplémentaires permettent de stocker 32 scènes après traitement et compression, en attendant la transmission. Ce volume est compatible avec le besoin de stocker en moyenne trois images par orbite pendant les onze orbites consécutives sans visibilité.

Tous ces besoins sont faciles à satisfaire en acceptant l'utilisation de composants militaires à la place des lots spatiaux qualifiés.

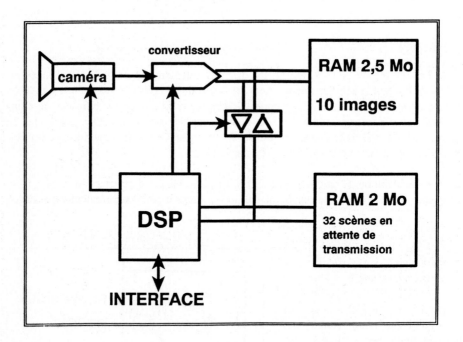

E.Plate-forme

La transmission peut être assurée dans la bande des 400 MHz, avec une puissance d'émission inférieure à 1,5 W. Cela nécessite de poursuivre le satellite avec une petite antenne pointée à quelques degrés près.

L'alimentation électrique est assurée par des panneaux solaires. La puissance crête nécessaire pendant la prise de vue et la transmission est assez élevée (plus de 10 Watt), mais cela ne dure en moyenne que 85 secondes par orbite (moins de 2% du temps). La consommation en veille peut être très faible (de l'ordre du Watt). Il est ainsi possible de fonctionner avec une puissance moyenne par orbite de moins de 3 Watt, permettant de se satisfaire des panneaux fixés sur quatre faces du satellite, de surface minimale 600 cm^2.

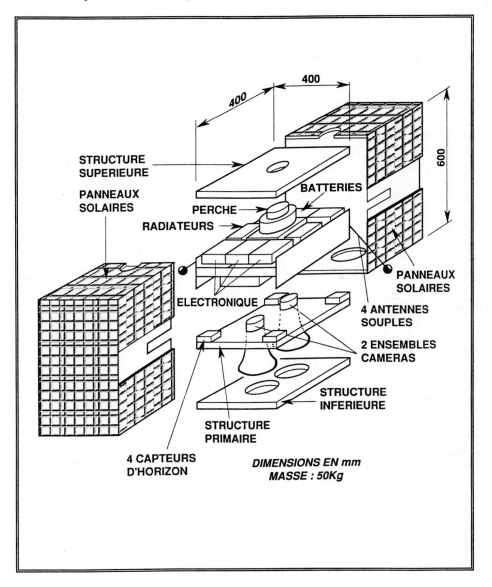

V.AMELIORATIONS POSSIBLES

L'objectif de la mission étant avant tout de démontrer l'intérêt de l'imagerie nocturne, nous utiliserons pour la plate-forme le maximum d'éléments existants. Au delà de cette mission probatoire, et en vue de missions opérationnelles ultérieures, de nombreuses améliorations de performances sont possibles.

A.Augmentation du rapport signal à bruit

La technologie des CCDs intensifiés progresse dans deux directions :

- photocathodes AsGa, dites de troisième génération
- augmentation du diamètre utile

Cette seconde voie semble la plus prometteuse pour l'observation par satellite. Elle permet d'améliorer la résolution par augmentation de la surface collectrice. Des photocathodes de 70 mm sont possibles : elles offrent un gain de FTM de 50% ainsi qu'une augmentation sensible du rapport signal à bruit. Des dispositifs de seconde génération de même taille commencent à apparaître. Ils offrent notamment des possibilités d'obturation plus rapides.

Les EB-CCD (Electron Bombarded CCD) font partie des voies d'avenir. Il s'agit d'un tube intensificateur dont l'écran photo-émissif est directement remplacé par un CCD. Celui-ci étant "éclairé" par des électrons et non par des photons, l'efficacité du système est améliorée en exposant sa face arrière. Le substrat doit être aminci. Ces dispositifs sont développés par le LEP. Ils ne sont pas encore disponibles mais promettent des performances intéressantes en gain et résolution.

B.Augmentation du champ et de la résolution

Ces deux exigences contradictoires passent par une augmentation du nombre de lignes que l'on peut résoudre sur la photocathode. Des productions spéciales utilisant de très grandes photocathodes associées à un CCD d'au moins 10^6 pixels sont envisageables sur des projets plus ambitieux et aussi plus couteux. Les besoins en contrôle d'attitude et en traitement de l'information à bord seraient augmentés.

C.Amélioration du contrôle d'attitude

La mission probatoire se satisfait d'une stabilisation passive peu performante. Un contrôle précis du lacet permettrait l'intégration par report de ligne (TDI) si les autres mouvements étaient suffisamment lents. L'influence du bruit de lecture du CCD serait ainsi diminuée.

Enfin des missions d'observation à haute résolution sont envisageables avec une plateforme très stable qui permettrait un traitement du signal analogique des scènes à très bas niveau de lumière. Il serait alors possible de couvrir la quasi-totalité des conditions d'éclairement.

D.Fréquence de prise de vue

Les aspects opérationnels de cette mission peuvent être améliorés en augmentant le nombre de satellites, ce qui améliore la fréquence de passage. Le nombre d'images prises par le satellite n'est limité que par la transmission des images par la télémesure et la mémoire de stockage. Cela peut être amélioré en augmentant le nombre de stations terriennes (stations de réception dans plusieurs stations météorologiques). Une puissance électrique plus importante permettrait également d'augmenter le débit de la télémesure.

Les progrès dans les algorithmes de compression d'images devraient permettre de diminuer les quantités d'information à stocker et à transmettre.

VI.CONCLUSION

Nous avons montré qu'il est possible d'obtenir des images de la terre dans le domaine visible quasiment sans interruption, depuis une orbite basse. La simplicité et le faible encombrement des dispositifs intensifiés permet d'adapter cette mission à des petits satellites. Le besoin de puissances de calcul importantes embarquées est évident pour ce type de mission. L'utilisation intensive de techniques de traitement d'images permet une prise de vue utile depuis des petites plate-formes.

Bien que fournissant des images moins résolues, la prise de vue nocturne ouvre de nouvelles possibilités d'observation qui devraient trouver des applications variées. On propose de valider les possibilités offertes par cette technique dans le cadre d'une mission probatoire sur un micro-satellite.

SYNTHESE DE LA SESSION
OBSERVATION DE LA TERRE

Depuis quelques années les programmes d'observation de la Terre font appel à des satellites de plus en plus lourds embarquant de nombreux instruments pour satisfaire des missions variées. Cette tendance, pour des raisons diverses (analyse de mission, raisons budgétaires, programmatiques...) s'est arrêtée voire inversée faisant appel à des satellites dédiés à une mission principale, par ailleurs les progrès de la technologie permettent de proposer des charges utiles et des plates-formes de taille réduite permettant de satisfaire certaines des missions précédentes.

Cette session, dédiée à l'observation de la Terre par minisatellite, a donné lieu à divers exposés en provenance d'agence spatiale (le CNES), de l'U.S. Air Force et d'industriels (Matra-Marconi Space et SODERN). Suite à ces présentations et aux discussions, il apparaît que les minisatellites sont particulièrement adaptés à la satisfaction d'une mission ou d'un service spécifique à l'échelle régionale ou à l'échelle mondiale en permettant l'optimisation d'une mission au moindre coût par le meilleur choix des paramètres (heure locale, orbite) et l'adéquation entre les besoins et les ressources. Ils autorisent une meilleure flexibilité (date de lancement, nombre de modèles déployés) et devraient permettre un délai plus court entre la définition de la mission et le lancement du satellite.

Plusieurs utilisations peuvent être envisagées :

– complémentarité avec un programme conventionnel,
– en redondance d'une charge utile défaillante embarquée sur un satellite multi-instruments, ils doivent, dans ce cas, être intégrés dans la conception système dès la phase de définition,
– concept autonome.

Les grands systèmes spatiaux, à cause du coût élevé induit par toutes les étapes du développement, doivent avoir des durées de vie élevées, les mini satellites dont les coûts de développement et de lancement sont plus faibles sont mieux à même de garantir des missions expérimentales de durée de vie plus courte, permettant soit de valider des technologies, soit de préparer des missions opérationnelles de plus longue durée.

Néanmoins un système d'observation de la Terre ne se limite pas au segment spatial, toutes les autres fonctions -calibration des instruments, qualité de la réception, archivage et distribution des données - doivent être remplies de façon à garantir des données utilisables et un système d'observation doit se concevoir comme un ensemble cohérent.

En conclusion, l'émergence des minisatellites -suite à une phase de maturation des produits offerts et à des analyses de missions adaptées, devraient permettre de satisfaire des missions et des services adaptés à des classes d'utilisateurs très variées dans le domaine de l'observation de la Terre.

SYNTHESIS OF THE SESSION
EARTH OBSERVATION

For some years, Earth observation programmes have been calling on ever heavier satellites carrying a large number of instruments to satisfy varied missions. For several reasons (mission analysis, budgets, programmes, etc.), this trend has been halted and even reversed, to bring into play satellites dedicated to one main mission. Moreover, technological progress has made available small payloads and platforms capable of fulfilling certain of the previous missions.

This session, devoted to Earth observation by mini-satellite, was the occasion for various talks from space agencies (CNES), the U.S. Airforce, and industry (Matra Marconi Space and SODERN).

From these presentations and the discussions that followed, it appears that mini-satellites are particularly apt to fulfil a mission or provide a specific service on a regional or world scale by optimizing a low-cost mission thanks to the best choice of parameters (local time and orbit) and the matching of needs and resources. They afford greater flexibility (launch date and number of models deployed) and should enable the delay between mission definition and satellite launch to be shortened.

Several uses can be envisaged:

– complementary with a conventional programme;
– as a backup to an ailing payload on a multi-instrument satellite. In this case, they must be integrated into the system design from the definition phase;
– independent concept.

Because of high costs induced by all the development stages, large space systems must have long lifetimes, whereas mini-satellites, with their lower development and launch costs, are in a better position to carry out shorter lifetime experimental missions that either validate technologies or prepare operational missions of longer duration.

Nevertheless, an Earth observation system is not limited to the space segment. All the other functions – instrument calibration, reception quality, data archiving and distribution – must be present in order to guarantee usable data, and an observation system has to be designed as a coherent whole.

In conclusion, the emergence of mini-satellites – following a phase where the products on offer reach maturity, and the right mission analyses – should provide missions and services suited to a wide variety of classes of users in the Earth observation field.

SESSION V

MOYENS SOLS

GROUND INFRASTRUCTURE

A PROPOSED GROUND SEGMENT DESIGN FOR SMALL SATELLITES

R.S.Thompson, C.J.Ashton and A.N.Pidgeon

VEGA Space Systems Engineering Ltd., Arden Grove, Harpenden, Herts., AL5 4SJ, England.

ABSTRACT

A number of missions involving small, low cost satellites are currently being planned or under development. The design of these missions is driven by the costs of the spacecraft, the launch, the ground segment and operations. This paper proposes a low cost ground segment comprising an integrated spacecraft control system and ground station, based largely on commercial hardware and making use of modern software technology. The feasibility, realiability, operations, hardware and software issues of such a system are discussed, as well as the potential cost savings which it could give.

1. INTRODUCTION

The monitoring and control of satellites has traditionally been performed by complex ground segments with expensive and lengthy development and implementation programmes. The scope of the ground segment includes the receiving/transmitting ground station(s), satellite control centre(s) and, where these are not co-located, the communications links between the two.

For small satellite missions, typically conducted within tight budget constraints by organisations not necessarily experienced in satellite operations, there is a requirement for an integrated ground segment, capable of processing and uplinking telecommands, receiving and processing telemetry, and providing facilities for on-line monitoring and control of the spacecraft and its payload. Depending on the nature of the mission and the design of the spacecraft, there may also be a requirement for tracking, orbit analysis, attitude reconstitution and manoeuvre planning.

This paper presents an approach for a low cost ground segment for geostationary and low Earth orbiting satellites. The approach presented is modular, in that alternative implementation options are identified for the main components, together with supporting cost and reliability trade-offs.

The scope of the paper includes the antenna, RF and baseband components of the ground station, and hardware and software solutions for satellite monitoring and control. Solutions based on current workstation technology and modern software techniques are considered. Elements which can be procured commercially, and those which need to be specially developed for the application are identified.

2. CHARACTERISTICS OF SMALL SATELLITE MISSIONS

Within Europe, many small satellites missions are associated with national space programmes and academic institutions. A common feature of small satellite missions is a desire to minimise costs, and this generally applies to all aspects of the mission: satellite, launch, ground segment and operations. Proposals exist for satellites to support a wide range of applications, including: space sciences; earth observation; environmental monitoring; microgravity; and low-cost communications systems.

The majority of small satellites are placed into Low Earth (**LEO**) or Geostationary Transfer Orbits (**GTO**), possibly as an auxiliary payload together with a larger satellite. Many have no capability for orbital correction, relying solely on the orbital injection precision of the launch vehicle. Attitude control may be provided by devices such as magnetorquers. In some instances, the concept of on-board orbit determination, using a Global Positioning Satellite (**GPS**) receiver, has been proposed. This removes the requirement for ranging of the satellite from the ground.

The resultant mission profile from the ground segment's viewpoint is, therefore, often one of periodic contact, with variable pass lengths. This requires steerable antenna with some form of automatic tracking. On-board data storage is frequently used, such that data can be downlinked when the satellite is in view of the ground station. This may imply higher data rates, with real-time data interleaved with the playback data, although total rates are not excessive. Telecommand schedules will normally be prepared in advance, for semi-automated uplink during the contact period.

Low-cost geostationary missions, featuring permanent ground contact and a capability for station-keeping, are also included in the discussion of architectures for low-cost ground segments. However, space segments comprising constellations of many small satellites are not considered, as the total mission costs may warrant greater investment in the ground segment.

3. APPROACH TO THE GROUND SEGMENT

The objective is to minimise the cost of the ground segment. It must be cheap to build, cheap to house, cheap to maintain, and cheap to operate! The proposed approach is to base the ground segment on small, standard and, wherever possible, "off-the-shelf" components. The use of standard hardware particularly applies to computer systems.

To minimise the implementation costs for an individual mission, the intention is to produce a highly modular generic architecture, both in terms of the hardware and software components, such that a mission specific system can be rapidly configured from standard elements.

The traditional requirement, particularly in Europe, for high availability, high reliability systems can be relaxed. It is assumed that a higher proportion of system down-time is acceptable, and that satellites will be capable of surviving for extended periods without ground contact (although any data down-linked during such periods would be lost). Redundant ground segment units are not provided by default, rather the availability and reliability of the system is maximised by using well tried and tested, commercially produced equipment.

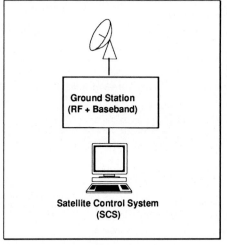

Figure 1 : Small Satellite Ground Segment

The removal of internal redundancy from the generic architecture simplifies the internal structure of the system, reducing overall costs by more than the cost of the redundant units alone, as there is no requirement for internal switching. If system reliability is a priority, then this can be provided by a duplicate system, possibly at an alternative site.

Operationally, there are significant implications of the need to minimise costs. For LEO and GTO missions, contact periods will be spread throughout the day, geostationary missions will be in permanent contact. In Europe, satellites are traditionally controlled around the clock. With a legal minimum of two people per shift, this can lead to an excessively large operations team, which is likely to be unacceptable for a small satellite mission. Consequently, satellites are more likely to be controlled on an intermittent basis, by a small operations team. The lack of permanent coverage implies control by exception and greater flexibility in the advance preparation of operational procedures (or command schedules) for automated up-link when no operations staff are present.

If this is to be performed with the same degree of security of operations, then this may actually necessitate more sophisticated automated operations tools than are normally found in larger satellite control centres, increasing the complexity of the ground control software.

The ground segment is made up of two main elements: the Ground Station and the Satellite Control System [see fig. 1].

The Ground Station comprises the antenna, radio frequency (**RF**) and baseband systems necessary for telemetry reception, tracking and commanding.

The Satellite Control System (**SCS**) is essentially a software system hosted on commercially available workstation computers. It performs telemetry processing and command scheduling functions, and provides the man-machine interface (**MMI**) for the satellite operator. It may also provide support for automated operations.

The two elements are assumed to be co-located, to avoid the requirement for long-distance communications links. The interface is at the level of a synchronised digital bit stream. The following sections describe each element in turn.

4. GROUND STATION ELEMENT

4.1. Background

Historically satellite Telemetry, Tracking and Command (**TT&C**) services have been associated with large ground stations, typically having antennas of greater than 10 metres diameter. This association was originally a consequence of the link performance - large ground stations were required to reliably reconstitute the weak radio signals received from satellites. Indeed with power levels of less than 1 Watt being transmitted from a spacecraft some 40,000 km distant, it is not surprising that large ground stations were required.

Since the early days of satellite communications the size of ground station antennas has consistently decreased, to the extent that there are now large numbers of small Television Receive Only (**TVRO**) antennas on houses throughout Europe. This is partly because of an increase in the power transmitted from satellites and partly because of improvements in ground equipment performance. These factors have not led to a commensurate reduction in TT&C ground station antenna size for a number of reasons.

The conservatism of TT&C operators led to larger operating margins being used. Thus improved satellite and ground station performance was reflected in a reduction in the probability of losing contact with the satellite during adverse weather conditions (for instance thunderstorms at the ground station site). Although such an approach may be prudent when dealing with a $50M spacecraft, few modern spacecraft would suffer should their command and telemetry links be lost every time a thunderstorm occurred at the TT&C station.

A second reason for using large TT&C antennas is that of angle tracking. One of the functions of a TT&C station is to accurately determine the orbit of the satellite. This is done by measuring the distance and angular extent of the satellite over a period of time, and putting them into a computer model. This requires the TT&C stations to be able to measure the azimuth and elevation of the satellite to great accuracy, typically ±0.01°. The tracking accuracy of an antenna is defined by several factors, one of which is the size of the antenna. Angle tracking requirements effectively replaced link budget constraints in antenna sizing.

The use of Navstar GPS receivers has been postulated as a means of providing accurate orbital information on LEO satellites for a number of years. This approach has great potential for reducing the ground station antenna size. For geostationary satellites, dual station ranging - measuring the satellite range from two TT&C stations spaced a large distance apart - also overcomes the requirement for a high angle tracking accuracy. In this case, the orbit determination software is able to perform some form of triangulation in order to pinpoint the satellite's position without requiring accurate azimuth and elevation data.

Another significant reason for retaining a large TT&C station is that of security. The possibility of satellite sabotage from a 2 to 3m terminal is not an attractive one. Limiting satellite TT&C access to large TT&C stations reduces satellite vulnerability. However, the increasing use of sophisticated command encryption on modern spacecraft effectively overcomes this eventuality.

Taking the above factors into account it is apparent that TT&C services may be possible from much lower cost ground stations than is currently the norm. This is particularly so in the case of small LEO satellites, where orbit determination can be achieved by using Navstar equipment on the satellite, the link distances involved are small and the high level of autonomy (essential for LEO spacecraft which spend large periods out of contact with their control centres during each orbit) enables lower link margins to be tolerated.

4.2. Typical RF Requirements

Tables 1 and 2 present link budgets for a hypothetical small LEO satellite. In this case an S-band TT&C system has been assumed, however, the results hold for several frequency bands. The budgets demonstrate that telemetry and command data rates of 20 kbps are feasible using a 3m ground station antenna, and indicate that a 2m antenna should be able to support data rates of 8 kbps. This is not achieved at great cost to the space segment either, since a 100 mW transmitter and 1dB LNA have been assumed with an omnidirectional antenna on the spacecraft.

4.3. Typical RF System Design

Figure 2 shows the block diagram of the small satellite ground terminal, no redundancy has been shown for clarity. It assumes a 3m antenna, and achieves performance parameters of 30 dBW and 14 dB/K, which are sufficient to handle data transfer rates of 20 kbps for both telemetry and telecommands, as illustrated in the link budgets in tables 1 and 2.

EIRF	dBW	-20.0
Space Loss	dB	-160.0
Earthstation G/T	dB/K	14.0
Boltzmann's constant	dBW/Hz/K	-228.6
C/No achieved	dBHz	62.6
Implementation Losses	dB	-2.0
Data Rate	dBHz	43.0
Eb/No achieved	dB	12.6
Eb/No achieved	dB	9.6
Performance Margin	dB	3.0

Table 1 : Telemetry Budget

EIRP	dBW	30.0
Space Loss	dB	-162.0
Satellite G/T	dB/K	-34.0
Boltzmann's constant	dBW/Hz/K	-228.6
C/No achieved	dBHz	62.6
Implementation Losses	dB	-2.0
Modulation Losses	dB	-5.0
Data Rate	dBHz	43.0
Eb/No achieved	dB	12.6
Eb/No required	dB	9.6
Performance Margin	dB	3.0

Table 2 : Telecommand Budget

The small antenna and its high power and low noise amplifiers are mounted on a suitable angle tracking mechanism. The small mass of the equipment to be moved reduces the cost of the mechanics required to move the antenna. In addition, the small antenna size results in a broad antenna beamwidth (some 3 degrees in this case) reducing the requirements on tracking accuracy and relaxing the tolerances on the mechanics.

To meet the EIRP requirement of 30 dBW requires a small solid state amplifier with an output of 250 milliwatts feeding directly into the

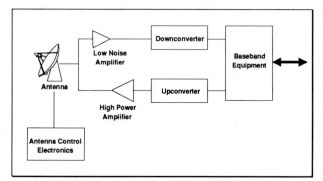

Figure 2 : Small Satellite Ground Terminal

antenna feed port. The small size of such an amplifier enables it to be mounted in a weatherproof box on the back of the antenna. This removes the requirement for long waveguide runs, and reduces the output RF losses. The G/T requirement of 14 dB/K is met by a low cost LNA of 1 dB noise figure, which is again mounted directly on the antenna feed port. Standard up and down converters interface the RF section of the ground station with the baseband electronics operating at an Intermediate Frequency (**IF**) of 5 MHz.

The baseband equipment is implemented using Digital Signal Processing (**DSP**) in order to reduce the high cost overhead usually associated with such dedicated satellite specific hardware. The input telemetry signals are sampled and converted to a digital bit stream for digital processing. The command data stream is generated digitally by a simple look up table sine wave generator and then converted to an analogue signal and filtered prior to upconversion. By selecting a 5 MHz IF, rather than the more conventional 70 MHz used in most ground stations, the baseband equipment design is simplified since it does not have to perform any frequency conversions to change DSP compatible frequencies to frequencies suitable for interfacing to the frequency converters.

4.4. Costing

A detailed cost analysis has not been performed for this hypothetical example as it would not be realistic. However, the two most costly elements in the RF portion of the ground station have been considerably descoped. The antenna has been more than halved in size, having a major cost saving impact. Indeed mass produced VSAT antennas would now be satisfactory, albeit with a modified mechanical mounting. The HPA system, costing around $100,00 each, has been replaced with a much cheaper solid state driver amplifier. This has the added benefit that it does not require large quantities of non-interruptible backed up power.

The simplificaitons to the baseband equipment reduce its complexity and should enable a more common approach to be adopted for several systems. In addition the use of standard DSP hardware should reduce the manufacturing costs significantly, making it more cost effective to hold sufficient spares at the ground station site.

5. CONTROL SYSTEM ELEMENT

5.1. Control System Architecture

Satellite control systems have evolved over the past few decades, to the extent that the basic processes involved, and techniques for implementation of these, are well understood. Traditionally, however, these systems have been implemented on centralised mainframe or mini-computers, with a network of terminal devices supporting the MMI for satellite operations. More recent systems have replaced terminals with workstation computers to provide more sophisticated MMIs, but have retained the centralised processing of telemetry and telecommands.

Prototype systems [ref. 1] have demonstrated, that the computing power available in modern desk-top workstation computers is sufficient to support all the traditional functions of an SCS, whilst providing an improved environment for satellite operations in two main areas:

- Sophisticated window-based MMIs, using high resolution interactive graphics to provide intuitive presentation of data and on-screen controls.

- Use of object-oriented and rule-based techniques to automate the execution of operations procedures.

A generic SCS for small satellite systems, should be capable of being configured to run on a single workstation class computer, or distributed over a Local Area Network (**LAN**) to provide multiple workstations. The same software architecture should support single-satellite, single-workstation; single-satellite, multiple-workstation; and multiple-satellite, multiple-workstation configurations.

It should also be sufficiently modular to support differing TM/TC standards (i.e. frame or packet-based), and to allow for the inclusion of optional components (e.g. ground based orbit determination).

5.2. Functional Components

The control system may be decomposed into the following functional components:

- Telemetry Frame Synchronisation
- Telemetry Acquisition, which depending on the telemetry standard employed may include packet reconstitution, frame/packet validation and routing.
- Telemetry History Filing and Retrieval.
- Telemetry Parameter Decommutation, including calibration of analogue values and interpretation of status parameters.
- Parameter [and Mode] Derivation.
- Parameter Monitoring, including validity tests; checking of numerical parameters against pre-defined limits and status parameters against expected states; and event detection.
- Alarm Handling and Event Logging.
- Real-time [and Historical] Display of Spacecraft Status.
- Telecommand Scheduling.
- Pre-transmission Command Validation.
- Command Frame/Packet Generation and Logging.
- Post-transmission Command Verification.
- Flight Dynamics, including orbit determination, orbit, attitude and geometrical event prediction, and manoeuvre planning as required.
- Summary Report Generation.
- Database Management and Maintenance.

5.3. Software Architecture

The proposed Software Architecture is based upon that demonstrated by the Meteosat Workstation (**MWS**) prototype [ref. 1]. The main feature of this architecture is a common *Blackboard* structure, which provides a means of communicating current status information between all components of the system. Information on the blackboard is represented as object structures, of which six major classes have been identified:

- Telemetry Parameters
- Telecommands
- Environmental Data [Flight Dynamics]
- Operational Modes
- Alarm/Anomaly States
- Operational Procedures

All relevant information about the item concerned, static as well as dynamic, is stored in the object, where it is accessible to data acquisition, data monitoring and display functions.

For the small satellite SCS the MWS blackboard would be replaced by the more flexible *Noticeboard* mechanism, developed in the context of the Expert Systems Tools (**EST**) study for ESTEC [ref. 2]. This has the added advantage of propagating events: the process 'reading' the noticeboard declares interest in an object, such that when the object is updated it is informed. In this way, parameter monitoring or display functions need have no knowledge of the origin of the parameter, but merely need to know of its existence to make use of it. This leads to a totally modular structure to the software [see fig. 3], such that telemetry acquisition processes for frame-based and packet telemetry can be interchanged, without impacting the telemetry monitoring or display processes. The Noticeboard supports the definition of classes of object, such as those listed above, derived parameters or ground station parameters.

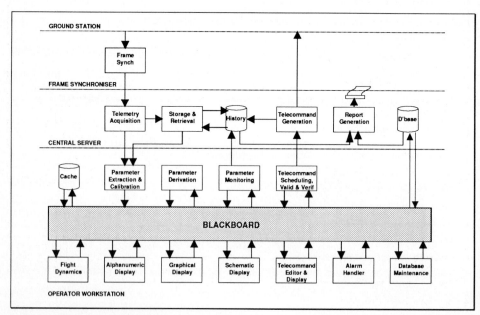

Figure 3 : SCS Software Architecture

Packet telemetry and telecommand handling components have been demonstrated in this environment by the Packet Utilisation Standard Verification Test Facility (**PUSV**) [ref. 3].

The noticeboard has the added advantage that it can be distributed across a LAN, which permits extension from a single to a multiple workstation system.

5.4. Computer System Architecture

The software components described above can be grouped to form three main software elements, each of which could be run on a separate computer, or conceptual processor:

- Frame Synchroniser
- Central Server
- Operator Workstation

It is recommended that a dedicated PC, or special processor card, with accurate hardware clock, be used to host the telemetry frame synchronisation function. This is to avoid placing a stringent real-time processing requirement on the workstation host, with its multi-tasking operating system.

The Central Server would perform the telemetry acquisition, filing and retrieval functions, command generation and logging, event logging, and database management. It may also support 'batch' processes such as summary report generation and certain flight dynamics functions.

The Operator Workstation would perform all other funtions, and could optionally include a local 'cache' history storage and retrieval function, which would store data in processed noticeboard format, rather than the raw frame/packet structures stored on the server.

In the simplest case [fig. 4] the Central Server and Operator Workstation would be combined on a single workstation computer (DEC VAXstation, DECstation, SUN SparcStation, etc.).

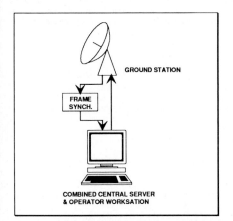

Figure 4 : Single Workstation SCS Configuration   **Figure 5 : Multiple Workstation SCS Configuration**

If more workstations were required to support a larger operations team, then this could be achieved by hosting the Central Server function on a server computer [DEC VAXserver, SUN SPARCserver, etc.) and linking this via a LAN to a number of Operator Workstations. In a multi-workstation configuration, individual workstations may be used to support specialist operations (e.g. Flight Dynamics), but all Operator Workstations would be functionally equivalent, such that any workstation could support any operational rôle. For a multi-satellite configuration, a single Central Server would handle parallel telemetry and telecommand streams, routing them to the appropriate Operator Workstation. A multiple workstation configuration is illustrated in fig. 5.

5.5. Man-Machine Interface

The Operator Workstation MMI is based on the concepts proven in the MWS prototype development [ref. 4], but would use X-windows and conform to either the Open Look or Motif standards for look-and-feel.

The windowing environment, together with a Graphical User Interface (**GUI**) tool-kit, would be used to generate a tiled display of non-overlapping windows, providing a combination of textual and graphical presentations of spacecraft status. This maximises information density, whilst minimising screen clutter, allowing rapid assimilation of information by the operator. Operator control of the system is primarily mouse-based, and uses a combination of pop-up menus and forms, on-screen widgets, and direct interaction with active graphical displays. Specific features of the MMI include:

- Tiled display, ensuring critical information is never obscured by overlapping windows.

- Use of colour, tone, shape and sound to encode status information in an instinctive and consistent manner.

- Alphanumeric displays of pre-defined and user-selectable combinations of telemetred parameters.

- Graphical displays of parameters plotted against time, with digital read-out from graphs using cross-hairs.

- Meter style displays for individual analogue parameters.

- Interactive 'Mimic' or schematic diagrams, with spacecraft status superimposed on block-diagrams of satellite sub-systems.

- Combined command entry, command schedule and command history display.

- Interactive control of historical data replay, via video recorder style interface.

- Dual screens, one for the standard TM/TC display, the other to display the mimic diagrams and off-line information.

5.6. Advanced Automation Features

Reduction of operational costs may be achieved by automating satellite operations. The control of unmanned satellites from Earth is almost universally carried out through the application of a set of pre-defined operations procedures. These procedures are designed to cover both routine operations and the diagnosis of, and recovery from, known or predicted failure conditions. Satellite operations procedures are produced in advance by highly qualified spacecraft engineers. These are validated, often against a satellite simulator, before they are released for interpretation and execution in real-time by trained spacecraft operators.

Several prototype systems have demonstrated the viability of automating these operations procedures, using object-oriented and knowledge-based techniques [refs. 5,6,7]. The latest version of the MWS prototype [ref. 1,8] includes such a procedure automation system, with the added advantage of allowing spacecraft engineers to specify the procedures in a special devised language, tailored to the requirements of satellite operations. Procedure scripts written in this language may then be compiled into an internal representation, which may be executed by the real-time procedure execution system. The procedure execution system itself is totally integrated with the basic SCS via the blackboard, which gives it full visibility of current status and enables it to inject telecommands into the system. The MWS prototype demonstrates that such a system can be built into a self-contained workstation-based SCS. The User Language Study [ref. 9] being conducted for ESOC has further refined and generalised the syntax used for specifying procedures in its Operations Language (**OL**).

5.7. Implementation Tools

Wherever possible, standard implementation tools should be used for development of the SCS, such that it is both portable and maintainable. To this end, a UNIX operating system is preferable, because of the large number of tools available for the environment and the high degree of portability across platforms from DEC, Sun, HP and others. Unix is also able to take advantage of the increasing processing power available on RISC workstations. DEC's VMS, whilst having certain real-time processing advantages is constrained to the VAX family of computers.

The MMI should be compatible with either the Motif or Open Windows standard and use the X-windowing system. Configurability and maintainability of the MMI is enhanced if standard GUI toolkits, such as DEC's VUIT or Sun's DevGuide, are used to build the interface. These do not, however, provide high level support for graphics primitives such as lines, rectangles and so on. Graphical displays and schematic diagrams can be constructed using specialist tools, such as V.I. Corporation's Dataviews, which provides an interactive drawing environment and enables 'animation' of drawings by linking graphical objects to dynamic data.

The C language has been used for many prototype developments, however, C++ tends to allow the development more robust software, promotes the reuse of software and is likely to be used increasingly in spacecraft control systems. C++ has already been successfully used on at least on prototype [ref 3]. The C language would still be used where appropriate for interfaces to other software and where efficiency is paramount.

Blackboard functionality can be provided by Vega's Noticeboard mechanism, either on a single machine in the single workstation SCS configuration or distrubuted over several machines in the multi-workstation configuration.

If procedure automation is required, then the procedure language compiler can be developed using an object-oriented derivative of Unix's standard compiler-compiler, such as YACC++.

5.8. Cost

The cost of the SCS is dependent on the required configuration, and as such there is no upper limit.

Hardware costs are minimised for the single workstation solution. A budget of $20,000 should be adequate for an entry-level workstation (eg. Sun Sparcstation IPC with two 16" colour monitors, 24 Mbyte memory, 400+ Mbyte disk and tape drive) together with a PC-based Frame Synchroniser.

The software costs do not reduce so dramatically with the minimal configuration, as essentially the same functionality is required, merely compressed into a single computer - multiple copies of application software are cheap. The cost of a purpose-built system is likely to be prohibitive. Hence the need for a low-cost *configurable* system, to which a licence can be purchased. The cost of such a licence will be dependent on the marketing strategy of the producer, but could be expected to be in the region of $100,000 - $200,000. To this would need to be added the cost of configuring the system for the specific mission.

6. CONCLUSIONS

The cost of the ground segment for a small satellite can be significantly reduced by making use of commercially available hardware and modern software technology and by collocating and integrating both the ground station and mission control system. The ground station component can be significantly descoped without major system implications, allowing a reduced cost antenna system, some 3 metres in diameter and low cost, 250 mW, solid state power amplifiers to be used.

The spacecraft control system component can make use of standard workstations, configurable software, graphical user interfaces and automated procedure execution to reduce the cost of the hardware, software and operations, whilst providing a high degree of flexibility to meet the specific needs of a given mission. The technology required for such a system has been demonstrated by a number of prototype developments, which have, in some cases, been used with real spacecraft.

The overall system cost can be greatly reduced by collocating both the spacecraft control system and the ground station, simplifying the interfaces between them. However, the proposed concept would still facilitate the separation of these components, for those missions, such as polar orbiting missions, which require it.

REFERENCES

1. Meteosat Workstation (MWS) 3.1: Software User's Manual, *Vega Space Systems Engineering Ltd., MWS.PNW.SUM.004, April 1992*, White P.N.

2. Expert Systems Tools: Final Report (Phase 2), *ESA Study Contract Report 8735/90/NL/JG(SC), , March 1992*, Spinks P.M., Keepence B.S. & Thyssen U.

3. Packet Utilisation Standard Verification Test Facility: Final Report, *ESA Study Contract Report 8975/90/D/IM, March 1992*, Melvin R.A.D. & Pidgeon A.N.

4. Man-Machine Interface (MMI) Aspects of Workstations for use in Spacecraft Operations, *Proc. 1990 ESA Conference on Ground Data Systems for Spacecraft Control,* Thompson R.S.

5. An Approach for the Application of Knowledge Based Systems to the Production and Execution of Spacecraft Operations Procedures, *Proc. 1990 ESA Conference on Ground Data Systems for Spacecraft Control,* Thompson R.S.

6. Expert Operator's Associate: an expert system for spacecraft control, *Proc. 1990 ESA Conference on Ground Data Systems for Spacecraft Control,* Nielsen M., Olalainty B., Lecouat F. & Wheadon J.

7. Expert System for Spacecraft Operations Planning and Execution (ESSOPE): Final Report, *ESA Study Contract Report 8168/89/D/IM(SC), June 1991*, Gusmeroli S., Monti M., Bjelogrlic Z. & Barone S.

8. Meteosat Workstation (MWS) FCP Syntax Translator: Software User Manual, *Vega Space Systems Engineering Ltd., MWS.PNW.SUM.005, April 1992*, White P.N.

9. User Language Study: Operations Language Syntax Definition, *Vega Space Systems Engineering Ltd., ULS.UT.REP.004, March 1992*, Thyssen U.

GROUND SEGMENT DEFINITION
FOR
THE SPANISH SMALL SATELLITE PROGRAM
(MINISAT)

F. Cancillo, L. Guzman, L.A. San Jose

INISEL ESPACIO

This paper describes the Ground Segment approach considered for the Spanish program of small satellites. The program is aimed at the development of a general-purpose platform to cover a wide range of missions, varying from digital communications to astronomy and Earth observation. The different characteristics of the mission force very stringent system requirements being set up to maintain the versatility of the platform, and consequently the associated Ground Segment.

Mission Scenario

The typical mission profile corresponds to operation from Low-Earth orbits (LEO) in equatorial ($0<i<40$) or polar ($70<i<100$) planes. These orbits, between 500 and 900 Km, will be achieved by means of a dedicated launch using Pegasus or Scout.

The kind of missions planned will require different stabilization approaches, being the most likely scenario the 3 axis stabilization.

The overall mass has to be between 200 and 450 Kg, and the average power per orbit around 120 W.

The spacecraft will be constituted by a platform, common for all missions, and a payload, specific for each kind of mission.

The minimum ground infrastructure requirements to control the mission is achieved by using one single earth station and a dedicated control center.

Due to the limited number of contact periods (1-2 per day) with short duration (5-12 minutes), and to the current trends in on board systems, the intelligence and autonomy on-board shall be increased. This concept implies in the ground segment to define a new policy for the mission planning and analysis.

General Requirements on the Ground Segment

The Ground Segment shall provide the usual TT&C/R services for a spacecraft control, including Telemetry, Telecommand and Ranging, and special services for specific payload data monitoring, control and analysis, that are mission dependent.

It shall be designed to allow easy upgrading to control new missions, starting with a kernel system for the first mission.

The Ground Segment shall take into consideration the geographical dispersion between the different components (Earth Stations, Satellite Control Center and Payload Control Center) and shall use at the maximum extent standard communication products for the interface between their components. Use of LANs and X.25 protocol is recommended.

It shall give priority to the data acquisition during the visibility period. Mission analysis and preparation may be deferred to the non-visibility periods.

For the implementation of the Ground Segment, the following aspects shall be taken into account:

- maximum use of standard products in the basic systems, concentrating the design effort at application level.
- incorporation of up to date technologies in the user interface aspects.

Ground Segment Architecture

In the baseline architecture, the Ground Segment for the minisatellite is composed of the Mission Control Center and the Earth Station both for TT&C purposes and for the reception of the payload data.

While the Mission Control Center would be installed in a location inside Spain, the Earth Station could be installed in other places, depending on factors such as type of orbit and mission to be carried out in the payload.

There is the possibility to add a second earth station to the baseline architecture. This second earth station would be operated as back-up of the main earth station. Also, it would allow to acquire more satellite passages, and therefore to increase the operation and performances of the system.

According to this baseline, the stated requirements and the functions that the whole Ground Segment have to carry out, its main components are: the Earth Station(s), the Communication Means, the Satellite Control Center and the Payload Control Center. Their architectural arrangement is depicted in the following figure 1.

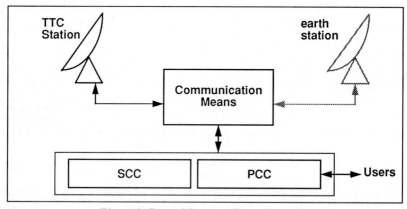

Figure 1. Ground Segment General Lay-out

As the figure shows, the Mission Control Center has been split, for modularity reasons, in two components: the Satellite Control Center (SCC) and the Payload Control Center (PCC), the second subsidiary of the first. This arrangement allows easier reconfiguration for each minisatellite: monitoring and control functions of the common platform are allocated in the SCC, and only minor changes will be needed on it for adapting the system to each payload and the monitoring and control functions of the payload are allocated in the PCC, a specific component for each kind of mission.

The Communication Means have been included as a separate module for allowing a mission independent definition of the external interface of each Ground Segment component. This black box strategy for the communications facilitates the implementation of each mission specific communications network without disturbing the other elements.

Earth Stations Design

The Earth Station will be designed to fulfill the requirements already mentioned, and moreover, taking into account the following performances:

- The earth station will support the mission both during the LEOP phase and during the exploitation phase. In the LEOP phase only TT&C functions will be executed. In the exploitation phase the reception of the payload data will be performed as well.

- Because of the successive missions can have different orbits the earth station will be capable of working in different physical locations. This fact imposes several constraints which will be commented in the following.

The block diagram for the earth station architecture is included in the figure 2, where the main subsystems are depicted.

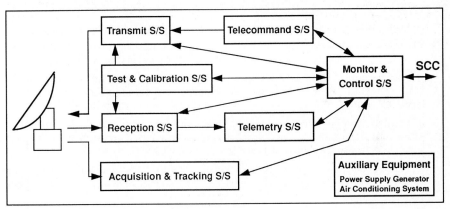

Figure 2. Earth Station Structure

After the analysis of the requirements and performances to be met it was decided to work with two basic configurations for the earth station: Self-contained Station and Transportable Station.

In the self-contained station option, the whole station, including antenna, electronics and operations shelter, air conditioner and power generator, would be integrated on a standard trailer. The components of the antenna (main reflector panels, structural trusses, sub-reflector and feed) would be housed in cabinets. Moreover, if it were possible, the antenna would be installed on the same trailer. On the one hand, this structure presents several advantages:

- This self-contained configuration allows the earth station to be operated independently of the usual infrastructure (building, primary ac power, ...)

- Both the assembly, to put the station in operational way, and the disassembly, to put the station in transport way, are very easy and quick.

333

- It is not required any type of civil works (antenna foundation) and the station can be put in service in a very short period of time (1 or 2 days) with a small crew.

On the other hand, there are some disadvantages to be taken in mind:

- The size of the antenna, and therefore its pedestal, is a critical factor because the antenna must acquire and track the satellite passages within the coverage area of the station.

- The mechanical design is very complicated and it is necessary to optimize the housing of all the equipment in the available space.

- The above mentioned constraints impact negatively on the station, making it more expensive.

The Transportable station option takes into account that the lifetime of the mission will be about two years and that during this time the station will be operated always on the same place. In this second case, the electronics are housed in a standard shelter which is used as operations room as well. The antenna, together with its structural trusses, feed, sub-reflector and pedestal, is transported inside other shelter. Previously to operate the station, the entire antenna subsystem has to be deployed on the ground. For this reason some civil works are now required to prepare the terrain and make the antenna foundation.

This configuration presents the advantage to be easier to implement, and therefore cheaper, than the other one. By the other hand, it requires more time to be assembled/disassembled and infrastructure (crane, primary ac power, for example) from the area where the station is being installed.

The main conclusions concerning the earth station are here below explained:

- The earth station should be designed in such a way to be capable of working in places with very different environment with the small number of changes in its configuration.

- It should be easily transportable and the tasks to install the station on site should not be complicated in order to avoid a big crew and a long period of time to put the system in operational way.

- The station should include a very reliable communication system with the Mission Control Centre. A system based on VSAT terminal is considered a good option, because the station has to receive also the payload data and send them to the MCC.

- At the beginning, the self-contained configuration is taken as baseline for the TTC/data reception station because it is easier to transfer to transportable configuration if it were further required.

Control Center Design

Concerning the functional aspects, the following figure 3 depicts the top level breakdown of the functions that the Control Center must carry out.

At lower levels, functions have been defined taking into account specific needs (like flight dynamics, on-board software management, communications management,...) and the necessity of monitoring and control all the subsystems.

From the analysis of the Mission Scenario and the Ground Segment Requirements the following main drivers for the Control Center design have been derived:

- Modularity and Extensibility. The need for having a Control Center easily adaptable to the different missions foreseen and for the different payloads that the satellite platform can accommodate forces the design of a control center that have to be modular -composed of a set of well defined and isolated elements- and extensible -adaptable to the specific needs of each mission-.

- Simplicity. The Control Center have to be easy to operate, easy to reconfigure for each mission and the computer platform shall be selected with this criteria in mind.

- Maximum use of standard products in the basic system, with design effort concentrated at application level.

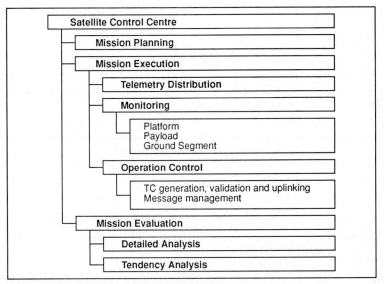

Figure 3. Control Center Functional Breakdown

In order to allocate the former functions into a well defined applicative modules, a mapping to the satellite operation domain has been considered as the best approach. The figure 4 depicts the agents of this domain.

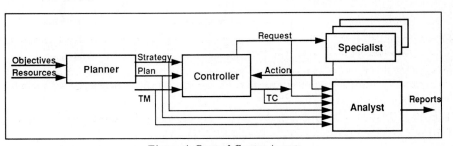

Figure 4. Control Center Agents

Each agent is in charge of performing a set of functions:

- *Planner*: mission planning for creating and updating plan(s), taking into account mission objectives and resources.

- *Controller*: monitoring and control at system level. This allows the evaluation of data that extends across subsystem boundaries and the control of each subsystem in conjunction with one other. The controller is supported by specialist. In order to coordinate their functioning, it elaborates request and receives activities to be performed. From that, the schedule of resources and actions is elaborated, and after that, it is ready for execution. The actual execution implies telecommand(s) generation, their validation and their uplinking. This task is condition-dependent: scheduled activities are activated when pre-conditions have been satisfied.

- *Specialists*: monitor and control a subsystem or give support for a specific need.

- *Analyst*: mission evaluation. It assesses degree of success or failure of an executed mission.

The Control Center top level architecture will be derived from the former diagram establishing a one-to-one correspondence between each agent and the corresponding application level module, which provides the necessary support for its activity (See figure 5).

This figure shows the applicative level (white boxes), and at lower level, a set of well-defined and well-known set of services (shaded boxes) for supporting the application level modules. It is a main driver for this project reusing existing software and standard products for these services.

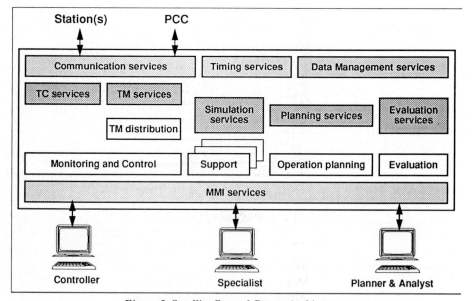

Figure 5. Satellite Control Center Architecture

All software will be housed on a single computer (desk-side type) with X terminals for users interaction. Only simulation services would require using external hardware for on-board computer and software simulation.

Payload Control Center Description

The Payload Control Center purpose is the monitoring, supervision and trend analysis of the Payload status and performances.

The Satellite Control Center performs a first level monitoring and control of the critical parameters concerning the payload that may impact in the performance of the overall mission. The Payload Control Center receives from the Satellite Control Center the TM/payload data relevant to the payload at any time it is available. This process may be deferred to the non-visibility periods if so required by the real time processes.

The general functioning of the Payload Control Center is based on the following:

- it files the received data into the Data Base, making the data available for the rest of Payload Control Center processes.

- the operator introduces in the Payload Control Center Data Base the configuration and expected behaviour of the Payload in use. This data base is dynamically updated during the mission. Also, he may introduce other types of data influencing the payload behaviour.

- it sends to the Satellite Control Center the commands needed to configure the payload. Based on this commands, the Satellite Control Center prepares the telecommands to be uplinked.

The Payload Control Center provides facilities to analyze the payload data and perform trend analysis on the future behaviour of the payload.

The received data and the processed data resulting from the analysis processes are archived into tapes, on a regular basis.

Additional support for delivering products to end-users is included in the PCC.

The figure 6 depicts the general arrangement of the PCC for performing the former activities.

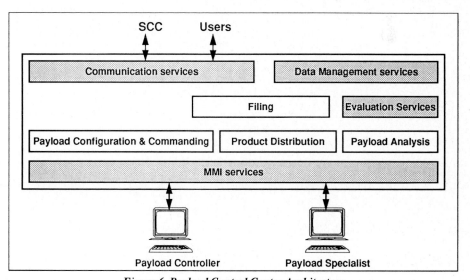

Figure 6. Payload Control Center Architecture

337

From the general requirements given before, the main functions of the Payload Control Center are summarized:

- Filing and archiving.
- Analysis.
- Payload configuration and commanding.
- Man-machine interface.

The only real-time function is the reception and filing of incoming data from the Satellite Control Center, being the other tasks post-processing functions conducted by the operator.

Related to the Payload Control Center addition to the basic configuration, the following points shall be highlighted:

- all functions may reside in the same Satellite Control Center computer or in a different one. In the latest case, the Payload Control Center computer architecture shall be based on the same family as that of the Satellite Control Center.
- the same Data Base product as for the Satellite Control Center should be used.
- it is recommended the use of LAN services, to communicate with the Satellite Control Center. In case of long distance, the use of bridges/gateways is desirable with X.25 as protocol.
- it provides a friendly MMI, using X-windows or equivalent.

Conclusions

This paper summarizes some aspects concerning the Ground Definition of the MINISAT. They have been extracted from the results of the Definition Phase for Spanish Small Satellite Program performed during 1991.

OREMUS: PROTOTYPE DE CENTRE D'ORBITOGRAPHIE

POUR LE CONTROLE DE MINI-SATELLITES

François LAPORTE
Geneviève CAMPAN
Huguette CONESSA

C.N.E.S
(Centre National d'Etudes Spatiales)
18 Avenue Edouard Belin
31055 TOULOUSE Cedex
Tél: 61.27.38.73

Les études menées actuellement en Mécanique Spatiale sur des projets futurs de mini-satellites ou de constellations de mini-satellites à défilement, ont permis de constater que malgré la diversité de ces projets, les problèmes se présentant pour la mise et le maintien à poste sont souvent similaires (acquisition de données, restitution d'orbite, calcul de manœuvres, ...).
Il apparaît donc nécessaire de disposer d'un produit unique (une boite à outils de fonctionnement aisé et homogène) regroupant les différentes fonctionnalités indispensables au contrôle de ces satellites.

En outre, le CNES dispose d'un vaste patrimoine de modules de calcul de Mécanique Spatiale développés dans le cadre d'analyse de mission ou pour le déroulement des opérations.
Il apparaît donc envisageable de réaliser, pour un coût modéré un prototype de segment sol de Mécanique Spatiale pour les opérations de satellites à défilement: projet OREMUS (Orbite, Restitution, Extrapolation, Manœuvres, Utilitaires, Simulateurs).

L'objectif du projet OREMUS est de montrer la faisabilité d'un système général permettant de répondre aux besoins exprimés par les différents projets clients de mini-satellites à défilement. Ce produit devra être adaptable et souple pour être utilisé par tous les projets en intégrant de manière simple les spécificités de chacun. Ses principales fonctionnalités seront:
- acquisition des données,
- restitution de l'orbite à partir des mesures de réseaux et DORIS,
- calcul des manœuvres orbitales,
- prévisions opérationnelles liées à l'orbite.

La validation des chaînes de traitement du prototype se fera en exploitant les mesures relatives à Spot2 et en comparant les résultats obtenus avec ceux issus des chaînes opérationnelles.

I. INTRODUCTION

Les études menées actuellement en Mécanique Spatiale sur des projets futurs de satellites ou de constellation de mini-satellites à défilement, ont permis de constater que malgré la diversité de ces projets, les besoins de calcul pour la mise et le maintien à poste sont souvent similaires (acquisition et décommutation de données, restitution d'orbite et d'attitude, calcul de manœuvres, prévisions opérationnelles, ...).
De plus, les caractéristiques indispensables des centres de Mécanique Spatiale doivent rester globalement les mêmes: fiabilité, ergonomie, sécurité, autonomie, ...

Le contexte de développement lié à certains projets de mini-satellites, par exemple S80 T, impose de nouvelles contraintes: moins de potentiel pour développer le centre de contrôle, délais réduits, spécifications parfois évolutives, ...
Ces nouvelles contraintes imposent de pouvoir réaliser des systèmes évolutifs pouvant fonctionner sur des architectures plus légères de type station de travail.

Ainsi, il semble nécessaire de pouvoir disposer d'un système unique, de type "boite à outils", de fonctionnement aisé et homogène, ayant les caractéristiques précédentes, et regroupant les différentes fonctionnalités indispensables au suivi et au contrôle de satellites. La réalisation d'un tel produit implique de disposer:
- de modules de calcul de Mécanique Spatiale,
- d'utilitaires de gestion de fichiers,
- d'une structure d'accueil permettant d'intégrer, d'interfacer et de coordonner les différentes fonctions du système.

Les utilitaires de gestion de fichiers et de compression de données existent de façon standard sur le marché.
Au CNES, le SDM (Service de Détermination des Manœuvres), au sein de la division MS, et le COO (Centre d'Orbitographie Opérationnel) disposent d'un vaste patrimoine de modules de calcul de Mécanique Spatiale développés dans le cadre d'analyses de missions ou pour le déroulement des opérations.
De plus, ces deux entités ont une grande expérience de systèmes intégrés: le système MERCATOR pour le SDM et SISSI pour le COO, sont tous les deux fondés sur le principe d'une structure d'accueil intégrant des modules de calcul de Mécaniques Spatiales. Toutefois, les approches de ces deux structures, spécifiées et développées de façon décorrélée, sont très différentes.

Ainsi, réalisant la synthèse de ces deux expériences, la division MS du CNES se propose de réaliser un système général de Centre de Mécanique Spatiale, dans le cadre du projet OREMUS (Orbite, Restitution, Extrapolation, Manœuvre, Uilitaires, Simulateurs).

Les deux premières parties de cette communication sont consacrées à la présentation des systèmes MERCATOR du SDM et SISSI du COO.
Dans la troisième partie nous présentons les grandes lignes du projet OREMUS.

II. EXPERIENCE DU SDM

MERCATOR (MEthodes et Réalisation pour le Contrôle de l'ATtitude et l'ORbite des satellites) est la structure informatique du Service de Détermination des Manœuvres. Ce service est un sous-ensemble du système sol de mise à poste des satellites géostationnaires du Centre Spatial de Toulouse. Responsable des aspects de mécanique spatiale, c'est une entité autonome qui reçoit ses informations de la télémesure du satellite et des mesures de localisation qu'il acquiert directement. Ses résultats sont transmis aux autres entités par diffusion vidéo.

On peut décomposer le SDM en deux parties distinctes :
- le système informatique,
- les logiciels de mécanique spatiale.

Nous allons nous intéresser plus particulièrement au système informatique nommé MERCATOR. MERCATOR est un système basé sur une architecture répartie modulaire tant du point de vue matériel que logiciel.

Le système opérationnel pour les mises à poste comprend quatre stations de travail identiques (SUN) reliées entre elles par un réseau Ethernet. Les diffusions vidéo, graphiques ou alphanumériques sont assurées via des PC ou des consoles.

Le logiciel du système opérationnel est composé de trois ensembles :
- acquisition et prétraitement de données,
- surveillance système,
- interface homme - machine, gestion des process.

Mais chaque station de travail supporte les mêmes logiciels. Le système peut donc être activé sur une seule station, le choix de quatre étant régi pour des considérations de redondance et d'ensemble de tâches à réaliser à un même instant de la mission.

MERCATOR correspond en fait à une structure d'accueil des logiciels de mécanique spatiale. Cette structure a été conçue pour que l'effort d'intégration dans le système d'un nouvel outil soit minimum, l'effort pouvant être donc porté sur l'outil lui-même.

Un autre aspect est la facilité de passage d'une mission à l'autre : environ une demi-heure pour configurer les logiciels d'un calculateur pour une mission : possibilité de présence d'une mission différente sur chaque calculateur en phase de développement et d'essais.

Une fois les logiciels de mécanique spatiale intégrés dans le système MERCATOR, l'ensemble permet alors de réaliser les tâches suivantes :
- acquisition de données et prétraitement (télémesure et localisation),
- restitution d'orbite en temps réel,
- calcul et suivi TR des manœuvres d'orbite et d'attitude,
- restitution d'attitude en temps réel,
- prévisions opérationnelles (éclipses, visibilités RF, visibilités senseur, ...),
- ainsi que divers supports pour l'interprétation des phénomènes et des résultats possibles grâce à l'ensemble des possibilités offertes à l'utilisateur et par la souplesse de leur choix : impressions, tracés interactifs, rejeux, enchaînement des fonctions, filtres sur les données, visualisation et tri des fichiers, ...

Les performances du système concourent évidemment à la bonne qualité de l'interface opérateur.

Par ailleurs, la compatibilité de l'application MERCATOR avec les fonctionnalités d'UNIX et du multifenêtrage permet d'avoir à disposition un grand nombre de possibilités d'analyse supplémentaires. Il faut noter également que tous les logiciels (analyse de mission comprise) sont aujourd'hui développés sur SUN et qu'il y a donc commonalité d'environnement de travail depuis les études préliminaires jusqu'aux opérations.

Un tel système présente des intérêts à divers niveaux :
- pour les utilisateurs dans sa souplesse et sa sécurité,
- pour l'organisation opérationnelle dans son autonomie et dans sa souplesse à le coupler à un CCS, entité supposée opérationnelle à plus long terme et au COR (Centre d'Opérations du Réseau : nœud de l'ensemble des lignes de données, de vidéo et de phonie et coordinateur des stations),
- par les possibilités d'ouverture au niveau de la mission. En effet, MERCATOR n'est pas dédié à une mission, il couvrira celle définie par les logiciels de mécanique spatiale implantés. D'où une possibilité d'extension à des satellites autres que géostationnaires, satellites à défilement, constellations, ...

Les nombreuses utilisations opérationnelles en font un produit fiable répondant parfaitement au souci des opérations : la mission d'abord.
. Utilisation lors des mises à poste TELE-X, TDF 2, INMARSAT-2/F1, F2, F3 et F4, TC2 A et B, puis HISPASAT, TURKSAT, ...,
. Utilisation dans les centres de contrôle TELECOM et TDF.
. Utilisation dans le cadre des opérations TOPEX pour la validation opérationnelle d'un navigateur à partir des mesures DORIS.

III. EXPERIENCE DU COO

La mission du COO (Centre d'orbitographie opérationnel) est principalement le calcul d'orbite dans un but de désignation de stations. Quotidiennement, il assure :
- l'acquisition et le contrôle des mesures de localisation du réseau 2GHZ,
- l'archivage de toutes les mesures reçues,
- suivi des satellites SPOT1 et SPOT2,
- service de prévisions permanent pour tout type de satellites opérationnels ou en phase d'étude,
- calcul et diffusions de données d'orbitographie (graphiques, tabulations).
En phase exceptionnelle :
- il participe aux analyses de missions (1ère acquisition),
- calcul de l'orbite et désignations des stations durant les mises à poste CNES,
- suivi des rentrées atmosphériques.
Services annexes :
- suivi de la qualité et calibration des mesures de localisation,
- rejeu des mesures
- simulations de mesures
- banques de bulletins.

III.1. Les besoins du COO en matière de logiciel

Le COO est un service opérationnel. Il est en contact avec de multiples projets et utilisateurs. Il a de nombreuses données à gérer (données de localisations, fichier stations, fichier satellites, bulletins d'orbite).

L'aspect opérationnel impose des logiciels ergonomiques, de présentation homogène, et fiables.
Du fait de la diversité des demandes, les logiciels du COO doivent être souples et adaptables facilement à de nouveaux besoins. Le COO étant installé sur des stations de

travail SUN, il est possible d'assurer une bonne ergonomie avec l'utilisation du multifenêtrage et de la souris. Mais, l'écriture de logiciels utilisant une telle interface provoque :
- un accroissement du temps de développement de chaque logiciel, en même temps qu'une surabondance de lignes de code. Cela entraîne une multiplication des erreurs qui sont souvent concentrés au niveau de l'interface homme-machine, et surtout cela occupe l'attention du programmateur au détriment du problème proprement dit qui se retrouve noyé dans le reste du code.
- une perte de souplesse, en cas de modification des données d'entrées: insertion de nouvelles données, ou boutons ...

Les besoins étaient donc les suivants :
- pouvoir facilement et rapidement transformer un module ou une "maquette" d'orbitographie en un programme opérationnel.
- se décharger de l'écriture de l'interface homme-machine, qui a pratiquement toujours la même structure, en la rendant automatique,
- concentrer la programmation sur le problème proprement dit, sans se préoccuper des aspects informatiques, traditionnellement source d'erreur,
- se décharger de la gestion des unités, et ne fonctionner que dans un système unique (par exemple: USI),
- se décharger de la gestion des fichiers, et pouvoir malgré tout manipuler de nombreuses données pouvant être différentes même à l'intérieur d'un même fichier (ex. 1 fichier station, avec des stations NASA, CNES, INTELSAT, où les types de données sont différents),
- pouvoir isoler le traitement du problème du reste du logiciel,
- avoir une interface homme-machine digne des stations de travail SUN (boutons, menus...), et néanmoins fiable (tests sur les données saisies).

III.2. L'interface homme-machine SISSI

III.2.a. Présentation générale

Sissi est un logiciel écrit par le centre d'orbitographie opérationnel pour répondre aux différents besoins exposés ci- dessus.
Il permet de générer du code FORTRAN à partir de fichiers décrivant les données d'Entrée/sortie et les écrans de saisie de ces données (Fichiers descripteurs).
L'appel des sous-programmes générés par SISSI dans un programme permet :
- d'avoir des fenêtres de saisie avec boutons, messages d'erreurs, menus, tableaux,
- d'afficher ou non des items de manière conditionnelle. La condition d'affichage peut être aussi complexe que nécessaire, car elle est décrite en FORTRAN dans le fichier descripteur, et retranscrite telle quelle dans le source généré,
- la gestion automatique des unités. Les unités fichiers et celles utilisées dans les programmes sont cohérentes. La transformation est reportée uniquement au niveau de l'interface homme-machine, et est totalement gérée par SISSI,
- d'afficher des menus déroulants,
- la gestion dynamique de tableaux : insertion ou suppression d'une colonne,
- gestion automatique à travers des boutons des fichiers associés aux données de l'interface homme-machine : sauvegarde des données saisies à l'écran, ou calculées, (chaque enregistrement d'un fichier est en fait lié à un descripteur d'écran, un fichier pouvant contenir plusieurs types d'enregistrements différents). Recherche d'un enregistrement particulier, lecture, écriture, suppression d'un

enregistrement, affichage de l'enregistrement suivant ou précédent, ...
- dissociation de l'interface homme-machine et du programme de traitement proprement dit. Les échanges de données entre l'interface homme-machine (processus père) et son programme de traitement (processus fils) sont assurés par des sous- programmes générés par SISSI,
- test des variables saisies, et association d'un message d'erreur en cas de non conformité au test.

III.2.b. Les points forts de SISSI

Sissi génère des sous-programmes. L'exécutable est crée à partir d'un programme définissant l'application qui fait appel aux sous- programmes générés. Il n'y a aucune perte de temps due à l'analyse d'un descripteur pendant l'exécution, et de plus cela permet d'insérer du code FORTRAN dans le descripteur, qui sera exécuté lors d'une action sur une donnée.

Sissi génère automatiquement un "Makefile" permettant la gestion de toute l'application (regénération des sources FORTRAN et recompilation des sources modifiées).

La partie graphique spécifique à la machine est concentrée dans un fichier de 2000 lignes en C. L'installation sur une autre machine avec une interface différente n'affecterait que ce fichier.

IV. LE PROJET OREMUS

L'objectif du projet OREMUS est de développer, pour mi 1993, un prototype de système général permettant de répondre aux besoins exprimés par certains responsables de projets de satellites. Ce produit devra être adaptable et souple pour être utilisable par les projets en intégrant de manière simple les spécificités de chacun. Il devra être ergonomique et de fonctionnement autonome par la mise en œuvre de fonctions automatiques.

Pour tenir compte des expériences opérationnelles du SDM et du COO la configuration informatique retenue pour ce prototype est une station de travail (aucune restriction n'est faite sur le modéle de station). On n'abordera pas, dans ce prototype, les problèmes de redondance et d'industrialisation.

Le développement de ce prototype de Centre de Mécanique Spatiale est fondé sur:
- la réalisation d'une nouvelle structure d'accueil bénéficiant des fonctionnalités de MERCATOR du SDM et de SISSI du COO,
- la récupération des modules de calcul de Mécanique Spatiale existants dans les systèmes opérationnels ou extraits de boites à outils d'analyse de mission.

L'interface homme-machine générée sera conceptuellement divisée en deux parties:
- un panneau de boutons permettant l'activation de tâches,
- un écran permettant la saisie et/ou l'affichage des informations. Toutes les informations transitant par l'interface homme-machine (données d'entrée, résultats de traitement, paramètres de fonctionnement, ...) sont regroupées en enregistrements.

Toute la logique et les types de présentation d'une page écran, visualisant et/ou renseignant le contenu d'un enregistrement à partir des saisies de l'utilisateur, est décrite dans un fichier descripteur d'enregistrement.

De même, toute la dynamique d'activation, de désactivation et de synchronisation des tâches, ainsi que le traitement d'évènements extérieurs (arrivée de données, fin de processus, ...) est décrit dans un fichier descripteur de tâches.

Ces fichiers descripteurs sont renseignés par l'utilisateur grâce à un langage de haut niveau. Les principales fonctionnalités que devra proposer le prototype sont celles qui doivent être disponibles dans un segment sol de contrôle[1] :
- acquisition des données: les réseaux sol que nous considérons sont: le réseau actuel 2 GHz, le réseau DORIS, et les stations spécifiques aux projets concernés. Les mesures de localisation considérées aujourd'hui, sont de type: distance, angulaire et doppler. L'acquisition et la décommutation des mesures se décomposent suivant les tâches:
  * acquisition ligne,
  * décommutation,
  * traitements paramétrés pour la télémesure,
  * pré-traitement pour les données de localisation.
- restitution de l'orbite, on considère deux types de restitution d'orbite:
  * orbite temps réel: elle correspond, par exemple, au calcul d'un bulletin d'orbite en utilisant les mesures doppler élaborées par le système DORIS. Dans ce cas, le traitement est effectué en utilisant le logiciel DORIS embarquable. Le principe est un ajustement temps réel avec un modèle dynamique et une méthode de filtrage-estimation adaptable aux types d'orbites et de satellites traités.
  * orbite temps différé:elle correspond, par exemple, au calcul d'un bulletin d'orbite en utilisant des mesures réseaux (réseau 2 GHz ou stations spécifiques) de type doppler, distance et angulaire. Le traitement peut se faire par ajustement moindres carrés avec un modèle d'orbite par intégration numérique.
- restitution de l'attitude: elle impose l'acquisition, la décommutation et le traitement de la télémesure. Ceci peut imposer un certain nombre de contraintes sur l'architecture du système de traitement, en particulier pour les volumes des données et du temps de traitement.
- calcul des manœuvres orbitales: le but du calcul des manœuvres est l'acquisition et le maintien des paramètres mission d'une orbite en respectant les contraintes propres au projet. On distingue deux types de manœuvres:
  * mise à poste: à partir de l'orbite d'injection fournie par le lanceur, elle correspond au calcul des différentes manœuvres permettant d'effectuer le rendez-vous avec l'orbite désignée pour la mission, en utilisant les mesures des réseaux sol et de la télémesure.
  * maintien à poste: il a pour but de calculer les stratégies optimales de manœuvres orbitales nécessaires au maintien des paramètres d'orbite dans les spécifications demandées par la mission, en respectant les contraintes satellite. La stratégie fonctionnera en utilisant les mesures des réseaux sol et de la télémesure.
- prévisions opérationnelles liées à l'orbite: on regroupe dans cette catégorie toutes les fonctions effectuant des traitements liés aux orbites:
  * calcul des désignations stations,
  * calcul des relations géométriques du satellite et de son environnement,
  * éclipses, angle d'éclairement panneau, ...

---

1. Le traitement de plusieurs satellites simultanément, est réalisé par l'application des différentes fonctions à chacun d'eux.

* couvertures d'instruments, visibilités inter-satellites,
* extrapolation pour la planification de la mission,
* calcul des paramètres de la mission.
- gestion des fichiers: la gestion des données technologiques, des mesures réalisées et des résultats obtenus doit être assurée. Ces informations sont stockées dans des fichiers. On s'attachera à utiliser des techniques efficaces de compactage des données afin de réduire au maximum le volume de ces banques de données.
- visualisations graphiques de paramètres: cette fonction permet d'assurer la gestion des tracés des divers types de données présentes dans le système.

Toutes ces fonctions sont réalisées à l'aide de modules dont l'enchaînement et les interfaces sont gérées par l'interface homme-machine.

V. CONCLUSION

Le développement de ce prototype de centre général de Mécanique Spatiale, piloté par la division MS, est fait en collaboration avec diverses entités du CNES pouvant y apporter une contribution:
- les différents départements de la division MS, pour:
    * l'expérience opérationnelle de MERCATOR,
    * les supports en Mécanique Spatiale, concernant les divers modules de calcul,
    * la définition des objectifs mission à satisfaire, en s'appuyant sur les résultats d'études d'analyse de mission,
    * la connaissance du système DORIS, pour la mise en œuvre du navigateur autonome DORIS,
    * l'expérience liée au développement de l'OMGS Spot,
    * ...
- le COO, pour son expérience opérationnelle liée à SISSI,
- le groupe Ada, pour leur support concernant les développements de certains modules de calcul (acquisition et décommutation de données, navigateur DORIS, ...).

Parallèlement au développement de l'interface homme-machine, les concepts d'OREMUS seront mis en œuvre dans différents contextes:
- reconstitution des fonctions de traitement de la chaîne opérationnelle de Spot2: ceci permettra la validation du prototype OREMUS, par comparaison de son comportement avec celui de la chaîne en exploitation:
    * restitution d'orbite: concernant l'orbite Spot2, nous disposons de trois sources de détermination d'orbite:
        . mesures du réseau 2 GHz,
        . mesures DORIS traitées par le navigateur embarquable,
        . résultats de l'orbitographie fine ZOOM.
        Si nous considérons que l'orbite fine délivrée par ZOOM est l'orbite de référence, nous avons ainsi la possibilité de valider la chaîne de restitution d'orbite grâce aux données du réseau 2 GHz. De plus l'établissement d'une liaison permettant de recevoir automatiquement les données DORIS montrera la faisabilité du fonctionnement temps réel du navigateur, ainsi que la qualité des résultats qu'il a fournis par une comparaison a posteriori avec l'orbite fine de ZOOM.

* calcul de manœuvres: parallèlement à cela, il est nécessaire de pouvoir valider les algorithmes de maintien à poste (phasage, inclinaison, excentricité, ...): cela sera possible en calculant les manœuvres à partir des conditions initiales réelles de l'orbite; celles-ci seront simulées par des modèles qui pourront être recalés grâce au suivi de l'orbite réelle. Ce type d'évaluation permettra de comparer l'efficacité de nouvelles méthodes par rapport à celles utilisées opérationnellement.

- l'expérience TOPEX-POSEIDON: le but est ici d'exploiter en temps quasi-réel, c'est-à-dire le plus proche possible du temps réel, les résultats du navigateur embarquable DORIS, intégré dans l'environnement MERCATOR, afin de le valider opérationnellement,

- réalisation du centre de Mécanique Spatiale pour le projet S80T, basé sur le générateur SISSI. Les fonctionnalités seront:
  * orbitographie du satellite: la mise en place d'un récepteur Doppler au pied de l'antenne permettra de disposer, pour un faible coût, de mesures Doppler sur la voie descendante. Ce qui rendra possible la restitution d'orbite du satellite.
  * localisation des brouilleurs: le traitement des courbes Doppler dans le nuage des mesures réalisées à bord, permettra de localiser les balises sol émettant dans une certaine bande de fréquence déterminée à priori.
  * restitution d'attitude,
  * prévisions opérationnelles,
  * tracés divers.

REFERENCE

[DORIS] C. JAYLES, H. RENAULT
On-Board Low-Earth Orbit Determination
AAS/AIAA Astrodynamics Specialist Conference august 19-22 1991

[FOLIA] J. FOLIARD
Présentation du développement de la partie Mécanique Spatiale d'un centre de contrôle de minisatellitesà défilement.
Note CNES, TE/IS/MS/AM/468 du 16 octobre 1991

[MERCATOR] B. BELON, J.C. BERGES, G. CAMPAN, P. LEGENDRE
MERCATOR, a new ground system for orbit and attitude control
Second International Symposium on Spacecraft Flight Dynamics, august 20-23 1986

[SISSI]
SISSI: Système Intéractif de Saisie et de Scrutation d'Informations
Notice d'utilisation, Version 1.0

LE SYSTEME INFORMATIQUE DE LA STATION SOL ARSENE

OUTIL DE CONTROLE ET DE DEVELOPPEMENT POUR PETITS SATELLITES

Jacques LAMAISON
Ingénieur au laboratoire d'Automatique
de l'Ecole Nationale Supérieure de
l'Aéronautique et de l'Espace
Sup'Aéro - Toulouse

Jean-Henri LLAREUS
Professeur
à l'Ecole Nationale Supérieure de
l'Aéronautique et de l'Espace
Sup'Aéro - Toulouse

L'objectif de cette publication est de présenter le système informatique de la station sol du mini-satellite ARSENE en mettant en avant les caractéristiques qui font son originalité et qui la rende particulièrement adaptée au contrôle et aussi au développement de petits satellites. Avant d'aborder, sur le plan technique, l'objet de notre communication, il nous semble important de la replacer dans le contexte du Projet ARSENE qui, après 13 ans de tribulations, est maintenant installé dans sa phase finale. Ceci, pour faire ressortir le caractère particulier de ce projet, quelque peu marginal, par rapport à un environnement de développement industriel et commercial classique, et aussi pour souligner l'extraordinaire aventure technique et humaine qui a marqué son déroulement.

LE PROJET ARSENE

Initiative de radio-amateurs du CNES groupés au sein de l'association Radio Amateurs Club de l'Espace (RACE), ARSENE (Ariane Radio-amateurs Satellite ENseignement Espace) est le nom donné à un programme de réalisation d'un mini-satellite pour les télécommunications de la communauté mondiale des radio-amateurs.

ARSENE est un mini-satellite de la classe des 150 kg, de forme hexagonale de 900 mm de diamètre et de 1100 mm de hauteur. Il est stabilisé par spin et le contrôle d'attitude est réalisé par un système de jets de gaz froids et d'un senseur Galiléo (terrestre et solaire). Il est équipé d'un moteur d'apogée en structure de carbone bobiné et de générateurs solaires AsGa. Sa charge utile est destinée aux télécommunications radio-amateurs.

Sans enjeu financier ou stratégique majeur, le projet est resté longtemps marginal, sans véritable budget, constamment à la recherche d'un groupe de projet structuré, de moyens de financement, de ressources matérielles et humaines. Porté à bout de bras par l'enthousiasme et la ténacité d'une poignée de personnes, le projet à toujours suscité et, même pendant les périodes les plus grises, sympathie, intérêt, voire attachement passionnel de la part des nombreux intervenants, que ce soit au niveau des individus : radioamateurs, étudiants, lycéens, ingénieurs, professeurs, appelés scientifiques, ouvriers et techniciens de tous métiers, secrétaires, retraités, bénévoles, que des organisations : industriels, organismes officiels, autorités…

Le projet a évolué, malgré tout, jusqu'à un niveau de crédibilité suffisant pour qu'en 1989, après une évaluation attentive, la Délégation Générale à l'Espace décide de fournir l'aide nécessaire pour terminer le satellite en milieu industriel en vue d'un lancement gratuit par Arianespace. Le vent avait tourné. Les concepts mis en œuvre pour ce satellite et son système d'embarquement, susceptibles d'autres applications, dans le cadre de l'intérêt grandissant pour les petits satellites, avaient fait leur chemin. Le combat changea d'âme. Les études papiers, les calculs, les schémas, les concepts, devinrent réalités physiquement palpables : un satellite intégré et en cours de tests fonctionnels à l'Aérospatiale de Cannes, une station de mise à poste mise en place à Sup'Aéro, un lanceur (Ariane vol n° 53), avec, en point de mire, ces quelques journées particulièrement exaltantes, et tant attendues, du mois de septembre 1992 qui concluront cette aventure : " ARSENE en orbite et fonctionnant pour le bonheur des radio-amateurs " et aussi pour celui de beaucoup d'autres.

Le projet ARSENE et l'enseignement

Dès l'origine, les initiateurs ont souhaité que le projet ARSENE soit la base d'une expérience pédagogique de grande ampleur en associant des établissements d'enseignement de toutes catégories, d'abord à l'étude, puis à la réalisation, et enfin au contrôle et à l'exploitation du système satellite ARSENE, véhicule et segment sol.

Il faut se féliciter de l'impact pédagogique du projet ARSENE, même si la prise en charge du projet dans son ensemble n'a pu se faire au sein d'une Ecole ou d'une Université, sans doute mal structurées pour une telle opération, comme ce fut le cas en Allemagne (Université de Marburg) ou en Grande Bretagne (Université du Surrey).

Plus de 300 collégiens, lycéens, étudiants, élèves-ingénieurs ont participé au programme ARSENE, encadrés par les personnels et les enseignants de leur institution. Ceux-ci appartenaient à 27 établissements d'enseignements : Grande Ecole, Université, IUT, Lycées, Collèges…Les participations ont été de natures diverses et variées : études papier, réalisation de maquettes, de sous-systèmes…Elles ont fait l'objet d'une thèse de Docteur-Ingénieur(Sup'Aéro), d'un mémoire CNAM (Sup'Aéro), de 90 projets ingénieurs dont deux primés par une médaille d'or IAF à Tokio et Rome (Sup'Aéro). Ces projets ont été réalisés dans le cadre de projets rémunérés et encadrés par l'industrie ou au sein de leur propre établissement.

Le projet ARSENE a permis, au travers de l'expérience concrètement vécue d'un projet à caractère industriel d'envergure, un rapprochement remarquable entre le monde industriel du domaine spatial et le monde de l'enseignement. Il a induit une sensibilisation aux contraintes de délais, aux modes de fonctionnement, à l'organisation du travail, aux normes et critères de qualité à mettre en œuvre pour obtenir, dans les délais prévus, des produits performants et de qualité. En associant des compétences diverses, il a largement contribué à la diffusion, à partir des établissements industriels ou étatiques (CNES, Aérospatiale, SEP, Arianespace…), de la culture scientifique et technique du domaine spatial.

Le projet ARSENE et Sup'Aéro

Tout à fait naturellement dans ce contexte, et compte tenu de sa vocation de formation dans le domaine spatial et des ressources humaines et matérielles dont elle dispose, Sup'Aéro a participé d'une manière particulièrement active au programme ARSENE.

Dans la phase amont des études de définition, de nombreux projets d'élèves et une thèse de Docteur-Ingénieur ont permis de spécifier, la mission du système satellite, la structure du satellite, son système de contrôle d'attitude, la propulsion, le segment sol. Dès 1983, il était décidé que la Station Sol de Contrôle ARSENE serait implantée à Toulouse et à Sup'Aéro. L'Ecole était chargée de la conception et de la réalisation de la partie informatique de cette station. En collaboration étroite avec les équipes compétentes du CNES, avec le RACE, Sup'Aéro assurera la mise en œuvre des ressources humaines et matérielles nécessaires aux opérations de mise à poste et de maintien à poste du satellite.

Quelle aventure et quel défi pour les personnels de l'Ecole et surtout pour les élèves ! Jusqu'à ce jour, dans le cadre d'activités pédagogiques variées, travaux d'initiation à la recherche, mini-projets, projets de fin d'études, thèse, en relation étroite avec les industriels du domaine, le CNES, le RACE, encadrés par les enseignants et les personnels de l'Ecole, en faisant participer des étudiants d'autres Ecoles, plus de 70 élèves de Sup'Aéro (près de 25 dans la phase finale) ont participé à cette aventure de longue haleine.

Depuis mars 1983, évoluant au rythme du projet ARSENE, les travaux relatifs à la conception et au développement du système informatique de la station de contrôle du satellite ARSENE se sont déroulés en 3 phases bien distinctes :
• De 1983 à 1984, réalisation des travaux de spécifications et de maquettages.
• De 1985 à 1989, conception et réalisation d'une première version de la station sol constituée de trois machines informatiques dédiées (Décodeur de Télémesure, Poste de Contrôle, Poste de Commande), construites à base de microprocesseurs 8 bits Intel 8085. Un de ces équipements a été utilisé par le CNES pour réaliser les tests, l'intégration et la validation des équipements embarqués à bord du satellite ARSENE.
• Depuis 1989, pour tenir compte de l'évolution des possibilités offertes par la micro-informatique moderne, étude et réalisation d'une deuxième version du système informatique de la station sol, à base de micro-ordinateurs compatibles IBM-PC. Livrée en juin 1991, il a été exploité et validé par l'Aérospatiale Cannes dans sa configuration Système d'Intégration et de Tests tout au long de la phase de développement et de validation du satellite. C'est cette dernière version qui est l'objet de cette communication.

LE SYSTEME INFORMATIQUE DE LA STATION SOL ARSENE

Le cahier des charges

Le système ARSENE a été conçu pour que les moyens à mettre en œuvre pour son contrôle soient aussi simples, peu coûteux, mais bien entendu, aussi efficaces que possible, en réduisant autant que faire se peut, le nombre et la complexité des opérations à réaliser.

1/ L'opérateur est dans la boucle. Pas de boucle automatique par le sol. L'opérateur prend connaissance de l'état des différents sous-systèmes du satellite, de son attitude, des aides de détermination de commande d'attitude et génère les commandes transmises au satellite

2/ Stabilisation d'attitude par spin.

3/ Pas de prétraitement d'informations à bord du satellite. Ce sont les informations brutes des capteurs qui sont transmises au sol par télémesure (ceci est particulièrement vrai pour les informations d'attitude et de spin issus des senseurs solaire et terrestres). La restitution de l'attitude du satellite en fonction des données senseurs et de la position du satellite sur son orbite (elle est obtenue par extrapolation à partir des caractéristiques d'orbite NORAD) est le résultat de calculs relativement complexes et volumineux.

4/ Contrôle d'attitude par système d'actuation à gaz froid (tuyère de spin , despin, de basculement. Des calculs, du même ordre que ceux définis ci-dessus et qui tiennent compte des caractéristiques mécaniques du satellite, permettent de définir le nombre de coup de tuyères et la durée d'émission de gaz nécessaires pour amener le satellite dans une attitude donnée à partir d'une attitude initiale.

5/ Pas de commande d'orbite (hors du transfert par tir du moteur d'apogée).

Les besoins opérationnels

Les différentes phases de développement, d'intégration, de validation, de mise à poste et de maintien à poste d'un système satellite nécessitent la mise en œuvre de procédures rigoureusement établies et appliquées et qui font appel à des outils de contrôle toujours plus sophistiqués, efficaces et qui doivent être suffisamment conviviaux pour les équipes d'opérateurs amenés à les manipuler sur leur poste de travail.

•Pour assurer une connaissance exhaustive de l'état des différents sous-systèmes embarqués, la position du satellite sur son orbite, son attitude…

- Acquisition et décodage des informations codées en binaire, organisées sous forme de trames, transmises par voies hertziennes (ou éventuellement par voies filaires dans la phase de développement) depuis le satellite vers le segment sol (télémesures, TM),
- Présentation de ces informations sous une forme compréhensible par l'opérateur,
- Vérification de la validité et de la cohérence des informations reçues,
- Mémorisation et datation des informations (heure, n° trame),
- Surveillance, observation de l'évolution des informations dans le temps, génération éventuelle d'alarmes.

•Pour assurer la commande des différents actuateurs qui permettent la réalisation des manœuvres nécessaires à la mise à poste du satellite, son maintien à poste et la gestion des différents équipements qui se trouvent à bord, plateforme et charge utile…

- Génération par l'opérateur des commandes à émettre, soit individuellement soit sous forme de séquences pré-enregistrées automatiques ou contrôlées,
- Vérification de la validité des ordres,
- Codage en binaire, construction de la trame de télécommande (TC).

Un segment sol ne peut être conçu sans la présence d'un système de simulation dynamique du comportement du satellite, attitude, orbitographie, fonctionnement des sous-systèmes. Un tel système apporte une aide indispensable dans les phases de développement et d'intégration, pour palier l'absence des équipements non encore intégrés, ou opérationnels. Il sert aussi à préparer et valider les procédures opérationnelles de manoeuvre prévues (cas nominal et cas dégradé), mais aussi non prévues, pour les phases de Mise à Poste et Maintien à Poste. Il faut souligner, également, le caractère pédagogique d'un tel système de simulation qui permettra, en Maintien à Poste et en exploitation, de réaliser des démonstrations, des essais de manœuvre, sans mettre en danger la vie du satellite.

On connait la puissance opérationnelle des systèmes de traitement de l'information qui permettent, entre autres, la réalisation d'interfaces confortables et efficaces entre des systèmes complexes (un avion, un système satellite, par exemple) et les opérateurs humains devant les contrôler. Il est tout naturel de faire appel à ces techniques pour réaliser les différents postes opérationnels d'un système de contrôle satellite dans les différentes phases de sa vie, en développement, au sol ou en orbite.

Les performances

Le nombre d'informations traitées ou stockées est relativement faibles : 110 informations de télémesure, 70 de télécommande.Elles sont codées en binaire et transmises en série à la vitesse de 128 bits/seconde.

Les traitements à effectuer sont essentiellement des codages, décodages, mises en forme, mémorisations. Ils peuvent être constitués de calculs plus ou moins complexes ou volumineux (orbitographie, restitution d'attitude), et, aussi, par une gestion d'enchaînements d'événements et d'opérations. Ces traitements sont, en général, on va le voir, peu contraints temporellement.

Les informations de télémesure sont organisées dans la trame sur 16 lignes de 64 octets (durée de transmission : 64 s). Chaque ligne est composée de 4 blocs de 16 octets dont 12 octets affectés à des informations du système de contrôle d'attitude (durée de transmission d'un bloc : 1 seconde). Autrement dit, les informations de contrôle d'attitude sont transmises toutes les une seconde. Les autre informations bord, analogiques ou numériques, peuvent être transmises de une à seize fois par trame.

Les contraintes temporelles ne sont pas très dures. Le temps de réponse est, en général, à l'échelle de la réaction humaine puisque, en tout état de cause, l'opérateur est dans la boucle, c'est-à-dire de quelques secondes ou de quelques minutes ; d'autant que les fenêtres de visibilité sont relativement longues (quelques heures) et que bon nombre de traitements peuvent être effectués hors fenêtre de visibilité.

Il faut cependant noter la forte indépendance des fonctions à générer et leurs conditions d'activation essentiellement différentes (notion de fort parallélisme). Ces fonctions peuvent être périodiques pour les actions permettant l'acquisition des trames de télémesure, leur décodage et leur pré-traitement. Elles peuvent être apériodiques pour les interventions humaines qui sont le fait d'opérateurs différents effectuant des tâches distinguées (exploitation des informations, stockage, génération des ordres…), et enfin périodiques pour la génération et la transmission des trames de télécommande.

Les contraintes

Il faut mettre en avant, pour la conception du système ARSENE, la recherche d'un rapport optimum entre les besoins opérationnels, les performances et les ressources nécessaires à leur réalisation ; cela pour des coûts aussi faibles que possible.

A notre sens, les principaux concepts qui doivent guider les choix techniques sont basés sur la réutilisation des ressources matérielles et logicielles mises en œuvre. Ceci favorise une évolutivité et une adaptabilité qui permettent de faire face aux modifications des différents besoins opérationnels et contraintes et prépare à un retour d'expérience tout à fait intéressant pour le développement de programmes ultérieurs.

Ce critère de réutilisation a également été choisi comme solution à l'assurance de bon fonctionnement du système en mode nominal ou mode dégradé dans les différentes phases de développement et de contrôle, mise à poste et maintien à poste, du système Satellite, il permet la duplication des ressources, la mise en œuvre de redondances chaudes et la possibilité de reconfigurations. Il favorise donc la maintenabilité du système.

Le concept de réutilisabilité ne peut être atteint sans une approche stricte des problèmes et passe par une recherche systématique, mais raisonnablement limitée par les coûts, de la portabilité des logiciels, la banalisation des ressources, essentiellement des ressources matérielles d'exécution. Il s'agit d'utiliser, aussi souvent que possible, les standards existants et de s'appuyer sur les règles et normes du génie logiciel.

L'architecture du segment sol

Si les postes opérationnels, tout au long de la vie du satellite, sont différenciés et d'un nombre pouvant varier dans un rapport de dix suivant la phase considérée (par exemple : phase de Maintien à Poste par rapport à la phase de Mise à Poste), il s'agit, en fait, de présenter à ces opérateurs qui travaillent de façon simultanée et d'une manière conviviale, les informations nécessaires à leur mission, éventuellement de les mémoriser ou de les traiter de façon adaptée pour préparer des décisions. Ces informations sont une partie de l'ensemble des informations d'état satellite pendant toutes phases de son cycle de vie. On peut dire que l'ensemble de ces informations constitue une ressource commune pour les différents postes opérationnels. Le bon fonctionnement est assuré par duplication des ressources d'exécution avec possibilité de reconfigurations. L'architecture du segment sol du satellite ARSENE est construite autour des entités suivantes :

Le système de contrôle

C'est l'ensemble des moyens informatiques distribués, faiblement couplés, permettant la réalisation du contrôle du satellite dans une des phases particulières du cycle de vie : le système de contrôle intégration et tests, le système de contrôle Mise à Poste (MIP), le système de contrôle de Maintien à Poste (MAP), des stations de contrôle spécialement configurées (station de contrôle de l'île de la Réunion),

Le poste opérationnel

Un système de contrôle défini ci-dessus, est constitué d'un ensemble de postes opérationnels. Un poste opérationnel permet la réalisation d'un ensemble de tâches représentant la mission d'un opérateur particulier (expert contrôle d'attitude, opérateur télécommande, chef de mission, responsable de détermination des manoeuvres...). Il est constitué d'un ensemble de ressources matérielles, d'interfaces particulières, mémoires de masse, imprimantes, ressources d'exécution sur lesquelles tournent les logiciels qui réalisent les fonctions nécessaires à la mise en oeuvre des tâches définies pour un poste opérationnel particulier.

Nous avons été amenés à distinguer les postes opérationnels suivants : poste de contrôle principal, poste de contrôle secondaire ou poste expert, poste de commande, poste orbitographie ou poste de localisation satellite, poste synoptiques, poste de simulation et de tests, poste de surveillance tuyères, poste balise de TéléMesure Réduite (TMR).

Tableau des fonctions des principaux postes opérationnels

Poste Opérationnel	Fonctions réalisées
Poste de Contrôle ou Poste de Contrôle Secondaire (Poste Expert)	• Acquisition des informations de télémesure prétraitées par le DTM (*), visualisation des informations reçues par l'intermédiaire de menus configurables par l'opérateur (A), surveillance des paramètres et gestion des alarmes (*), calcul restitution d'attitude (*), mémorisation des informations reçues ou calculées (*), dépouillement des informations mémorisées (courbes évolution temporelle) (B), aide à la détermination de commande (C). • Les fonctions A, B et C sont exécutées en exclusion mutuelle, les fonctions * sont exécutées en parallèle des fonctions A ou B ou C. •Les paramètres d'orbite du satellite sont des informations externes (NORAD).
Poste Synoptiques	• Visualisation synthétique sous forme graphique de l'état des différents sous-systèmes du satellite et des éléments de contrôle, historique des télécommandes. • Synoptiques sous-systèmes accessibles par menus, synoptiques animés par des informations de télémesure et de télécommande. • Rôle pédagogique. Convivialité efficace.
Poste de Commande	• Sélection par l'opérateur des ordres à émettre, soit individuellement ou sous forme de séquences pré-programmées contrôlées par l'opérateur ou envoyées automatiquement, transfert vers la partie RF des trames de télécommande (*), contrôle bonne réception satellite de l'ordre transmis par retour de télécommande via la télémesure, mémorisation des ordres transmis, recherche et dépouillement des ordres antérieurement transmis. • La fonction * est exécutée en parallèle des autres fonctions (environ 75 o/s). • L'accès aux commandes du poste de commande est protégé par un mécanisme de mots de passes hiérarchisés. Le mot de passe de la personne habilitée est demandé à l'initialisation du système et pour la génération de commandes critiques (par exemple pour le tir du moteur d'apogée).

Poste Opérationnel	Fonctions réalisées
Poste Surveillance Tuyères	• Permet la détection des fuites tuyères. • Visualisation des informations des senseurs terrestre et solaire reçues chaque seconde dans la trame de télémesure, calcul de la vitesse de spin et des angles d'attitude du satellite
Poste Orbitographie	• Visualisation de la trace du satellite sur une projection des continents, visualisation de l'attitude du satellite, de sa position sur son orbite, prévision des visibilités électriques et des visibilités senseurs, visualisation des visibilités géométriques des différentes stations, détermination des commandes antennes du segment sol. • Les paramètres d'orbite du satellite sont des informations externes (NORAD).
Balise de TéléMesure Réduite TMR	• Version dégradée du Poste de Contrôle. • Visualisation et mémorisation des informations de la trame réduite. Pas d'information du système de contrôle d'attitude.
Poste de Simulation / Tests	• Génération de trames de télémesure, saisies au clavier, mémorisées antérieurement ou résultats d'une simulation, acquisition des trames de télécommande, simulation du comportement de sous systèmes du satellite, calculs et génération des tops senseur déterminés à partir des données d'orbite, de l'attitude et de la vitesse de spin du satellite obtenus par simulation dynamique en réponse aux signaux de commande des tuyères acquis sur une interface particulière. • Les paramètres d'orbite du satellite sont des informations externes (NORAD). • Plusieurs utilisations et configurations possibles : Simulation du fonctionnement du satellite en fermant la boucle télémesure - opérateur - télécommande, ceci dans toutes les phase de la vie du satellite : élaboration et validation des sénarios opérationnels, entraînement des personnels lors de la phase de qualification opérationnelle, pour des démonstrations, ou une exploitation pédagogique. Test et validation de la station sol. Validation de la boucle de contrôle d'attitude. Validation du Codeur TéléMesure et Décodeur TéléCommande embarqués sur le satellite.

Les ressources d'exécution :

Les ressources d'exécution sont banalisées et autonomes. Ce sont des micro-ordinateurs standards de grande diffusion, compatibles IBM-PC, connectés à des périphériques standards (imprimantes, liaisons séries…). Ces micro-ordinateurs sont relativement peu coûteux, ont atteint un niveau de fiabilité suffisant et pemettent des interfaces homme-machine conviviales et performantes.

Les différents postes opérationnels sont configurés, premièrement, par la mise en place, directement dans le micro-ordinateur, et lorsque cela est nécessaire, de cartes d'interfaces particulières, et, deuxièmement, par l'exécution d'un logiciel spécifique au poste. Ce logiciel particulier peut être installé sur toutes les ressources d'exécution à condition, bien sûr, que la constitution matérielle du poste le permette. En particulier, les cartes d'interfaces spécifiques et les périphériques nécessaires doivent être présents.

Les cartes d'interfaces spécifiques à implanter directement dans le micro-ordinateur sont de trois types.

- • la carte Génération Trame : Sérialisation des trames de télécommande et de télémesure.
- • la carte Acquisition Trame : Désérialisation des informations des trames de télécommande et de télémesure.
- • la carte Interface Equipements Satellite (LCA-EMA). Cette carte réalise l'interface avec la Logique de Contrôle d'Attitude du satellite, logique de commande tuyères et avec l'Electronique de Mesure d'Attitude du satellite (acquisition tops senseurs). Elle est utilisée uniquement dans le poste de simulation pour la phase de développement et d'intégration.

Tableau de configuration matérielle des postes opérationnels

La ressource d'exécution de base est constituée d'un micro-ordinateur compatible IBM-PC 386 équipé d'une carte écran VGA, d'un lecteur de disquette 3,5", d'un disque dur de 40 Mo, deux liaisons série dont une pour la souris. Le micro-ordinateur doit posséder, dans son châssis, un certain nombre d'emplacements libres pour l'accueil de cartes d'interface standard (parallèle ou série) ou de cartes spécifiques. La connexion d'une mémoire de masse amovible (Data Pack) ou d'une imprimante laser ou à aiguille dépend de la configuration particulière du poste.

Poste Opérationnel	STANDARD			SPECIFIQUE		
	Data Pack amovible	Disquette 5,25"	Coproces-seur arithmétique	Carte Génération Trame	Carte Acquisition Trame	Carte Equipe-ments satellites LCA-EMA
Poste de Contrôle Principal	1	1	1	0	0	0
Poste de Contrôle Secondaire (Poste Expert)	optionnel	0	0	0	0	0
Poste Balise TMR	optionnel	0	0	0	0	0
Poste Orbitographie	0	0	1	0	0	0
Poste Surveillance Tuyères	0	0	0	0	1	0
Poste Synoptiques	optionnel	0	0	1	1	0
Poste de Commande	optionnel	0	0	1	0	0
Poste Simulation /Tests	0	0	1	1	1(*)	1(*)

(*) L'absence de ces cartes spécifiques supprime les fonctions associées réalisées par le logiciel.

Le Décodeur de Télémesure
Le Décodeur de TéléMesure, (DTM) est un élément essentiel du système de contrôle satellite ARSENE.

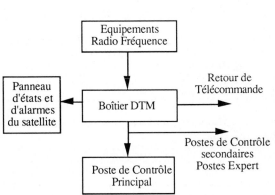

Le DTM réalise l'acquisition et le décodage de la trame TM en principe issu de la partie Radio-Fréquence. Il gère un panneau, optionnel, d'états et d'alarmes du satellite, informations critiques présentées, dès leur réception, le plus souvent sous leur forme brute. Il réalise le prétraitement des infor-mations, leur diffusion par liaison série vers le poste de contrôle principal et les postes de contrôle secondaires (postes Expert), le transfert du retour de télécommande vers le poste de commande.

Le DTM est une machine informatique spécifique, construite, dans sa version actuelle, autour d'un microprocesseur 8 bits, qui est gérée par un exécutif temps réel et qui, associé à un automate de désérialisation, réalise les fonctions d'acquisition, de désérialisation et de prétraitement des informations de trame, de façon indépendante, ce qui permet d'obtenir les temps de réponse requis pour un bon fonctionnement du système.La version actuelle du DTM assure parfaitement la gestion du flux d'information acquis à 128 b/s. Elle doit évoluer pour permettre la prise en compte de débits de télémesure plus importants, jusqu'à 20 kb/s, et des traitements plus sophistiqués.

Les logiciels

Les logiciels du Segment Sol ARSENE sont exécutables sur des micro-ordinateurs compatibles IBM-PC. Ils s'appuient sur les ressources logicielles du système d'exploitation MS-DOS et du BIOS. Ils représentent environ 30 000 lignes de TURBO-PASCAL (version 5.5).

Ce langage a été choisi car il induit une qualité des programmes conforme à nos objectifs (déclarations systématiques, typage des informations, structuration des programmes), il donne accès à des fonctions graphiques et d'interface homme-machine suffisamment performantes, ainsi qu'une formulation efficace pour le développement des différents modules de calculs (orbitographie, restitution d'attitude) à mettre en œuvre dans le système. Les contraintes de temps de réponse et d'occupation mémoire étant peu critiques dans notre application, les performances du Turbo-Pascal, sont, à cet égard, tout à fait acceptables.

Le logiciel a été conçu pour être facilement adaptable dans des contextes d'exploitation différents. Si la ressource d'exécution reste le micro-ordinateur IBM-PC, ce logiciel supporte facilement les modifications et les évolutions et il permet la réalisation de postes opérationnels variés et de systèmes de contrôle adaptés à des satellites différents.

La portabilité par rapport aux systèmes de contrôle, aux postes opérationnels et au satellite à contrôler, repose sur une conception modulaire, une approche objet, en particulier pour les interfaces homme-machine, et par la mise en œuvre de bases de données technologiques spécifiques au segment sol et au satellite contrôlé. Certaines de ces données sont figées pour toute la vie du système de contrôle et du satellite ; elles sont regroupées dans des fichiers de déclarations au niveau source et peuvent être modifiées par recompilation : format de trames, identification des paramètres et messages visualisés associés, description des sous-systèmes satellites, arborescence des menus d'accès...D'autres informations peuvent évoluer pendant la vie du satellite et doivent pouvoir être modifiées dynamiquement. Ces informations sont regroupées au niveau des exécutables dans une unité commune à tous les postes opérationnels et sont modifiables par un logiciel à accès protégé, exécuté à partir du poste de contrôle principal : informations d'orbite NORAD, courbes de réponse, plages de fonctionnement des capteurs qui sont susceptibles de vieillissement ...

Les logiciels segment sol du satellite ARSENE sont fournis sous forme de répertoires correspondant aux différents postes opérationnels mis en œuvre.

REPERTOIRE	MISSION
COMMUN	Base de données technologiques du satellite et exécutable de gestion de cette base.
CONTROLE	Logiciels de gestion du poste de contrôle (principal et secondaire) et fichiers associés.
COMMANDE	Logiciels de gestion du poste de commande et fichiers associés
SYSTEST	Logiciels de gestion du poste de Simulation et de Tests et fichiers associés
BALISE	Logiciels de gestion du poste Balise de TéléMesure Réduite (TMR) et fichiers associés
TUYERES	Logiciels de gestion du poste de Détection des Fuites Tuyères et fichiers associés
ORBITOGRAPHIE	Logiciels de gestion du poste Orbitographie (localisation satellite) et fichiers associés
SYNOPTIC	Logiciels de gestion du poste Synoptiques et fichiers associés

L'ensemble de ces répertoires sont regroupés sur une même disquette 3,5". Ils peuvent être installés et exécutés sur n'importe quel compatible IBM-PC, ressource d'exécution commune à tous les postes opérationnels. Le logiciel relatif à un poste opérationnel sera convenablement exécuté si la ressource d'exécution est convenablement configurée par la mise en place des périphériques (imprimantes, mémoires de masse), des connexions standards (liaisons série, parallèles) et des cartes spécifiques nécessaires.

On voit donc qu'un poste est facilement et rapidement configuré ou reconfiguré, en cas de panne par exemple, par une éventuelle reconfiguration matérielle et par l'exécution du logiciel approprié, à partir d'une disquette commune. Ainsi, le poste de contrôle peut facilement devenir poste de commande ou poste synoptique.

Schéma de configuration d'un poste opérationnel

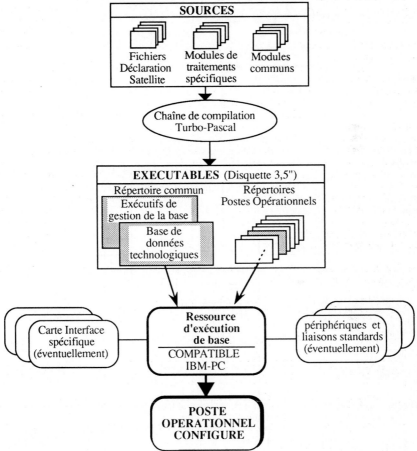

Les systèmes de contrôle satellite de la Station Sol ARSENE.

A partir des postes opérationnels configurés, définis ci-dessus, nous avons pu constituer les systèmes de contrôle du segment sol ARSENE. Ils sont aujourd'hui opérationnels. L'effort de configuration a toujours été limité et nous avons pu répondre aux sollicitations opérationnelles et aux évolutions du cahier des charges dans des temps relativement courts ; par exemple trois mois pour le système de Mise à Poste.

Composition d'un système de contrôle

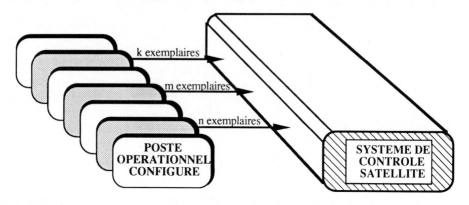

Tableau de configuration des systèmes de contrôle de la Station Sol ARSENE

Poste opérationnel Système de contrôle satellite	Con- trôle	Com- mande	Expert	synop -tiques	Orbito	Tuyè -res	Simu /tests	Balise TMR	DTM	Panneau Etats Alarmes
Système Intégration et Tests (AsCa + Kourou) 3 postes opérationnels TM-TC	1	1					1		1	1
Système de Mise à Poste (Sup'Aéro Toulouse) 29 postes opérationnels TM-TC	1+1(*)	1+1(*) (1)	12	6	3	2	1	1	1+1(*)	1+1(*)
Système de Maintien à Poste (Sup'Aéro Toulouse) 10 postes opérationnels TM-TC	1+1(*)	1+1(*)		1	2	1	1	1	1+1(*)	1+1(*)
Station Ile de la Réunion 4 postes opérationnels TM seule (2)	1+1(*)					1	1 (3)		1+1(*)	

Les chiffres présentés ne tiennent compte que des redondances chaudes (*) et non des postes de secours et des stocks de maintenance prêts à être configurés.

(1) Une recopie d'écran télécommande est distribuée sur 9 postes opérateurs.
(2) Info TM transmise par MODEM vers la station de Mise à Poste Sup'Aéro Toulouse.
(3) Sans tops tuyères.

Les évolutions du système informatique de la Station Sol ARSENE

Les concepts qui ont guidé la réalisation du segment sol ARSENE ont permis de répondre, de façon efficace et dans les temps impartis aux demandes fonctionnelles formulées et aux performances requises. Ils sont porteurs d'adaptabilité et d'évolutivité. L'aventure technique n'est donc pas terminée et des améliorations des postes opérationnels du segment sol ARSENE sont d'ores et déjà prévues :

Développement d'un nouveau décodeur de télémesures

Il sera totalement intégré au poste de contrôle. Il est en cours d'étude et de développement (délai 6 mois). Ce nouveau DTM, machine informatique spécifique à base de micro-processeur 16 bits apportant une puissance de traitement accrue, sera totalement configurable et géré à partir du poste de contrôle principal pour s'adapter à différents types de trames de télémesures et de satellites : débit, mots de synchronisation, format de trame (affectation des paramètres dans la trame, organisation temporelle et spatiale, longueur, nombre de bits, de mots...), messages à afficher sur les postes de contrôle, messages pour le panneau d'états et d'alarmes. La liaison DTM-Poste de contrôle se fera par Mémoire Double Accès, ce qui permettra de porter le débit d'acquisition de trame à 20 kbits/seconde. Ce nouveau DTM assurera aussi la diffusion des informations de trame, de la base de données technologique du poste de contrôle principal vers tous les postes expert ou autres postes opérationnels.

Prise en compte de l'état satellite pour le contrôle des télécommandes générées

A l'heure actuelle la validité des commandes envoyées au satellite est conditionnée par la qualité du travail des opérateurs qui analysent l'état du satellite et définissent les commandes ou les séquences de commandes à générer sur le poste de commande. Ils sont aidés dans leur travail par des procédures manuscrites préalablement définies.

Dans sa nouvelle version, le poste de commande recevra du décodeur de télémesure un certain nombre d'informations d'état du satellite qui seront utilisées pour conditionner l'envoi des commandes, soit de façon automatique, soit sous le contrôle de l'opérateur qui, de toute manière, sera informé du déroulement des opérations et pourra éventuellement intervenir.

Contrôle du panneau d'états et d'alarmes

Le contrôle du panneau d'états et d'alarmes sera réalisée par une machine informatique spécifique connectée au DTM par une liaison série standard.

Nouveau panneau d'états et d'alarmes satellite

Intégration des postes opérationnels synoptiques actuels pour la définition d'un nouveau panneau d'états et d'alarmes.

Système de télésurveillance de la station sol

Etude et réalisation d'un système de télésurveillance du bon fonctionnement de la station Sol par une liaison téléphonique vers les responsables en astreinte.

Il est certain que cette liste de modifications en cours d'étude n'est pas close aujourd'hui et que, au cours de la vie d'ARSENE, de nouveaux besoins opérationnels apparaîtront et feront évoluer la station actuelle.

CONCLUSION

Ainsi donc, voici le mini-satellite ARSENE pourvu d'un Segment Sol opérationnel, conçu et développé au sein d'un établissement d'enseignement et dont le bon fonctionnement a été éprouvé lors des phases du développement par un industriel spécialiste du domaine. Il tourne actuellement pour les épreuves de qualifications opérationnelles. Il est utilisé par l'équipe d'opérateurs et d'experts composée d'élèves, de personnels de Sup'Aéro et du CNES, pour se former, se préparer au Grand Soir ou le lanceur ARIANE lâchera ARSENE sur son orbite de transfert et à ces heures exaltantes de la Mise à Poste qui suivront.

Pour nos élèves et pour tous les autres, le rêve deviendra réalité, ce rêve, issu de ces images d'"Objectif Lune" et de "On a marché sur la lune", de ces salles de contrôle de Cap Kennedy, en cette nuit du 21 Juillet 1969 où le premier être humain foula le sol lunaire.

On pourrait comparer le développement du projet ARSENE et de sa station sol au déroulement d'un conte qui décrirait les tribulations scientifiques et humaines de personnages en butte aux attaques des dragons de la lassitude, du renoncement, de l'indifférence et de l'oubli, évoluant dans un environnement semé d'embûches (pas d'enjeu financier, peu d'argent, organisation difficile à mettre en place dans des milieux hétérogènes), mais qui poursuivent leur objectif avec astuce, intelligence et détermination et qui, en fin de compte (ou conte) se retrouvent aux portes du palais de la princesse pour subir les dernières épreuves (le lancement, la Mise à Poste).

La formule utilisée pour la fin d'un conte est traditionnelle : " ils vécurent heureux...". En fait, est-ce bien la fin du conte, ou le début d'une nouvelle histoire ? Car enfin, oserait-on laisser se perdre un tel retour d'expérience, les concepts d'ARSENE, petit satellite simple et robuste, de la classe des 150 kg, pourvu d'un moteur d'apogée, du lancement sur ARIANE en troisième passager, d'une station de développement et de contrôle évolutive utilisant au maximum des éléments banalisés et peu coûteux, le rapprochement productif des milieux industriels et de l'enseignement, la diffusion de la culture espace. Aucun doute, c'est le début d'une nouvelle histoire.

SATELLITE CONTROL

A Comprehensive Approach

By: J.T. Garner

ESA, Noordwijk, The Netherlands

Abstract:

Post launch satellite control is undertaken by the Telemetry Tracking and Telecommand (TTC) system elements that are operated under the executive control of the Earth Segment. Satellites which have been produced under the auspices of the European Space Agency (ESA) have also been controlled by telemetry and telecommand facilities during pre-launch operations.

On the communication satellite programmes of ESA the European Test and Operations Language (ETOL) has been actively engaged for satellite control purposes during satellite construction and launch. ETOL is also employed for monitoring the condition and status of ESA's communication satellites that are in orbit.

If pre-launch satellite activities are a simulation of expected post-launch conditions then common equipments and methodologies could be employed throughout the complete life cycle of the satellite. This approach has not been actively employed on programmes which have produced large satellites for ESA. On programmes of other authorities for smaller satellites such a comprehensive approach for satellite control has been undertaken. In such a case pre-launch activities can be regarded as being control and test whilst post-launch activities are control and use. The commonality of satellite control via telemetry and telecommand for pre and post launch activities therefore gives opportunities for re-using equipment and methodologies. This can present cost effective solutions which from a comprehensive satellite life cycle standpoint could be commercially attractive besides enhancing safety of system operations.

Satellite Operations

The operational life cycle of a satellite should be considered to begin before launch and terminate at End of Life (EOL) in orbit. During this period, which can last for several years, the satellite is controlled by telemetry and telecommands. The control activities embrace satellite condition and status besides maintaining orbital requirements.

Satellites which have been constructed on programmes of the European Space Agency ESA have been controlled before and after they are launched. Prior to launch vehicle lift-off satellite operations have involved control and verification, whilst after separation from the launcher satellite operations have embraced control and utilization. Consequently a common factor from an overall system standpoint is satellite control. This can be considered as a process that embraces the monitoring of satellite health; condition and status. If unwanted criteria are attained then either automatic or manually instigated recovery actions are undertaken. For satellite health control this process is performed by telemetering from the satellite, analogue values and digital status, analyzing the results and if necessary transmitting commands to relieve an unwanted situation. Similarly the satellite's orbit is controlled as a post-launch activity employing orbital tracking facilities. Obviously this is not performed before launch but functional tests are undertaken and criteria established for attaining and maintaining operational orbits.

The complete operational life cycle of a satellite from a comprehensive stand point can therefore be considered to commence when all on-board satellite subsystems are integrated and system level activities commence. The life cycle terminates in orbit either due to malfunctions or after expenditure of all available on-board fuel.

Comprehensive Control

The functional architecture of complete aerospace systems in fully operational states are shown in principle on Figure 1. It will be seen that the Earth Segment is composed of User facilities and elements which are employed to support spacecraft control. The control facilities are usually known as the Ground Segment and the term Ground Control Segment would perhaps be more correct today. The overall system requirements for a complete aerospace system will embrace both the Space and Earth segments and encompass pre and post launch operations. Figure 2 shows the Earth Segment for post-launch activities and Figure 3 shows the Earth Segment for pre-launch operations of ESA's communication satellites.

The satellite design process should emanate from post launch requirements of the satellite users. Consequently satellite Assembly, Integration and Verification (AIV) can embrace simulations of expected conditions that the satellite will experience after its integration with the launch vehicle upto its End Of Life (EOL) in orbit. This AIV process can involve the testing of on-board redundancies and any automatic recovery actions. The satellite

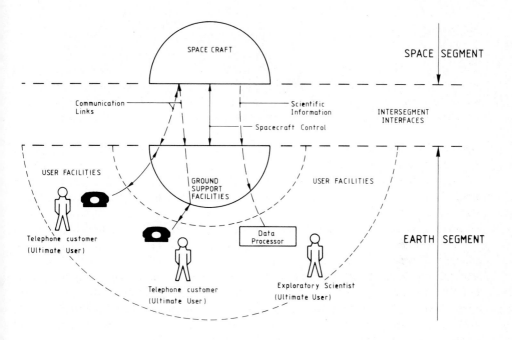

Figure 1.   Functional Architecture of Fully Operational Aerospace Systems

AIV programme can be a dominant factor for Ground Control Segment element re-use for a single satellite besides Aerospace programmes which require a series of similar satellites. Such a re-use may be considered as vertical rationalization commencing with the production of a fully integrated satellite and terminating at EOL. If this complete vertical rationalization is not achieved similarities between satellites of different programmes can enable horizontal rationalization to be achieved. An overview of horizontal and vertical rationalization for satellite operation can be assessed from Figure 4. No matter how much horizontal or vertical rationalization of working practices are achieved satellite control is the centre piece for all operational tasks as is depicted in Figure 5. for the complete lifecycle

Technology Re-use

The re-use of equipment, for unmanned launches on expendable launch vehicles, will be dominated by the baseband components of the Ground Control Segment. However some re-use of the satellite's ultimate users equipment can occur. This re-use of ultimate user equipment for pre and post launch activities is more likely to be attractive for a satellite engaged on a scientific mission.

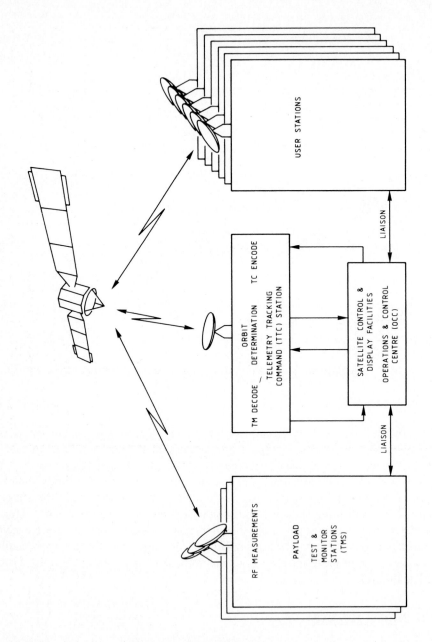

Figure 2   Post Launch Earth Segment

Geostationary Communications Satellite

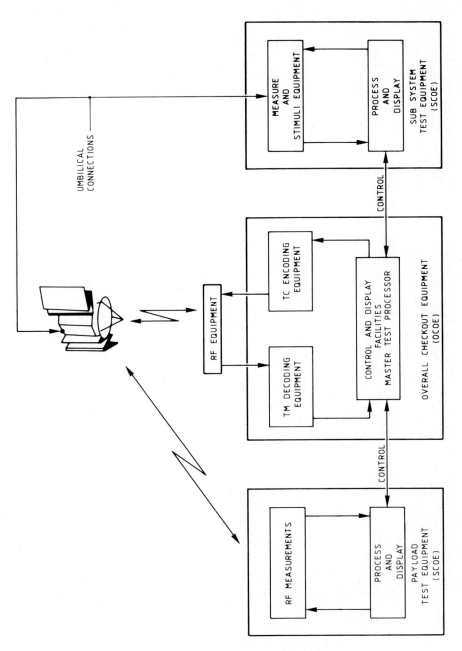

Figure 3 Pre Launch Earth Segment

Geostationary Communications Satellite

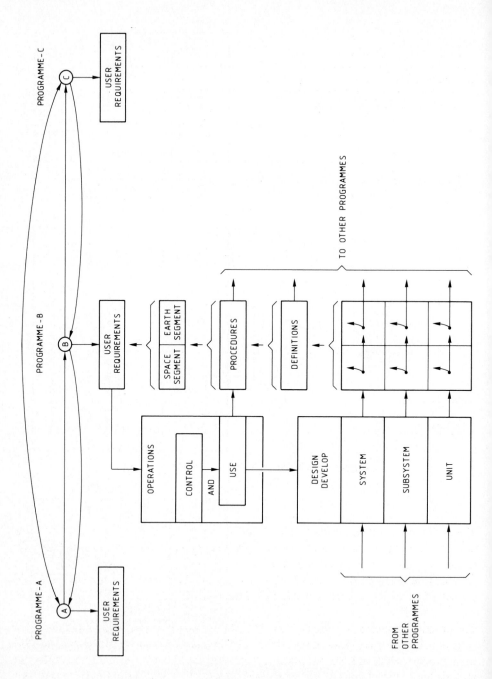

Figure 4   System Rationalization Methodology

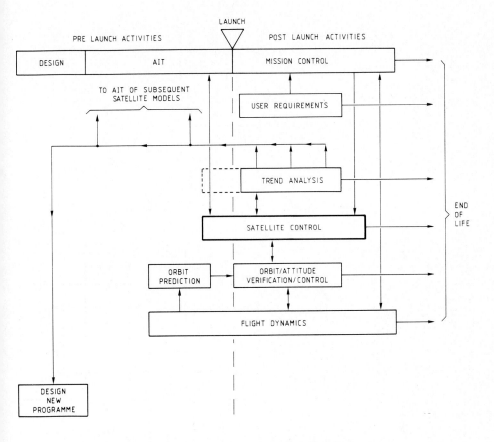

Figure 5   Complete Lifecycle of Satellite Operations

The system level functional architecture for the control of a large geostationary commu-nications satellite is given in Figure 6. The elements which present an opportunity for re-use on both scientific exploratory and commercial exploitation satellite programmes are the Telemetry decoding and Telecommand encoding equipment together with the executive controller and its associated workstations.

The practical re-use of any ground control elements may not, from a satellite production schedule, be attractive. However re-use can be the result of a single design and develop-ment process which produces duplicate identical equipment and methodologies. This can include the re-use of computer software, which was developed during satellite construc-tion, for post-launch operational activities.

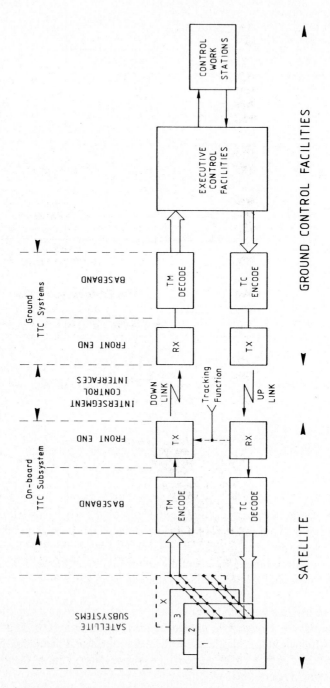

Figure 6   Functional Architecture for Satellite Control

ESA Experiences

The experiences of ESA on Communication Satellite Programmes has enabled both vertical and horizontal rationalization to be achieved to some extent. System elements, particularly computer software, have been re-used for monitoring the satellite's condition and status via telemetry both before and after launch. Horizontal rationalization has allowed the pre launch executive controller to be practically identical for satellites of the European Communications Satellite (ECS) and the Maritime European Communications Satellite (MARECS) programs as well as other non ESA programmes. Developments have also enabled re-use from these programmes to be applied for the pre and post launch operations of the ESA Olympus satellite. The prime system element which has allowed both vertical and horizontal rationalization to occur is the European Test and Operations Language (ETOL). Its unnamed forerunner was used on ESA's first communication satellite OTS. From this ETOL was developed and used on MARECS a year after the successful OTS launch in 1978. Since then ETOL developments have embraced directly the requirements of MARECS, ECS and other non ESA satellite programmes followed by Olympus which was launched on 12th July 1989.

A version of ETOL for post launch monitoring of ESA's communication satellites operates on a Communication Satellite Monitoring Facility (CSMF) stand alone work-station. Such a workstation decommutates the satellite telemetry baseband signal and processes the results with a personal computer. The display of processed telemetry data is almost identical to that which was employed with the pre-launch executive controller during satellite Assembly, Integration and Verification (AIV).

ETOL Developments

ETOL developments have been a co-operative effort by ESA and Industry. Such developments have been undertaken to meet the requirements of scientific and applications spacecraft. ETOL enables users to be actively involved in the configuration of satellite control software to meet their requirements which can include the automation of procedures and display facilities. Synoptic pictures can be developed and a zoom capability can be achieved for the display of telemetry data. Displays of telemetered data can also be made in a purely alpha-numeric form besides displays which present only textual explanatory information.

The current status of ETOL for ESA communication satellites enables a mini computer based system to be employed. Developments regarding ETOL and the mini computer are being undertaken by industry for the ESA Data Relay Programme with the Agency playing a monitoring role. ETOL developments for personal computer applications with the CSMF stand-alone workstations for communications satellites are under direct ESA control but with industrial partners.

CSMF Status

The ESA Communication Satellite Monitoring Facilities (CSMF) that employ ETOL are:

a)   The CSMF Centre

This is a development of the pre-launch executive control centres that were employed on all ESA communication satellite programmes. The pre-launch control centres are more commonly known as Overall CheckOut Equipments (OCOE). The CSMF centre can construct and operate all databases and automatic routines that enables a satellite to be monitored via ETOL in real-time.

b)   CSMF Stand-Alone Workstations.

These take satellite telemetry signals in PCM form as the input and after processing display the results in real-time in the same manner as the CSMF centre and consequently the OCOE. Any modifications to the ETOL databases that operate on a stand alone workstation need to be made on the central system and downloaded to the personal computer of these workstations.

ETOL developments for communication satellites commenced in the late 1970's and have continued to give the CSMF stand alone workstation which actively supports in orbit operations of Olympus. Indeed such a workstation is employed at the Olympus user coordination centre which is located in Redu, Belgium.

Applications to Small Satellites

The use of ETOL for small satellites could give an opportunity for employing facilities which have been developed and employed on large satellites. Some small satellite programmes have adopted a control methodology which has exploited pre and post launch commonalities. ETOL could provide a means to this end for expanding the field of activities which involve the control of small satellites. Certainly in the area of communication systems a significant number of small satellites in polar orbits could be the Space Segment of a future communications system. In addition small satellites in Polar orbits could complement large satellites in geostationary positions in the future. So perhaps the Ground Control Segments and the re-use of experiences before launch will be passed over to post launch operations more directly than has happened in the past.

This handover can give cost effective solutions that embraces a number of resources including manpower, equipment hardware and documentation besides computer software associated with telemetry and telecommand. The resources that have been proven for both vertical and horizontal rationalization regarding ESA communication satellites can perhaps be employed on small satellite programmes and give a commercially attractive solution for satellite control. The attractions of employing such a methodology can reduce risk and increase safety if the pre launch space segment AIV programme is based upon the post launch operational activities giving a comprehensive solution with commercial attractions. Furthermore a single development activity for satellite control equipment and procedures will ease production schedules and promote a coordinated core team that can efficiently handle complete satellite operations.

Bibliography

This paper is based upon the principles outlined by J.T. Garner and M. Jones in the the publication of the Ellis Horwood Library of Space Science and and Space Technology entitled "Satellite Operations - Systems approach to design and control".

SYNTHESE DE LA SESSION
MOYENS SOLS

1 - Le segment sol des petits satellites, comprenant la station d'émission/réception TM/TC et la station de contrôle est réalisable avec de petits moyens en utilisant des matériels et logiciels standards. On peut, à cet effet, citer les stations sol type ARSENE ou UOSAT, réalisées avec 1 ou 2 PC et le projet espagnol avec des stations de travail. Une approche intégrée, prenant en compte les besoins et les contraintes de la composante sol dès le début du projet, est importante afin de permettre par exemple l'utilisation de la station pendant l'intégration du satellite.

2 - Le choix ou la répartition entre un environnement existant (logiciels de contôle, stations...) et le développement de moyens spécifiques reste à effectuer en tenant compte des coûts d'exploitation associés aux moyens tels que les stations de réception actuelles.

3 - De nouveaux travaux doivent être entrepris pour, d'une part, développer des matériels de communication peu coûteux adaptés à ce type de satellite et, d'autre part, réfléchir à des segments sol utilisables non pas pour un petit satellite, mais pour les constellations à nombreux satellites envisagées.

SYNTHESIS OF THE SESSION
GROUND INFRASTRUCTURE

1) The ground segment for small satellites, comprising the TM/TC transmission-reception station and the control station, can be set up with limited means using standard hardware and software. The ARSENE and UOSAT ground stations, with 1 or 2 PC's, and the Spanish project using work stations are examples of this. An integrated approach, taking the needs and constraints of the ground component into consideration from the start of the project, is important if the station is to be used, for example, during satellite integration.

2) The choice or distribution between the use of an existing environment (control software, stations, etc.) and the development of specific means remains to be made, taking into account the running costs associated with facilities such as current receiving stations.

3) New work needs to be undertaken in order to i) develop inexpensive communication equipment suited to this type of satellite and ii) think about ground segments usable not for one small satellite but for the constellations of numerous satellites that can be foreseen.

SYSTEMES
DE RADIOCOMMUNICATIONS
ET LEURS APPLICATIONS

RADIOCOMMUNICATIONS SYSTEMS
AND APPLICATIONS

REGULATION OF LOW EARTH ORBIT SATELLITES

Don Jayasuriya

Radiocommunications Agency, Dept. of Trade and Industry, United Kingdom

Introduction

There has been a growing interest in utilising small satellites in Low Earth Orbits (LEO) to provide services ranging from low speed data to voice communications. The WARC-92 Conference held in February 1992 allocated a number of frequency bands to the Mobile Satellite service within which LEO systems could operate.

The allocation of these frequency bands within the spectrum used by other radio services has caused a great deal of difficulties for the establishment of the inter service[$] frequency sharing criteria and the regulatory procedures for the Coordination and Notification of frequency assignments. The intra service[¥] frequency sharing also causes difficulties because of the complex sharing mechanisms between LEO and Geostationary/LEO systems. The studies on frequency sharing with the existing services have been continuing for many years within the CCIR and some of the preliminary results have been published as the CCIR Report to the WARC-92. As a result of these findings the frequencies allocated by the WARC have been subjected to a number of provisos included in the Radio Regulations under various provision numbers, called "Footnotes" to the Table of Allocations.

This paper describes the allocations made by the WARC-92 and their associated inter and intra service frequency sharing difficulties. Various provisos introduced by the WARC-92 which impact on the operation of LEO systems are also highlighted. The regulatory aspects such as type approval and licensing are briefly presented.

Frequency Allocations

The discussions on frequency sharing aspects, anticipating the allocation of certain frequency bands to the Mobile Satellite Service (MSS) for the use by LEO satellites, have continued within CCIR Study Group 8 for a number of years, in preparation for the WARC-92. Following the decisions of WARC-92 these studies are expected to continue for several more years until the their conclusions are adopted as CCIR Recommendations.

The additional allocations of frequency to the MSS made by the WARC-92 are given in the Tables 1 and 2. These only include allocations made on a "worldwide" basis and made within the main body of the Table of Allocations (i.e. excluding Footnote allocations).

$ -   Inter service: Frequency sharing between the networks of different radiocommunication
      services

¥ -   Intra service: Frequency sharing between different networks of the same
      radiocommunication service

Allocations below 1 GHz:

TABLE 1

Frequency band MHz	Service	Footnotes
137 - 138	MSS/mss (segmented Primary and Secondary) /space to Earth	599A*, 599B
148 - 149.9	MSS/Earth to space	599B, 608X*, 608Z
149.9 - 150.05	LMSS/Earth to space	599B, 609B, 608Y*
400.15 - 401	MSS/space to Earth	599B, 647X*

* - application of Resolution COM 5/8

Note: MSS designates a Primary MSS allocation
         mss designates a Secondary MSS allocation

Allocations above 1 GHz:

TABLE 2

Frequency band MHz	Service	Footnotes
1525 - 1530	MMSS/lmss Region 2 MSS Regions 1 and 3 space to Earth	726B, 726X*
1610 - 1610.6	MSS/Earth to space	733E, 731X*
1610.6 - 1613.8	MSS/Earth to space	733E, 731X*
1613.8 - 1626.5	MSS/Earth to space mss/space to Earth	733E, 731X*, 731Y
1980 - 2010	MSS/Earth to space	746X*, 746U
2170 - 2200	MSS/space to Earth	746X*, 746U
2483.5- 2500	MSS/space to Earth	753X*
2500- 2520	MSS/space to Earth	760X*
2670 - 2690	MSS/Earth to space	764A*

* application of Resolution COM5/8

Note: MSS designates a Primary MSS allocation
         mss designates a Secondary MSS allocation

Radio Regulatory Aspects

The Coordination and Notification of the frequency assignments to space stations are covered by the Articles 11 and 13 of the Radio Regulations. Whilst it has been recognised that these regulations have served adequately for the satellite systems operated from the Geostationary Satellite Orbit (GSO), concern has been expressed over a number of years that these regulations do not sufficiently cover similar aspects of non-GSO satellite systems.

The WARC-92 having considered this and noting the growing interest in non-GSO applications, adopted an interim regulatory procedure, under Resolution COM 5/8, for the Coordination and Notification of assignments of non-GSO satellite networks. This Resolution, which replaces the provisions in Articles 11 and 13, applies only to those systems to be operated within frequency bands where a specific mention is made to it under a Footnote to the allocation in the Table of Allocations. The Resolution COM 5/8 has entered into force from 4 March 1992. The provision of LEO systems within all frequency bands listed in Tables 1 and 2 will be subjected to this Resolution. The Footnote in the Radio Regulations which refers to the Resolution is identified by an asterisk in the Tables.

The procedure described in the Resolution establishes the need for assignments within MSS to seek coordination with the assignments of existing or planned satellite networks or terrestrial networks as shown below.

non-GSO satellite network	-->	GSO satellite network
non-GSO satellite network	-->	non-GSO satellite network
GSO satellite network	-->	non-GSO satellite network
non-GSO space station	-->	terrestrial stations[1]
non-GSO earth station	-->	terrestrial stations[1]

[1]   The coordination as proposed in the Resolution applies in certain instances where the power flux density on the surface of the Earth (for a space station) or at the border of the territory of another administration (for a mobile earth station) which has been specified in the Radio Regulations is exceeded.

The sharing of frequencies between the networks of MSS and other services (for example Mobile and Fixed) comes under the classification of "inter service" frequency sharing. The frequency sharing between different networks within the MSS referenced as "intra service" frequency sharing.

Inter Service Frequency Sharing

The degree of complexity associated with the inter service frequency sharing situations is very much depended upon other radio services which have co-primary and secondary allocations within the band. Any other provisos associated with the allocation, of course, add to this complexity. The sharing situations arising from most of these allocations (Tables 1 and 2) have been addressed by the CCIR and a brief summary of the current status is shown in the Tables 3 and 4. The provisos set by the WARC-92, for the protection of existing and planned services, are also mentioned briefly in the Tables. Frequency coordination will be required if the limits set by various provisos are breached, for example by exceeding the stated Power Flux Density (PFD) on earth. The coordination could be conducted according to the methods prescribed by the CCIR in its Recommendations. However, some provisos, for example the requirement for not to claim protection from, or not to cause harmful interference to, certain services are absolute and can not be violated.

Allocations below 1 GHz

TABLE 3

Frequency band MHz	Sharing Situations	WARC Provisos	CCIR
137 - 138	Space Operations (space to Earth) Met. Satellite (space to Earth) Fixed, Mobile	PFD on Earth -125 dB(W/m²/4kHz) Protection of radio astronomy	examination of: FDMA LEO -> Mobile CDMA LEO -> Fixed, Mobile, Met systems
148 - 149.9	Fixed, Mobile	PFD at national boundary -150 dB(W/m²/4kHz) claim no protection from, or cause no harmful interference to, fixed or mobile in most countries (a large number of European countries)	examination of: FDMA LEO -> Mobile CDMA LEO -> Fixed, Mobile
149.9 - 150.05	Radionavigation-satellite	PFD at national boundary -150 dB(W/m²/4kHz) not to constrain the development of radnav. satellites	
400.15 - 401	Meteoro. aids, Met. satellite (space to Earth), Space Research (space to Earth), Space Operations (space to Earth)	PFD on Earth -125 dB(W/m²/4kHz) Protection of radio astronomy	

The primary allocations to MSS shown in Table 3, available for LEO systems, are subjected to a number of provisos set by the WARC-92. The limit on the space-to-Earth link, -125 dB(W/m²/4kHz), is only 1 dB below the PFD level on Earth required for FDMA systems as identified in the CCIR Report to WARC-92. The corresponding level for CDMA systems is -160 dB(W/m²/4kHz). It is worthy noting that further Footnotes require the MSS to protect the radio astronomy service in the bands 150.05 - 153 MHz and 406.1 - 410 MHz, by taking all practicable steps to limit out of band emissions.

The Earth-to-space primary allocation at 148 - 149.9 MHz band is shared with the Mobile Service. This band is used or planned to be used extensively for the mobile service (land mobile applications) in a number of countries. The MSS (or LEO) systems are required to limit the emissions from the mobile earth stations outside the national boundary to -150 dB(W/m^2/4kHz) and required not to claim protection from, or not to cause harmful interference to, Fixed and Mobile Services in most countries. Thus, in addition to the limitations placed on the mobile earth station emissions, the satellite receiver shall not claim protection from the stations of the Fixed or Mobile services in certain countries listed under the Footnote 608Z.

The following draft Recommendations are currently under study within CCIR Study Group 8:

Document 8D/TEMP/13-E: Method for determining sharing between stations in the Mobile Service below 1 GHz and FDMA non-GEO mobile Earth stations.

Document 8D/TEMP/15-E: Criteria for sharing between the Mobile Satellite Service and other services in certain frequency bands below 1 GHz.

Document 8D/TEMP/36-E: Methods for analyzing sharing between existing Fixed and Mobile and Meteorological systems and spread-spectrum CDMA LEO MSS below 1 GHz.

Allocations above 1 GHz:

TABLE 4

Frequency band MHz	Sharing Situations	WARC Provisos	CCIR
1525 - 1530	Space Ops. (space to Earth), Earth Exploration Sat., Mobile, Fixed, Maritime and Land mobile sat.	PFD on Earth, limit in No. 2566	no specific CCIR Recommendations
1610 - 1610.6	Aeronautical radnav., fixed (730), airborne electronic aid to air navigation (732)	Mobile Earth station eirp limit -15 dBW/4kHz to protect FN 732 systems, elsewhere -3 dBW/4 kHz, and protection of the radio astronomy service	as above
1610.6 - 1613.8	Radio astronomy, Aeronautical radnav., fixed (730), airborne electronic aid to air navigation (732)	as above	as above
1613.8 - 1626.5	Aeronautical radnav., fixed (730), airborne electronic aid to air navigation (732)	as above	as above
1980 - 2010	Fixed, Mobile	PFD on Earth, limit in No. 2566	as above
2170 - 2200	Fixed, Mobile	--	as above
2483.5 - 2500	Fixed, Mobile, RDSS (space to Earth), Radiolocation	PFD on Earth, limit in No. 2566	as above
2500 - 2520	Fixed, Mobile	PFD on Earth, limit in No. 2566	as above
2670 - 2690	Fixed, Mobile, Earth exploration sat., Radio astronomy, space research	--	as above

Although the frequency bands listed in the Table 4 can be used for non-GSO applications, the paper concentrates on two frequency bands, namely, 1610 - 1626.5 MHz and 2483.5 - 2500 MHz, widely identified as candidates for a number of LEO systems proposed by various organisations. As for the former frequency band, the WARC-92 in addition to setting a general eirp density level of -3 dBW/4kHz for the mobile Earth stations, required the stations of the MSS not cause harmful interference to, or not to claim protection from, fixed service and other stations operating under the Footnote 732*. In the part of the band where systems operate under Footnote 732 an eirp limit of -15 dBW/4kHz was applied to the mobile Earth stations. These MSS stations are also required not to cause harmful interference to the Radioastronomy Service using the band 1610.6 - 1613.8 MHz. As for the latter frequency band (2483.5 - 2500 MHz) the PFD limits specified in the Radio Regulation provision No. 2566 apply. These limits vary from -152 $dB(W/m^2/4kHz)$ (for 0 to 5 degree elevation) to -142 $dB(W/m^2/4kHz)$ (for 25 to 90 elevation).

---

* The Footnote 732 states "The band 1610 - 1626.5 MHz is reserved on worldwide basis for the use and development of airborne electronic aids to air navigation and any directly associated ground-based or satellite-borne facilities. Such satellite use is a subject to agreement obtained under the procedure set forth in Article 14"

The are no CCIR Recommendations or draft Recommendations which deal with these specific inter service frequency sharing situations.

Intra Service Frequency Sharing

The question of intra service frequency sharing has also been raised by the Resolution COM5/8. This matter has not been fully addressed within the CCIR and it is expected that further studies will be initiated within the CCIR Study Group 8. This is an important issue since these studies will determine the number of competing satellite systems that could operate within the spectrum allocated to MSS.

The ongoing work within CCIR Study Group 8 relates to the following two issues:

> Document 8D/TEMP/34-E: Interference criteria for the Mobile-Satellite Service operating between 1 GHz and 3 GHz.

> Document 8D/TEMP/10-E: Frequency sharing involving Geostationary (GSO) and Low Earth Orbit (LEO) RDSS/MSS satellite systems for 1 - 3 GHz.

Type Approval and Licensing

In a region such as Europe where pan-European applications have been considered under the land mobile satellite service, a key element would be the ability to cross national borders without any restrictions. This requires the administrations concerned to adopt a common licensing regime based on mutual recognition of licences. An approach based on mutual recognition of licences has been adopted by the CEPT to facilitate the transborder operation of the terminals of specific systems; namely, Inmarsat-C and Euteltracs.

The mutual recognition of licenses is subjected to the type approval of equipment to agreed performance specifications. These specifications generally examine the safety, potential interference to other services and wider electromagnetic compatibility issues. The specifications for European applications are being drawn up by ETSI and are known as European Telecommunications Standards (ETSs). The ETSI committee responsible for this activity, ETSI SES5, has completed its work on ETSs for following applications:

- Land Mobile Earth stations operating in the 1.5/1.6/2.5 GHz bands providing low bit rate data communications;

- Land Mobile Earth stations operating in the 11/12/14 GHz bands providing low bit rate data communications;

and

- Network control facilities for land mobile earth stations operating in the 1.5/1.6/2.5 GHz and 11/12/14 GHz bands providing low bit rate data communications.

The Committee has just embarked on drafting a standard for the high speed data and voice systems operating in the 1.5/1.6 GHz bands. It has also placed on its work programme to prepare ETSs for LEO terminals operating within the 1 - 3 GHz bands.

Conclusions

The frequency bands within which LEO systems could be operated have been allocated to the Mobile Satellite Service by the WARC-92. The operation of LEO systems are subjected to a number of provisos relating to the protection of existing or planned services. The LEO systems, prior to their implementation, will have to show the possibility of operating within the stated provisos. The breach of these provisos will require detailed frequency coordination with the affected administrations.

The regulatory regime required for pan-European operations has been reasonably well established by the CEPT for earlier GSO systems and may be extended to cover LEO terminals, if a way could be found to resolve difficulties arising from the use of certain frequencies. The type approval of terminals to an agreed European standard or ETS will be a pre-requisite for pan-European operation.

A STUDY ON AN EXPERIMENTAL COMMUNICATION SYSTEM USING MICROSATELLITES

R. SUZUKI*, Y. HASHIMOTO*, R. MIURA*, M. TANAKA*, T. OBUCHI**,
K. MIYAZAKI**, O. NAKAGAWA**, M. MATSUI**, N. MURANAKA**

* Communications Research Laboratory, MPT   ** NEC Corporation

ABSTRACT

A simple communication network by microsatellites is studied. A few microsatellites pick up and deliver voice and some digital information from/to ground stations, and/or from/to satellites. 9.6 kbps and 1.2 kbps are used for the ground link and the inter-satellite link respectively with on-board digital processing techniques. It uses the formation of the microsatellites in one orbit, to widen the real-time communication area. The microsatellite is 50 kg of dumbbell shape with an expandable mast.

1. Introduction

Currently, the satellite communications are realized by using the geostationary satellite, because the satellite can be used as a fixed relay station in the sky. However, the geostationary orbit is only one orbit and the capacity of the number of the satellite should be limited. Also, the recent development of the communication satellite goes to the large scale, multipurpose design. And, the life time of the satellite is extend in order to reduce its operating cost. Therefore, the satellite designs become more and more complex and require higher reliability. On the other hand, the altitude of the geostationary satellite is high and propagation delay time for the two way communication through the satellite is large. And also, big antennas and the high power amplifiers are needed in order to compensate for serious propagation loss.

As a way to prevent difficulties of geostationary satellites, low earth orbit (LEO) satellites are widely noticed, and are discussed in many organizations. In the case of the LEO satellites, small size antennas and low power transponders can be applicable because of the low propagation loss of the satellite link. The size of the satellite can also be reduced. In contrast to geostationary satellites, the visible time of LEO satellites is limited. Multi-satellite systems are proposed, such as the Iridium system, the Orbcom system, the Starnet etc. in order to extend the availability of the satellite link.

An electronic mail system using LEO satellites is discussed as another approach to satellite communication. Real-time communication is desirable within a region with small time difference. However, real-time communication is not essential to communication between two regions having a big time deference. An electronic mail system which transfers data within a 24 hours can be applicable to that kind of communication. A LEO microsatellite system with store and forward function can easily carry electronic mail or facsimile data to the destination within 12 hours.

Furthermore, the microsatellites can be easily launched with low risk and low cost. Therefore, the microsatellite system is suitable not only for the communication and observation, but also to space prove new electric devices and/or new communication systems. The merits of the proposed network system are summarized as follows:

1) It will realize lower G/T and lower EIRP than the GEO communication satellite network.
2) It will provide a simple global system with a store and forward function.
3) It is a low cost system consisting of the world wide dispersed information collection ground terminals using a personal computer.
4) A small, light-weight, low cost satellite bus can be developed by effective applications of existing designs.
5) The space segment of this system can be launched economically with H-II piggy back, ASAP (the Ariane Structure for Auxiliary Payloads), PEGASUS.
6) Because of its low cost, the microsatellite is suitable to space prove on-board equipments which use novel technology entailing high risk.

CRL/NEC cooperative team is currently designing a store and forward type of digital message delivery system with the microsatellites, as shown in Fig. 1. The authors hereinafter discuss the microsatellite and the experimental communication system.

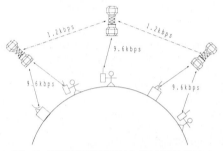

2. Experimental communication system with microsatellites

2.1 System design of microsatellite communications

Fig. 1 EXPERIMENTAL SATELLITE COMMUNICATION SYSTEM IMAGE

To provide a continuous communication to LEO satellites, twenty-three satellites are necessary in the case of randomly distributed satellites of 894 km altitude orbit as shown in Fig. 2. More satellites are required for the polar orbit satellites system because the density of satellites increases around the pole.

Various type of orbit and constellation are possible depending on the service objectives considered. To study the possibility and characteristics of a simple satellite communication network, the experimental system is composed with a number of microsatellites which provides communication links for the ground and between satellites. The store and forward type of digital data transmission is used in this system. All satellites in the

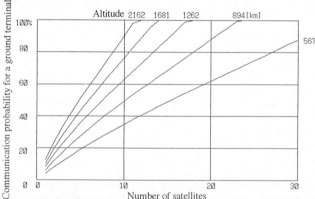

Fig. 2 COMMUNICATION PROBABILITY FOR A GROUND TERMINAL
(RANDOMLY DISTRIBUTED SATELLITE SYSTEM)

system are put into the same orbit. The orbital position of each satellite is selected in order that the coverage of each satellite can overlap the other. Then, the earth terminals covered by one satellite zone can communicate with each other through the satellite in real-time basis with data and/or voice. Also, the earth terminals covered by different satellite zone at the same time can communicate with each other through the inter-satellite link among the satellites in real-time basis. The data and/or voice packet transmission to the earth terminals outside the zones of the satellites can be carried out by the store and forward communication.

By using the formation of the microsatellites in one orbit, the area of the real-time communication can be widened, and the communication period, which is a disadvantage of the LEO satellite, in the same satellite path can be extended. Table 1 shows the visible time period of the satellites as a function of the altitude of the satellites. In the event that the three satellite are put into an orbit of 1681 km altitude, total visible time can be extended to two and half hours.

Table 1 TOTAL SERVICE TIME

Altitude (km)	Time (min)		
	1 sat.	2 sat.	3 sat.
567	20	35	50
894	34	56	82
1262	55	84	113
1681	68	105	146
2162	105	171	241

Table 2 shows the link budget calculated for the up/down link to/from the satellite and the inter-satellite link. In this case, data transmission rate of 9.6 kbps is used for the up/down link between the earth terminal and the satellite and 1.2 kbps is used for the inter-satellite link. For the up/down link, 400 MHz band is suitable in order to reduce propagation loss, because the satellite antenna should cover the wide area on the earth so that the antenna gain is low. On inter-satellite link because high gain satellite antennas can be used.

Table 2 LINK BUDGET

LINK from/to	ground/sat.1	sat.1/2	sat.2/3	sat.3/ground
Frequency	400MHz	2.5GHz	2.5GHz	400MHz
Distance (km)	3941	4007	4007	3941
Tx power (dBW)	0	0	0	0
Feed loss (dB)	0.5	1.5	1.5	0.5
Tx Ant.Gain(dBi)	0	8	8	0
Path loss (dB)	156.4	171.3	171.3	156.4
Rx Ant.Gain(dBi)	3	8	8	3
Feed loss (dB)	0.5	1.5	1.5	0.5
Rx power (dBW)	-154.4	-158.3	-158.3	-154.4
Noise (dBW/Hz)	-203.8	-203.8	-203.8	-203.8
C/No (dB/Hz)	49.4	45.5	45.5	49.4
Req. Eb/No (dB)	8.3	7.8	7.3	6.8
Bit rate (kbps)	12.9	5.9	6.6	18.2

Altitude = 1681 km

2.2 The radio link for ground stations

The radio link budget is shown in Table 3. The earth station is assumed to be the small mobile terminal with 0 dBi gain omni-antenna. The satellite's orbital height is around 1000 km and it is designed to achieve a radio link of more than 5 degrees elevation. The modulation type is BPSK. In case of the required C/No >= 46.8 dBHz, the radio link for 400 MHz needs EIRP >= 27.5 dBm, also for 2.5 GHz needs EIRP >= 42.4 dBm. To realize these EIRPs, the EIRP breakdown is as follows.

Table 3 RF LINK ESTIMATION

ITEM		CASE 1 (140MHz)		CASE 2 (400MHz)		CASE 3 (1.5GHz)		CASE 4 (2.5GHz)	
		UP	DOWN	UP	DOWN	UP	DOWN	UP	DOWN
EIRP	(dBW)	7.0	-2.5	7.0	-2.5	7.0	6.0	7.0	12.4
Path Loss	(dB)	-145.2	-145.2	-154.3	-154.3	-165.8	-165.8	-170.2	-170.2
G/T	(dB/K)	-33.1	-24.0	-32.1	-23.0	-22.6	-22.0	-16.2	-22.0
Rx Ant. Gain(dBi)		-0.5	2.0	-0.5	2.0	8.0	2.0	14.4	2.0
Feeder Loss (dB)		-2.0	-	-2.0	-	-2.0	-	-2.0	-
Rx No (dBWHz)		-140.7	-145.7	-149.8	-154.8	-152.8	-157.8	-150.8	-157.8
C/No (dBHz)		57.8	56.9	49.2	48.8	47.2	46.8	49.2	46.8

Orbit Altitude: 1000 km,　Slant Range (Ln) of Elevation 5':3105 km,
Required C/No 46.8 dBHz

387

one case

Transmitter Output Power	: 30 dBm
Feed loss	: 2 dB
Antenna gain for 400 MHz	: >= -0.5 dBi
Antenna gain for 2.5 GHz	: 14.4 dBi

another case

Transmitter Output Power	: 33 dBm
Feed loss	: 2 dB
Antenna gain for 400 MHz	: >= -3.5 dBi
Antenna gain for 2.5 GHz	: 11.4 dBi

Then, 400 MHz band can realize the radio link by on-board omni-antenna, and 2.5 GHz band can realize the radio link by on-board seven elements micro stripe antenna.

2.3 Inter-satellite radio link

Inter-satellite links for non-geostationary satellites provides the following advantages:

(1) the direct access area can be enlarged by increasing the number of satellites.
(2) inter-satellite links between satellites in different orbits can reduce the delay of message delivery.

The possible transmission rate depends on the link budget which is determined by the antenna gain and the output power achievable in the limited size, weight and generated power of the microsatellite. Two configurations of antennas were studied, One is to apply the same antenna used for the ground link to the inter-satellite link. The other is to install the array antenna having four or more elements to get the petal type of patten. The transmission rate is also affected by the satellite orbit. The higher the altitude of the satellites, the longer the propagation length becomes, although greater coverage is obtained. The possible transmission rate for the link between two satellites on 1681 km altitude is 1.2 kbps under the condition of 1 w output power and 8 dB antenna gain as is shown in Table 4. On the other hand, 7 kbps is possible for neighboring satellites in the configuration assumed above.

Table 4 INTERSATELLITE LINK BUDGET

Altitude	(km)	894	1681	2162
Frequency			S band	
Distance	(km)	2558	4007	4801
Tx power	(dBW)	0	0	0
Feed. loss	(dB)	1.5	1.5	1.5
Tx Ant	(dBi)	8	8	8
Path loss	(dB)	167.4	171.3	172.9
Rx Ant	(dBi)	8	8	8
feed. loss	(dB)	0.5	0.5	0.5
Rx power	(dBW)	-154.4	-158.3	-159.9
noise	(dBW/Hz)	-203.8	-203.8	-203.8
C/No	(dB/Hz)	49.4	45.5	43.9
Req. Eb/No	(dB)	7	7	7
Bit rate	(kbps)	17.4	7.1	4.6

The feasibility ad the utility of the simple communication system with microsatellites will be evaluated through the communication techniques demonstration test, where large Doppler effect and satellite attitude will be considered.

3.Conceptual Design of the Satellite Bus System

The satellite weight is selected less than 50 kg so as to increase the launch opportunities. The satellite system block diagram is shown in Fig. 3. The system consists of the power subsystem, the attitude control subsystem, twin structures and harness and also mission subsystem. The weight and power of the bus portion is 32 kg and 8 W, and that of mission portion is 18 kg and 27.6 W.

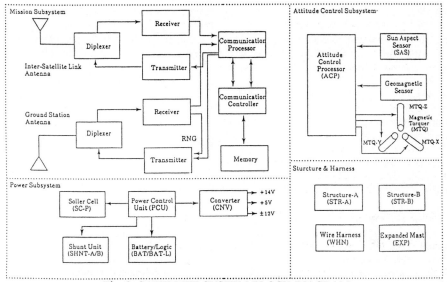

Fig. 3 SATELLITE SYSTEM BLOCK DIAGRAM

The satellite features twin structures of twenty-six-hedron using the sate-of-art JAS-1 microsatellite bus. The twin buses are connected to each other by an expanded mast. The solar cells ate mounted on the each panel of the twin bus structures. After being launch into LEO, the twin structures are fixed 2.5 meter apart by expanding the mast as shown Fig. 4. The stowed configuration size during launch phase is 440 mm (phi) * 2970 mm (H). The merits of this structure are as follows.

1) There are two areas to install on-board equipment, and it corresponds to versatile requirements.
2) The structure strength is kept by a central tube, then the outer frame shape can change easily, depending in mission requirements.

3-axis stabilization type of the attitude control system (ACS) is preferred for achieving the communication link between the G/S and the satellite, and/or the inter-satellite link. The satellite's antenna has to set the earth directed plane (yaw plane) for achieving the radio link.

There are two methods of attitude control. One is active attitude control using momentum wheels, and the other is a passive one using a gravity gradient torque saturated mass with magnetic torquers, or fine optical gyros. If the active momentum wheel consumes too much power, then the latter one is adopted for this satellite.

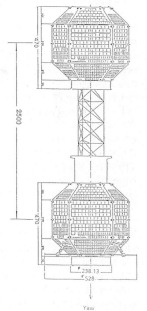

Fig. 4 MICROSATELLITE

The satellite attitude is controlled by using a gravity gradient torque. In this case, the attitude accuracy is proportionate as follows.

Attitude accuracy = Disturbance torque / Gravity gradient torque per angle (phi)

The vibration around the stabilization axis, so-called, libration is induced by the thermal expansion and contraction torque due to Sunshine/Sun shade trangent, residual magnetic dipole torque, solar radiation pressure torque and air pressure torque.

The libration is reduced by magnetic torquers. Fig. 5 shows the attitude accuracy vs., a expanded mast length. It shows that the attitude accuracy can be controlled within 1.0 degree for 2.5 meter expanded mast. This attitude data is gathered with a two-dimensional sun sensor and an geomagnetic earth sensor, or fine optical gyros.

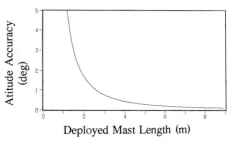

Fig. 5 ATTITUDE ACCURACY AS A FUNCTION OF MAST LENGTH

4. Design of microsatellite antenna

In order to install the high gain antenna on the microsatellite, new design of microstrip antenna is developed. For the inter satellite link, more than 8 dBi of antenna gain at S-band frequency is essential. Two elements of microstrip antenna is suitable, because of its light weight and conformal structure. However, high gain antenna need large area of the surface of microsatellite, and the area of the solar cells should be reduced. Then, the microstrip antenna with solar cells is designed.

Fig. 6 shows the construction of the microstrip antenna. Antenna radiation is mainly generated from the edge of the antenna elements, so that the solar cells can be put on the microstrip antenna except the edge of the elements. Fig. 7 shows the radiation pattern of the antenna with and without solar cells. By using this technique, high gain microstrip antenna can be installed on the surface of the microsatellite without no reduction of the solar power.

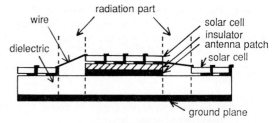

Fig. 6 MICROSTRIP ANTENNA WITH SOLAR CELL

5. Design of the store and forward transponder

The configuration of the store and forward type transponder installed in the microsatellite is shown in Fig. 8. The transponder consists of RF units, which are 400 MHz band unit for the up/down link, and 2.5 GHz band unit for the inter-satellite link, and the store and forward data control unit. The digital signal processing architecture is employed for the modems. However, another modem with conventional circuits is prepared for the TT&C system in order to keep redundancy.

The store and forward data control unit consists

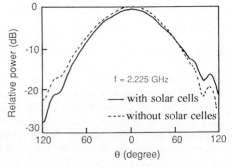

Fig. 7 RADIATION PATTERN OF MICROSTRIP ANTENNA

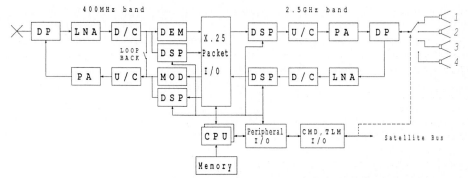

Fig. 8 BLOCK DIAGRAM OF STORE AND FORWARD TRANSPONDER

of the microprocessor, the data memories and the peripheral circuits. The function of the unit are to keep the message data, to control the packet transmission and reception, reception of the command packet for the satellite control, transmission of the telemetry packet and 2.5 GHz antenna direction control. A memory size of 4 to 16 MByte is essential in order to store up to three minutes length of the voice packet which is coded to 9.6 kbps data.

For the purpose of finding the best transmission protocol in the experiment, the modulation method and communication protocol can be changed by downloading the control program from the earth station. Moreover, some part of the memory unit is made from the dynamic memory chip in order to maximize the memory capacity and to test the reliability of the chip in space.

6. Conclusions

The authors explained the experimental communication system using microsatellites whose purpose is as follows.

1) To confirm the validity of store and forward mail communication between ground stations and microsatellites.
2) To experiment with the possibility of a delay time reduction for package message communication using the inter-satellite link.

The microsatellite features twin structures of twenty-six-hedron connected to each other by an expanded mast. Based on this unique satellite design, the authors intend to proceed with the detailed design.

REFERENCES

[1] "JAS-1b", JARL News, Nov. 1988-Nov. 1989
[2] M. KAN et al., "Digital Communication System by Amateur Satellite JAS-1", IECE National Conversion Record, 1986, S25-6
[3] Y. HASHIMOTO et al., "A STUDY ON A SIMPLE COMMUNICATION NETWORK BY MICROSATS", 14th AIAA Int'l Communications Satellite Systems Conference, Mar. 22-26, 1991

LEOCOM-SPES: LOW COST MESSAGE COMMUNICATIONS

G. Barresi, L. Caporicci, R. Del Ricco, S. Di Girolamo (1)
B. Pavesi, G. Rondinelli (2)

(1) ITALSPAZIO - Via V.E. Orlando, 83 - 00185 Roma (Italy)
(2) Previously with ITALSPAZIO

ABSTRACT

Communication systems based on constellations of satellites deployed in Low Eart Orbits (LEO) represent a valuable opportunity
for commercial use of space. Several companies are proposing constellations of small satellites provided with highly integrated
electronics. The major features are the low cost of spacecraft
production and an easy interface with user terminals.
Since 1990, ITALSPAZIO is considering the adoption of LEO systems. In particular, ITALSPAZIO has defined a system based on a
sparse constellation applicable to message/data communications:
LEOCOM/SPES, "Space Pony ExpresS".
The purpose of the paper is to highlight the results of the study. The mayor system elements, as the orbiting constellation, the
ground segment and the user terminal are briefly outlined together with an assessment of the economical feasibility of the proposed system.

1. INTRODUCTION

LEOCOM-SPES is a message packet communications system based on
the use of a constellation of satellites deployed in low earth
orbits (LEO). The basic services offered by the system are the
transmission of data messages (electronic mail), facsimile,
computer data files, which will arrive to the addressees within a
maximum delay of few hours from the submission. The envisaged
costs of the satellites, the relevant launches and the earth
terminals are relatively low, permitting to offer the service at
lower costs with respect to other communication means. In the
basic version for operation at lower rate, the user's terminals
have the dimension of a robust walkie-talkie, thus offering very
easy installation and/or mobility.

2. LEOCOM SYSTEM ARCHITECTURE

LEOCOM system is composed by:

- a space segment, consisting of a constellation of low earth orbit satellites with regenerative payloads and mass memories,
  deployed in several orbits, with orbital planes and satellite
  phasing suitably displaced in order to grant world-wide but di-
  scontinuous coverage;
- a ground control system capable to control satellites, communication payloads and network operations;

393

- gateway stations to serve major communications centers of private, national, regional networks;
- low cost small size user terminals of various types and costs, which will support different bit rates according to user's needs and services.

```
┌─────────────────────────────────────────────────────────────────┐
│ LEOCOM System Major Features:                                    │
│                                                                   │
│ . Service coverage      : world-wide, discontinuous              │
│ . Service type          : data message communications            │
│ . Users                 : mobile to mobile                       │
│                           fixed to mobile and viceversa          │
│ . Coverage area         : 5000 Km diam.                          │
│ . System coverage avail.: variable, 40% min. at equator          │
│ . User terminal         : RF pocket size + lap top computer      │
│ . Data rates            : 1.2 to 9.6 Kbps user to communication centers │
│ . User's links freq.    : UHF; 400 MHz down; 500 MHz up (typically) │
│ . Control links freq.   : C-band; 4 GHz down; 6 GHz up           │
│ . Space segment         : 24 to 32 satellites                    │
│                         : 6 to 8 sat.s per plane                 │
│                         : constant phasing among satellites      │
│                         : orbit height: 780 Km                   │
│                         : orbit inclination: polar               │
│                         : orbit period: 1 h., 40 min.            │
└─────────────────────────────────────────────────────────────────┘
```

LEOCOM mission provides two types of communications: a) store & forward message communications between users everywhere located; b) real time message data communications between users located inside the same satellite coverage area only; that is when originator and addressee users have simultaneous visibility towards the same satellite.
Communications between distant users are possible through the storage of the messages on-board the spacecraft. The delay time between sending and receiving the messages may result several hours, when the satellite constellation will consist of few satellites. By increasing the number of satellites, the maximum delivery delay may be kept at the level of 2-3 hours or less. The efficiency of the system also increases by introducing a routing process via a master network center, the Central Control Station. This station will provide message switching from one satellite to another satellite, selected according to its ability to reach the addressee users in shorter time delays.
The communications characteristics are conditioned by the type of satellite in terms of constellation density (or availability), payload memory, Space-Earth-Space interfaces. The service efficiency derives from a convenient combination of above parameters, which impact on spacecraft mass and power. Aspects such waiting time, queuing length for users inside the same visibility area, message length, relations with the orbit geometry and delivery time are the peculiar parameters governing the system architecture.
The satellite orbits will be circular. The preference is addressed to polar orbits with altitude lower than 1000 Km in order to reduce space-radiation effects. At the selected altitude 780 Km, the satellite foot-print is circular, with 5000 Km diameter about. Of course, the coverage area moves along the satellite subtrack. Due to the earth rotation the satellite sub-tracks shift about 25° West from one orbit to the following orbit. For this reason, a numerous constellation is required in order to provide the service with acceptable discontinuities.
With a system coverage availability in the order of 50%, the system transport capability, that is the delay time between

sending and receiving the messages, is drastically improved by the routing process provided with the Central Control Station.

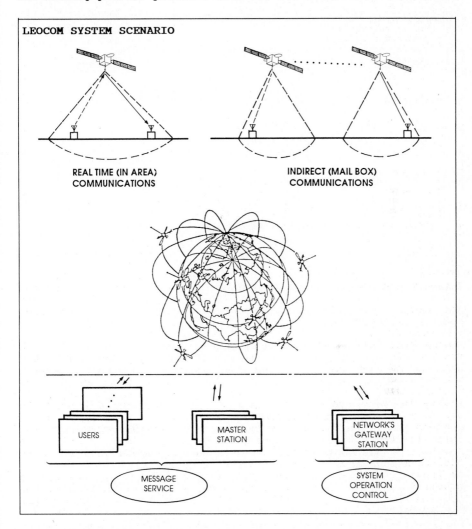

LEOCOM SYSTEM SCENARIO

REAL TIME (IN AREA)
COMMUNICATIONS

INDIRECT (MAIL BOX)
COMMUNICATIONS

USERS

MASTER STATION

NETWORK'S GATEWAY STATION

MESSAGE SERVICE

SYSTEM OPERATION CONTROL

The resulting system architecture is:

. a fleet of 24 to 32 satellites in polar orbit;
. a Central Control Station fully integrated with the space segment.

The Central Control Station implements the function of a network node. Through an adequate selection of the site of this node, visibility of all satellites every orbit must be provided. This occurs in few localities on the Earth. The most convenient site is Svalbard Island 80°N-15°E, where a 100% visibility towards all satellites in polar orbit is possible every orbit revolution (with the assumed orbital parameters). This site is the preferred location of the system master station (Central Control Station).

```
LEOCOM Network Operation:

a) User link data rates:
   . Simple terminals                              1.2 Kbps
   . Enhanced terminals                            9.6 Kbps
   . Gateway stations (star network hubs)          16 Kbps
   . Signalling                                    Slotted Aloha

   Access                   Channel assignment

   Modulation:              Typically QPSK

   Channel organization:    Packet mode

   Coding:                  1/2 Viterbi for signalling  and selected modes
                            of communications

   Routing functions:       . for in area communications, on-board the sat.s
                            . for optimum selection of message paths,
                              in the Central Control Station

b) Feeder links/TT&C:
   Satellite to/from Central Control Station       2 Mbps

c) BER:                                            10⁻⁶ unfaded
```

3. ORBIT AND CONSTELLATION SELECTION

The major criteria adopted to define a suitable satellite constellation, have been:

a) The orbit altitude is selected:
   . to minimize the RF power demand of satellite and terminals;
   . to provide sufficient coverage area in order to allow real-time communications, also considering a 10° coverage mask angle;
   . to avoid frequent orbit corrections for atmospheric drag and reduce the space radiation effects.
b) Orbit inclination shall be such to allow frequent interconnections with a single network center.
c) Orbit planes must be staggered in such a way as to provide almost homogeneous world-wide service characteristics.

Adequate satellite phasing in the orbit will allow user's waiting time periods (before each satellite pass) to be almost equal world-wide.

A polar orbit with altitude 780 Km satisfies above requirements. The altitude 780 Km has been traded-off with an altitude 1200 Km. The 1200 Km altitude provides a larger coverage with respect to the 780 Km altitude and is capable to support a higher volume of real-time traffic. This circumstance would allow a simplification of the on-board equipment requiring less memory for message storing. However, adopting this orbit:

. there is not a drastic reduction in the number of satellites in the constellation when an equivalent service availability is required,
. there is an increase of propellant consumption for achieving the higher orbit altitude,
. there is an increase of RF power demand on-board.

Thus, the 780 Km altitude has been selected. The resulting satellite foot-print at this altitude still allows a satisfactory degree of real-time communications.

The selection of the number of satellites, on which it relies the traffic carried-out by the system, is made by applying the following criteria:

. Initial orbital constellation must provide an acceptable service for at least 30% of the total users envisaged at system saturation.

. Additional satellites, as required to face higher traffic demand, will be injected into the initial orbit planes.

. Phasing of satellites in adjacent planes will be such to reduce the overlapping of coverages, typically at poles for polar orbits.

Several computer runs have been implemented in order to assess the most convenient constellation parameters, capable to provide the required service with the minimum number of satellites:

. minimum waiting time/service availability,

. acceptable system performances connected with a gradual deployment of the satellites,

. suitable coverage for full constellation.

The major parameters adopted in the assessment of a convenient constellation have been:

. Satellite altitude	: 780 Km
. N. of orbit planes	: 4
. Orbit period	: 6027 sec
. Mask angle	: 10 degrees
. Satellite cone antenna aperture	: 2 x 60.4 degrees
. Visibility time from any point on the earth	: 569 sec, typical

With these parameters, the percent of visibility has been determined as the average time during which selected zones at different latitudes are in visibility of the satellites.

The results obtained for the constellations:

. 32 sat.s, deployed into 4 orbit planes, with 8 sat.s per plane,
. 24 sat.s, deployed into 4 orbit planes, with 6 sat.s per plane;

are presented hereinafter.

The configuration with 32 satellites appears a convenient solution. The typical coverage is also shown.

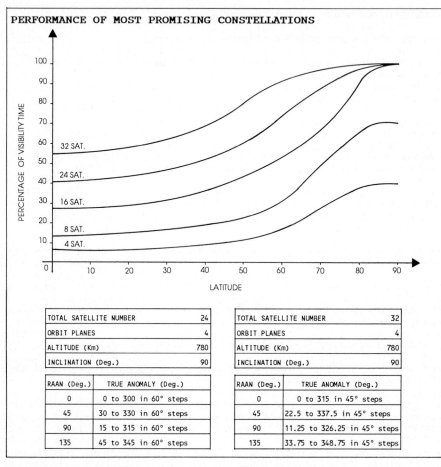

PERFORMANCE OF MOST PROMISING CONSTELLATIONS

PERCENTAGE OF VISIBILITY TIME

LATITUDE

32 SAT.

24 SAT.

16 SAT.

8 SAT.

4 SAT.

TOTAL SATELLITE NUMBER	24
ORBIT PLANES	4
ALTITUDE (Km)	780
INCLINATION (Deg.)	90

RAAN (Deg.)	TRUE ANOMALY (Deg.)
0	0 to 300 in 60° steps
45	30 to 330 in 60° steps
90	15 to 315 in 60° steps
135	45 to 345 in 60° steps

TOTAL SATELLITE NUMBER	32
ORBIT PLANES	4
ALTITUDE (Km)	780
INCLINATION (Deg.)	90

RAAN (Deg.)	TRUE ANOMALY (Deg.)
0	0 to 315 in 45° steps
45	22.5 to 337.5 in 45° steps
90	11.25 to 326.25 in 45° steps
135	33.75 to 348.75 in 45° steps

SPOT COVERAGES WITH 32 SAT.s: 4 ORBIT PLANES, 8 SATs PER PLANE

ITALSPAZIO CAD

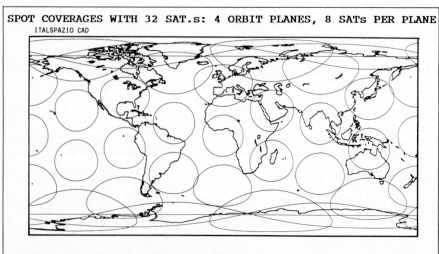

4. TRAFFIC SCENARIO AND REQUIREMENTS

In order to assess a convenient system architecture, the coverage considerations must be supported by a projection of LEOCOM-SPES traffic during the operation life. The major user's categories have been identified. For each of them projections of traffic demand and market penetration have been assessed; finally, suggested transmission rates has been established.

. Trucks, car, man packs   1200 bps
. Sites of construction companies   1.2 or 9,6 Kbps
. Small ships   1200 bps
. Big ships   1.2 or 9.6 Kbps
. Benevolent institutions, Red cross   1.2 or 9.6 Kbps
. Vatican, U.N. bodies,   1.2 or 9.6 Kbps
. World weather watch   1200 bps
. Oil rigs   1.2 or 9.6 Kbps
. Foreign offices - Embassies   1.2/9.6/16 Kbps
. Commercial traffic   1.2/9.6 Kbps.

The expected traffic can be private, national, regional and international. It is foreseen that the system will operate through a multiplicity of networks having different configurations: a) star networks formed by several simple user terminals located in isolated areas and one hub/gateway station located in a zone of high density traffic; b) meshed networks among the gateway stations. The star network structure will face the traffic requirements by adopting different rates for the links satellite/gateways stations with respect to the rates of the links satellite/user terminals, since the incoming and outgoing traffic from the gateway stations implies high transmission rates, while the remote terminals, with a reduced number of messages, can operate at low transmission rates.
Through market analysis and enquiries on the acceptability of the system concept and operation capability, the expected traffic of LEOCOM has been derived. The results give the total traffic per day in terms of bytes loaded into the memories on-board the satellites of the constellation. The difference between minimum and maximum traffic figures mainly derives from different assumptions of service penetration for the commercial traffic. The commercial traffic can be, considered, the wider and most important category of users.

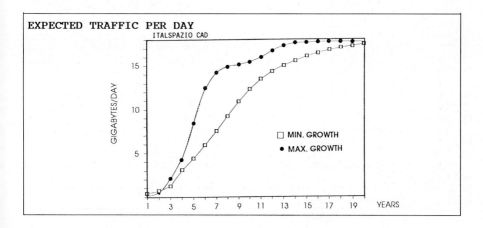

5. ECONOMIC SCENARIO

The following implementation schedule is considered for LEOCOM.

TRAFFIC FORECAST		
AT YEAR	TRAFFIC PER DAY, Gbytes	
1st	0.5 min	0.5 max
2nd	0.6	0.7
3rd	1	2
4th	3	4
5th	4	8
6th	6	12

SYSTEM IMPLEMENTATION		
LAUNCHED SATELL.	IN SERVICE SATELL.	IN ORBIT SPARES (*)
6	4	2
6	10	2
6	14	4
12	26	4
6	32	4
SECOND GENERATION		

(*) NOTE: in orbit spares can be used to face higher traffic demands.

An overall throughput of 6.5 Gigabytes/day has been fixed for reference, also in consideration of a conservative market capture. For constellation deployment, the following assumptions are made:

. a first generation system is initially deployed, adopting a satellite design concept compatible with a life time 5 years,
. the service operation starts with a reduced constellation of satellites. The full 32 satellite constellation will be operational at the beginning of the 5th year from initial operation,
. a second generation of more powerful spacecraft will be gradually deployed in substitution of the first generation spacecraft which reached EOL.

The implementation schedule proposed is in line with these assumptions. The rate envisaged for satellites manufacturing is 8 satellites per year, with a mass production in batches of 4 satellites per batch. Up to 6 satellite launches per year are foreseen, using a S-ELV, typically a launcher of Pegasus class.
The continuation of the operational phase during the subsequent years (operational years 6, 7 etc.) would require to manufacture and launch satellites which will gradually replace the first generation satellites. The manufacturing and launch rate of the second generation spacecraft will be dictated by the market acceptance.

Anyhow, an additional design effort and other non recurring costs might be needed at that time, both for technological up-dating and for a review of the system and satellite capacity according to the effective traffic growth.

We therefore consider that, for the purpose of evaluating the costs of the services and the possibility to make profits by investing in this system, we must compare the costs of implementation of 36 satellites (32 sat.s + spares) with the revenues coming from the expected traffic during the 5 years period of initial operation. For what concerns the implementation of user terminals and gateway stations, we consider that the manufacturing will be performed by specialized companies upon specifications prepared by the Agency or the company/venture capitalist who will be the LEOCOM-SPES owner.

IMPLEMENTATION SCHEDULE OF LEOCOM-SPES 1st GENERATION

ACTIVITY	YEARS: -3	-2	-1	I	II	III	IV	V
Satellite specifications & design	X X X X X X X X							
Manufacturing batches 1: 4 F.U.			X X X X					
2: 4 F.U.			X X X X				
3: 4 F.U.				X X X X			
4: 4 F.U.				X X X X			
5: 4 F.U.				X X X X			
6: 4 F.U.					X X X X		
7: 4 F.U.					X X X X		
8: 4 F.U.					X X X X		
9: 4 F.U.						X X X X	
Launch sequence: 2 F.U. per launch				2 2 2 2	2 2 2 2	2 2 4 2	4 2 2	
Service Go-ahead				◊				
Total Satellites available for service				4	12	20	32	
Central Control Station, install. & SW	X X X X X X X X X X X X							
User terminal specifications	X X X X X X							
User terminal validations			X X X X X X					
Operational phase				X X X X X X X X X X X X X X X X X X X X X X X X				
Management & billing center	X X X X X X X X X X X X X X X X X X X X X X X X X X X X X X X X X X X X							

Satellite Costs: The costs of the satellites have been evaluated on the basis of the results of earlier ITALSPAZIO studies for ESA. With a 70/30 ratio between NRC & RC, the resulting unit cost of the first satellite is:

$$92 \text{ K\$/Kg}$$ of which:

- NRC, non recurring cost = 61 K\$/Kg,
- RC, recurring cost = 31 K\$/Kg.

With production organized in batches of four satellites, the unit cost of the first batch is 92 K\$/Kg. The costs of the satellites will be:

	UNIT COST K\$/Kg	COST OF BATCHES MILL. US\$
Batch 1 (4 FU)	92	55.2
Batch 2 (4 FU)	22	13.2
Batch 3 (4 FU)	19	11.4
Batch 4 (4 FU)	17	10.2
Batches 5 to 9 (4 FU x batch)	16	48.0

Since the satellite dry mass will be 150 Kg each, the envisaged production cost applicable to all 36 FU spacecraft (including four spares) will be: a) 36600 K$ for non recurring costs; b) 101400 K$ for recurring costs, summing up to an overall figure of about:

138 millions of US$

Launch Costs: The mass of the LEOSTAR satellite, for LEOCOM-SPES mission, has been defined so to permit to carry two satellites each launch operation. Making reference to Pegasus, the injection strategy is to launch into a circular polar orbit at 200 Km altitude. No out-plane maneuvers are required to achieve the final orbit. An optimum strategy, minimizing the overall propellant consumption, will allow to reach the final circular polar orbit, 800 Km altitude. The optimal number of burns at apogee and perigee of the transition orbits along with the thrust level of each burn, is derived once fixed extremal orbits, time limit and gravity losses.
The injection sequence covers three main phases:

. a perigee burn, that allows to acquire an elliptic orbit;
. a sequence of intermediate burns at perigee and at apogee;
. a final apogee burn, to reach the wanted circular orbit.

Taking into account that the program would require 18 launches with the sequence of minimum 3 launches per year, we consider that a discount could be obtained through appropriate cost/service negotiations. The expected launch costs is assumed 12 M$, corresponding to 6 M$/satellite and a total launch cost 216 M$. The insurance is assumed 17% of the launch cost.

Investment Costs for Central Control Station, Other Costs: The Central Control Station (CCS) is considered part of the space segment. The cost estimate is as follows:

. Construction of CCS station building	1500 K$
. Construction of personnel housings	2500 K$
. Antennas + radomes (redundant)	500 K$
. Modems and RF (redundant)	500 K$
. Computers (redundant)	1000 K$
. Monitor and control (redundant)	500 K$
. Installation, testing, doc. & manag.	1000 K$
. Spare parts (one equipment set)	1250 K$
. Control softwares	500 K$
. Traffic management softwares	8000 K$
Total investment costs	**17250 K$**

The relevant expenditure schedule is: 20%, 40%, 40% respectively in the years preceding the launch operations. The CCS operational costs are estimated in the order of 2000 K$ per year. These expenditures also covers software maintenance and are effective, from the beginning of service operations. Other costs are expected, which will include:

a) the system management, billing and administration,
b) the operation costs relevant to the overall system deployment (EOP costs),

c) the standardization of the user's terminals, inclusive of specifications and validation tests of hardware/software elements.

RESUME OF COSTS	
. Satellite Non Recurring Costs	36600 K$
. Satellite Recurring Costs	101400 K$
. Launch Costs	216000 K$
. Insurance (15% of launch cost)	32400 K$
. CCS Investment	17250 K$
. CCS Operational Costs (5 years)	10000 K$
. EOP (3% of Satellite costs)	3000 K$
. Billing and management (8 years)	12000 K$
. Spec. & Valid. of User Term.	1500 K$
Total	430150 K$

6. USER CHARGES

Following the assumptions made in the previous paragraphs, the
calculations of LEOCOM-SPES user charges indicate a cost of the
space segment amounting:

0.013 $/Kbit

In addition to this cost, to be paid to the service provider, the
users will incur the cost of their terminals, through a leasing
fee or a purchase cost.

Comparisons with similar services offered by other organizations
indicate that the cost of the space segment is sensibly lower
than the cost of other satellite services or terrestrial packet
switching services, for which the following indicative figures
apply:

. Inmarsat type C   : 0.7 $/Kbit (space only),
. PTT VSAT   : 0.25 $/Kbit (space only),
. PTT Terrestrial packet-switch: 0.15 $/Kbit.

It has to be remembered that the above listed competing services
are in real time, while the LEOCOM-SPES services are generally
non real time. Nevertheless, we consider that LEOCOM-SPES will be
capable to gain a valuable share of traffic especially in the
zones of poor or unreliable infrastructures.

7. SUMMARY PERFORMANCES OF LEOSTAR

LEOCOM-SPES mission is possible through the adoption of LEOSTAR
spacecraft. LEOSTAR is a three axis gravity gradient stabilized
satellite designed by ITALSPAZIO for operation in low altitude
earth orbits. Its shape is hexagonal, with four solar panels and
a deployable boom for attitude stabilization. The antennas, which
provide the required coverage through wide beams, are fixed on
two lateral panels. When the spacecraft reaches the final orbit
position, the antennas are deployed and result oriented towards
the Earth.

LEOSTAR presents a high level of autonomy: the satellite functions and the operation management are performed by two on-board processors which can be programmed for each mission and for each configuration.

Attitude control system is based on semi-passive gravity gradient concept. This type of control allows a considerable mass saving with reduced construction complexity while providing high system reliability levels with optimized design, development and manufacturing costs.

LEOSTAR MASS & POWER BUDGETS		
Payload	48 Kg (max)	175 W (max)
Structure	20 Kg	-
Electric Power	33 Kg	190 W(*)
Attitude Control	7 Kg	6 W
System Management Processor	20 Kg	20 W
Thermal control	5 Kg	7 W
Propulsion	10 Kg	12 W
Telemetry and command	8 Kg	15 W
Total dry mass	151 Kg	
Propellant mass	27 Kg	
Interfaces (double launch)	3 Kg	--
TOTAL S/C AT LAUNCH	181 Kg	425 W

(*) Battery charge

8. CONCLUSIONS

For all the user categories which do not need real time connections, LEOCOM-SPES is an economic and attractive alternative to the personal communications system currently proposed by private companies and international organizations.

From the user point of view, LEOCOM-SPES seems to offer services at lower costs and better coverage than the corresponding services offered by the current technologies.

From the service provider point of view, there is no doubt about the fact that LEOCOM-SPES potentially offers high profits.

9. BIBLIOGRAPHY

[1] ITS-TR-171.B/91: "Studio sulle Tecniche di Messaggistica con Satelliti LEO".
[2] ITS-TR-170.1/91: "Study for Definition of LEOSTAR".
[3] ITS-TR-176/91 : "LEOCOM Mission Concept Analysis".

10. ACKNOWLEDGEMENT

The authors wish to acknowledge the advise and support of A. Teofilatto, President of ITALSPAZIO. Special tanks are addressed to Mr. D. Brown and Mr. K. Galligan of ESA for their stimulus on this innovative field.

TAOS (S80) : UN SYSTEME LEO-MSS POUR DES SERVICES DE LOCALISATION ET DE TELEGESTION

par A. GAUTIER et P. DUMONT

Centre National d'Etudes Spatiales -

18, Av. Edouard BELIN
31055 TOULOUSE

1.   Résumé

L'objectif de cette publication est de présenter un système de localisation et de télégestion basé sur l'utilisation de mini-satellites (masse< 150 kg). Les études de définition et de faisabilité sont actuellement réalisées par le CNES.

Les caractéristiques principales du système sont le faible coût de développement et d'utilisation du service ainsi que sa vocation mondiale et sa grande capacité (> 500 000 terminaux par région).

Ce type de système est économiquement intéressant pour les utilisateurs gérant des parcs importants de terminaux. Il est particulièrement adapté à une utilisation ponctuelle ne nécessitant pas de court temps de réponse (environ une heure).

2.   Introduction

Les services mobiles récemment développés ou en cours de développement (e.g. Inmarsat, Omnitracs / Qualcomm, Datatrack) offrent habituellement un service de localisation (position reporting) en plus des transmissions classiques de la voix et/ou des données. Leur utilisation reste néanmoins coûteuse.

Les autres systèmes dédiés à la localisation (GPS, Loran C, Omega) fournissent celle-ci au mobile dans un but de navigation sans possibilité de connecter celui-ci à une base de rattachement.

S80 vise à offrir un service de localisation (position reporting) et de télégestion pour un investissement et un coût d'utilisation limités.

3.   Rappel historique

Dès la fin des années 60, le programme Eole (localisation de ballons) préfigurait ce qui allait devenir, avec le programme Argos, puis Sarsat et Doris, un domaine d'excellence du CNES reconnu au niveau international grâce à des coopérations bilatérales ou multi-latérales.

Depuis plus de deux décennies ont été perfectionnées par le CNES et les industriels français les techniques de localisation et de collecte de données basées sur l'utilisation de satellites en orbite basse fortement inclinées et de fréquences inférieures à 500 MHz.

Les trois thèmes d'applications développés par le CNES se résument donc comme suit :

- ARGOS : étude et protection de l'environnement,

- COSPAS-SARSAT : sauvegarde de la vie humaine,

- DORIS : localisation ultra-précise (géodésie).

Pour des raisons réglementaires d'attributions de fréquences, seules les applications d'étude et de protection de l'environnement ont accès au service ARGOS.

4. Des etudes de marché ...

Dès 1990 s'annonçait la possibilité d'utiliser des bandes de fréquences en dessous de 1 GHz pour des systèmes mobiles basés sur des satellites en orbite basse (LEO-MSS [1]) et pour des services publics.

Ainsi, avec un système "Post-ARGOS", il devenait possible de toucher un marché beaucoup plus large laissé vacant par les services existants. De plus, l'utilisation de fréquences VHF/UHF et de satellites défilants laissait entrevoir des prix de développement et d'utilisation intéressants.

Dans ce contexte, le CNES a fait réaliser une étude de marché en Europe et en Amérique du Nord visant à recenser la clientèle potentielle d'un service de localisation et de télégestion peu coûteux et à vocation rnondiale.

Les principales caractéristiques d'un tel service sont les suivantes :

- Les clients sont principalement des opérateurs de mobiles terrestres : compagnies de location de véhicules, transporteurs, compagnies de chemins de fer, conteneurs et dans une certaine mesure, les véhicules grand public.

- Le service principal consiste en la localisation d'un mobile rattaché à une base propriétaire. Sur requête de la base ou du mobile, la localisation est effectuée et fournie à cette base. Les applications sont typiquement liées à la gestion et à la surveillance de parcs de mobiles. La précision de localisation requise est comprise entre 100 m et 1 km.

- Le service secondaire consiste en l'envoi de messages courts (quelques caractères alphanumériques) de la base vers un mobile lui étant rattaché et inversement. Aucune messagerie conversationnelle n'est requise. Néanmoins, le client doit être sûr que son message a été correctement remis.

- Un temps de réponse de l'ordre de l'heure est toléré, contrairement aux services assurant des liaisons quasi temps réel. Aucun besoin de dialogue conversationnel depuis une base jusqu'au mobile n'a été exprimé. Ceci rend possible l'utilisation de constellations sans couverture permanente des zones d'intérêt.

- Le profil d'utilisation : une localisation et une messagerie en moyenne tous les trois jours (utilisation ponctuelle).

- Les régions à fort potentiel sont l'Amérique du nord (USA, Canada, Mexique), l'Europe (CEE, Scandinavie, Europe Centrale) et l'Asie (Japon, Corée, Taiwan).

- Les contraintes clients : hors son faible coût (quelques milliers de francs), le terminal sera compact et autonome pour des raisons d'installation et de discrétion.

- La capacité requise du système est de minimum 500 000 mobiles par région.

5. ... Au système

5.1. Architecture d'ensemble

Après analyse des éléments de mission ci-dessus, un segment spatial composé d'une constellation de mini-satellites en orbite basse (circulaire et fortement inclinée) a été choisi :

- Compte tenu des performances demandées sur de telles orbites (puissance, stabilisation), de petits satellites (masse < 150 kg) peuvent convenir.

- Un déploiement progressif de la constellation est possible, parallèlement à l'exploitation.

- Des moyens de lancement appropriés à de tels satellites pourront être disponibles à court terme (Pegasus, Scout), à un coût compatible avec celui des satellites.

- Enfin, de telles orbites rendent possibles l'utilisation des techniques Doppler pour la localisation des terminaux.

---

[1] LEO MSS : Low Earth Orbits Mobile Satellite System.

La charge utile est constituée d'un répéteur, sans démodulation à bord. Les liaisons sont alors possibles lorsqu'il y a visibilité mutuelle de la station sol de connexion et du mobile. Le mobile s'accroche sur le signal continu émis par la station et relayé par le satellite (voie aller) et renvoie de courts messages (voie retour) vers cette station.

Quant au segment sol, il devra être adapté afin d'assurer l'exploitation du système dans les trois régions considérées.

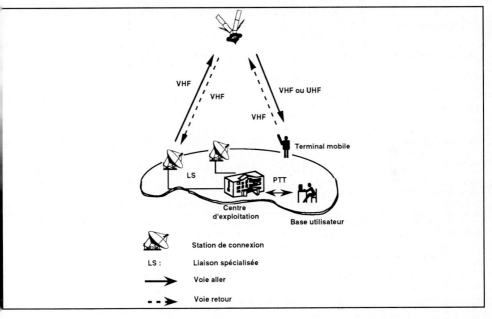

Figure 5.1.a Architecture système

5.2. Aspects réglementaires

La Conférence Mondiale des Radiocommunications (WARC 92) autorise le développement de systèmes LEO-MSS dans les bandes de fréquences suivantes (pour la mission):

- [137-138 MHz]: liaisons espace vers Terre : statut co-primaire sauf [137,025-137,175 MHz] et [137,825- 138 MHz] (statut secondaire). Flux maximum autorisé : -125 dB(W/m^2/4kHz).

- [148-149,9 MHz] : liaisons Terre vers espace : statut co-primaire.

- [149,9-150,05 MHz] : liaisons Terre vers espace : statut co-primaire pour les systèmes mobiles terrestres par satellites à partir du 1er janvier 1997.

- [400,15-401 MHz] : liaisons espace vers Terre : statut co-primaire. Flux maximum autorisé : -125 dB(W/m^2/4kHz).

5.3. Plans de fréquence

Les bandes de fréquence mentionnées sont déjà utilisées par d'autres services. Dans ce contexte, le choix final des fréquences dépendra de l'analyse des bilans de liaisons, confortés par les résultats de l'expérimentation S80T (Température de bruit et brouillage). La nécessité de cohabiter avec les systèmes existants a amené l'utilisation de techniques spectre étalé au moins pour la voie retour (CDMA).

	Liaison montante	Liaison descendante	Bande utilisée
Option 1			
Voie aller	[148-150,05]	[137-138]	1 MHz SSMA[1]
Voieretour	[148-150,05]	[137-138]	1 MHz CDMA
Option 2			
Voie aller	[149,9-150,05]	[400,15-401]	30 kHz
Voie retour	[148-149,9]	[137-138]	1 MHz CDMA

Figure 5.3.a Plans de fréquence

Option 1 :

Les deux voies utilisant la même bande de 1 MHz dans [148-150,05 MHz] se brouillent mutuellement. Néanmoins, la charge utile, constituée d'un simple répéteur 148-137 pour les deux liaisons, reste très simple. Toutes les liaisons s'effectuent en spectre étalé.

Option 2 :

Ce scénario constitue l'alternative la plus intéressante à l'option 1 car les voies aller et retour sont découplées. De plus, la réception terminal s'effectue avec des techniques classiques en bande étroite.

Note : Un scénario intermédiaire SSMA/CDMA en UHF/VHF fait aussi l'objet d'études non présentées ici.

5.4. Segment spatial

5.4.1. Constellation

Compte tenu des performances lanceurs attendues, l'altitude des satellites est comprise entre 800 et 1500 km.

L'optimisation des constellations a porté sur les délais d'attente des liaisons. Différents outils d'analyse mission ont été développés dans ce but[1]. Deux approches ont été effectuées [2] :

- une méthode numérique par optimisations successives (Adaptative Random Search),

- une méthode quasi-analytique basée sur les théories de Walker, Ballard et Beste [Réf 1].

Les deux types de simulations tendent à prouver que les géométries optimales sont du type des constellations de Walker. Pour un objectif de temps d'attente d'une heure pour 90% des requêtes utilisateurs, une constellation constituée de cinq satellites sur cinq plans d'orbite répartis uniformément sur 360°, d'inclinaison 57°, avec un phasage relatif entre deux plans de 216° est optimale pour une zone comprise entre 20 et 60° de latitude, principale zone d'intérêt. L'altitude adoptée est de 1208 km (13,5 orbites par jour). Les durées de visibilité mutuelle sont alors de 15 minutes en moyenne.

---

[1] SSMA : Spread Spectrum Multiple Access.

CDMA : Code Division Multiple Access.

[1] LEONART : Low Earth Orbits Numerical Analysis I Research Tool, développé en collaboration avec l'ENST sous contrat CNES.

[2] Les études préliminaires des constellations S80 ont été effectuées par l'ONERA - Site de Châtillon. Une analyse complémentaire sur le maintien à poste de ces constellations est en cours.

5.4.2. Satellites

En l'absence de mini-satellites sur le marché européen, des études plate-forme et charge utile ont été lancées [3]. Le lanceur considéré pour les optimisations est Pégasus, seul lanceur dédié pour des mini-satellites disponible à ce jour.

La configuration plate-forme retenue à ce jour possède les caractéristiques suivantes :

- Générateur solaire : quatre pétales d'environ 3 m^2. La puissance moyenne fournie par les générateurs solaires est de 270 Watts,

- Stabilisation : < 5 deg (3σ) sur les trois axes,

- Propulsion : gaz foid, six tuyères 0,1 N.

- Contrôle thermique : passif, caloduc entre les différentes faces du satellite,

- Alimentation : batterie Ni-Cd,

- Gestion bord : centralisée,

- Masse : < 150 kg,

- Consommation électrique moyenne : 50 Watts plate-forme, 100 Watts charge utile.

- Antennes : lobe formé compensant la dynamique des pertes d'espace. Cette compensation est limitée par les fréquences utilisées (VHF) et par le volume disponible sous coiffe.

- Durée de vie : 5 ans (fiabilité 0,6).

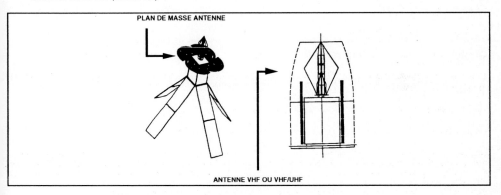

Figure 5.4.2.a Vue d'ensemble du satellite (deployée et stockée)

Selon le plan de fréquence retenu, la charge utile sera uniquement VHF ou UHF/VHF.

---

[3] Etude plate-forme menée par l'Aerospatiale Cannes. Les études charges utiles sont en cours.

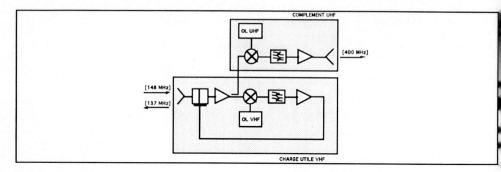

Figure 5.4.2.b Description fonctionnelle charge utile

5.5. Segment sol

Le segment sol et notamment les stations de connexion aux satellites doivent permettre l'exploitation sur les trois régions considérées. Néanmoins, la vocation mondiale du service nécessite de prévoir l'introduction de nouvelles stations.

a) Segment sol mission.

Les études des temps de réponse ont montré qu'une seule station de connexion était suffisante en Europe et en Asie tandis que deux sont nécéssaires en Amérique du Nord.

D'autre part, un centre d'exploitation par région assure l'interface avec les bases utilisateurs. Il sera donc relié au segment spatial au moyen d'une ou plusieurs stations sol. Les conflits potentiels entre stations dûs aux visibilités multiples seront gérés au niveau de ce centre d'exploitation. Afin d'assurer un fonctionnement global (localisation indifféremment sur les différentes régions), ces centres d'exploitations seront interconnectés.

Les antennes sont dimensionnées pour permettre l'acquisition satellite à partir de 5° de site.

b) Segment sol de contrôle

Il assure le contrôle des satellites (TM/TC, mise et maintien à poste). Cette composante pourra utiliser les moyens du segment sol mission afin de limiter les coûts globaux.

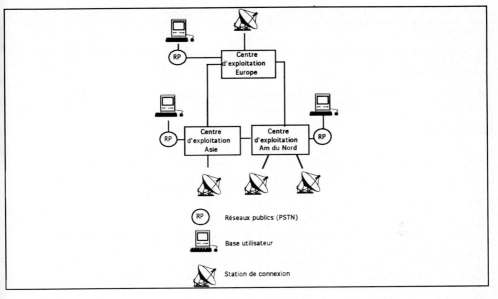

Figure 5.5.a Segment sol mission
Anneau mondial - Etoile régionale

5.6. Terminaux mobiles

Les technologies liées à l'utilisation de fréquences VHF et UHF permettent de concevoir un terminal simple et peu coûteux.
Ce terminal a deux fonctions principales : assurer les liaisons avec les stations de connexion et fournir les moyens de localisation à cette station.

a) Liaisons de connexion

Après correcte réception du canal de signalisation (voie aller), le terminal accède à la voie retour par répartition de code (CDMA).
Les liaisons avec la station sol de connexion s'effectuent en half-duplex afin de faciliter le couplage des voies émission et réception.
La couverture antenne est quasi-omnidirectionnelle pour éviter tout pointage. En l'absence de masques, l'antenne sera optimisée afin de permettre les liaisons pour des angles de vue du satellite d'au moins 10°.
Différentes méthodes sont envisagées afin de minimiser la consommation du terminal (prévision de passage, réveil cyclique, canal de signalisation, détection du passage satellite).[1]

b) Fonction localisation

Deux techniques sont envisagées pour remplir la fonction localisation :

- Mesures mixtes Doppler /Distance :

---

[1] Une analyse des technologies à mettre en oeuvre dans le terminal et des coûts qui en résultent a été effectuée par Mors-Terminaux en 1990-91.

411

Le terminal reémet en synchronisme avec la liaison aller (station vers mobile) un message contenant la mesure Doppler de la liaison aller. La station sol effectue une mesure Doppler et la mesure de distance sur la voie retour et en extrait la localisation.

Les précisions requises nécessitent au plus trois mesures. La localisation est donc strictement issue des liaisons de communications mobile-station. Cette technique nécessite une bonne stabilité des horloges et des synthétiseurs de fréquence du terminal.

Ce type de localisation est facilitée par des liaisons intégralement en spectre étalé (SSMA/CDMA, option 1).

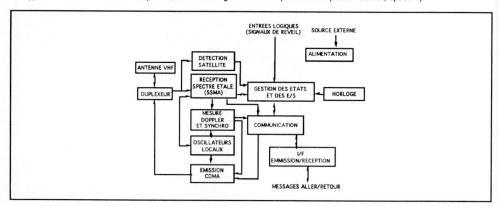

Figure 5.6.a Description fonctionnelle
Terminal S80 (localisation dédiée, VHF)

- Mesure externe type GPS

La faisabilité de la localisation Doppler/distance à un coût raisonnable pouvant s'avérer délicate, une solution alternative est envisagée : à l'aide d'un système annexe, la localisation est effectuée dans le terminal. Cette information est ensuite retransmise à la station de connexion sur la voie retour.

Cette technique est particulièrement bien adaptée à une réception en bande étroite (option 2).

Le moyen de localisation envisagé est le GPS. Les performances de précision, d'intégrité ainsi que les coûts des récepteurs dans les cinq années à venir en font le partenaire approprié.

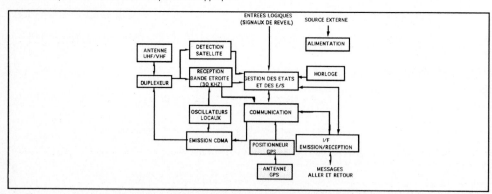

Figure 5.6.b Description fonctionnelle
Terminal S80 (localisation GPS, UHF/VHF)

6. Bilans de liaison

Les bilans de liaison sont présentés pour l'option 1 CDMA/SSMA VHF en supposant une modulation du type BPSK.

	Liaison aller		Liaison retour	
Montant	**148 MHz**	**Montant**	**148 MHz**	
Débit	14 kbit/s	Débit	1,2 kbit/s	
Code conv.	28 kHz	Code conv.	2,4 kHz	
Code d'étalement	1 Mchip/s	Code d'étalement	1 Mchip/s	
Pire station	12,8 dBW	Pire terminal	0,7 dBW	
Pertes d'espace	-147,4 dB	Pertes d'espace	-146,3 dB	
Autres pertes	-2 dB	Autres pertes	-3 dB	
G/T sat	-30,5dB/K	G/T satellite	-31,6 dB/K	
Boltzmann	228,6	Boltzmann	228,6	
C/No montant	61,5 dBHz	C/No montant	46,7 dBHz	
Descendant	**138 MHz**	**Descendant**	**138 MHz**	
Puissance signal	7,8 dBW	Puissance signal	-6 dBW	
Pertes d'espace	-145,6 dB	Pertes d'espace	-146,7 dB	
Autres pertes	-5 dB	Autres pertes	-4 dB	
G/T terminal	-36,2dB/K	G/T station	-17,6 dB/K	
C/No descendant	49,6 dBHz	C/No descendant	54,3 dBHz	
C/Io (Acc. S80)	68,7 dBHz	C/Io(Acc. S80)	68,7 dBHz	
		C/Io (voie aller)	45 dBHz	
C/Io (Brouilleur)	53,6 dBHz	C/Io(Brouilleur)	38,9 dBHz	
C/No tot	47,9 dBHz	C/No tot	37,2 dBHz	
Eb/No (BER 10^{-5})	4,4 dB	Eb/No (BER 10^{-5})	4,4 dB	
Marge	2 dB	Marge	2 dB	

Figure 6.a Bilans de liaison Option 1

Les pertes d'espace libre sont calculées pour un site minimum de 5° pour la station de connexion et de 10° pour le mobile.

Les températures de bruit antenne sont évaluées comme suit :
Satellite (148 MHz) :   2000 K
Terminal mobile (137 MHz) :   5000 K
Station de connexion (137 MHz) : 2000 K.

Le calcul de brouillage considère quatre accesseurs simultanés au système (accès aléatoire) ainsi qu'un brouilleur bande étroite de 18 dBW dans la bande [148-149,9 MHz].

L'option 2, non exposée ici présente des marges comparables.

7. Les protocoles de communication

Seul le protocole lié à une localisation dédiée, à l'initiative de la base utilisateur sera présenté ici. Les fonctions liées à la localisation du type GPS et/ou aux transactions à l'initiative du terminal font l'objet d'études annexes.

a) Le centre d'exploitation met à jour en permanence les requêtes provenant des bases et les réponses des terminaux tout en gérant les conflits potentiels entre stations.

La liaison aller contient les messages de synchronisation, l'identification de la station ainsi que toutes les informations à destination de terminaux spécifiques (requêtes, acquittement, messages). Cette voie sert de plus à contrôler les terminaux afin d'optimiser le fonctionnement du système (gestion des priorités, autorisation à émettre, configuration interne du terminal).

b) Le satellite retransmet continûment le signal provenant de la station sol.

c) Lorsque le satellite est en visibilité mutuelle de la station et du mobile, celui-ci se synchronise. Il peut ainsi répondre à toute requête de localisation et de messagerie.

Localisation : Le terminal re-émet en synchronisme avec la voie aller des messages permettant à la station sol de le localiser. La station sol acquitte la correcte réception de 3 messages successifs. Ceci permet de localiser le mobile même en présence de pertes de signal fugitives (arbres, évanouissements, accesseurs simultanés, etc.). Les instants d'émission seront optimisés afin de limiter le nombre d'accesseurs simultanés au système. Ceci garantira une capacité maximale.

Messagerie : le terminal émet un acquittement afin d'assurer la station sol de la correcte réception du message. Cette dernière peut ainsi éliminer ce terminal de la liste à interroger et garantir à la base la correcte transmission du message.

Une analyse détaillée est actuellement en cours au CNES. Les simulations de ces protocoles sont développées sur le logiciel OPNET, particulièrement bien adapté à ce type de système.

8.   Performances système

8.1. Capacité

Le système est dimensionné pour prendre en compte un parc de 700 000 terminaux par région d'exploitation. Chaque terminal est localisé en moyenne une fois tous les trois jours. La longueur des messages est de 256 bits maximum.

8.2. Temps de réponse

Le système garantit un temps d'attente maximal de 60 minutes pour 90% des requêtes de localisation et messagerie. Dans le pire des cas, l'attente n'excède pas 90 minutes.

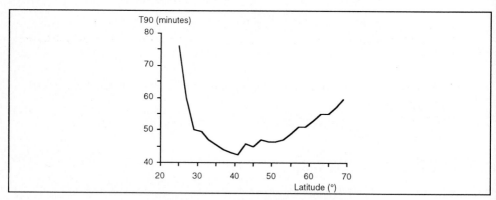

Figure 8.2.a Temps d'attente pour 90% des requêtes
(Zone Europe, longitude 1°, station à Toulouse)

8.3. Disponibilité et fiabilité

Une étude paramètrique a été menée au CNES afin d'évaluer la disponibilité du système. En optimisant la stratégie de déploiement et de maintien du segment spatial, une disponibilité de 0,95 pour 4 satellites (service dégradé) et de 0,8 pour le service nominal à 5 satellites peut être garantie pendant la phase opérationnelle.

9.   Démonstration de la faisabilité : S80T

Deux éléments critiques ont été identifiés dans les études préliminaires:

- En l'absence de données suffisantes sur le sujet, l'occupation de la bande [148-149,9 MHz], élément dimensionnant la qualité des liaisons, nécessite des mesures directes (bruit résiduel et brouilleurs).

- La faisabilité des mesures Doppler et de distance dans cette bande de fréquences est limitée par les erreurs de propagation ionosphérique.

Ces deux points seront prochainement étudiés au moyen d'un satellite technologique, S80T développé par Matra Espace associé à Dassault Electronique et à l'Université du Surrey. Ce micro-satellite, dont le lancement sur Ariane en accompagnement de Topex Poséidon est prévu en juillet 1992, aura une durée de vie de un an.

Les moyens sol sont dimensionnés afin de pouvoir éxécuter ces expérimentations en Europe et dans les autres régions.

10. CONCLUSION

Un système de localisation et de télégestion à faible coût de développement et d'utilisation a été présenté.

Basé sur l'utilisation de mini-satellites (masse < 150 kg) et de terminaux portables autonomes, ce système garantit des délais d'attente de l'ordre d'une heure entre une demande de localisation émise par un client (compagnie de transport, loueur de voitures, sociétés de surveillance) et la remise de la localisation du terminal associé.

La capacité de S80 est évaluée à 700 000 terminaux par région (Europe, amérique du Nord, Asie).

La localisation sera effectuée grâce à des techniques Doppler et distance ou au moyen de récepteurs GPS.

La cohabitation avec les utilisateurs actuels des bandes de fréquences allouées est obtenue grâce à des techniques de spectre étalé.

Les études de définition conduites par le CNES font appel à diverses études et expertises d'industriels français et européens. La faisabilité du système sera vérifiée grâce à l'expérimentation en vraie grandeur conduite au moyen du satellite S80T.

11. REFERENCES

[REF 1] Rosette constellations of Earth satellites, A.H. Ballard. IEEE Transactions on Aerospace and Electronic Systems. Septembre 1980.

The ORBCOMM System

Martin Deckett

Orbital Communications Corporation

The ORBCOMM^{sm} data communications and position determination system is designed to bring low-cost mobile communications to every country throughout the World. It uses a constellation of small satellites in low-Earth orbits to give complete geographic coverage without the need for thousands of tower-mounted radio transmitters and receivers.

A typical communications need is illustrated in Figure 1. User A is the dispatcher for a fleet of long distance trucks, two of which are shown at A1 and A2. He needs to send messages to the trucks. He also needs to be able to receive messages from the trucks and know where they are. There is also another user, Type B. He needs to obtain data from a large number of remotely located sensors, such as the one shown on B1, that measure snow depths, rainfall rates and lake levels. Based on these data, he will then want to send commands to operate reservoir gates, which may also be located in places that are difficult to access, such as the one shown as B2.

Both these users have a common need - a two-way data communications network configured in a star pattern, with a central hub and a large number of remote

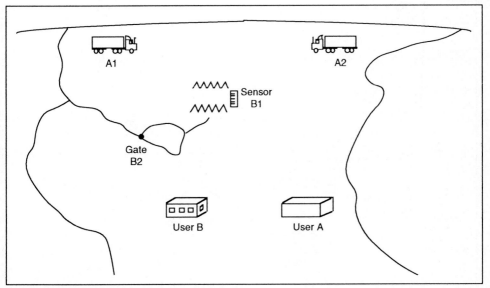

Figure 1. The Communications Need.

terminals. The truck dispatcher's problem is compounded by the fact that his remote terminals, the trucks, are mobile and, in most parts of the World, beyond the range of tower-based radios. Also, he needs to know where they are. The water resources controller's problem is not that his remote units are moving, but that they are located in generally hard-to-access places, where it is extremely expensive to run telephone lines, and very inefficient and costly to depend upon a person to physically inspect the sensors.

Clearly satellites can overcome the problems of communicating with mobile and remote terminals. To a limited extent, this is now being done, using geostationary satellites. However, this technique requires fairly large, high power and expensive terminals on the ground. The disadvantages result from the long transmission distance from Earth to a geostationary satellite and the need to use microwaves (L-Band and above) to form narrow beams on the satellites.

The advent of small satellites and the low-cost rockets with which to launch them has changed the nature of the satellite solution. The ORBCOMM system is one of these solutions. Satellites are in low-Earth orbit and operate at VHF. The remote terminals are now pocket-size, can operate for months on battery power and have simple 50 cm long whip antennas.

The way in which ORBCOMM solves the needs of users A and B is shown in Figure 2. There will be a constellation of small LEO satellites, two of which are illustrated. As they pass over a country, they will be used as relays by the

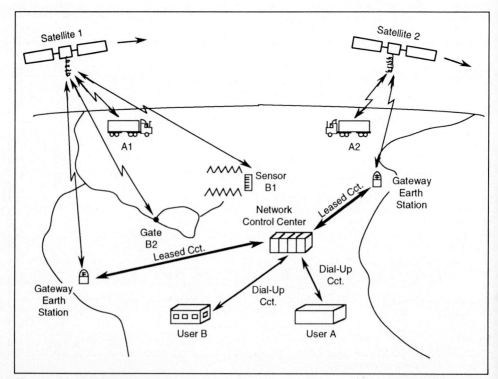

Figure 2. The ORBCOMM Solution.

418

ORBCOMM network in that country. On the ground there will be a simple Network Control Center (NCC) and, depending upon the size of the country, one or more Gateway Earth Stations. Two are shown in the illustration. The Network Control Center is connected to each of the Gateways by 56 or 64 kbps duplex leased circuits. These could be on terrestrial microwave or cable. Alternatively, they could use a geostationary communications satellite with VSATs. In many networks, both methods may be used, with one as the redundant back-up to the other. The key point is that existing, publicly available data links are used. ORBCOMM is not a telephone bypass system.

At its central office, each user will have a desk top computer. This is the "hub station". This computer can be connected to the NCC computer, again using the existing telephone data network, but on a call-up basis and not by a permanently leased line. With the computer, each user can "use the network" as and when needed. This also allows use of a variety of existing electronic mail systems. Many of these are already integrated into office local area networks.

For example, the User A dispatcher may wish to send re-routing instructions to his truck A1, or User B may wish to close a sluice gate at location B2. He enters these data on his computer and sends it to the NCC. The computer decides which gateway and hence which satellite to use and sends these data, together with data from other users, over the leased circuit to the chosen gateway. The selection is made by the NCC and is dynamic. It depends upon the approximate location of the terminal (if, indeed, this is known) the positions of all the satellites in view, and the current traffic loading.

The data stream is radioed to the satellite on a 50 KHz wide channel in the 148-150 MHz band. In the satellite, messages are separated and radioed downwards on one of a number of 10 KHz wide channels in the 137-138 MHz band and so received at the remote terminal.

Inbound messages, from the remote terminals to the user's hub station, follow the same route, but in reverse. These messages can be initiated at the terminal unit or polled, that is requested from the hub station. Thus, the truck dispatcher can poll a truck to send back its position, without requiring any action by the driver. And, of course, the controller at user B's hub can poll any sensor and have it respond with the data it has been collecting and storing.

With inbound messages, there are many options for completing the last leg, that from the NCC to the user's hub. The data can be stored in memory at the NCC and then, at the user's convenience, he can access that memory using his own computer and obtain the data -basically an E-mail process. If the inbound message was polled, then it can be relayed through to the user hub over the dial-up line opened by the user to send the polling request to the NCC. Some inbound messages will be initiated at the terminal unit and cannot be delayed. These are emergency alerts and represent an important service provided by ORBCOMM. They are recognized as priority messages throughout the ORBCOMM network and will be sent from the NCC to the user hub without delay.

The remote terminals can be designed to measure the doppler shift on the downlinked signals. In addition, each satellite determines its own position and velocity using the Global Positioning System and transmits these data down to all terminals. With these measurements and data, the terminals are able to determine their position, generally with an accuracy of better than 100 meters.

Thus, the user hub station consists of nothing more than a desk top computer and a modem for connecting it to the public switched network, that is to a dial-up telephone line, and hence to the computer at the Network Control Center. The NCC itself is just a computer. Part of the computer is accessible by the users. Much of it is not, and is concerned with traffic routing, billing and other central control functions. The Gateway Earth Stations are unattended and located where they have unobstructed views of most of the horizon. The VHF antenna at each Gateway is steerable, and tracks one of the satellites as it crosses the sky. The Gateways will be fully redundant and will have uninterruptable power sources.

The satellites will be quite small and simple. The antenna will provide coverage over the entire visible Earth. The satellites will be in a circular orbit at an altitude of approximately 775 km. Thus, the half-beamwidth will be close to 60 degrees, and the footprint diameter about 4600 km. The pattern will be designed to have increased gain away from the boresight so as to compensate for the longer path lengths to terminals that are near the edge of the footprint.

The first two satellites will be launched into a polar, or near-polar orbit. These will be followed by 24 more, with 8 equidistantly placed in each of three planes. These planes will be inclined at 45 degrees to the Equator. This is illustrated in Figure 3. The main coverage is provided by the 24 satellites in the included planes. The 2 polar orbiting spacecraft provide an extension of coverage into the high latitudes. As the system develops and demand grows, a further 8 satellites will be launched into a fourth inclined plane.

Initial Deployment	2 Satellites in 1 Plane	785 km Altitude 90 deg Inclination
Main Deployment	24 Satellites in 3 Planes (8 in Each)	785 km Altitude 45 deg Inclination 0,135 and 270 deg Long. of Asc. Node
Expansion Deployment	8 Satellites in 1 Plane	785 km Altitude 45 deg Inclination 90 deg Long. of Asc. Node

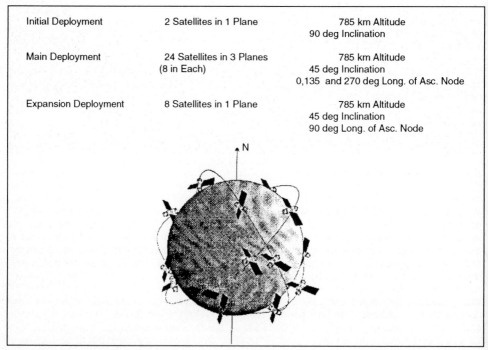

Figure 3. The ORBCOMM Constellation.

Figure 4 shows an instantaneous snapshot of the footprints of the 24 inclined orbit satellites. It also illustrates the unsuitability of this type of presentation of coverage, which is much more applicable to geostationary satellites. The pattern of footprints of a constellation of LEO satellites is continually changing, with the non-covered zones moving all the time. A far more useful chart is shown in Figure 5. This shows average availability contours. ORBCOMM satellites do not have large memories - they do not operate in the store and forward mode. Thus, the availability of an ORBCOMM link requires that one of the satellites has simultaneous sight of the remote terminal and a Gateway Earth Station. The generation of these availability contour charts depends upon the number and location of the gateways. This chart was completed for availability in the mainland USA, with just four Gateways, one near each corner of the country. As can be seen, most of the region has availability times well in excess of 95 percent. It is planned to increase this by installing one or two more Gateway Earth Stations and, at a later time, by placing another 8 satellites in orbit. For other regions of the World, we will use this technique of availability contours to determine the required number of Gateways and their locations.

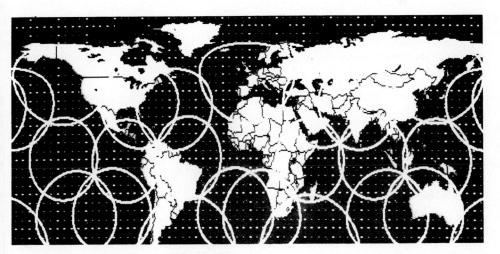

Figure 4. Instantaneous Coverage Footprints.

There is another important piece of information which even the availability contour charts do not show. That is, the statistics of the outage periods. For example, an availability at a certain remote terminal location of 98 percent means that, on average, there will be a communications outage there for 2 percent of the time, or for 29 minutes in each 24 hour period. This does not mean that there will be a single outage every day lasting nearly a half-hour. On the contrary, the outages will be frequent and short and fairly uniformly distributed in time. Other calculations show that, for the example depicted in Figure 5, 90 percent of the outages will last for less than 5 minutes.

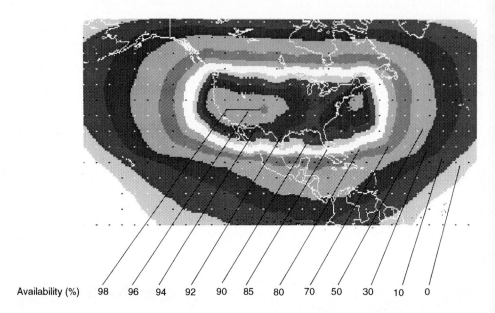

Availability (%)   98   96   94   92   90   85   80   70   50   30   10   0

Figure 5. Availability Contours For 24 Inclined Orbit Satellites and 4 Gateways.

Of very great importance to the acceptance of these communication systems is the size, mass and cost of the remote terminal units. There will be several different types of these units, which will be manufactured and marketed by a few different companies who are already in the consumer electronics business. One very simple type may be designed to operate within the case of some other equipment, and provide only some of the features of ORBCOMM. It will accordingly, sell at a very low price. At the other extreme, a unit may be completely self-contained, with its own battery, antenna and case, and be designed to provide all of the ORBCOMM features, including personal interface, with an alphanumeric key pad for data entry and a LCD screen for displaying received data. This type of remote terminal unit is shown in Figure 6. The unit will measure 7x15x3 cms and weigh less that 300 grams.

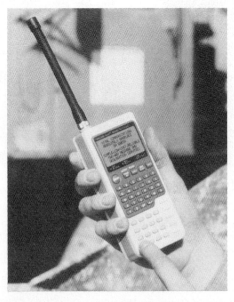

Figure 6. Full Capability ORBCOMM Terminal Unit.

There are several different services which ORBCOMM can provide. Basically, there are three generic types. Depending upon the type of remote terminal unit purchased, the user will be able to use any one of these generic services, or combinations of them. This is shown in Figure 7. The first type of services is SecurNet^sm , the emergency alerting service. By pushing a button, or by sensing an external switch closure, the remote terminal unit will send a short emergency alert message, inbound to the user's hub station. The unit will continue to send the alert until it receives confirmation of its receipt. Applications for this simple service include advising central station alarm systems of an intrusion into protected property, or sending immediate reports that a pressure or temperature in remote machinery or a pipeline has gone out of limits.

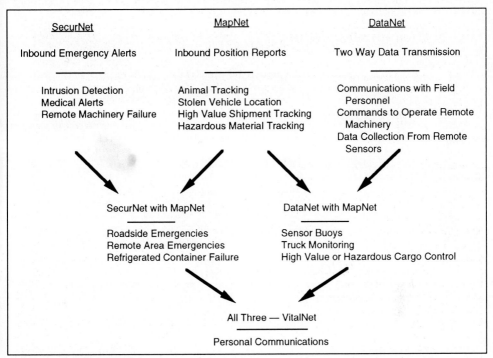

Figure 7. The ORBCOMM Services.

The second generic service is MapNet[sm], which transmits the position of the remote terminal unit. As stated earlier, the units can be designed to measure the downlink doppler shifts and to receive the position and velocity of the satellites. By processing these data (in a Kalman filter), the unit is able to determine its own position. The accuracy of this determination depends upon the period of time during which the data are collected and the accuracy of knowledge of the terminal's own speed, if it is mobile. Also, if doppler measurements are made on only the VHF signals (in the 137-138 MHz bands), there is a major error source in the uncertainly of the ionospheric refraction. Thus, standard position determination for ORBCOMM will have an uncertainly of about one kilometer. This will be considerably reduced, to less than 100 meters, by measuring the doppler on the downlink UHF signals too. (Each satellite will transit time signals and other data in a single UHF channel at 401 MHz). The MapNet only service will find applications in animal tracking, in tracking free-floating buoys, and in locating stolen vehicles or misplaced high value assets. It may be noted that a MapNet only terminal can be discretely mounted on a car and connected to the standard entertainment radio antenna. Thus, it can be polled to transmit its position without a thief being aware of its existence.

Another generic service is DataNet[sm], the communication of data. For outbound communication, the data may consist of an alphanumeric message for display on the remote terminal unit, or for entry into a palm-top computer. Or the data may be an encoded command to operate a switch on remote machinery. All communications through ORBCOMM are digital, and there can be an RS 232 dataport on a terminal unit to connect it to other equipment. Inbound data may be entered into the remote unit by a person, using a keypad, or read from a memory buffer in adjacent and attached equipment. There are clearly a very large number of possible applications for DataNet.

Finally, these generic services may be combined in the design of the terminal unit. One such combination is to have both SecurNet and MapNet. Thus, an emergency alert can be sent to the user hub station accompanied by the position of the remote unit. These units could be installed quite cheaply in cars and trucks. An emergency alert could be sent by the driver pushing a button or automatically after a crash by using the air-bag deployment command. Also, it is anticipated that there will be a large demand for units which combine all the basic services and which have personal interface (key pad and display screen) as well as a dataport access to ancillary equipment. This full combination is called the VitalNet[sm] service.

At this point it is worthwhile to look at the many design choices which were made for ORBCOMM. They are summarized in Figure 8. The underlying motive was always to achieve low cost service for modest needs that are either unserved or underserved. Thus, the system is designed for fairly low rate digital data, and not for voice or high speed data. The outbound data rate is set at 4800 bps, with the inbound rate at 2400 bps. The messages will be short, typically

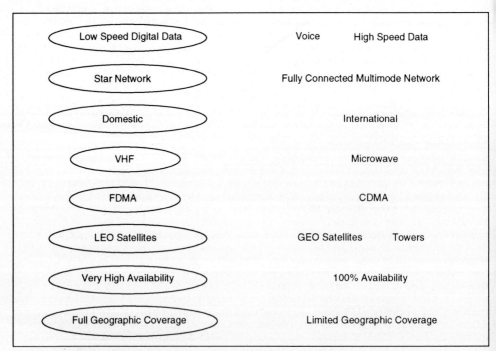

Figure 8. ORBCOMM Design Choices.

computers, although it can be used by a mobile palm top computer to access the memory of a large static computer. Secondly, domestic star networks are provided and not international multipoint-to-multipoint networks. This simplifies the satellites by eliminating cross-links. Remote-to-remote connections are possible, by effecting a turn-around either at the Network Control Center or at the user hub station. The "inconvenience" of this double hop process, which we expect to be infrequently used, allows considerable cost savings in the space segment. Similarly, international links are obtained by tying in a domestic ORBCOMM network to the existing international communications infrastructure at the user hub station. This is much more cost effective than designing ORBCOMM to emulate the existing point-to-point international networks.

Limiting the traffic to fairly low speed digital data allows the use of narrow band VHF channels. This is an extremely important design choice for low cost, since it not only lowers the mass and cost of the satellites but also allows the low cost manufacture of the remote terminal units.

The low cost features of using LEO satellites, compared with GEO satellites or terrestrial towers, has already been discussed. The number of satellites and their orbits was selected to provide very high availability values, but not 100 percent. For many data applications and for many parts of the World, low cost communications with high, but not continuous availability is economically feasible. The cost increase to ensure 100 percent availability all too often results in zero availability, because the service becomes too expensive and will never be implemented.

That ORBCOMM is low cost and affordable is illustrated in Figure 9. The cost of a remote terminal will depend upon the number of service capabilities it is designed to provide. It will range from as little as $50, for units integrated with other equipment, up to less than $400 for full capability VitalNet units. The installation cost are zero or negligible. No special equipment is needed at each user's hub other than a general purpose desk top computer and telephone modem. These probably already exist in most users' offices. There will be access charges, varying from $5 to $45 per terminal per month, and usage charges, expected to be in the region of half a cent per byte. These costs make ORBCOMM far cheaper than GEO satellite mobile services or LEO satellite voice services. They are also comparable with tower-based data services, but without the geographic limitation of any terrestrial network.

Capital Costs	
Remote Terminal Units	$50 – $400 Negligible Installation Costs
Hub Station	Shared Use of A Desk Top Computer and Modem
Operating Costs	
Access Charges	$5 – $45 Per Month, Per Terminal
Usage Charges	Around $0.005 Per Byte

Figure 9. Cost Elements.

Orbital Communications Corporation will build, launch, operate and, when necessary, replace the satellites. It will also build and operate the Network Control Center and the Gateway Earth Stations for the USA network. For the rest of the World, domestic communication entities, either a government agency or a private company, will operate the system under license. They will procure, install and operate the NCC and gateways and use the satellites as they pass overhead. Typically, the cost to start the network in a country is less than two million dollars.

In February 1992, the World Administrative Radio Conference of the International Telecommunications Union reallocated the use of the VHF and UHF frequencies. The ORBCOMM frequencies can now be used, on a primary basis, for LEO mobile satellite services throughout the World. Each government can give a license for an ORBCOMM network in its country in strict observance of the internationally-agreed allocations. Orbital Communications Corporation has been granted an initial license to operate the system in the USA with 2 satellites. These will be launched in mid-1993 and we will then start the U.S. Network with intermittent service. We anticipate receiving the full license before the end of this year, so that we will be able to launch the rest of the constellation in 1994. Agreements are being made with communication companies in many other countries so that other domestic networks will be in operation within just a few years.

MAGSS-14: A Medium Altitude Global Mobile Satellite System with Enhanced Regional Coverage

J. Benedicto, J. Fortuny, P. Rastrilla
Radiofrequency Systems Division
Electrical Systems Department, ESTEC
P.O.Box 299, Noordwijk, NL

1 Abstract

Non-geostationary circular Earth orbits at medium (MEO) or low (LEO) altitudes are being considered for the fourth generation mobile satellite systems (MSS) as an effective way to provide voice communication services to users equipped with hand-held and portable terminals.

This paper describes the basic parameters and performance of a Medium Altitude Global Satellite System (MAGSS-14) based on 14 medium-size satellites in a MEO constellation. MAGSS-14 offers significant advantages in terms of gradual build-up and Global coverage with respect to other systems proposed until now. The constellation parameters have been optimised to enhance the coverage in terms of minimum elevation angle in the regions contained between 30° and 60° of latitude.

2 Introduction

As early as 1976 the use of geostationary satellites was regarded as the appropriate solution for providing communication services to mobile users on sea, air and ground. In accordance with it, current first and second generation satellites make use of a Global beam to offer these services, requiring the mobile users to be equipped with fairly large and powerful terminals.

Third Generation satellites are planned to provide higher gain spot beams on Global (INMARSAT III) or regional basis (MSAT, ARTEMIS), which will increase further the capacity and scope for frequency reuse.

With the rapid growth of Terrestrial Cellular Networks which offer a variety of services (including toll quality voice) to users equipped with small portable vehicular (PV) and even hand-held (HH) terminals, non-geostationary LEO and MEO Mobile Satellite Systems are being studied and proposed (Iridium, Odyssey, Globalstar,...) to complement those, offering equivalent services to users outside urban areas.

PV and in particular HH type terminals have to be equipped with very low gain antennas (close to 0 dBi) and limit the transmit RF power below 1 Watt in order to reduce the radiation exposure to the user. Such constraints impose very stringent requirements to the design of a suitable space segment.

In the selection of the optimum satellite constellation a number of options can be considered, namely: LEO (Low Earth Orbit), HEO (Highly Elliptical Orbit), GEO (Geostationary Orbit) and MEO (Medium Earth Orbit). The different aspects related with the adoption of each of these options can be summarized as follows:

1) Voice links to HH terminals from GEO are very demanding in terms of spacecraft RF power consumption and size of the on-board antenna, which has to be large also to achieve a significant degree of frequency re-use. Such antennas generate a large number of beams over the visible Earth, requiring novel payload routing and beamforming concepts. From GEO, latitudes above 60° (N and S) are poorly covered with elevation angles below 10-20°, and round trip delays in the link are relatively large, about 250 ms.

2) Traditional HEO options cannot provide global coverage, unless they are combined with other GEO satellites or the satellites are used throughout the complete orbital period. Apogees of optimized HEO orbits are in the range of 20000 to 30000 km or more, so that very large spacecrafts must be used for an HH-type of service, and large round trip delays are to be expected. Furthermore, these spacecrafts would pass frequently through the Van Allen belts increasing the spacecraft radiation exposure. On the other hand, this option is optimum for regional or multi-regional coverage, providing elevation angles above 50° or 60° in high latitude regions.

3) Spacecrafts orbiting at altitudes in the range of 2000 Km to 9000 Km would suffer from high radiation doses. Thus, a "LEO" option must be designed at orbital altitudes below 2000 Km. At these altitudes polar orbit constellations are optimum but provide highly non-uniform coverage. Furthermore, many satellites and therefore many gateway stations and/or ISLs are required, links would suffer from higher Doppler shifts, and global coverage can only be provided with very low elevation angles (in the range of 10° or less). Therefore, impact of Doppler, multipath and shadowing due to the low elevation angles would degrade very much service quality and system availability. On the other hand, operating at low altitudes means that lower path losses and transmission delays are to be expected.

4) Medium Altitude Orbits (MEOs), i.e. around 10000 Km, have shown to be optimum for an HH type of service from the point of view of coverage performance. They provide global coverage with the maximum guaranteed elevation angle minimising the number of satellites involved. The size of the spacecraft (for an HH-type of service) and the network complexity remain also within practical limits. Additionally, MEO systems offer a good scope for frequency re-use, relatively short round trip delay and the radiation doses are well below other HEO or high LEO options.

Consequently, a medium altitude (MEO) orbit at 10,350 Km (6-hour period) has been selected as the baseline Global Personal Communication Satellite System which is described in the following section.

3   MAGSS-14: system description

MAGSS-14 (*Medium Altitude Global Satellite System*) is a satellite system that has been designed to provide global mobile communication services such as voice and data to *Hand-Held* (HH) and *Portable/Vehicle* (PV) terminals.

The satellite network proposed (illustrated in Fig. 1) consists of the following elements:

- The user terminal which can be HH or PV of characteristics as shown in table 1.

	Hand-Held	Portable/Vehicle
Antenna Gain (dBi)	0	7
RF TX Power (W)	0.5	2
EIRP (dBW)	−3	10
DC Power (W)	2.0	8
G/T (dB/K)	−25	−18

Table 1: *Mobile Terminals technical parameters.*

- The space segment consisting of 14 medium altitude satellites.

- A number of Earth Gateway Stations (EGS), distributed around the Globe (a minimum of 14 is required to avoid the need for ISLs) which provide the interconnectivity between the satellites and the Terrestrial Networks.

- The Network Control Center which is connected to all EGSs and performs the function of Network management in terms of satellite power and spectrum resources utilisation.

The satellite links with the mobile users are at L-band and the links with the EGS can be either at C-band or at Ka-band (20-30 Ghz). Using C-band for the EGS links would be advantageous from the points of view of link availability and EGS cost but the issue of interference with other GEO systems using the same bands should be deeply analysed before adopting such approach.

The satellite constellation, shown in Fig. 2, provides 24/24 h Global coverage with a minimum angle of elevation worldwide of 28.5 degrees, although a given user will experience in average a much higher elevation angle, above 50 degrees. Since the time during which each satellite is covering a given user is quite large (about 1 hour), the satellites could adjust for every call the TX power level according to the mean angle of elevation expected during the call (which could be up-dated on ground every few minutes in case the call is still in progress). This would result into a significant on-board RF power saving.

Another important feature provided by this constellation is that of inherent flexibility in the location of EGSs (which may be subjected to geoadministrative constraints) and multiple satellite-EGS interconnectivity. By providing a mobile service zone with relatively large (28.5°) minimum elevation angle as illustrated in Fig. 3, the feeder link coverage can be extended further (down to a lower elevation angle) so that a given EGS can simultaneously handle traffic from various satellites. The EGS coverage zone could be as large as 2 times the mobile service zone, and could be defined by a minimum angle of elevation of, say, 5 to 10 degrees.

3.1   Orbital Parameters

MAGSS-14 constellation is the best single visibility *Rosette* [2] for a number of 14 satellites slightly modified. Its main orbit parameters are:

- 10354 Km orbit altitude.

- 6 Hours orbit period.

- 56° orbit plane inclination, instead of the 54° corresponding to the best single-visibility *Rosette* of 14 satellites .This inclination angle is the result of an optimization process to enhance the coverage between the latitudes 30° and 60°. Such difference does not degrade at all the global minimum elevation angle, still being around 28.5°.

3.2   Elevation Angle Statistical Variations

MAGSS-14 offers global coverage 24 h/24 h with elevation angles always above 28.5°, and moreover, this coverage is enhanced in elevation angle in the regions between 30°-60° latitude (North and South hemispheres). Fig. 4 shows a snapshot of the elevation angle contours for a MAGSS-14 satellite above Europe while Fig. 5 shows the statistics of the minimum elevation angle, i.e. the percentage of time during which the elevation angle is above a certain value (in this case 50°) as a function of the latitude of the observation point (it does not depend on the longitude). It can be calculated [3] that between 30°-60° latitude the elevation angle is above 30°, 40° and 50° in 100%, 95% and 75% of the time, respectively.

Plotting the variations of the minimum elevation angle versus time from a 50° Latitude point, the corresponding user-to- satellite hand-over sequence can also be calculated [3]. It can be seen that hand-overs from the Equator would occur regularly every 1/6 of the orbital period, i.e. about 1 hour.

Regional distributions of the minimum elevation angle for Europe, North-America, and East Asia have also been analyzed [3]. It can be said for illustration that the distribution for Europe shows several long periods (about 3 hours) of time where more than 90% of the locations are above 50° of elevation angle.

3.3   Payload design

The MAGSS-14 satellite payload has been preliminary evaluated in its complexity. A transparent analog repeater payload has been assumed so far, although techniques of on-board DSP will be investigated to enhance the space segment capacity.

Fig. 6 shows typical 37-beam coverage of the European region from one of the MAGSS-14 satellites. Such coverage can be provided from an aperture of 1.8 meter diameter, which would generate 24 dB edge-of-coverage gain beams.

It has been assumed preliminary that such antenna could be realised with a direct radiating phased array of 37 elements 1.3 lambda each, which would be fed by 37 L-band SSPAs of 3.5 watts RF power. The total 126 watts RF power generated on-board would provide a total EIRP of 43.5 dBW. This figure takes into account 3 dB edge of coverage gain loss and 1.5 dB transmit output network losses.

The total payload mass including a Ka-band gateway feeder link transponder is estimated in 140 Kg and the payload DC power consumption below 500 watts.

3.4 Link budgets and system capacity

Forward and Return link budgets are provided for illustration in table 2.

FORWARD LINK (1.5 Ghz)	
elevation (deg)	30
satellite EIRP (dBW)	17.2
path loss (1)	178.1
atmospheric loss (dB)	0.2
mobile G/T (dB/K)	-25
down-link C/N_o (dBHz)	42.5
overall C/N_o (dBHz)	42
required C/N_o (dBHz)	42
margin (dB)	0

RETURN LINK (1.6 Ghz)	
elevation (deg)	30
mobile RF power (W)	0.5
mobile antenna gain (dBi)	0
mobile EIRP (dBW)	-3
path loss (2)	178.5
atmospheric loss (dB)	0.2
satellite antenna diameter (m)	1.8
repeater noise temperature (dBK)	28
satellite G/T (dB/K)	-3.45
up-link C/N_o (dBHz)	43.45
overall C/N_o (dBHz)	42
required C/N_o (dBHz)	42
margin (dB)	0

(1) includes slant range loss at edge of coverage
(2) includes slant range loss at edge of coverage

Table 2: *Forward and return link budgets*

The payload described in the previous section would lead to a satellite capacity (see for reference table 3) of 1,333 hand-held voice circuits or the equivalent of 6,665 portable/vehicular voice circuits (C/N_o=42 dBHz).

With the assumptions of 10 mErlang user activity factor (equivalent to 15 minutes per day per user) and that 80% of the total Global traffic is carried by only 6 of the 14 satellites, the worldwide number of users that could be served by this system would be 1,000,000 equipped with hand-held terminal or the equivalent of 5,000,000 equipped with portable/vehicle terminals.

Over Europe, MAGSS-14 could provide service to about 133,300 users equipped with hand-held terminals or about 666,500 users equipped with portable terminals.

EIRP/channel (dBW)	17.2
voice activation (dB)	4.0
power control advantage (dB)	1.0
satellite antenna diameter (m)	1.8
satellite antenna EOC gain (dBi)	24
ONET loss (dB)	1.5
total number of channels	1333
total satellite EIRP (dBW)	43.5
RF power (W)	126
DC power (W)	380
s/c DC power (W)	500

Table 3: *Satellite RF power requirement for hand-held voice circuits (1.5 Ghz).*

3.5   Gradual system build-up

A very important feature of constellations with large number of satellites is that of being able to start providing service with a reduced number of satellites and allow a gradual build-up of the complete network capability.

MAGSS-14 has been designed such that it can start providing worlwide service with a minimum elevation angle of 7.5° using only 7 out of the 14 satellites. Such start configuration is a constellation of 7 satellites distributed in 7 orbital planes of 56° at 10354 Km of altitude which would cover the entire Earth optimally.

The elevation angle statistics for this start-up constellation have also been calculated [3] for all latitude points and for elevation angles greater than 10, 20 and 30 degrees. It should be noted that for all regions contained between 15 and 65 degrees of latitude (Northern and Southern Hemispheres) the elevation angle is better than 30 degrees for more than 80 percent of the time with only 7 satellites.

4   Conclusions

In this paper a MEO system called MAGSS-14 has been presented. This system results very attractive for the introduction of hand-held voice services with medium-size satellites based on well proven technology. MAGSS-14 features 28.5 degrees of minimum angle of elevation worldwide with only 14 satellites. The constellation has been optimised to provide enhanced coverage over the region contained between 30-60° of latitude. Improvement of the statistical angle of elevation has been demonstrated, showing to be as high as 50 degrees for 75% of the time on those regions. A build-up configuration using only 7 of those satellites has also been analysed and proven to provide continuous Global coverage with 7.5 degrees minimum angle of elevation, comparable in performance to other proposed systems based on a much larger number of satellites. The system has been sized to provide worlwide service to 1,000,000 hand-held terminals or the equivalent of 5,000,000 portable/vehicle terminals.

5   Acknowledgements

The study reported here has been performed in the Radiofrequency Systems Division of the Electrical Systems Department, ESTEC. The authors would like to thank Mr.M.Lopriore, Mr.R.Coirault and Mr.W.Greiner for the encouragement received during the development of this work.

References

[1] W.S. Adams and L. Rider. *Circular Polar Constellations Providing Continuous Single or Multiple Coverage Above a Specified Latitude.* Journal of the Astronautical Sciences, Vol. 35, No. 2, April-June 1987.

[2] Ballard, A.H. *Rosette Constellations of Earth Satellites.* IEEE Transactions on Aerospace and Electronic Systems, Vol. AES-16, No. 5, September 1980.

[3] Fortuny, J., Benedicto, J. and Rastrilla, P. *Satellite Constellations for a Global Personal Communication System at L-band.* ESA-EWP 1661, May 1992.

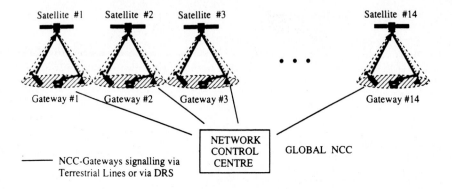

Figure 1: *Network topology*

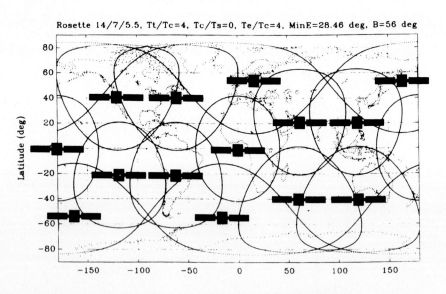

Figure 2: *Snapshot of the MAGSS-14 constellation showing the coverage for a minimum elevation angle of 28.5°.*

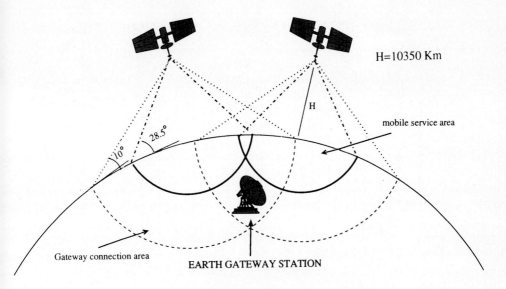

Figure 3: *EGS-satellites connectivity.*

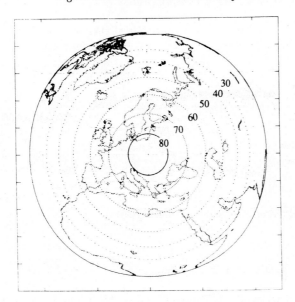

Figure 4: *Elevation angle contours for a MAGSS-14 satellite over Europe.*

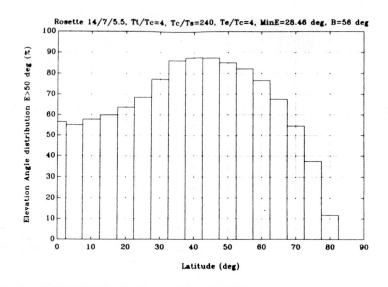

Figure 5: *MAGSS14 Minimum Elevation angle statistics above 50°.*

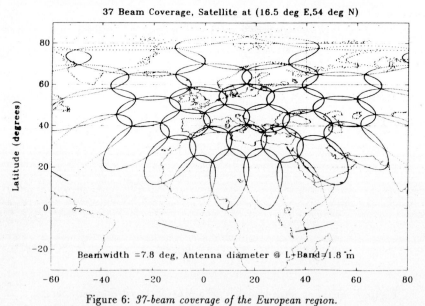

Figure 6: *37-beam coverage of the European region.*

FEASIBILITY STUDY OF A PERSONAL COMMUNICATIONS SYSTEM IRIDIUM-Like

L. Caporicci, R. Del Ricco, S. Di Girolamo, C. Soddu **(1)**
G. Rondinelli **(2)**

(1) ITALSPAZIO - Via V.E. Orlando, 83 - 00185 Roma (Italy)
(2) Previously with ITALSPAZIO

ABSTRACT

The paper outlines a candidate architecture applicable to personal communication systems, via LEO satellites. The results of a study performed by ITALSPAZIO for the European Space Agency (ESA) are presented.

According to the ESA directions, the concept of the IRIDIUM Motorola system has been adopted as derived from the available public documentation. The following topics have been covered:

- System architecture,
- Constellation, coverage and frequency reuse,
- Traffic management: access, routing and networking,
- Spacecraft and payload architecture definition,
- Organization aspects.

1. IRIDIUM-Like CONCEPT

The Motorola IRIDIUM system will provide mobile/voice data communications. The system will operate through a fleet of 77 LEO satellites and user terminals having cellular radio size.

The overall space/ground infrastructure will consist of:

- The space segment, that is 77 LEO satellites interconnected via intersatellite links (ISL) for 100% world continuous coverage.
- The network earth stations: gateway (GTW) stations and associated facilities world-wide distributed.
- The control segment: a) telemetry, tracking and command (TT&C) stations, b) Satellite Operation Control Centres (SOCCs) and c) Network Operation Control Centres (NOCCs).

The space infrastructure supports an adequate interface with the user segment, that is millions of terminals which may be portable, mobile, transportable, voice and/or data and RDSS terminals, according to the specific user needs.

Major System Features: The system provides world-wide service coverage with extensive frequency reuse in the user's links.

- The interface with the users adopts a cell grid coverage implemented by a multibeam antenna system (37 beams) on-board the spacecraft.
- FDM/TDMA operation of user's links, with two sets of carriers

437

for up/down links, with spot beam switching slaved to the TDMA operation.
- TDM/TDMA gateway links with on-board antenna beam agility and synchronous operation with other links;
- Inter satellite TDM links (ISL) of each satellite with 2 satellites (forward and after) in the same orbit plane and 2 + 2 satellites in the adjacent planes.
- Centralized network control: spacecraft TT&C & monitoring of earth segment.

. Potential beam overlapping of satellites in adjacent planes avoided through gradual spot beam disabling from equatorial to polar regions.
. Routing mechanization on board each satellite with alternative routing selection, addressed by the on-board logic system.
. Minor helping system functions from ground segment, such as updating of position of mobile users roaming across wide regions.
. Assignment of channels to identified users only, with user's position determined by the system itself or by other localization means.

Based on above concepts, ITALSPAZIO has developed the overall design of an IRIDIUM-Like system:

- capable to support world-wide services for 2-4 millions users;
- provided with system autonomy, with operation controlled by the earth segment.

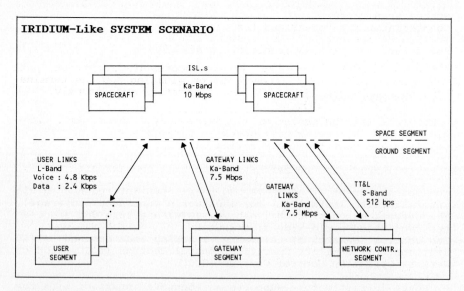

Network Operation: The network will support:

- traffic data flows: signalling and true traffic user-to-user bit streams, which is the overall traffic supported by the user access channels, ISL.s and gateway trunks;
- system house-keeping and infrastructure control data, network operation of the gateway stations,
- gateway status and control, satellites status and control,
- system supervision operated by the master control center, billing data.

. Communications between two mobile subscribers involve only channels of satellite user links if both users
  are covered by the same satellite.
. If users are not covered by same satellite, one or more ISL hops are needed to interconnect the two satellites which are in direct communication with the subscribers.
. When a communication is established between a mobile subscriber and a PSN subscriber through a gateway,
  also a channel of Gateway links is involved.
. User links, GTW links, ISL.s adopt particular TDMA structures to fulfill the specific link requirements.
. Time-consuming reformatting is avoided by adopting common clock, basic timing diagrams and messages where
  possible.

In the user links, the cell pattern of satellite foot print moves
rapidly: communication payload must periodically hand-off the
"active" links. At the appropriate time, the hand-off is executed
and the "new" channel path is established before the "old" channel path be released. Hand-offs can be a) internal, inside same
satellite from current cell to an adjacent cell; b) external,
from current cell of one satellite to the adjacent cell of another satellite.
Hand-off procedure involves coordination control between the satellites and the user terminals. The satellite currently servicing the user terminal initiates and manages the hand-off operation.

The satellites:
. Select the potential hand-off cells and identify the most appropriate "next" cell.
. Inform the user terminal on the hand-off timing, the new carrier frequency and the time slot.
. Set-up a "new" talking path in the satellite network.
. Release the "old" talking path in the satellite network.
. Inform the gateway station about the new call reference number.

Routing Concept: The routing scheme chooses the shortest path
which minimizes the ISLs between the originating and the terminating nodes, with the satellite nodes operating autonomously.

Information used during call routing:
. position of mobile user
. position map of satellites
. position map of gateway stations
. connectivity matrices
. routing tables
. status of output buffers
. status of active cells.

The connectivity matrix is established among the co-rotating satellites, due to criticality of ISL between counter-rotating satellites.

Earth Segment Operation: The gateway stations interface satellites with PSTN.

. Gateway stations provide billing and registration of assigned mobile users, support call processing, validate registered mobile users.
. TT&C and SOCC maintain, monitor and manage the orbiting satellites, determine their ephemeris, perform
  station keeping duties.
. Satellite ephemeris are up-dated every orbit to enhance navigation performances and are distributed to
  all gateways for tracking.

The NOCC provides overall management of communications network.
It supports the network operation sending to satellites and gate-

ways instructions for normal operation and corrective actions.

System Data: System data will support system operation:

a) control data of user traffic;
b) control data of constellation;
c) monitoring and control data of gateway stations.

Due to the impact on the availability of channels for true traffic, system data volume shall be maintained as small as possible, but compatible with a sound management of the system operation.

. Gateway stations monitoring consists of in-out data exchanges with Central Control Station(s). Information from the gateways in visibility of one satellite are real-time transferred to the Central Control Station via the ISLs and feeder (GTW) links.
. Telemetry and command data from/to each satellite are linked to the Central Control Stations and, possibly to selected gateways.
. Traffic control data and billing data support the traffic management:
 - up-dating of subscriber list, to/from each gateway;
 - up-dating of position of all subscribers, to/from each gateway;
 - call data relevant to each active user, to/from each gateway;
 - transfer of information subscriber status and traffic data among the gateways;
 - transfer of selected items of above information to/from the Central Control Station;
 - alarms.

Traffic Loading Capability: The system is dimensioned in order to support 4070 users max in each spacecraft coverage.

. for user links   : 4070 calls/sat
. for gateway links : 2600 calls/sat, typ., 5200 calls/sat max
. for ISLs   : 5400 calls/sat typ., 6200 calls/sat max

Gateway operation is typically 2600 calls/sat. To accept peak traffic, the actual figure can be doubled through the use of two additional carriers: a total 4 carriers can be handled; 2 each TWTA of the gateway link on-board payloads.

Due to the effective satellite coverage at latitudes between 45° and 60° in the northern earth emisphere, the total call number per satellite ranges from 3000 to 2500 about. Since at such latitudes the adoption of a personal communications system could be extensive, a large margin on gateway links capability can be convenient to accept peak traffic since most of the mobile originated or addressed traffic will be connected to PSN.

Another system margin is foreseen, as 1400 Kbps for each ISL carriers, (tot. 1400x4) equivalent to about 800 call/sat. For ISLs, the margin can represent about the 50% of the traffic of one satellite. This margin can be used for rerouting of communications in the case of failure of another satellite.

2. CONSTELLATION CHARACTERISTICS

The orbit characteristic of the IRIDIUM-Like constellation, are:

- Seven orbital planes. The first plane has 27.046° RAAN (Right Ascension of Ascending Node). The angular distance between adjacent orbit planes is 27.046°, with the exception of plane 1 and plane 7 which are separated 17.724°.

- All satellite orbits have the same semiaxis 7143 Km and inclination of 90° (polar orbits). The orbital period is 6008 sec. that is: 1 h, 40 min., 8 sec..
- Each plane contains 11 satellites. Satellites in odd planes have alternate phasing (true anomaly) with respect to satellites in even planes.
- All orbits present a common small eccentricity (0.002) but different argument of perigee among odd planes and even planes. In this way, the satellite of each orbital plane have different altitude when reach the polar zones. Thus, the risk of collision between spacecraft is avoided in principle.

IRIDIUM-Like CONSTELLATION PARAMETER

PARAMETER	VALUE	ERROR LIMIT	SYMBOL
Orbital Period	6008 s	±1 s	P
Eccentricity	0.002	±0.0006	e
Inclination	90.00°	±0.005°	i
Right Ascension of Ascending Node for Plane j (j=1,...,7)	27.046° x j	±0.10°	Ω
Argument of Perigee	Any value 0 to 360	Between two odd or two even planes j and l $30 \le \| \omega_j - \omega_l \| \le 330$	ω
True Anomaly, Even planes: Sat. 1 to Sat. 11 Odd planes : Sat. 1 to Sat. 11	16.36° to 346.64° 0° to 327.27° in steps 32.73°	±0.10° ±0.10° ±0.10°	ϑ

3. USER LINK AND FREQUENCY REUSE

For user links up and down, the satellite foot print on the earth is composed by 37 L-band spot beams, resulting a continuous hexagonal pattern with one central spot beam surrounded by three rings of equally sized beams.
A combination of TDMA/FDMA access scheme supports the user links. Vocoded voice and data signals are QPSK modulated.
The user Tx/Rx scheme is applied to the 37-cell satellite coverage, where the spot beams are active in sequence and with simultaneous activity of spot beams sufficiently far away.

Each user link operates in a burst mode. The bursts are controlled to occur at the proper time in the TDMA frame.
Several carriers are involved in the same beam, both in transmission and in reception.
In order to have a high number of user channels with reduced frequency band occupation an extensive frequency reuse scheme is adopted: a) using narrow spot beams, b) re-using same carrier frequencies with a separation of 1 to 2 spot beams, c) both up and down links use in time sharing the same frequency band.

With the adopted 37 cell grid the frequency reuse per satellite is 5.23 (maximum). The effective instantaneous reuse factor depends by the actual satellite latitude, since the outermost spot beams are disabled to eliminate un-necessary overlaps with beams belonging to adjacent satellites.

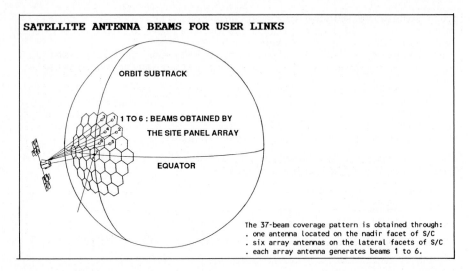

SATELLITE ANTENNA BEAMS FOR USER LINKS

ORBIT SUBTRACK

1 TO 6 : BEAMS OBTAINED BY
THE SITE PANEL ARRAY

EQUATOR

The 37-beam coverage pattern is obtained through:
. one antenna located on the nadir facet of S/C
. six array antennas on the lateral facets of S/C
. each array antenna generates beams 1 to 6.

The strategy for the spot beam activity is function of the satellite latitude. Up-dating of active beams occurs at high latitudes: change of the simultaneously active beams configurations is
implemented with the following constraints:

- a separation of two not-active spot beams is provided between
  any couple of active beams of external coverage rings;
- a separation of one not-active spot beam is provided between
  any couple of active beams generated by different satellites.

The number of cells active in time sharing within the single satellite depend by the latitude of the satellite orbit position.
The total number of active spot beams required to fully cover the
earth results 1758. A global coverage is achieved during one TDMA
frame.

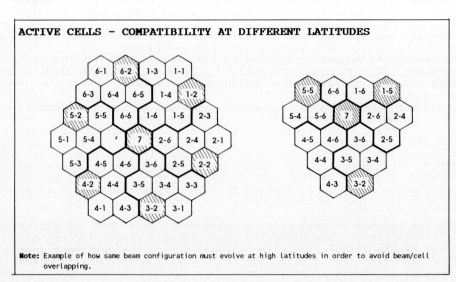

ACTIVE CELLS - COMPATIBILITY AT DIFFERENT LATITUDES

Note: Example of how same beam configuration must evolve at high latitudes in order to avoid beam/cell
overlapping.

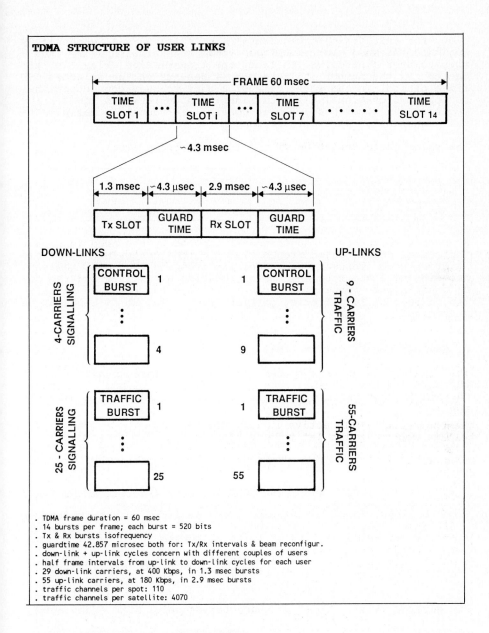

TDMA STRUCTURE OF USER LINKS

- . TDMA frame duration = 60 msec
- . 14 bursts per frame; each burst = 520 bits
- . Tx & Rx bursts isofrequency
- . guardtime 42.857 microsec both for: Tx/Rx intervals & beam reconfigur.
- . down-link + up-link cycles concern with different couples of users
- . half frame intervals from up-link to down-link cycles for each user
- . 29 down-link carriers, at 400 Kbps, in 1.3 msec bursts
- . 55 up-link carriers, at 180 Kbps, in 2.9 msec bursts
- . traffic channels per spot: 110
- . traffic channels per satellite: 4070

4. ISL LINKS AND FREQUENCY REUSE

A total of six antennas per satellite is envisaged to establish
intra-plane links (forward and backward satellites) and inter-
plane links (two satellites for each adjacent plane). However, a
maximum of four intersatellite links may simultaneously operate:
1 each side and 1 each fore and aft. The TDMA format for ISL is
based on the same timing as the user link TDMA, but using as frame period the time slot duration of the user link TDMA. The adop-

443

tion of a multiframe format containing 14 frames is essentially due to the need to reduce the total transmission delay for a user-to-user connection. In fact, the transmission delay is affected by the number of ISL.s and it depends on the selected ISL frame period. In the worst case of a user-to-user connection where the two originating and terminating nodes are two counter-rotating satellites passing over equator, it results a maximum total transmission delay of 310 msec.

The major characteristics of the ISL TDMA frame are:

. Transmission Rate	: 10 Mbps	. Guard Time, max	: 500 microsec
. Multiframe Format	: 14 frames	. Satellite ch.s per Superframe: 616 min.	
. Multiframe Period	: 60 msec	. TDM Efficiency (min/max)	: 63/78%
. Frame Period	: 4.2857 msec	. Satellite Link Capacity, min : 5400 traffic ch.s	

A proper frequency reuse scheme is imposed by the need to reduce the number of allocated frequencies and the constraint to avoid interferences between the spacecraft crossing the polar regions. Assuming no links between counter-rotating satellites and the same inter-plane frequencies properly shifted for the same satellites, a pool of 18 different carrier frequencies at Ka-band may be sufficient.

5. GATEWAY COMMUNICATION LINKS

The spacecraft antenna system for gateway links provides earth coverage in the overall cone of visibility of the spacecraft through 12 spot beams cyclically enabled for transmission and reception:

- two Tx/Rx chains are envisaged to support communications inside two different sets of 6 spot beams;
- a maximum of two spot beams may be active per time, one per chain, allowing transmission/reception of one, maximum two carriers per beam;
- TDMA frame length and spot beam activity strategy of gateway links are flexible;
- guard times, about 500 microsec, are required between bursts of different spot beams for on-board antenna switching;
- positions and durations of traffic bursts are managed by the spacecraft in visibility;
- burst time plan is updated on-board the spacecraft and transmitted to each gateway in visibility.

For gateway links, the major characteristics of TDMA frame are:

. Transmission Rate	: 7.5 Mbps
. Frame Period	: 60 msec
. Guard Time (max)	: 500 microsec
. Satellite channels per frame	: 630 (*)
. Frame efficiency	: 80% (*)
. Gateway link capacity	: 1400 traffic DSI ch.s/carriers.

(*) TDMA frame utilization efficiency depends on the number of gateways actually in visibility and their distribution inside the spot beams. Above figures refer to 6 gateways in visibility, 1 gateway per spot beam of feeder link antenna coverage.

7. PAYLOAD AND USER LINK ANTENNA

The IRIDIUM-Like payload implements three main Tx/Rx functions, for user links, gateway links and ISLs.

In addition on OBP provides payload operation management/control and traffic routing. The payload is composed by:

- 6 phased array side antennas and 1 central antenna for user links. Active array antennas, with Tx/Rx functions switched, via OBP are foreseen;
- 7 Tx/Rx channels (baseband to RF and viceversa) interfacing user link traffic with the OBP;
- GTW link Tx/Rx equipment interfacing at baseband with the OBP;
- simple GTW link antenna: 12 Tx + 12 Rx horns, switched by ferrite latching switches commanded via OBP;
- ISL Tx/Rx equipment interfacing at baseband with the OBP;
- two fixed (aft & forward) ISL antennas, four gimbaled lateral antennas;
- TWTA for Ka-band transmission, gateway links and ISLs;
- OBP, for traffic routing, payload operation management & control;
- payload management unit including telemetry and command;
- frequency source and distribution devices.

PAYLOAD OVERALL DIAGRAM

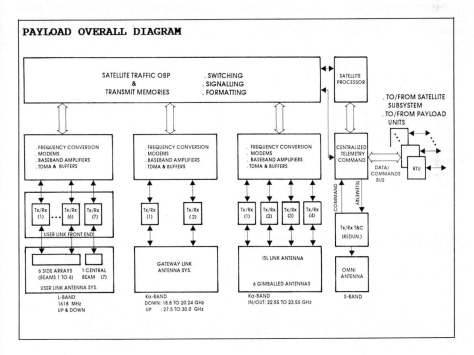

The use of different bands is foreseen in order to implement the links towards users, gateway stations and other spacecraft:

- L-band communications between each spacecraft and individual user terminals;
- Ka-band intersatellite links;
- Ka-band communications between spacecraft & gateway stations;
- S-band TT&C links, for telemetry, command and RR&R operations.

A summary budget for the overall payload has been derived:

PAYLOAD MASS/POWER BUDGETS		
	MASS (Kg)	POWER (W)
User link packages	164	340 *
ISL packages	22.5	140
Gateway packages	13.5	134
OBP	6	30
Frequency synthes. & ref.	7	11
Ancillary electronics	20	22
TOTAL	233.0	677**

Max power consumption (W): * 365, ** 702.

User Link Antenna System: In terms of design complexity, the most demanding element is the array antenna system for user links. Moreover its dimensions are key parameters impacting on the overall spacecraft configuration. The user link antenna is composed six side panel arrays and one central beam antenna element. Through a wide conical beam the central element provides coverage around the nadir direction. The six side panels provide each one six beams squinted at different angle from nadir, up to the boundary of the spacecraft coverage, with a mask angle of about 10%. Each side panel is mounted on one side panel of the hexagonal spacecraft.

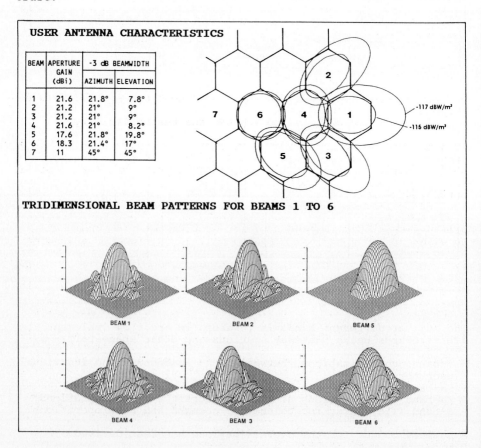

USER ANTENNA CHARACTERISTICS

BEAM	APERTURE GAIN (dBi)	-3 dB BEAMWIDTH	
		AZIMUTH	ELEVATION
1	21.6	21.8°	7.8°
2	21.2	21°	9°
3	21.2	21°	9°
4	21.6	21°	8.2°
5	17.6	21.8°	19.8°
6	18.3	21.4°	17°
7	11	45°	45°

-117 dBW/m²

-115 dBW/m²

TRIDIMENSIONAL BEAM PATTERNS FOR BEAMS 1 TO 6

BEAM 1   BEAM 2   BEAM 5

BEAM 4   BEAM 3   BEAM 6

The array panels are inclined 42° with respect to the spacecraft body. Such a solution has been adopted in order to:

- limit the scan losses by reducing the beam scan angles,
- illuminate the earth with almost uniform power density,
- reduce sidelobe level, through scanning reduction.

Antenna design is based on the isoflux method. In simple words, this method allows to balance range losses with delta antenna gains cell by cell, as far as the range to the users from the spacecraft increases from subsatellite point to the boundaries of the coverage zone.

8. LEOSTAR-E SPACECRAFT DEFINITION

The LEOSTAR-E spacecraft, defined by ITALSPAZIO for an IRIDIUM-Like mission, will be capable to support the operation of the defined payload. The major requirements to be taken into account are:

. Attitude control : ±0.5° all axes	. Orbit correction : mission lifetime compatible
. Nominal orbit : circular, H = 1361 Km i = 90°	. Lifetime : 5 years with in orbit storage &
. Launcher : ARIANE 44, compatibility with	optional de-orbiting capability
multiple launches	. Autonomy : scheduled operations,
. Payload mass : 233 Kg	re-programmability by ground
. Payload power : 700 W	. TT&C : ESA standard, S-band
. Payload operation: full operation during eclipses	

The satellite design has been accomplished according to the following guidelines:

- already proven design concepts for most of spacecraft subsystems;
- limited new design areas to improve the bus reliability.

The major innovation is the spacecraft autonomy: due to the high number of satellites in the constellation, each satellite must be able to navigate and operate in unattended mode for one orbital period, at least, in order to avoid an overload of the ground control segment.
The spacecraft is a three-axis stabilized vehicle with sun pointing solar arrays. The structure consists of 6 aluminum longitudinal trusses with a square empty section for the frame of the satellite. The subsystems and the payload equipment are accommodated on 3 horizontal panels while 6 lateral panels support the payload antenna and the Tx/Rx equipments. The panels are aluminum honeycomb sandwiches core with aluminum face skins.
The S-band TT&C subsystem allows RR&R measurements, for orbit control and ephemeris up-dating. Moreover, it provides telemetry & command operation during orbit injection and emergency phases. The use of TT&C ESA standard equipment is foreseen.
The main elements for the attitude determination, with the required accuracy of 0.2° around each axis, are a conical earth sensor mounted on the bottom panel; a wide angle sun sensor, needed for normal operation initialization, mounted on one of the two solar panels. A digital sun sensor is adopted on the other solar panel in order to maintain solar array sun pointing during normal operation. The attitude control is obtained by a pitch momentum wheel, a yaw reaction wheel and twelve 3N thrusters for wheel desaturation. The thrusters are also utilized for orbit injection correction and orbit keeping maneuvers.

447

The power subsystem makes use of Nickel Hydrogen batteries with a load power of 910 W. The solar panels make use of GaAs cells and are maintained always perpendicular to the sun by a solar array drive and power transfer assembly (SADAPTA). The solar array area required to support the spacecraft power requirements is 12 m^2 (2253 W BOL).

All satellite functions are managed by a redundant on-board computer. The overall mass and power budgets for LEOSTAR-E are shown in the following:

MASS & POWER BUDGETS		
SUBSYSTEM	MASS (Kg)	POWER (W)
Payload	233	702 max, 667 AOE[*]
Structure	39.8	
TT&C	15	20
Attitude determination	6.2	20.4
Attitude control	7.2	5.0
Propulsion	7.9	0.3
Power	86.0	81.8
Management processor	5.9	24
Thermal control	14.6	/
Total dry	415.6	818.5
Propellant	60	
Margin (>10%)	47.4	83.8
Total S/C at launch	523.0	902.3
Battery charge		821.4
Total panel load		1723.7

* AOE (Average Out of Eclipse)

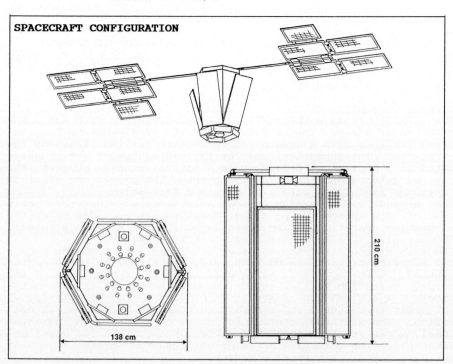

SPACECRAFT CONFIGURATION

210 cm

138 cm

9. ORGANIZATIONAL ASPECTS AND MANUFACTURING STRATEGIES

The establishment of a proper manufacturing policy is a key element to the success of a Personal-Service Communications system (PSC). The role of a "general contractor" could be identified as the prime responsible for the successfull delivery in orbit of the constellation.
This general contractor could be or a single firm or a consortium among operators, financial entities and selected manufacturers, for which responsibility and risk shares shall be carefully allocated.
According to this approach, the satellite system will be accepted in orbit. The performances of each single satellite are established by the customer and agreed by the manufacturer, who is responsible to procure suitable launchers and correctly position the satellite in orbit.
This mode of operation leads to establish an industrial team responsible to: contract for item suppliers/producers, control the quality and the specification responsiveness of produced items, provide a centralized program control, establish a centralized documentation control system, edit-issue and authorize interface control drawing and documents, select qualified suppliers, perform cost management, periodically review and approve CCN, establish and conduct quality inspection and product effectiveness plans, control that suppliers responsively perform production and test programs.

10. CONCLUSIONS

The study performed by ITALSPAZIO, demonstrated the feasibility of an IRIDIUM-Like mission from a system point of view.
Additional efforts will be required in order to assess a convenient cost/technology trade-off and the economic the program.
In addition, the large production volume, as required to built the whole constellation satellites, will cause umpreceeded manufacturing problems to be deeply investigated.
Moreover, the proposed communications and networking scheme seems to be too complicate to fit the basic low cost requirements; for this reason some system elements will require additional refinements in order to reduce the complexity and costs.

BIBLIOGRAPHY

[1] MOTOROLA to FCC.
[2] ITS-TR-175.D/91: "LEO System Study for a Definition of MINISTAR (IRIDIUM-Like)

ACKNOWLEDGEMENT

The authors wish to acknowledge the advise and support of Mr. A. Teofilatto, President of ITALSPAZIO and Mr. G. Barresi, Director of ITALSPAZIO. Special tanks are addressed to Mr. D. Brown and Mr. K. Galligan of ESA for their stimulus on this innovative field.

S 80/T : un micro-satellite
qui combine hautes performances et ressources limitées

par

Jean-Claude LLORENS
Centre National d'Etudes Spatiales, Toulouse, France

1. INTRODUCTION

S 80/T (T pour technologique) est un micro-satellite expérimental qui a été réalisé dans un délai de un an par Matra Marconi Space pour le compte du CNES. Il sera lancé en passager auxiliaire par Ariane lors du vol V 52 Topex-Poséidon.

Ce premier micro-satellite est destiné à la préparation du programme de radiolocalisation et de messagerie S 80 par :

- la mesure du bruit radioélectrique dans la bande VHF 148-149,9 MHz attribuée par la Conférence Mondiale des Radiocommunications de 1992 aux systèmes mobiles par satellite à orbite basse,
- la réalisation d'une expérimentation de messagerie bidirectionnelle et de localisation par des techniques de modulation à base de spectre étalé,
- la détermination de la localisation de mobiles par mesure de distance et d'effet Doppler.

La réalisation de S 80/T a permis au CNES et à MMSF de tenir un pari difficile en réalisant dans un temps très court, inférieur à un an, le satellite et le segment sol associé.

Afin d'aboutir dans les délais prévus, de nouvelles méthodes de travail, un nouveau concept de qualité et des rapports adaptés maître d'oeuvre-client ont dû être mis en place.

Par ce document, on s'attachera à montrer qu'il est possible de réaliser très rapidement et à faible coût une expérimentation préparant un programme opérationnel.

On commencera par décrire l'expérimentation complète : aspects système, composante spatiale et système sol. On mettra en évidence les difficultés rencontrées au cours du projet afin d'en tirer un maximum d'enseignement sur des projets futurs du même type.

2. MISSION S80/T

Dans la continuité du programme Argos, le CNES envisage de mettre en place un système de localisation et collecte de données plus adapté aux différents marchés potentiels.

Début 91, en avance de phase par rapport aux décisions de la CAMR 92, le CNES décidait de mettre en orbite un satellite capable de recevoir l'intégralité des bandes 148 à 149,9 MHz (liaison terre-espace du LEO MSS) et de réémettre en utilisant la liaison descendante LEO MSS 137-138 MHz. Grâce à cette liaison aller-retour, le satellite peut remplir une double mission :

- une mission prioritaire d'analyse du canal 148-149,9 MHz,
- une mission secondaire de test des types de modulation (CDMA ou TDMA) à utiliser par S80 dans les conditions de bruit rencontrées.

3. DESCRIPTION DU SYSTEME

Un synoptique d'ensemble est présenté figure 1.

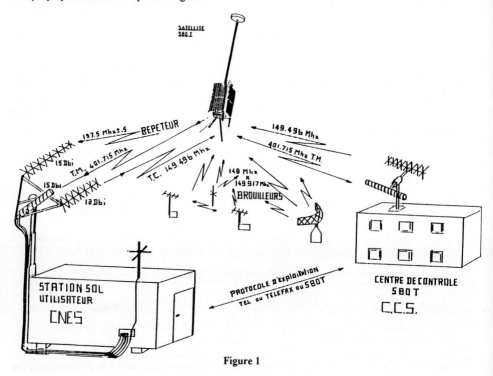

Figure 1

3.1. PLATE-FORME ET CHARGE UTILE S80/T

La plate-forme est un micro-satellite de 50 kg, type UOSAT de l'Université du Surrey. La stabilisation est donnée à $\pm 1,5°$. La charge utile développée par Dassault Electronique est constituée par un répondeur linéaire capable de mesurer des températures de bruit de l'ordre de 300°K et de délivrer des puissances de sortie entre 5 et 8 watts.

L'antenne bifréquence 137-150 MHz est à polarisation circulaire droite pour les besoins de l'expérimentation. Elle possède un gain de -3 dB en émission et en réception. L'énergie de bord est conçue pour un fonctionnement moyen de la charge utile pendant 20% de la période d'orbite.

3.2. MISE A POSTE ET CONTROLE SATELLITE

Les opérations de mise à poste et de contrôle du satellite seront effectuées à partir de l'Université du Surrey par SSTL.

3.3. STATION SOL UTILISATEURS

La station sol utilisateurs est constituée de trois parties :

- une fourniture SSTL/MMSF comprenant les trois fonctions télécommande, télémesure, poursuite satellite et antennes,

452

- le système d'acquisition et de traitement des signaux en provenance du répéteur conçu et réalisé par le CNES, incluant la localisation du satellite et des brouilleurs discrets,

- un ensemble émission-réception CDMA QPSK conçu et réalisé par la société belge SAIT sous contrat ESA.

Cette station sol utilisateurs est une station automatique mobile installée en début d'expérience dans un shelter situé au Centre Spatial de Toulouse.

En plus de cette station mobile lourde, le CNES a conçu et réalisé une station mobile simplifiée permettant l'observation du canal 148-149,9 MHz dans d'autres zones que la zone Europe, à la demande de différents utilisateurs potentiels.

4. ANALYSE DU CANAL

4.1. PRESENTATION DES TRAITEMENTS ENVISAGES

Ils 'agit d'effectuer l'analyse spectrale des bandes VHF 148-149,9 MHz. Cette analyse est basée principalement sur l'utilisation d'un analyseur de spectre temps réel Tektronics 3052. Sur celui-ci, on effectuera, durant les passages satellites en visibilité d'une station sol du CNES, des relevés de spectre de puissance conduisant à l'étude des flux réels reçus par le satellite. Les principaux traitements consistent en :

4.1.1. Traitements statistiques sur le bruit ramené à l'entrée du répéteur satellite

Pour cela, on décompose le bruit en une composante bruit large bande et une composante brouilleurs discrets.

La première composante amène à une notion de température de bruit à la sortie de l'antenne S80/T, permettant ensuite de déterminer le flux à l'entrée de l'antenne S80/T.

La seconde composante concerne l'étude des brouilleurs discrets. Il s'agit de connaître leur nombre, leurs niveaux, leurs occupations spectrales, leurs instants, leurs durées d'émission et leurs fréquences d'apparition. En ce qui concerne les niveaux, on effectuera une correction après localisation des brouilleurs permanents (ou quasi-permanents).

4.1.2. Traitement des événements de courte durée (200 µs)

Pour cela, on fera sur l'analyseur de spectre Tektronics l'acquisition de séries pouvant aller jusqu'à 500 spectres consécutifs autour d'un déclenchement effectué soit en mode manuel (par un opérateur) soit en mode automatique (par dépassement de gabarit programmé sur l'analyseur). Ces relevés de spectre seront stockés sur l'analyseur de spectre et ne font pas l'objet de traitements dans la station sol.

4.1.3. Traitements à partir du signal temporel

On utilise ici un enregistreur magnétique dont le rôle est de pouvoir rejouer les passages sur l'analyseur de spectre Tektronics de manière, en temps différé, à :

- modéliser le canal (association d'une loi de probabilité, étude des variations des principaux paramètres μ et σ),

- aider à la simulation sur des logiciels de télécommunication en utilisant le modèle réel du canal pour la définition de l'architecture de S 80.

4.2. STRATEGIE ET MESURE DE CALIBRATION

4.2.1. Principe

A partir des mesures effectuées sur l'analyseur de spectre, il s'agit de remonter à la puissance réelle à l'entrée du répéteur, puis au flux à l'entrée de l'antenne.

4.2.2. Passage à la mesure de puissance à l'entrée du récepteur

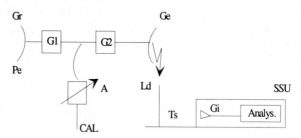

Figure 2

On cherche à connaître Pe à partir de P mesuré sur l'analyseur de spectre (θ = température de fonctionnement du système).

$$\frac{\text{Pe(f) . G1 (f.}\theta\text{) . G2 (f.}\theta\text{) . Ge (f) . Ld(f) . Gs(f) . G3 (+Ts)}}{} > \text{Pmesuré}$$

$$\frac{\text{CAL . A ((}\theta\text{) . G2 (fo.}\theta\text{) . Ge (fo) . Ld(fo) . Gs(fo) . G3 (+Ts)}}{} > \text{CALmesuré}$$

Or, Ld(f) $\approx$ Ld(fo) et Gs indépendant de la fréquence.

On a $\dfrac{\text{Pmesuré}}{\text{CALmesuré}} = f1 \ (f,\theta) \ . \ f2 \ (f) \ . \ \dfrac{\text{Pe}}{\text{CAL}}$

avec $f1 \ (f,\theta) = \dfrac{G1(f,\theta) \ . \ G2(f,\theta)}{A(\theta) \ . \ G2(fo,\theta)}$

f1 est une caractéristique du répéteur fourni par Dassault Electronique, tout comme CAL.

$f2(f) = \dfrac{Ge(f) \ . \ Gs(f)}{Ge(fo) \ . \ Gs(fo)}$

f2 est une caractéristique de l'antenne fournie par MMSF lors des essais d'antenne.

4.3. RELATIONS ENTRE LA PUISSANCE REELLE A L'ENTREE DU REPETEUR ET LA PUISSANCE DE BRUIT CAPTEE PAR L'ANTENNE

4.3.1. Bruit large bande

Si Pin = puissance de bruit à l'entrée de l'antenne :

$$Pe \approx 1/4\pi \ \iint\Omega o \ Pin \ GR \ . \ d\Omega \qquad\qquad (1)$$

Ωo = angle solide par lequel la terre est vue depuis le satellite. La formule (1) est valable dans la mesure où la température du ciel est négligeable.

Nous avons : $Pin = 4\pi \dfrac{1}{\displaystyle\iint_{\Omega o} GR\,.d\Omega}\,Pe$

4.3.2. Brouilleurs discrets

La station sol permettra d'établir une cartographie des brouilleurs discrets avec leur puissance d'émission (PIRE). La localisation des brouilleurs permanents sera assurée par mesure Doppler. La PIRE de chaque brouilleurs sera déterminée à partir de la puissance reçue par la relation :

$$PIRE = \frac{Pe}{L(\alpha).G(\alpha)}$$

où $L(\alpha)$ = pertes d'espace libre du brouilleur et $G(\alpha)$ = gain de l'antenne de réception dans la direction α.

4.4. Séquencement des mesures, exploitation

Le signal à analyser dans la bande 148-149,9 MHz est essentiellement composé de bruit. Il est transmis au sol à 137 MHz. Il s'avère nécessaire de séparer le bruit au sol à 137 MHz du bruit en provenance de la liaison 148 MHz.

Dans le temps, il est effectué successivement les mesures suivantes :
- Relevé du niveau de bruit au sol à 137 MHz, soit TsB,
- Mesure du signal de calibration avec la bande d'analyse B du bruit au sol,
- Mesure du plancher de bruit ($NoB_{mesuré}$ + TsB), on en déduit NoB bruit mesuré dans la bande 148 MHz.

4.4.1. Evaluation de bruit

Connaissant la fonction de transfert $CAL_{mesurée}$ en fonction de CAL, on a :

$$\frac{NoB}{A} = \frac{CAL}{f1(f,\theta).f2(f)} \cdot \frac{NoBmesuré}{CALmesuré}$$

Si : $\dfrac{CAL}{f1(f,\theta).f2(f)} = REF$

$$No = A/B \ .\ REF \ .\frac{NoBmesuré}{CALmesuré}$$

NoB représente la densité de puissance de bruit par Hz à l'entrée de l'antenne.

4.4.2. Evaluation des brouilleurs

La PIRE de chaque brouilleur de la cartographie sera :

$$PIRE = \frac{REF}{L(\alpha).G(\alpha)} \cdot \frac{NoBmesuré}{CALmesuré}$$

5. Architecture de la station sol utilisateur (SSU)

Elle est composée de trois parties principales (voir figure 3) :

- une partie MMS/SSTL (Université du Surrey)
- un calculateur interface,
- une partie mesure et traitements CNES.

5.1. TM, TC, poursuite

Elle comprend les trois fonctions de télécommande, télémesure et poursuite. Un calculateur PC est dédié à chacune de ces fonctions. Chacun des calculateurs comprend une carte d'interface réseau Lantastic. L'existence de ce réseau permet :

- le partage des périphériques,

- la synchronisation des calculateurs,

- la circulation, pendant le passage du satellite, d'informations de poursuite émises par le calculateur de tracking.

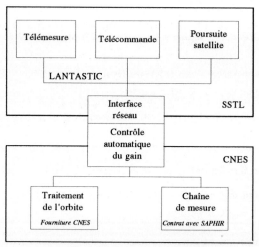

Figure 3 : Station Sol Utilisateur (SSU)

5.2. Calculateur interface

Un calculateur CNES monté sur le réseau Lantastic assure principalement deux fonctions :

- une fonction interface réseau,

- une fonction temps réel d'interprétation des télémesures et d'envoi de télécommandes vers la plate-forme.

5.3. Mesures et traitements

La seconde partie mesures et traitements, directement à la charge du CNES, concerne l'acquisition et le traitement des signaux en provenance du répéteur. Le synoptique de l'ensemble de mesures est présenté par la figure 4. On y voit deux chaînes indépendants :

- La chaîne 1, ou chaîne principale, disposant d'un récepteur qui permet de s'accrocher sur un signal de calibration émis à bord du satellite. On compense ici le Doppler de la liaison descendante et, à l'aide d'un fréquencemètre déclenché à intervalles réguliers et précis, on réalise l'acquisition de couples temps-fréquence permettant la localisation du satellite. La mesure du niveau du signal de calibration se fait par lecture d'une tension analogique à la sortie du répéteur (celui-ci effectue un CAG sur le signal de calibration sur lequel il s'accroche, mais pas sur le reste du signal). En bout de chaîne, l'analyseur de spectre temps réel Tektronics 3052 permet l'acquisition des spectres de puissance à étudier.

- La chaîne 2, ou chaîne de secours, disposant d'un synthétiseur de fréquence qui commande un changement de fréquence grâce à l'information Doppler calculée à partir des prévisions d'orbite). En bout de chaîne, un analyseur de spectre HP 70000 à balayage assure en mode dégradé les mêmes fonctions que l'analyseur Tektronics.

Enfin, le synoptique (figure 4) permet de voir un enregistreur analogique à bandes magnétiques positionné sur l'une et/ou l'autre voie.

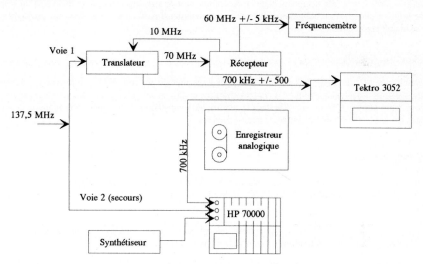

Figure 4 : Synoptique de la chaîne de mesure

Les deux chaînes de mesure et l'enregistreur sont pilotés par le "calculateur de mesure" dont les programmes ont été développés par la société Saphir (Chambéry).

L'ensemble de la chaîne de réception sol est synchronisée par un récepteur GPS utilisé en tant que base de temps TU. Le temps TU sert de référence de temps à l'ensemble des mesures.

Un autre calculateur, pris en charge totalement par le CNES, est dédié à la localisation et à l'orbitographie.

6. CONSIDÉRATIONS SUR LE DEVELOPPEMENT DU PROJET S80/T

Un projet de satellite en moins d'un an à faible coût, tel est le pari engagé pour S80/T. Ce pari semble être tenu à ce jour. Les difficultés rencontrées pendant la durée du projet nous conduisent à tirer un certain nombre de conclusions.

6.1. PHASES DE DEROULEMENT DU PROJET

Le budget d'un projet satellite, même s'il est réduit, reste quand même important. Les quatre phases classiques de développement d'un projet (faisabilité, définition, conception, réalisation) devront être engagées successivement sans suppression totale de l'une d'elles, et devront être optimisées afin d'être réalisées dans les budgets et délais prévus. En règle générale, la réduction des coûts et du temps de réalisation sera vécue comme une optimisation permanente.

6.2. ORGANISATION

Un projet à faible coût implique une équipe réduite très performante, apte à traiter tous les problèmes afin d'en dégager les points durs et faire appel aux spécialistes des disciplines concernées en cas de besoin.

Etant donné le nombre des tâches et leur diversité, le schéma classique de spécialistes s'occupant de chacune des tâches dans chacune des phases est en effet incompatible avec les coûts et les délais.

La maîtrise des coûts et des délais implique au départ une gestion rigoureuse du projet de la part du responsable de projet. Celle-ci passe obligatoirement par une connaissance parfaite de l'ensemble des problèmes posés afin de limiter les surprises.

6.4. QUALITE, FIABILITE

Un certain nombre de points clés devront être prévus, permettant un contrôle des réalisations effectuées. Il faudra s'assurer essentiellement que les équipes chargées de la réalisation et des essais effectuent leurs tâches avec un degré suffisant d'auto-contrôle dans la mesure où les méthodes habituelles, trop lourdes, ne sont pas directement applicables à la réalisation de micro-satellites.

7. CONCLUSIONS

L'utilisation d'une plate-forme type micro-satellite est possible pour toutes les applications pouvant s'accommoder de puissances moyennes de l'ordre de 25 watts et de précisions de pointage de l'ordre de quelques degrés.

Des domaines aussi variés que les applications scientifiques, commerciales et militaires devraient pouvoir bénéficier de coûts et délais attractifs et d'un niveau de performances acceptable.

Dans ces conditions, il serait souhaitable de créer de petites cellules autonomes (pouvant être intégrées à des entités beaucoup plus importantes) pour s'occuper de tels développements. Ces cellules, tout en permettant une gestion technique et contractuelle optimale, devraient constituer des foyers d'excellence, sources de recrutement d'idées neuves pour les grands projets.

THE ELLIPSO^{TM} SYSTEM: ELLIPTICAL LOW ORBITS FOR MOBILE COMMUNICATIONS

David Castiel, Ellipsat, Washington, DC USA

ABSTRACT

The ELLIPSO^{TM} system is aimed at providing combined position determination and mobile voice services via satellites located in low-earth elliptical orbits and operating in the 1610-1626.5MHz and 2483.5-2500 MHz bands. ELLIPSO^{TM} uses a spectrum efficient combination of FDMA and CDMA techniques. The technical characteristics of the ELLIPSO^{TM} constellation provide a platform for the provision of mobile voice at costs comparable to cellular.

I.OVERVIEW

ORBITAL CHARACTERISTICS

The ELLIPSO^{TM} satellites, in a constellation of up to twenty-four satellites, will be placed into the following elliptical orbits:

- perigee at 426 kilometers,
- apogee at 2903 kilometers in the Northern Hemisphere,
- argument of periapsis of 270°
- eccentricity of 0.1541,
- orbit inclination of 63.4° North, and
- period of the orbit at exactly 2 hours (1/12 of a sidereal day).

ELLIPSO^{TM} provides maximum time coverage in its orbits over the Northern latitudes, up to 37 minutes for the continental United States. This coverage is assured with antenna characteristics as follows:

- transmit, four elliptical beams @ 60°x 20° beamwidth
- receive wide beam with 60° width for mobiles
- receive spot beam with 10° widths for control stations.

The coverage with only twelve such satellites, six in each of two elliptical orbits, is illustrated in Figure 1 below.

Figure 1. Coverage with 2 Planes @ 6 Satellites/Plane

Ellipsat has modeled a grid in CONUS and computed satellite availability over a twenty-four hour period. The statistical results for availability with a twelve satellite-constellation are as follows:

Elevation ->	5°	15°
Coverage:		
Maximum (best location)	100.0%	100.0%
Minimum (worst location)	95.6%	60.4%
Average	99.7%	89.5%

Ellipsat intends to deploy nonetheless 18 satellites for capacity considerations, by adding 3 satellites per orbital plane, and thus availability is expected to exceed 99% at all points in CONUS.

Coverage of the Southern Hemisphere can be incrementally achieved by adding six satellites in one equatorial orbit. Figure 2 below shows how virtual global coverage is obtained with only twelve Northern and six Equatorial satellites.

Figure 2. Coverage of 2 Planes x 6 Satellites Constellation
with 6 Additional Equatorial Satellites

The Equatorial satellites, in addition to closing the gaps in the Southern Hemisphere where needed, provide additional capacity to the Northern points, thus supplementing the Northern constellation. ELLIPSO™'s communications channels will be activated during coverage of CONUS, and switched off elsewhere.

Ellipsat's orbital strategy provides a way to deploy the constellation in stages, assuring service in preferred areas first and reducing cash flow constraints and ultimately costs to the end-user. Ellipsat's elongated lapse over CONUS eliminates the need for on-board switching, thus reducing the costs of its satellites.

ACCESS AND MODULATION METHOD

ELLIPSO™ utilizes Code Division Multiple Access (CDMA) in compliance with the technical requirements of the RDSS bands. CDMA is implemented within frequency "segments" to achieve an innovative and efficient FDMA/CDMA scheme.

Each satellite has a bandwidth of operation of 16.5MHz on the transmit side and an equivalent 16.5MHz on the receive side. These bands are further divided into frequency "segments" of 1.4MHz each, within which CDMA modulated signals between the mobile terminals and the Ground Control Stations (GCSs) are passed. Common channel signalling is performed by two separate signalling channels, one for uplink transmissions and one for downlink transmissions. No processing of the signal other than frequency translation and amplification is done on the satellite. The schematic representation of the segments is shown in Figure 3.

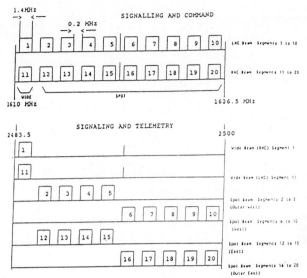

Figure 3. ELLIPSO^{TM} Frequency Plan

The transmission channels (Nos. 2 to 10 and 12 to 20) are divided into the four transmit spot beams, with 20°x60° beamwidth at 3dB. The total coverage at apogee including the overlaps, is an area approximately 2000km x 1600km in size.

Frequency reuse isolation is obtained by cross polarization isolation as well as beam isolation. As the system uses the same frequency bands for feeder links to the GCS, mobile users enter the satellite via the "wide-beam" and the appropriate channel number selection; these transmissions are then passed to the 'spot' beam (10° beamwidth) and received by the GCS. The GCS in turn transmits back to the mobile unit via the receive 10° beam on the satellite and the 20° x 60° transmit beams. It is not possible for a mobile unit to communicate directly with another mobile unit via frequency or beam allocation. Doppler correction is required for both the GCS and the mobile terminals, as for these the Doppler shift varies with their geographic location.

ELLIPSO^{TM}'s capacity restriction is that imposed primarily by power and flux density limitations, that apply to each frequency segment. In the proposed constellations, all satellites operate on all segments which are assigned to specific GCS-supported geographical areas. A total of six GCS is planned for the entire United States. Inter-GCS traffic is routed via the public telephone network. The multiplicity of satellites and GCSs provide inherent system redundancy, traffic diversity, and increased capacity through frequency reuse.

The useable bandwidth of 1.4MHz provides guard bands of .2MHz between the segments. The number of CDMA "channels", or carriers, is dependent upon coding and available power within each segment. These 1.4MHz useable segments are compatible with digital cellular implementations, thus the same CDMA chips, handsets and other components can be used for both digital CDMA cellular and ELLIPSO^{TM} satellite service; satellite service requires only the installation of add-on L- and S-Band RF modules, and a dual antenna.

The CDMA carriers use 1.28Mcps chip rate and FEC coding at rate 1/2 and K=7. They provide the equivalent of 4.8kbps digital voice, and thus are equivalent voice channels.

III. ELLIPSO^{TM} SATELLITES AND GROUND EQUIPMENT

A typical ELLIPSO^{TM} satellite is illustrated in Figure 4, reproduced from Ellipsat's FCC filing of June 3, 1991. It has the following parameters:

```
Spacecraft Basic Parameters
   Orbit                         Elliptical, Apogee 2903 km
                                            Perigee 426 km
                                 Eccentricity, 0.1541
                                 Periapsis Argument 270°
                                 63.4 ° North Inclination
   Mass                          380 lbs
   Stabilization                 Momentum Wheel & Propulsion
   Station Keeping               +/- 5°
   Lifetime                      5 years
   Eclipse Capability            Full

Communications Subsystem Parameters
   Receive Frequency             1610-1626.5MHz
   Receive G/T                   -17dB/°K Widebeam
                                  -3dB/°K Spotbeam
   Receive Antenna Beamwidth     60° and 10° with
                                 frequency reuse
   Polarization                  Dual Circular
   Transmit Frequency            2483.5-2500MHz
   Bandwidth per Segment         1.4MHz
   RF Amplifier Power (Total)    170Watts (RF)
   Transmit Antenna Beamwidth    four @ 60°x20°
   Polarization                  Circular
   Total EIRP (all channels)     35dBW
```

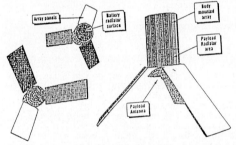

Figure 4. Typical ELLIPSO™ Satellite

ELLIPSO™ achieves frequency reuse via four elliptical spot Transmit beams on its satellites. Two Receive beams, one narrow (10°) for GCS support and one wide beam (60°) for the mobiles, provide interference protection to and from similar systems. The antenna systems patterns are depicted in Figure 5.

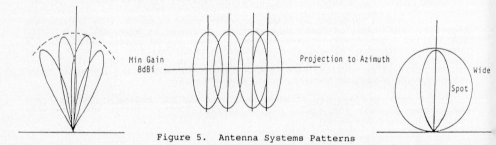

Figure 5. Antenna Systems Patterns

As the satellites sweep the United States, action by the momentum wheel achieves pointing of the 60° x 20° beams toward the served area, with the 10° beam being constantly directed toward a specific GCS.

The ELLIPCELL™ mobile unit and the GCS have the following parameters:

```
ELLIPCELL
Transmit Frequency Range    1610-1626.5MHz
Modulation                  CDMA
Beam Peak Above Horizon     15°
Polarization                Circular (RHCP)
Transmit EIRP               11dBW

Receive Frequency Range     2483.5-2500MHz
Beam Peak Above Horizon     15°
Polarization                Circular (LHCP)
Receive G/T                 -21dB/°K @ 15° elev
                            -24dB/°K @ 5° elev.

GCS
Transmit Frequency Range    1610-1626.5MHz
Modulation                  CDMA
Polarization                Circular (RHCP)
Antenna Size                8 meters
EIRP per Segment            11dBW

Receive Frequency Range     2483.5-2500MHz
Polarization                Circular (LHCP)
Receive G/T                 +25dB/°K

Antenna Pattern: Conforming to CCIR,
                 High Gain, Tracking Dish
```

III. THE GEOBEACON SERVICE

In addition to mobile voice service, ELLIPSO™ supports position determination embedded in the overall system. The technique used by Ellipsat is based on a concept developed at the Massachusetts Institute of Technology (MIT) and implemented by Interferometrics, an Ellipsat shareholder. Interferometrics has also patented this implementation, called the Geobeacon system (Figure 6).

The Geobeacon system compares Time Differences Of Arrival (TDOAs) to execute ranging measurements, and increases accuracy and speed of position detection by performing Frequency Difference Of Arrival (FDOA) measurements. FDOA is unique to the Ellipsat's RDSS. TDOAs provide the Positions Computer at the GCS a "line" of possible positions. FDOAs provide an orthogonal "line". The intersection of these two "lines" is the actual position of the mobile transmitter. The accuracy depends on the location and number of satellites that relay the sample signal, the number of samples per unit time and the history of the actual sampling. A depiction of the system is given in Figure 6.

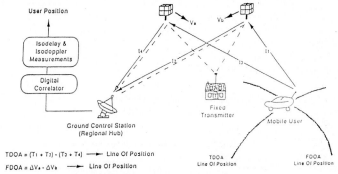

Figure 6. Schematic Representation of the Geobeacon Technique

STARSYS: A VIEW AFTER WARC-92

ASHOK KAVEESHWAR

and

RAUL RODRIGUEZ

STARSYS GLOBAL POSITIONING, INC.

ABSTRACT

Advances in technology for military, space and commercial organizations have generated a growth industry in new space communications which are designed for the broad, consumer market. STARSYS is one such effort, marrying the experience of two highly regarded high-technology firms to bring to the marketplace a new dimension in affordable, personal, global communicating. North American Collection and Location by Satellite (NACLS), a U.S. company in Landover, Maryland, provides satellite-based location and data collection value-added services using the Argos system for its French parent, CLS. ST Systems Corporation (STX) of Lanham, Maryland, is a leader in space activities such as earth observing technologies, satellite remote sensing, space data management for NASA, and satellite ground stations. NACLS and STX jointly formed Starsys Global Position-ing, Incorporated.

The STARSYS system goal is to provide low-cost global positioning and messaging by satellite. STARSYS is a data only system (no voice) which uses very brief message transmission times, thus accommodating millions of customers world-wide.

STARSYS plans to use Code Division Multiple Access (CDMA) for frequency sharing. This digital technique enables transmitted data to be coded for unique user identification and enhanced transmission privacy. CDMA also enables STARSYS to employ Doppler and radio ranging to determine the geographical location of a transmitting terminal.

The STARSYS system is composed of the field receiver/transmitter, the low-earth orbit satellite constellation, and the ground station elements. Ground computers will be able to determine the location of remote terminal transmissions to within 100 meters. Each message transmission will be able to contain up to thirty two (32) digital characters.

STARSYS has been pursuing a license from the U.S. Federal Communications Commission (FCC) for more than two years. Progress is being made. Recently the FCC approved an experimental license for a system on which the company will begin tests and demonstrations beginning this fall. The U.S. "Little LEO"[1] applicants will be working soon to complete a negotiated rulemaking for the new service, after which the licensing efforts with the FCC will become more intense. STARSYS anticipates licensing by late fall of this year, allowing us to launch the first operational satellite by early 1995.

Market applications for a global positioning and messaging system are numerous. We believe a low-cost system will create a large demand for these services. Some of the most lucrative market applications are theft control, vehicle and logistic tracking and messaging, personal communications, and utility and environmental data acquisition and transfer. Market surveys indicate that very large markets exist for low-cost positioning and messaging services, and that the advent of a low-cost service commercial positioning and messaging service will cause demand for applications not now envisioned.

The success of the "Little LEO" frequency allocation at WARC-92 provided a strong demand for these systems among developing countries. In fact, developing nations were among the strongest supporters for us at the Torremolinos, Spain, conference earlier this year. Achieving co-primary allocations for "Little LEO" systems has resulted in accelerating interest from potential customers, investors, and the press. Although the amount of frequency allocation for LEO MSS[2] < 1 GHz is small, it is sufficient for initial operations by several companies.

---

[1] Low Earth Orbit, satellite companies communicating in radio frequencies below 1 GHz   [2] Mobile Satellite Service

The STARSYS System

The three basic components of the STARSYS system are: 1) the field receiver/transmitter; 2) the array of low-earth orbiting satellites; and 3) the ground stations which translate the messages and manage the system.

The transmitter/receiver units, also referred to as User Terminals, will be available in a variety of sophisticated electronic configurations depending on customer need and desire. The terminals may be simple, hand-held, battery-operated devices about the size of a pocket calculator, stand-alone units used for remote sensing or monitoring, or they may be integrated in a package with other equipment. The transmitter will operate at one to two watts power in the VHF frequency band, broadcasting in 100 millisecond bursts. Such short operating times extend the field life of battery operated units.

Display options for the User Terminals will range from a simple illumination device acknowledging receipt of transmission, to a liquid crystal display for the thirty two character digital message. Input options can vary from a simple on/off switch, which, for example, could signify an emergency, to a small keypad for individual messages, and digital inputs when used in a sensing mode.

STARSYS units will transmit only very short messages, and are not expected to be used frequently, thus allowing the system to accommodate millions of users. At the same time, the spread-spectrum technology allows the same frequencies to be used by others without noticeable signal loss. CDMA encodes each transmission and provides each with its own unique "signature," assuring message privacy.

At maturity the STARSYS system will have twenty four specially designed satellites in orbit. The satellites will be launched into a 60° inclined circular low earth orbit of 1300 kilometers altitude.

The advanced design orbiters, lightweight and efficient, will have a life span of about five years. Launch can be accomplished by a variety of systems, including ARIANE, PEGASUS, MICRO-SPACE, and others, giving STARSYS not only choice, but flexibility for economies in launch costs, payloads and schedules.

The satellite functions primarily as a relay, and uses a "bent pipe" transponder concept to retransmit data between the user terminals and the fixed ground station. The satellites will be solar powered, with on-board thermal control features to maintain the precise temperatures needed for the batteries and electronic systems to work properly.

A unique aspect of STARSYS' satellite technology is the ability of the system to determine the accurate geographic position of a user terminal within one hundred meters without relying on other navigation systems. This is accomplished by combining doppler frequency shift measurements and distance ranging techniques. Data acquired by each satellite is relayed to the fixed ground station where it is processed and analyzed to provide an accurate location for the emitting terminal.

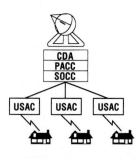

The fixed ground station is separated into several distinct management functions. Four interconnected sub-systems operate in parallel to accomplish data transmitting and receiving, data processing, network and satellite control, and information flow with the customer service bureaus. The control and data acquisition elements perform the broadcasting and receiving functions to and from the satellites. Two of these stations will be located in the United States, supported by a master processing, analysis and control center. The master data processing, analysis and control center is the computer nerve center for the entire system, processing and analyzing the information needed to make STARSYS work, controlling the satellites, and coordinating with the world-wide STARSYS network. A STARSYS Opera-tions and Control Center will be the administrative headquarters for the system, and will ensure quality control and overall supervision for the STARSYS system. The fourth ground component, the various customer service bureaus, will operate the customer contact portion of the system for different applications.

Each User Segment Application Center (USAC) will operate its own community or business service. "Vehicle Protection Services Company," for instance, might provide simple locator devices to individuals and car rental agencies, suitable for theft control purposes. The "Logistic Tracking Services Company" might sell terminals to transportation companies desiring to track high-value cargo shipments from portal to portal. Whatever the service, each customer service bureau will market its own capabilities, collect its own fees and charges, purchase, resell or lease and maintain its own mobile terminals, provide resources for originating and receiving user data and messages, and generally perform all the direct contact business functions with subscribers. A service company can operate on a city/state/region basis, or nationwide, or, in some situations, on a world-wide basis.

The USAC will have direct contact with the customer to process and distribute messages and information from the STARSYS system. Customers in turn will have access to messages and location information through a variety of means, depending on the type of service subscribed to, such as voice mail or digital mail box, using a phone, computer, or a dedicated system such as a teletype.

Each Application Center will buy STARSYS satellite capacity in bulk. The service bureaus in turn will charge customers directly, based on one of several low-cost user-option plans for their particular service. Our goal is to keep costs to the user in the vicinity of what he or she would pay for a good telephone service, depending on the amount of use.

The reusability of the STARSYS satellites' capacity and frequencies world-wide will allow the STARSYS system to operate in any country which desires the service. In developing countries STARSYS provides the opportunity for two-way, low-cost messaging and positioning which cannot be matched by any other communication system.

Regulatory Status

Since filing the original application to provide a mobile satellite service in May 1990, Starsys has achieved several important milestones toward achieving its license for operation. Perhaps the most important was the highly successful outcome of WARC-92 in March 1992. Establishment of a co-primary frequency allocation for the "Little LEO" service was a major accomplishment, achieved via the strong and vocal support of the developing countries.

WARC-92 did not happen overnight. The U.S. Government position to support that allocation was the result of approximately one and one-half years of work on the part of the "Little LEO" applicants to convince not only the U.S. agencies of the need for such a service, but to prove that the service could co-exist with existing users in the bands around the world. Numerous CCIR meetings addressed various aspects of the LEO MSS < 1 GHz in Finland, Mexico City, Melbourne, and Geneva, in addition to several regional meetings with Canada and Mexico. U.S. Government support at WARC-92 was a major boost in achieving the final allocation.

Following the WARC, in April 1992, the FCC granted Starsys an experimental system license. Currently we are developing our program and hardware for testing and demonstrating the STARSYS spread-spectrum communication system in conjunction with a satellite transponder. We are excited about the coming tests this fall as they will tell us much about the existing interference in the frequency bands, and will allow us to construct the operational satellites with certain knowledge of our system requirements.

Currently Starsys and the other "Little LEO" applicants are engaged with the FCC to accomplish the "rulemaking" process, which is required before licensing any new service. We expect a fairly expeditious resolution to the rulemaking. The companies are relatively close together on our respective views for the LEO MSS service. Only a limited number of companies are attempting to establish the service. One of the unresolved issues is equitable sharing of available spectrum among the applicants, each of whom has a unique approach to frequency sharing.

Once the "rulemaking" is complete, the FCC will be able to address licensing issues with the individual companies. Each of us will have to demonstrate financial ability to initiate and operate our respective systems. The FCC will grant initially a one-year conditional license, after which each company must provide proof of funding for the first year of operations in order to begin construction and launch of the initial satellites.

Starsys believes the licensing process is on-track after more than two years of effort, and that we can anticipate the conditional license by late fall. Based on that schedule, we anticipate the first launch of an operational satellite by early 1995, and initial operations shortly thereafter.

Market Analysis

Starsys has spent more than two years evaluating the market potential for a satellite positioning and messaging system. We are confident that a significant market exists now for the service, and that a low-cost system will generate the development of significant new markets for Starsys type services which do not yet exist. One only needs to see the exploding marketplace demand for Global Positioning System services to appreciate how low-cost satellite based positioning and messaging can follow the same pattern.

Some of our markets are obvious: theft control for vehicles and cargo; personal communications for travel and vacationing; and remote data transfer by pipelines and other utilities. These markets are large, they are world-wide, and they are large enough to accommodate several providers of the service. In the U.S. alone there are more than 190,000,000 vehicles and boats registered, with 11,000,000 new vehicle registrations each year. Over five million shipping containers exist world-wide, with no ordinary means of keeping track of them. Car thefts are increasing world-wide, with more than 1.4 million in the U.S. alone in 1990. Many vehicles are never recovered. Truck and bus thefts are at a rate of 180,000 per year, while boats disappear to theft at more than 25,000 per year.

These statistics are only the tip of the iceberg, so to speak, but they serve to identify the magnitude of the potential market just for theft control. Due to the queries we have received from interested organizations, we believe that additional large markets also exist for tracking of high-value cargo shipments, for vehicle fleet control, for environmental monitoring, and for many other related applications involving messaging for sales force personnel, delivery services, etc.

We also believe that another major market for positioning and messaging services in the industrialized countries is the automatic transfer of utility data. The potential cost savings to utility companies through automatic and regular transfer of routine consumption data represents a large market for those satellite communications systems that can provide data relay services at a reasonable cost.

We have been approached by large, lesser-developed countries with a strong interest in a "Little LEO" type system to avoid the infrastructure costs of laying miles of telephone cables. These countries look for the "Little LEO" companies to be a communications system of the future. One of the first applications these countries seek is vehicle tracking to improve efficiency and reduce delivery times of over-the-road truck shipments. A Starsys type system is ideal for this type of application.

To "jump start" the marketing of STARSYS we are offering an "Early Entry" program to introduce potential STARSYS customers to the concept of low-cost positioning and messaging via satellite. We are able to use a small number of ARGOS terminals to provide one-way location and data information to key potential customers. With this approach we will be able to demonstrate the commercial advantages of a Starsys type system, and we will be able to learn much about customer requirements for positioning and messaging information services. Potential customers are already in contact with us.

Additional information on Starsys marketing will be presented in the poster session.

Impact of WARC-92 Results

Since the successful allocation of co-primary frequency to "Little LEO" at WARC-92, we have seen an acceleration of the regulatory process in the U.S., and significantly increased interest from potential customers, manufacturers, investors and the press. In essence, the successful WARC allocation has "put us on the map," so to speak, as an up and coming space communications system which will be able to provide valuable services for many applications.

The WARC-92 results, in terms of frequency allocation, exceeded our administration's position by virtue of the Canadian recommended addition of 150 KHz in the 149.9-150.05 MHz uplink band. This additional allocation is not large, but it is an indication that many countries supported the concept of the "Little LEO" global positioning and messaging service. The WARC allocation provided about 3.4 MHz of spectrum primary allocation, plus an additional 500 KHz of secondary spectrum, and the three U.S. "Little LEO" companies are working together to find a way to share the allocation equitably. The "Little LEO" group,

and the U.S. government, had a goal of achieving about 5 MHz of spectrum allocation in order to facilitate two different types of radio frequency systems (CDMA and FDMA) and allow for multiple service providers. At this point we believe there is enough spectrum to start operations by the three applicants in the U.S.

WARC-92 ALLOCATION FOR LEO MSS < 1 GHz

149.9 MHz

Uplink
(-150 fpd limit)

148.0 MHz   150.05 MHz

Downlink   P
(-125 fpd limit) S   P   S

137.0 MHz   138.0 MHz   400.15 MHz   401.0 MHz

[P] Co-Primary   [S] Secondary   [▨] Secondary until 1997, then P

Despite the significant success achieved at WARC, we did not achieve all our goals. A number of countries opted to confine LEO MSS operations in the uplink band in their country to "secondary" use vice the "co-primary" allocation we sought. The impact of this restriction on uplink transmissions is that implementation of a Starsys, Orbcomm, or even a VITASAT has no protection from other communications systems operating in the same bands. Thus, before developing a "STARSYS" capability in one of these countries, negotiations with the host regulartory agency would be required to insure protection of such an investment. Unfortunately, many of the developing countries planning to rely on the installation of a LEO MSS service may be unable to find investors if the uplink band service remains hostage to the "secondary" allocation status. However, in the long run we may find that this problem solves itself as the public demand for a satellite positioning and messaging service in their country puts pressure on the regulatory agency to exit the "secondary" status footnote to the uplink band.

WARC-92 also firmly established the restrictions and established the parameters for coordination of the LEO MSS < 1 GHz service. It is restricted to non-voice, and stringent power limits have been established for the satellite transmissions in order to protect the existing services in the bands. If the service stays within the power limits, no coordination is required. The WARC has put new companies on notice that they must not provide harmful interfence to existing users, yet they must accept whatever interference exists already in the bands from the other primary users. To comply with the WARC restrictions on the LEO MSS service, the satellites must either avoid the channels in use by the meteorological satellites and other space services, or transmit at power levels which will not impact their operations.

The restrictions impact proposed CDMA and FDMA systems in different ways. For Starsys, one of the more positive aspects of WARC was the opportunity to coordinate face-to-face with countries concerned about out-of-band transmissions by CDMA systems impacting radio astronomy. By addressing the issues on the spot we were able to illustrate how CDMA systems can be engineered to avoid harmful interference to the valuable radio astronomy networks in India. Criteria established in the footnotes to the "Little LEO" frequencies in the WARC Final Acts were the direct result of similar engineering discussions with Australia, New Zealand, Indonesia, and other countries, and enhanced support for the "Little LEO" allocation. Many similar WARC on-site discussions occurred with other countries which did not have in-depth knowledge of the CDMA or FDMA technology, and these discussions also helped to achieve widespread support for the "Little LEO" spectrum allocations.

Because WARC provided the opportunity to meet with the many intrested countries face-to-face on sharing issues for this new service, knowledge of the system benefits has created expectations and demand for the low-cost positioning and messaging service. Many countries have become aware of the potential advantages of the service, and are now pushing for implementation. WARC-92 not only created world-wide demand which supports our progress, it also fostered efforts by other countries to implement their own services. The WARC-92 meeting found that the Russians were a strong advocate for the service, and they brought several proposals for similar systems to the conference. France identified its efforts for a low-earth orbit system, and recently we have seen a filing with the ITU for use of the frequencies by Tonga, in the name of Tongasat. By our own success at the WARC we have created our own competition world-wide, and we must now proceed with due speed to achieve implementation of our programs.

SYNTHESE DE LA SESSION
SYSTEMES DE RADIOCOMMUNICATION
ET APPLICATIONS

Je définierais la situation comme suit :

Don JAYASURIA a fait le point de la situation en présentant les éléments cruciaux de l'environnement de la régulation radio mis en évidence par le WARC 92, nous faisant prendre conscience des réalités des dépôts de brevets et des homologations des différents types.

Puis, sans que cela soit nécessairement dans un ordre chronologique, fut présentée une série d'articles étudiant les éventuelles missions Télécom (le LEOCOM de l'ESA en est peut-être un bon exemple) exposant les limites des techniques, suivie par une série de rapports relatifs à des systèmes expérimentaux tels que S80 T grâce auquel un nouveau pas vers la « réalité » a pu être franchi.

Nous avons ensuite assisté à la présentation d'une troisième série d'articles utilisant une autre approche philosophique et dont les auteurs originaires principalement d'Amérique du Nord étudiaient des systèmes qu'ils préconisaient dans le but de fournir un service opérationnel (même si certaines de ces propositions incluaient un régime expérimental ou pilote). STARSYS peut être considéré comme un bon exemple de tels systèmes. Puis furent présentés des rapports très stimulants, tel celui concernant les NAONOSATS de M. ELLIOT.

Ces articles mirent en évidence une différence d'approche dans le passage de l'idée à la création d'un système. Ils nous ont bien entendu également fait prendre conscience des différents régimes de régulation et des approches commerciales existant en Amérique du Nord et en Europe notamment, à la fois pour ce qui concerne le style et peut-être l'extension géographique de la couverture.

On ne peut cependant nier qu'à cette occasion, les participants ont une nouvelle fois montré qu'ils pensent qu'il y a de la place pour des services autres que l'offre quelque peu monolithique que présentent les opérateurs actuels, par exemple, un service de boîte postale à coût très faible (0,01 $ par Kbit) mais avec un temps de transmission relativement long.

Il existe de nombreuses solutions permettant à de petits satellites de fournir un point de départ à de nouvelles opportunités commerciales. Cette affirmation devrait cependant être tempérée en faisant remarquer qu'une approche de « radio-amateurs » ne peut fonctionner dans un environnement commercial supposant des investissements lourds, qui exige des responsables (ingénieurs) hautement expérimentés mais néanmoins ouverts d'esprit. Le seul regret est que TERMISAT, peut-être le premier petit satellite conçu et financé par un opérateur Télécom, n'a pas été décrit au cours de cette session.

SYNTHESIS OF THE SESSION
RADIOCOMMUNICATIONS SYSTEMS
AND APPLICATION

I would characterize the situation as follows:

Don JAYASURIA set the scene with the hard facts of the radio regulatory environment that emerged from WARC 92, bringing us to the realities of licensing and type approval.

Then not necessarily chronologically, were a group of papers exploring possible Telecom missions (ESA's LEOCOM perhaps being a good example) where the limits of techniques were explored, followed by papers of experimental systems such as S80 T where one more step towards "reality" was made.

But then we heard in a third series of papers where a different philosophical approach was used were the authors largely from North America explored systems that they were promoting to provide operational service (although some of these proposals embodied an experimental or a pilot regime). STARSYS was perhaps a good example of this. Then there came papers to stimulate us such as that on NAONOSATS by Mr. ELLIOT.

The papers highlighted difference in approach to the transition from idea to creating a system. Also of course we became aware of the different regulatory regimes and the commercialisation approaches that existed in North America and Europe, in particular, both in style and perhaps geographical extent of coverage.

What could not be denied howewer was that time and again people showed that they believed there was room for services other than the somewhat monolithic offering currently presented by today's operators. E.g. for a mailbox service at very low cost ($ 0.01 per Kbit quoted) but with comparatively long delivery time.

Many solutions are available for small satellites to provide an entry point to new business opportunities. However that statement should be tempered with the warning that an "amateur-radio" approach will not work in a high investment commercial domain, where highly experienced, albeit, openminded engineer-managers will be required. The only regret was that TERMISAT perhaps the first small satellite to be specified and funded by a Telecom Operator was not described in this session.

SESSION VII

ARCHITECTURE SATELLITE

SATELLITE ARCHITECTURE

UoSAT: A Decade of Experience Pioneering Microsatellites

J M Radbone
Prof M N Sweeting

Surrey Satellite Technology Ltd
University of Surrey
Guildford, Surrey GU2 5XH
United Kingdom

1. INTRODUCTION

Small satellites have recently become popular as cost-effective options for a wide range of potential missions - however small satellites are not new: the space age began with the launch of Sputnik in 1957 weighing only 75kg. The need for ever-larger, more capable and more complex satellites led to a natural upward growth (Sputnik-2 weighed 400kg!) - limited initially by launcher capability and then, later, by finance.

Advances in VLSI digital microelectronics now enable very sophisticated functions to be achieved within tight constraints of mass, volume and power - giving rise to a new 'species' of capable satellite, the microsatellite. Whether a particular satellite is considered 'large' or 'small' depends upon viewpoint and so the following classification has become widely accepted:

Large satellite	>	1000 kg
Small satellite	500 -	1000 kg
Mini-satellite	100 -	500 kg
Micro-satellite	10 -	100 kg
Nano-satellite	<	10 kg

Mini- and & micro-satellite missions are not intended to replace large satellites, but rather to act in a complementary role for certain well-focused or exploratory objectives. Indeed, as the funding for new space programmes is scrutinised ever more closely, as demonstrated by the current re-evaluation of the ESA programmes, the role of smaller, lower cost missions must now receive serious attention.

The real questions are thus:

a) what can mini/microsatellites usefully contribute?

b) how can cost, risk, and performance be managed on a low budget and a sustainable commercial environment?

This paper examines the latest two satellites constructed at Surrey as examples of low cost missions and describes the technical and management techniques employed. These have been developed gradually and represent the cumulation of a decade of experience in the design, construction and orbital operation of low cost microsatellite missions.

2. UoSAT MICROSATELLITE MISSIONS

The University of Surrey has pioneered cost-effective microsatellites during the last decade through its UoSAT missions - designed, constructed and operated in orbit from the University. The applications of microsatellites has been demonstrated by five UoSAT spacecraft carrying payloads supporting:

- digital store-&-forward communications
- medium-resolution Earth imaging
- small-scale space science
- technology demonstration
- education

The five UoSAT microsatellite missions built, launched, and operated in orbit during the period 1981-1991 [Table-1] have been well documented elsewhere [see refs.]. UoSAT-5, the most recent microsatellite launched in July 1991, provides a good example of multi-payload mission, carrying: store-&-forward communications for SatelLife (USA); a medium resolution Earth imaging experiment sponsored by SSTL; a total radiation dose monitor; and solar cell technology demonstration payload for DRA (UK).

Following the initial demonstration of the feasibility and technical capability of low cost microsatellites by UoSAT-1 & 2, a University company, Surrey Satellite Technology Ltd (SSTL), was established to provide an effective means of interfacing to payload customers and to introduce microsatellites into the commercial market-place. The introduction, by Arianespace, in 1990 of the Ariane Structure for Auxiliary Payloads (ASAP) provided the first regular, commercial, means of launching microsatellites at an affordable cost and was a key element in catalysing a sustained microsatellite programme. Payloads from customers have been included on the UoSAT-3,4 & 5 missions, whilst the latest Surrey microsatellites (KITSAT-A & S80/T) to be launched in 1992 represent the first fully-commercial microsatellite missions undertaken through SSTL.

2.1 KITSAT-A Microsatellite

KITSAT-A is an experimental mission within a collaborative programme on satellite engineering between the UK and South Korea. Based at the University of Surrey, a joint team of engineers from the Korean Advanced Institute of Science and Technology (KAIST) and Surrey Satellite Technology Limited (SSTL) has designed and built the first Korean satellite and illustrates the use of microsatellites for training and technology transfer to developing space nations.

The Programme has run for three years and comprised:

academic training - via a post-graduate Masters' degree course

on-the-job training - through participation in the UoSAT-5 microsatellite
                       mission

project training - integrated within a team building and operating the
                    KITSAT-A microsatellite

national facilities - establishing a satellite tracking/control groundstation
                      and satellite laboratories in Korea to build KITSAT-B

KITSAT-A is based on the successful UoSAT-5 microsatellite platform and provides digital store-&-forward communications, a Digital Signal Processing experiment, a wide-field and narrow-field Earth imagining payload, and a Cosmic Radiation experiment.

Executed via a commercial contract and although KAIST are the 'customer', they are at Surrey to learn satellite engineering techniques and hence are willing to execute the mission following the design philosophies and approaches as used on previous UoSAT missions - without additional technical or administrative requirements.

478

2.2 S80/T & CERISE Microsatellites

An example of a more constrained industrial application of microsatellites, S80/T is a demonstration mission to evaluate the use of VHF frequencies for future LEO communications systems. Surrey Satellite Technology Ltd have built the S80/T platform as sub-contractor to Matra-Marconi Space (Toulouse) who are the prime contractor for the customer - CNES.

In contrast to KITSAT-A, the S80/T platform has been provided to organisations which were normally required to work within the constraints imposed by the traditional space industry and which have been developed to handle satellite projects with large budgets and long timescales. These mechanisms cannot be simply 'geared down' to cope cost-effectively with quick-response (1 year), micro-budget (FF10M), microsatellite missions!

Surrey Satellite Technology Ltd are also manufacturing a modified microsatellite platform for Alcatel Espace which will carry a classified payload for the CERISE mission. Although on a longer timescale, CERISE is for a customer who is accustomed to working in the most traditional aerospace manner and thus represent even tighter constraints.

It has become clear through the experience with the UoSAT microsatellites that the successful completion of a low-cost, rapid-response microsatellite mission requires an entirely different technical and managerial approach to that employed in traditional space industries.

Whilst the KITSAT-A, S80/T and CERISE microsatellites are based on the flight-proven UoSAT-5 platform and therefore inherited technical trade-offs undertaken during previous missions, the management aspects of each of these missions has been driven directly by the individual customer's requirements - and which, in each case, have led to quite different management techniques.

3. KEY ISSUES IN MICROSATELLITE MISSIONS

At first sight, a microsatellite can look deceptively simple and, indeed, each individual element should present little problem to any competent engineering laboratory or company - but it is a microcosm of larger satellite projects and a prime example of the whole being _far_ _greater_ than the sum of the parts! It is easy to under-estimate the integrated demands of technology and management on a project which must result in a product which must meet an immovable delivery date and then operate largely unattended in a remote and hostile environment where any shortcoming in design or workmanship may prove fatal to the outcome of the mission - and all achieved within FF10m!

There is no real 'secret ingredient' in successful microsatellite missions - success is only achieved by a combination of imaginative engineering and management with dedication to the task - and (in the case of UoSAT/SSTL) some 20 orbit-years of vital operational experience!

3.1 Technical Issues

The constraints on power, mass, volume and cost imposed upon microsatellite designs call for imaginative and innovative technical solutions. Whilst each mission has its own specific requirements and constraints, it is possible to draw some general conclusions and recommendations.

Simple & realistic interfaces

UoSAT/SSTL have periodically investigated adopting standard interfaces developed by ESA, military, computing, or international bodies. When examined for use with microsatellites, adoption of such standards has usually been found to be inefficient (in various combinations of complexity, power, mass or volume) and hence simpler interfaces have been evolved - better matched to the application.

Realistic interface specifications should be applied following frank discussions directly between the designers of the platform and the payload. It is interesting to note that on a recent mission both platform and payload designers were given specifications which included a hidden 'safety margin'. This not only led to an unnecessary and significant design modification but, instead of providing a safety margin, in fact resulted in an additional set of performance problems!

These interface problems inevitably arise more frequently in programmes where the platform and payload are designed and constructed by different, and geographically separate, organisations. Platform and payload teams should be co-located and work closely together, particularly during the design phase, if costs and timescales are to be kept to a minimum.

Flexible design

The ability to optimise the microsatellite at as late a stage in the project as possible can have a dramatic influence upon the eventual 'value for money' returned to the customer from the mission. Considering the very short gestation period usually associated with microsatellite projects, it is unlikely that sufficient time will have elapsed to allow all aspects of the mission to have been thoroughly explored well in advance of manufacture. This is particularly the case with spacecraft and groundstation software.

The accepted procedure within traditional space projects is for all hardware and software interfaces and design specifications to be completely frozen at a Critical Design Review (CDR) quite early on in the project. This has not been the approach used for UoSAT microsatellite missions, which have what could be described as a 'design solidifying phase'. This phase can, in the case of some sub-systems or payloads, continue right up until final hardware assembly and, indeed, the software is being continually improved and may never really be considered as frozen - merely at a certain version. In this environment the designs freezes gradually, as needed for manufacturing, rather than from the need to present a final and completed picture to the customer at an arbitrary point in the project. The continued evolution of spacecraft software and the ability to upload new software to the satellite in orbit improve the mission operations by adapting to new mission requirements, unexpected opportunities or anomalous conditions.

The UoSAT microsatellite platform design is highly flexible - particularly in terms of its on-board data handling (OBDH) architecture. An interlinked hierarchical architecture (which has layers of sophistication from a basic level of reliable and proven devices up to state-of-the-art processors which may be unflown in space) can achieve both high reliability, high performance and graceful degradation through the use of a diversity of technologies. SSTL have thus been able to use the same basic platform in support of both S80/T and KITSAT-A with changes in configuration and software which support different mission operations. This flexible, modular approach was one of the key factors that enabled SSTL to undertaken the S80/T mission within a schedule of less than 1 year from mission definition to launch.

Control of Requirements & Modularity

Particularly in the case of S80/T, short timescales and low cost were accepted at the start as key programme drivers. In fact, in all the UoSAT missions which included integration of external payloads it has been recognised that one of the most important, and most difficult, issues is to keep the customer requirements firmly under control. This applies both to the technical

480

performance and the contractual conditions - it is just not possible to have your cake and also eat it!

The ability to meet the short timescales demanded for the recent UoSAT missions has been founded upon the technical choices made during UoSAT-3 & 4 to establish a modular, multi-mission platform capable of supporting a range of payloads. With minimal hardware changes, the same platform has been used to support both KITSAT-A and S80/T with their completely different payloads. This modularity and ease of integration of external payloads has come from a fundamental design philosophies, such as standardised module boxes machined by CNC machine stacked together which give a variable height payload module space; provision of a large number of telecommand and telemetry channels which may readily be re-allocated; an on-board computer (OBC) running a generic software kernal with mission-dependent changes only required to be made to applications programmes; and the ability of the OBC to provide a highly flexible means for automatic control of and data handling for the payloads.

Quality & Product Assurance

It has become clear in the execution of S80/T and CERISE microsatellites that the whole area of PA/QA is one where there is a significant discrepancy between the approach taken by UoSAT/SSTL and the traditional space industry.

A formal PA/QA programme, including FMECA and reliability analysis, is feasible but increases the cost of the programme. For S80/T, no reliability analyses were undertaken as there was insufficient time to implement any changes anyway. For CERISE, on a longer timescale, reliability analyses have been made but not to influence significantly the overall design of the microsatellite, but rather to identify any serious localised risks that could be avoided. Overall, UoSAT/SSTL employs a more practical engineering approach and applied a total quality approach relying on individual engineers taking a high degree of responsibility for maintaining appropriate levels of quality and providing rigorous peer review. It is interesting to note that external inspections of work undertaken during the manufacture of S80/T at SSTL highlighted a variation in style and technique rather than a lack of resulting quality. This approach does imply, however, the need for a team of highly motivated and reliable personnel, working within a compact team.

The experience over a decade of microsatellite research, including the selection of components, has resulted in the conclusion that low cost and long lifetime are not necessarily mutually exclusive. A thorough understanding of the space environment and its effects, together with a knowledge of the production processes used for the components in question, are vital to correct selection. The willingness to consider non-space-qualified components for inclusion on-board UoSAT microsatellite has resulted in a very wide variety of component specifications being flown - from commercial quality, high volume components to high-reliability space qualified parts. It has been SSTL's experience that special self-imposed test procedures applied by UoSAT/SSTL to low cost commercial devices has resulted in reliable systems at a fraction of the cost of components that have been subjected to a traditional qualification process - and that also the use of 'space-qualified' components is no guarantee against failure! The proof of this philosophy comes from the UoSAT-1 & 2 who both have exceeded 8 years operation in orbit.

Further, for missions with short timescales, it is often impossible to procure high-qualification devices and so lead-time is also a factor in the component selection philosophy. Whilst many of the components flown by UoSAT are not formally accepted as 'space qualified', it has been acceptable for S80/T to select components which have a flight heritage from previous UoSAT missions.

Launch

In order to minimise cost, time and potential for error, it has proven to be beneficial that all technical interfacing to Arianespace, as the launch agency, has been the responsibility of SSTL as the platform manufacturer particularly having previous experience of using the ASAP. This is an extension of the philosophy of keeping the communications channel short and direct, and hence the resulting documentation concise but complete.

3.2 Key Management Issues

Effective and responsive management is essential to complete a microsatellite project within a short timescale and micro-budget. The most important ingredient of all is 'team spirit' with a completely integrated effort across technical and management issues.

Contract Conditions

It is an obvious statement that constraining contract conditions will have a direct impact on cost! Ensuring compliance with severe contract conditions may add 50% to the mission cost to the customer - which does not match the philosophy of low cost access to space. For a minimum cost mission, a realistic contract based upon mutual 'best efforts' understanding is important. Such a contract is appropriate in light of the fact that the manufacturer (SSTL) is a small and highly motivated motivated team that are completely committed to making the mission a success for their own satisfaction, pride and survival - neither manufacturer nor customer benefit from a failed mission. Under these circumstances, a more cost-effective approach is to protect against failure by taking out suitable insurance cover for launch and orbital operations rather than costly constraints built into the contract.

The inclusion of penalties in the contract linked to firm milestone dates have a high probability of being applied and therefore the supplier must include suitable allowance in the contract price - increasing the mission cost but with no greater or lesser risk of missing the launch. The most satisfactory missions have been executed within 'best efforts' contracts where a real team spirit is developed between supplier and contractor and both sides work closely together to solve problems. The shorter the project schedule and lower the cost of the mission the more the 'best efforts' approach is necessary - SSTL could not have undertaken the S80/T mission in any other way.

Project length

It has been observed that there appears to be an optimum point between the programme being so short that there is a huge surcharge on the procurement for short delivery, and so long that the task merely expands to fit the time and the costs increase proportionately. A project length of 18-24 months provides a good compromise. Short projects often result in a need for more pragmatic solutions to engineering problems and practical testing has often been found to give a faster more meaningful solution that extensive analysis.

Concise documentation

Documentation is important, but must be scaled to match the project resources. Concise but complete documentation is another key to low cost missions and is to some extent more easily achieved on programmes where the platform and payload engineers are co-located.

Efficient Meetings & Communications

If minimum cost and timescale for the mission are to be achieved, the time spent in meetings must be carefully apportioned. Technical meetings, which are needed to solve technical issues, should be frequent and indeed are much more efficient than lengthy written specifications for ensuring true understanding of the technical interfaces and highlighting potential problems early on in the project. Progress meetings, which are needed to inform the customer of satisfactory progress to generate confidence, and the preparation required for them, should be cut to the absolute minimum. The people attending the meetings from the spacecraft manufacturer are generally the same people who are building it to the tight schedule! There is pressure for regular (and lengthy) meetings when working with a new customer on the first mission, particularly if the customer/contractor is an aerospace organisation itself, whereas on follow-on missions confidence and trust has been established and the manufacturer can proceed with fewer interruptions.

During both technical and project meetings, and indeed in all communications, frankness and directness are absolutely vital. It is important that unrealistic requirements are challenged and problems tackled as early as possible - this again is more likely to occur within the context of a 'best efforts' contract.

Integrated and co-located team

It is perhaps obvious that it is most efficient to have an integrated and co-located team - thus enabling regular technical meetings to be organised rapidly as needed on an informal basis - and seconding external payload engineers seconded for periods to work at Surrey has proved an effective approach. The traditional project management structure comprising a prime contractor, several sub-contractors, and various divisions within the sub-contractor is just not appropriate for a microsatellite mission.

The importance of cross-checking and peer review within a small team was high-lighted during the KITSAT-A project. When the number of Korean engineers working on KITSAT-A increased to the extent that Korean was spoken instead of English, the number of avoidable problems also increased and it become apparent how much automatic cross-checking is achieved through 'over-hearing' discussions in the same laboratories and offices.

Flexibility of Organisation & Personnel

As the development cycle of a microsatellite is very short, each part of the construction cycle is perhaps only a matter of weeks and when unexpected events occur, as they always do, the organisations involved must possess sufficient flexibility to respond rapidly, eg. being able to arrange (and authorise) to travel to the USA that afternoon, place procurement orders rapidly, have personnel on hand who have flexible family commitments, etc. Since personnel are such a key element, it is important to understand their personal constraints, interests and motivating factors in order to maintain the crucial team spirit.

3. CONCLUSIONS

Low-cost, quick-response, microsatellite missions have a wide range of applications - complementary to rather than competing with large traditional satellites. Such missions are, in fact, a microcosm of their larger counterparts in complexity, however a different management structure and technique is required to be able to meet tight timescales and a micro-budget. Microsatellites for sustainable research and commercial programmes are not achieved through the use of cheap student labour - in fact quite the reverse. They are achieved by a small team of highly motivated, professional engineers of the best calibre who are able to take full responsibility for the application of 'good engineering' in its broadest sense to the project. Real cost savings can be made through efficient interfaces with external organisations who are able to work in a flexible and imaginative manner. The S80/T project has demonstrated that a highly integrated team, using the flight-proven, modular UoSAT platform, can provide opportunities to orbit a new payload in a timescale of less than 12 months and within a budget of less than FF10M on a commercial basis.

The future looks attractive for UoSAT and SSTL with an increasing emphasis on the role of small satellites. SSTL has enjoyed the position of being the only European supplier of microsatellites with extensive in-orbit experience and has thus been able to establish procedures and techniques appropriate to the scale of production of microsatellites at very low cost whilst maintaining minimal risk. This pragmatic approach has enabled SSTL to enter contracts for further microsatellite missions with Korea and Portugal who seek low cost access to space as a way of stimulating a new space industry, and with organisations such as SatelLife who seek low cost access to space in order to provide affordable communications to remote regions and developing countries.

4.   ACKNOWLEDGEMENTS

The authors would like to thank colleagues in Matra-Marconi Space (France), CNES, Alcatel Espace, KAIST and SSTL for their support and, in particular, their willingness to approach microsatellite missions in a constructive and imaginative manner.

5.   REFERENCES

1.   'Space Science & Remote Sensing with Low Cost Microsatellite Missions'
     Sweeting M.N.
     ESA Euro-Latin America Space Days Proceedings, Nov 1991

2.   'Can small satellites be used for really useful tasks?'
     Radbone J.M.
     42nd Congress of IAF, Montreal, Oct 1991

3.   'Microsatellite Technology'
     Sweeting M.N.
     Space Technology International, pp. 55-59, 1991

4.   'SMALLSATS & LIGHTSATS - Do They Have a Future?
     Radbone J.M.
     Presented at European Space Conference, Paris, Apl 22-24, 1991

5.   'Into Space on a Small Budget'
     Sweeting M.N.
     Graduate Scientist & Engineer, Vol. 11, No. 7, 1990

6.   'How Do You Build An Inexpensive Spacecraft?'
     Radbone J.M.
     Proc. Low-Cost Access to Space Conference, Paris, France, May 22, 1990

7.   'Construction of Low Cost Spacecraft - The UoSAT Programme'
     Radbone J.M.
     Proc. Low-Cost Access to Space Conference, Paris, France, Jun 6, 1989

8.   'Small Satellites: The UoSAT Experience'
      Sweeting M.N
      Proc. First European Workshop on Flight Opportunities for Small
      Payloads, ESRIN, Frascati, Italy, Feb 8-10, 1989

9.   'UoSAT Microsatellite Missions'
      Sweeting M.N.
      Electronics & Communication Engineering Journal on Space Systems &
      Technology, IEE, Special Issue, June 1991

10.   'Small Satellites, Large Pictures'
      Space Technology International, pp. 51-52, 1992

TABLE-1

THE UoSAT MICROSATELLITE MISSIONS

UoSAT-1
launched: 1981 (NASA), 560 km polar orbit
status: re-entered 1989 (whilst operational)
Payloads: Geiger detectors
                HF & microwave propagation beacons
                CCD imager
                Technology demonstration (microcomputers)
                Educational experiments for schools

UoSAT-2
launched: 1984 (NASA), 700 km polar orbit
status: operational
payloads: auroral particle-wave analyser experiment
                store-&-forward communications experiment
                CCD imager
                Technology demonstration of microcomputers
                & attitude stabilisation
                Educational experiments for schools

UoSAT-3
launched: 1990 (Ariane ASAP#001), 800 km polar orbit
status: operational
payloads: cosmic particle detector experiment
                store-&-forward communications transponder
                Technology demonstration of micro-computers,
                VLSI RAM, attitude stabilisation & control

UoSAT-4
launched: 1990 (Ariane ASAP#001), 800 km polar orbit
status: failed (communications lost after 30 hrs)
payloads: Technology demonstration of solar cells,
                Transputers, attitude sensors
                CCD imager with on-board processing

UoSAT-5
launched: 1991 (Ariane ASAP#002), 765 km polar orbit
status: operational
payloads: store-&-forward communications transponder
                for medical teams and disaster relief in
                remote regions; technology demonstration of
                Transputers, solar cells; remote sensing
                demonstration using CCD imager with
                on-board image & data processing

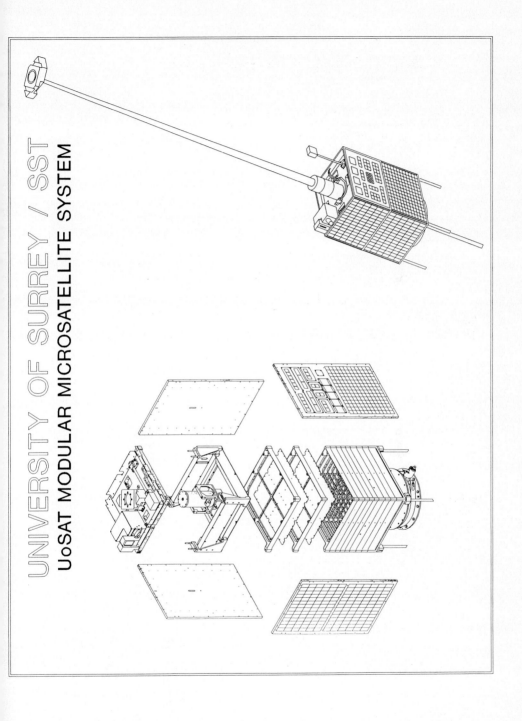

UNIVERSITY OF SURREY / SST
UoSAT MODULAR MICROSATELLITE SYSTEM

LE SYSTEME MICROSATELLITE CERISE

J. KACED

ALCATEL ESPACE
26 rue J.F. Champolion
BP1187
31037 TOULOUSE Cedex

1 INTRODUCTION

Depuis février 1989, ALCATEL ESPACE, sous contrat avec la DME (Direction des Missiles et de l'Espace) a étudié un système spatial appelé "CERISE" bâti autour d'un microsatellite de masse inférieure à 50 Kg. Agissant en tant que maître d'oeuvre, ALCATEL ESPACE en assure actuellement la réalisation avec un objectif de lancement dans le courant de l'année 1994 en charge auxiliaire avec HELIOS.

La mission principale de CERISE est d'effectuer une mesure et une caractérisation de l'environnement radioélectrique à bord d'un satellite en orbite basse, dans une large bande de fréquences.

Le système CERISE se décompose en :
- un microsatellite comportant :
    . une plateforme microsatellite dérivée de celle d'UoSAT construite par la société SSTL en tant que sous-traitant sur laquelle un minimum de modifications ont été apportées pour remplir les exigences de besoin mission,
    . une charge utile conçue et réalisée par ALCATEL ESPACE et THOMSON-CSF en tant que sous-traitant.
- une station sol de commande/contrôle du microsatellite conçue et réalisée par SSTL sur la base de celle utilisée pour les UoSAT avec des modifications mineures ;
- une station d'exploitation des télémesures scientifiques de la charge utile conçue et réalisée par ALCATEL ESPACE

Une contrainte importante de ce type de projet reste la minimisation du coût qui induit des choix et des procédures de travail souvent très différents d'un projet spatial "classique".

Le paragraphe 2 évoque, d'une part, un certain nombre de questions qui peuvent se poser dans le choix d'une solution microsatellite lorsqu'un industriel doit répondre à un besoin mission précis et, d'autre part, les avantages associés à cette solution.
Le paragraphe 3 donne une description du système CERISE.

2 LE CHOIX DU CONCEPT MICROSATELLITE

Dans le cadre d'un projet à caractère scientifique, la question de l'utilisation d'un microsatellite en tant que vecteur d'une expérience destinée à être placée en orbite peut se poser au maître d'oeuvre lorsqu'une contrainte de <u>faible coût</u> est placée en première priorité.

Cependant, l'utilisation d'un microsatellite conduit à respecter un certain nombre de contraintes qui ne sont pas forcément acceptables pour n'importe quelle mission :

2.1 En tout premier lieu, un microsatellite est lancé en <u>charge auxiliaire</u> en compagnon du (ou des) satellite(s) principal (principaux). De par ce fait, <u>l'orbite</u> effective du microsatellite n'est pas choisie par l'utilisateur final mais dépend de l'opportunité de lancement. Cela suppose que l'objectif de mission puisse être tenu dans une gamme d'altitudes et d'inclinaisons suffisamment large, compte tenu des opportunité offertes.

2.2 D'autre part, l'expérience embarquée sur microsatellite doit pouvoir s'accommoder de <u>l'absence de contrôle d'orbite</u> qui a pour conséquence une dérive progressive de l'orbite du satellite donc de faire apparaître des conditions de phasage et d'éclairement variables dans le temps.

2.3 Le <u>contrôle d'attitudes</u> du microsatellite est souvent de conception simple (stabilisation passive, par exemple) et par là-même d'une précision limitée dans les 3 axes (plusieurs degrés). En revanche, la précision de restitution d'attitudes peut être meilleure lorsque cette restitution est opérée au sol en temps différé (inférieur au degré).

2.4 Les <u>capacités de stockage</u> d'informations à bord (quelques dizaines de Ko) ainsi que les débits TM/TC, échangés entre la composante bord et le sol (quelques Kbit/s) sont limités. Dans le cas d'expériences de télécommunications ou technologiques, cette limitation est moins critique que dans le cas d'expériences d'observation fondées sur le recueil de mesures tout au long du déplacement du microsatellite.
Enfin, la <u>durée de vie</u> du segment bord liée à la fiabilité prévisionnelle n'est pas un contrainte en soi mais reste un objectif raisonnable (durée de vie de l'ordre de quelques mois).

Les quelques contraintes exposées ci-dessus peuvent conduire à la conclusion que le concept microsatellite est mal ou pas adapté à la mission envisagée.

Dans d'autres cas, quelques modifications mineures d'un concept existant associées à une évolution non critique de la mission amènent à permettre l'utilisation d'un microsatellite et de bénéficier des avantages apportés par cette solution que sont :

- la réalisation de <u>l'objectif de faible coût</u> par l'utilisation d'une plateforme microsatellite et d'une station sol existantes, la mise en place d'une équipe projet intégrée réduisant au minimum les circuits de décision.

- une <u>autonomie</u> et une certaine <u>souplesse</u> dans le développement du système par rapport, par exemple, à une solution "passager" d'un gros satellite qui impose son calendrier de développement, son plan de mission, sa priorité etc...

- une contrainte de disponibilité au niveau du lancement réduite au strict nécessaire en termes de préparation, de points de rendez-vous et de tests (concept ASAP d'ARIANESPACE, par exemple).

3   **LE CONCEPT MICROSATELLITE DANS LE PROJET CERISE**
Le système CERISE est construit à partir du concept UoSAT proposé par la société SSTL de l'Université du Surrey. Ce concept déjà éprouvé par l'envoi sur orbite par ARIANE de 3 microsatellites (UoSAT 3, 4, 5) présente l'avantage de se présenter comme un standard en Europe.

Pour remplir la mission allouée au système CERISE, un certain nombre de modifications ont été apportées à la conception d'UoSAT-5 pris comme référence. Celles-ci, ont été minimisées pour éviter de perdre le bénéfice d'un coût réduit par l'obligation d'une qualification coûteuse au sol.

Elles consistent principalement en : (voir ci-après la figure 1 illustrant la "configuration nominale du microsatellite CERISE")

- l'adjonction de 4 panneaux solaires déployables en plus des 4 panneaux fixes pour augmenter la puissance électrique disponible pour la charge utile (avec les modifications correspondantes du sous-système de puissance et l'adjonction de mécanismes de déploiement et de gerbage).
- une nouvelle implantation de la face terre pour y loger, outre les senseurs destinés au contrôle d'attitudes et les antennes TM/TC (télémesures/télécommandes), le dispositif de gerbage des panneaux solaires déployables et les antennes charge utile.

- la modification du logiciel vol pour tenir compte de la gestion de la charge utile

- l'augmentation du débit de TM pour passer de 9600 bps à 38400 bps pour transmettre la télémesure charge utile.

- la modification des fréquences TM/TC.

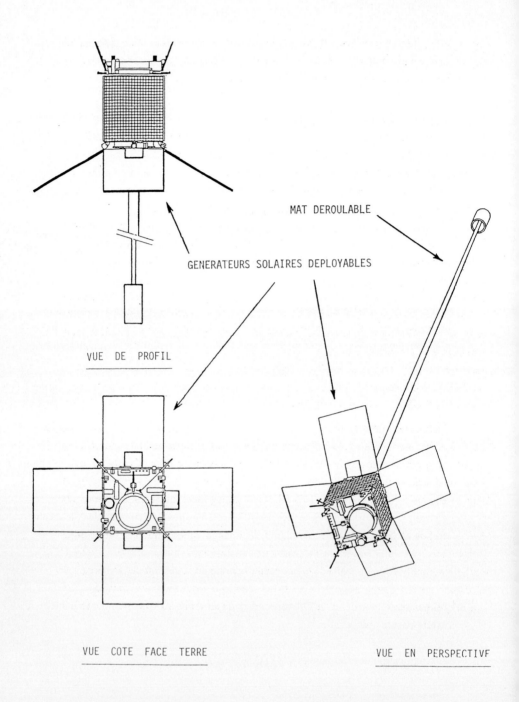

MAT DEROULABLE

GENERATEURS SOLAIRES DEPLOYABLES

VUE DE PROFIL

VUE COTE FACE TERRE

VUE EN PERSPECTIVE

FIGURE 1 - CONFIGURATION NOMINALE MICROSATELLITE CERISE

492

Ces modifications ont motivé une phase d'études en préliminaire à la phase C/D et ont donné lieu à un prototypage et à des tests de validation pour les mécanismes de déploiement et de gerbage, les modifications de logiciel et de débit de TM.

La charge utile CERISE est développée de façon spécifique pour la mission souhaitée. Elle a été implantée en tenant compte du caractère modulaire de la plateforme microsatellite UoSAT. L'élément de base ou module de celle-ci constitue une "tranche" du microsatellite de hauteur variable (voir ci-après en figure 2, la vue éclatée du microsatellite). Trois de ces modules contiennent l'électronique de la charge utile, le reste de celle-ci étant constituée des antennes placées sur la face Terre.

La charge utile comporte un calculateur identique à celui de la plateforme et peut accéder à toutes les ressources de celle-ci. Par le jeu du téléchargement des logiciels plateforme et charge utile, les deux calculateurs peuvent ainsi travailler en redondance complète.

La charge utile comporte également un capteur hyperfréquence large bande, spécifique à la mission, développé sous contrat avec THOMSON-CSF. Le synoptique du micro-satellite (fourni ci-après en figure 3) permet de situer la charge utile complète dans l'environnement microsatellite.

Les bilans masse, consommation de la charge utile aboutissent aux chiffres suivants :

masse :   12 Kg
consommation :   20 W (en jour et nuit)

Le déroulement de l'A.I.T. (Assemblage, Intégration et Tests) du satellite s'initialisera à partir de la livraison par SSTL de la plateforme et des moyens de tests sol associés. Dans un deuxième temps, le satellite et la station sol seront testées ensemble en usine de manière à valider complètement les différents dialogues et traitements prévus dans le système.

La charge utile sera donc testée et validée directement à l'aide de la plateforme et de la station sol, dans l'environnement électrique définitif et subira des essais d'environ-nement thermique et mécanique tel que prévu sur le lanceur et en orbite. On évite par là-même une validation intermédiaire de la charge utile avec des moyens de tests spécifiques et souvent complexes puisqu'ils simulent en général l'environnement satellite plus ou moins complètement.

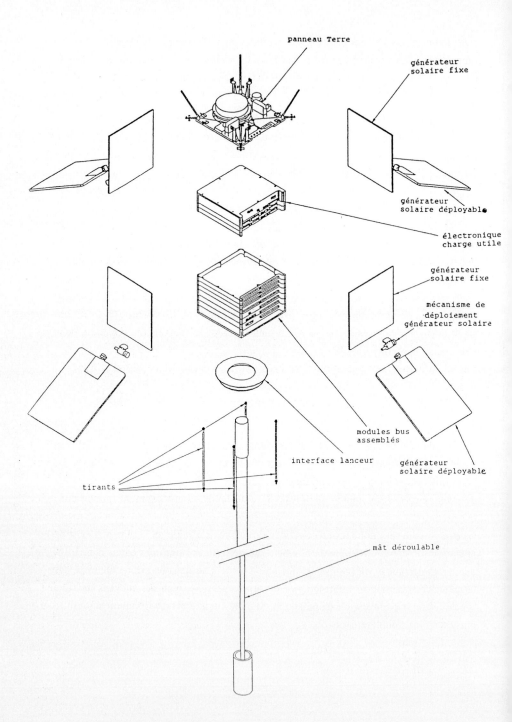

Figure 2 - Vue éclatée microsatellite CERISE

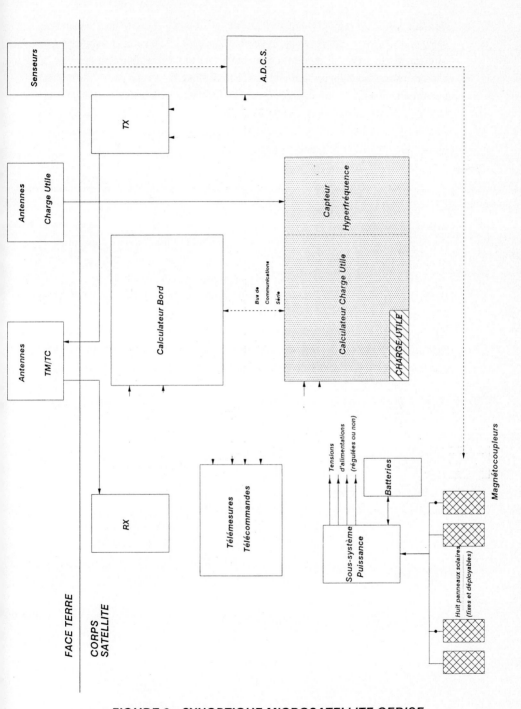

FIGURE 3 - SYNOPTIQUE MICROSATELLITE CERISE

La station sol CERISE développée en grande partie par SSTL sera installée en France et servira, dans un premier temps, à la mise à poste et à la recette en orbite du micro-satellite. Cette station comportera également une unité d'exploitation des TM de la charge utile, développée par ALCATEL ESPACE. Cette unité est intégrée naturellement dans la station grâce au réseau local existant dans celle-ci et par l'inter-médiaire duquel s'effectuent tous les échanges de données entre les ordinateurs de la station. A noter qu'une fonction de mémorisation de toutes les TM par disque optique numérique (WORM) de grande capacité est actuellement prévue.

4   CONCLUSION

Le système CERISE constitue le premier exemple d'utilisation d'un concept microsa-tellite existant pour remplir une mission précise de type expérimental et scientifique financée par un client comme la DME à un industriel "clés en main".

La livraison d'un tel système sera réalisée en orbite et une station de commande/contrôle du microsatellite et d'exploitation des mesures sera livrée à la DME.

De plus, certaines modifications étudiées et réalisées dans le cadre de ce projet ont permis d'améliorer le concept UoSAT dans certaines de ses caractéristiques (puissance électrique disponible, débit de TM, capacité de mémorisation bord etc...)

Impact of Advances in Technology

on

Future Spacecraft Design

F. Gampe

ESA/ESTEC
Postbus 299
NL-2200 AG Noordwijk
The Netherlands
Tel.: +1719/84636
Fax: +1719/85184

G. Lippner

Dep. RSX
Dornier GmbH
Postfach 1420
D-7990 Friedrichshafen
Tel.: +7545/89946
Fax: +7545/85686

Abstract

The paper presents the status of the ESTEC study 'Impact of Advances in Technology on Future Spacecraft Design'. The study objective and the study approach are discussed. Surveys on Advanced Technology, Advanced Management and Engineering Approach, Launchers and Application Fields have been performed. Potential Model Missions are identified and discussed and an outlook on the future study activities is given.

1. Introduction

There is a continuing development in spacecraft technology towards miniaturization and performance improvement. Advanced Technologies lead to a considerable reduction in mass, volume and power-demand of components, still providing enhanced capabilities and increased reliability.

As a consequence new mission and commercial concepts evolve leading to a new kind of **"small but smart"** spacecraft, offering high performance at lower procurement cost.

The compelling motives for this evolution are the following

- advanced technology allows to build smaller, lighter satellites
- these satellites may allow cost effective splitting of missions/platforms into multiple missions and spacecraft
- the development time will be reduced and the 'application turn-over' for the user will be improved: > **more frequent opportunities for more users** <
- new mission and commercial concepts are arising, e.g. IRIDIUM, Globalstar
- the penalty of launching standardization or communality will be reduced
- new launcher concepts are arising.

497

This process was and is promoted currently primarily by military applications in the USA and the former USSR. Within Europe there were only sporadic attempts in this field. To make up leeway, ESA has initiated this study: 'Impact of Advances in Technology on Future Spacecraft Design'.

The role of the study within the "Small Satellites Systems and Services" scenarios is shown in Fig 1-1 and the main topics are presented in Fig. 1-2.

Considering these topics the study objectives are characterized by four basic questions:

- What is the potential of reducing project duration?
- Is the trend to heavier spacecraft and payload packaging efficient or does it just follow the increase of launcher capabilities?
- Is the management approach, the architectural design and modular concept of today's spacecraft optimized or could it be improved?
- Can "small but smart" satellites compete commercially in small business segments?

The ESA study is performed by Dornier/Deutsche Aerospace with the subcontractor Sagem (France) and the consultancy of IKI (Russia) and DSI (USA).

Special support was provided by Ross Jones and Rex Ridenoure from Caltech, Pasadena, as well as Herbert A. Roeder from Perkin-Elmer and James Hoffman from Space Instruments Inc. (all USA).

The presentation covers the first results of the initial five months (total duration = 12 months) of the study.

ESA / ESTEC / FSD

Dornier
Deutsche Aerospace

I A T - F S D

DATE: 01.07.92

PAGE: 15

New Missions & New Services by Smalll Satellites with Conventional Technologies	Micro and Experimental Satellites	Integrated Approach New Missions and New Services by Satellites with:
• Satellite Constellations • Gapfiller Satellites to Replace Failed Ones • Smaller Countries • Small Satellites for First-Class Science	• University Satellites • Technology Satellites 'Microspacecraft with Miniaturization Pushed to its Limits'	• (very) Advanced Technologies • Advanced Design/ Operations Concept • New Mission Concepts • New Commercial Approach

SMALL SATELLITES SYSTEMS AND SERVICES, ARCACHON, FRANCE, 29. JUNE - 03. JULY 1992

Fig. 1-1: Role of the IAT-FSD Study Within the "Small Satellites Systems and Services Scenarios"

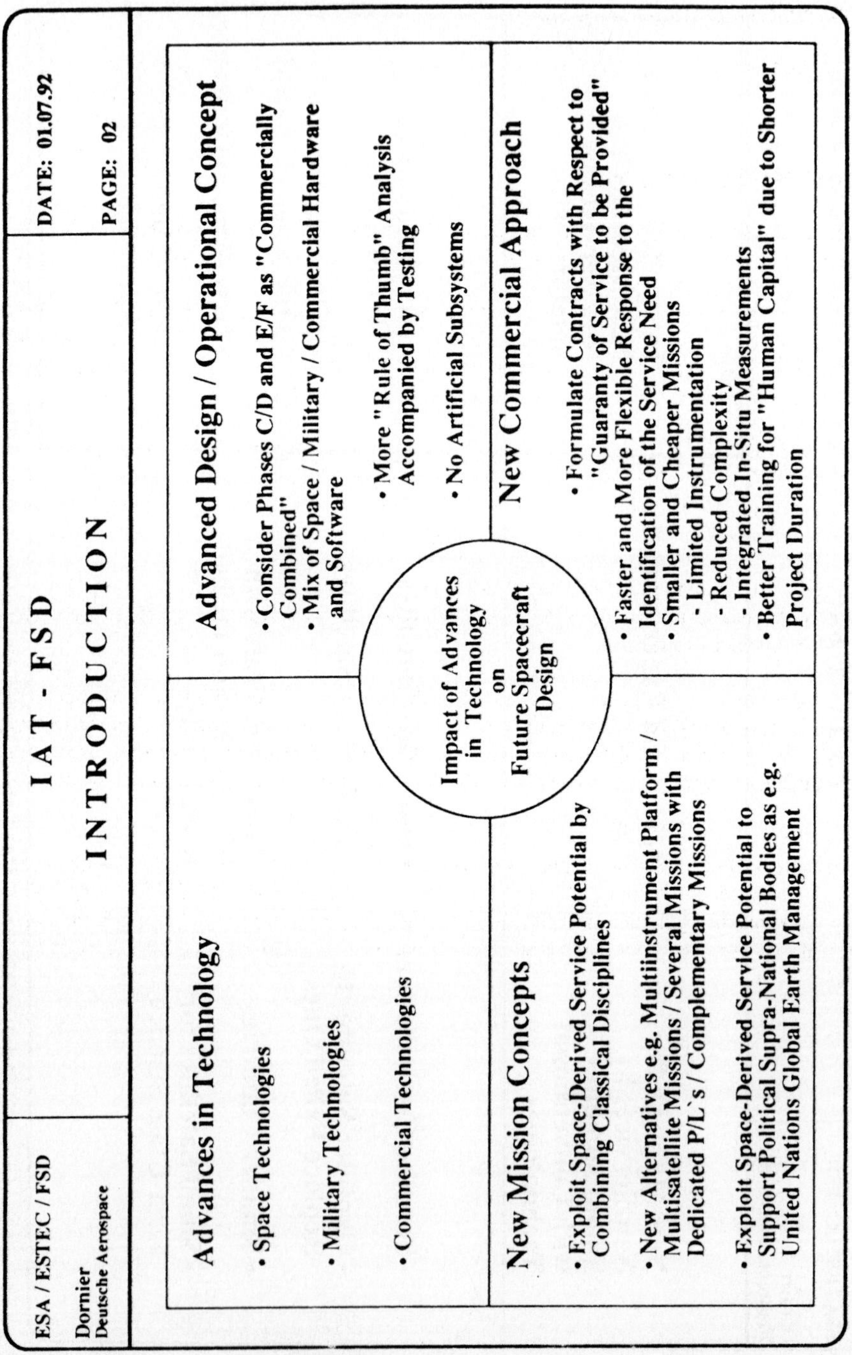

ESA / ESTEC / FSD
Dornier
Deutsche Aerospace
IAT - FSD
INTRODUCTION
DATE: 01.07.92
PAGE: 02
Advances in Technology
• Space Technologies
• Military Technologies
• Commercial Technologies
Advanced Design / Operational Concept
• Consider Phases C/D and E/F as "Commercially Combined"
• Mix of Space / Military / Commercial Hardware and Software
• More "Rule of Thumb" Analysis Accompanied by Testing
• No Artificial Subsystems
Impact of Advances in Technology on Future Spacecraft Design
New Mission Concepts
• Exploit Space-Derived Service Potential by Combining Classical Disciplines
• New Alternatives e.g. Multiinstrument Platform / Multisatellite Missions / Several Missions with Dedicated P/L`s / Complementary Missions
• Exploit Space-Derived Service Potential to Support Political Supra-National Bodies as e.g. United Nations Global Earth Management
New Commercial Approach
• Formulate Contracts with Respect to "Guaranty of Service to be Provided"
• Faster and More Flexible Response to the Identification of the Service Need
• Smaller and Cheaper Missions
- Limited Instrumentation
- Reduced Complexity
- Integrated In-Situ Measurements
• Better Training for "Human Capital" due to Shorter Project Duration
SMALL SATELLITES SYSTEMS AND SERVICES, ARCACHON, FRANCE, 29. JUNE - 03. JULY 1992

Fig. 1-2: IAT-FSD Study Main Topics

2. Study Objectives and Study Approach

The study objectives are summarized in Fig. 2-1 and the study approach is presented in Fig. 2-2.

3. Survey of Background Data

The main foundation for the study is the Survey of Advances in Technology. This survey is based on a review of the domains shown in Fig. 3-1. Examples are given in Fig. 3-2.

It is followed by a review of the programmatic aspects of the current environment in which the various space programs are planned and executed in Europe. This review includes the **Marketing, Management and Engineering Approach** currently applied in Europe by the National and International Agencies as well as recommendations for future advances (see Fig. 3-3).

It is evident that a comprehensive review of the impact of Advanced Technologies must include current and future Launcher Concepts. Therefore a **Survey of Launchers** is included in the study. **Survey of Application Fields** has been established. This survey presents the current status and discuss the trends of future missions for each Application Field.

The survey is followed by a collection of attractive ideas for future missions (see Fig. 3-4). This collection of ideas serves as a pool of **Potential Model Missions** from which three missions are chosen for further investigations.

Finally the System Level Impact of Advanced Technologies on Spacecraft Design was evaluated. However it must be understood that such a 'system-impact per technology-domain' presentation can not cover the full range of effects of advanced technologies. The reason is that there are complex interdependencies between technology domains as well as follow on effects form one domain to others.

To demonstrate how strong the impact is on Mission level there are 3 out of the 14 above mentioned potential Model Missions selected for a detailed analyses. The Model Missions and Advanced Technology are discussed in Fig. 3-5, the Advanced Design in Fig. 3-6, the launch opportunities in Fig. 3-7, the Ground Segment Approach in Fig. 3-8, and the Commercial Approach in Fig. 3-9.

ESA / ESTEC / FSD	I A T - F S D	DATE: 01.07.92
Dornier Deutsche Aerospace	S T U D Y O B J E C T I V E S	PAGE: 03

Identification of

- Promising Advanced Technologies for Future Spacecrafts

- The Application Potential of "Small-and-Smart" Satellites Either by

  - Enabling New Missions or

  - Performing Planned Missions in a More Efficient Manner

- The Cost Reduction Potential of "Advanced" Technologies

- Those Advanced Technologies Providing Most Likely the

  Maximised Operational Benefit (Cost, Capabilities, Performances)

Fig. 2-1: Study Objectives

502

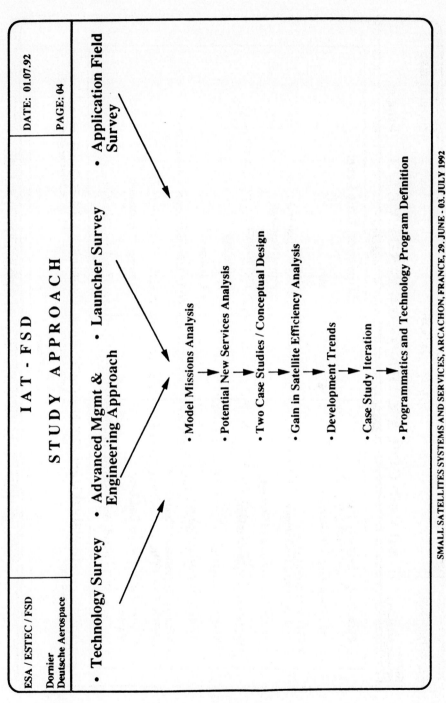

ESA / ESTEC / FSD

Dormier
Deutsche Aerospace

I A T - F S D

S T U D Y   A P P R O A C H

DATE: 01.07.92

PAGE: 04

- **Technology Survey** • **Advanced Mgmt & Engineering Approach** • **Launcher Survey** • **Application Field Survey**

- Model Missions Analysis

- Potential New Services Analysis

- Two Case Studies / Conceptual Design

- Gain in Satellite Efficiency Analysis

- Development Trends

- Case Study Iteration

- Programmatics and Technology Program Definition

SMALL SATELLITES SYSTEMS AND SERVICES, ARCACHON, FRANCE, 29. JUNE - 03. JULY 1992

Fig. 2-2: IAT-FSD Study Approach

503

ESA / ESTEC / FSD	I A T - F S D	DATE: 01.07.92
Dornier Deutsche Aerospace	ADVANCED TECHNOLOGY SURVEY 1	PAGE: 05

Technology Survey in

- Data Porcessing and Storage
- Telecommunications
  (Incl. Antenna Technology)
- Power Generation and Storage
- Structure and Mechanisms
- Thermal Control
- Attitude and Orbit Control
- Mission Operations / Flexibility /
  System Autonomy
- Ground Infrastructure and User
  Support

Impact on Unit Level

- Mass
- Volume
- Power Demand
- Performance
- Reliability
- Lifetime
- Tolerance to Space Environment
- Cost
- Testing / Verification

General Tendency

- Less Mass
- Less Volume
- Less Power

- Higher Performance

SMALL SATELLITES SYSTEMS AND SERVICES, ARCACHON, FRANCE, 29. JUNE - 03. JULY 1992

Fig. 3-1: Survey of Advances in Technology

ESA / ESTEC / FSD	**I A T - F S D**	DATE: 01.07.92
Dornier Deutsche Aerospace	**A D V A N C E D T E C H N O L O G Y**	PAGE: 06

Technology Area	Unit Level Advances (Time Frame, 5 years)	System Design Drivers	System Impact
Data Processing	• Chip Technology • Packaging Technology • Processor Technology Projected Improvement Factors: Mass 10 Volume 3 Power 10 Performance TBD	**1. S/C Bus** • S/C Mission Management (incl. TM/TC I/F) • S/C System Management (FD/R etc.) • HK Data • Control Layout (Complexity) • Power Management **2. Payload** • Payload Management	• Strong System Mass, Volume, Power and Performance Improvement • Reliability Improvement • Very High Improvement for P/L data processing --> impact on overall processing and distribution concept --> Potential New Services
Solar Generator	• Cell Efficiency • Cell Thickness Projected Improvement Factors: Mass specific Power < 2 Area specific Power < 3	**1. S/C Bus** • Mission (e.g. ecclipses) • Power Consumption profile of S/C Bus electrical units • Heater Power Requirements **2. Payload** • Power Consumption Profile of P/C	• Strong System Mass, Volume Decrease Influencing - Configuration (Deployable/Fixed) - Free FOVs (Sensors, P/L) - Launch Mass - AOCS (e.g. drag, eigenfrequencies) - Structure (load, hold points) - S/C Mission Management

• Complex Advanced Technology System Interactions to be Analysed on the Basis of Model Missions

SMALL SATELLITES SYSTEMS AND SERVICES, ARCACHON, FRANCE, 29. JUNE - 03. JULY 1992

Fig. 3-2: Example for Advances in Technology and Corresponding Impact on System

ESA / ESTEC / FSD	I A T - F S D	DATE: 01.07.92
Dornier Deutsche Aerospace	ADVANCED ENGINEERING APPROACH	PAGE: 07

- A Small and Cost Effective Payload is the Key to a Cost Effective Mission

- Deletion of Artificial Subsystem

- Subcontractors have to be Minimized

- Activities which Ensure Mission Success have to be Performed in an Engineering Way (e.g. Parts Traceability, Efficient Functional Redundancy, Testing)

- Deletion of Overloaded Administrative Reporting and Documentation but e.g. "As Built" Doc`s have to be Available in a Professional State

- More Flexible Hardware Approach

- Use H/W which is Proven to be Cost Efficient and Reliable Unmodified
- Parts Level Should be no Dogma
- Where Necessary and Possible "Conventional" H/W is Upgraded, e.g. TV Testing of Several Commercial Alternatives, Upgrading and Shielding
- Build H/W as soon as possible

- Minimise Analysis where Effective

- Adapt Organisational Structure, "Lean Management"

Fig. 3-3: Recommendations for an Advanced Engineering Approach

ESA / ESTEC / FSD			IAT - FSD	DATE: 01.07.92
Dornier Deutsche Aerospace		POTENTIAL MODEL MISSIONS		PAGE: 08
Model Mission	Mission Objective	Space Segment		• Payload
Hydrosat	• Global & Regional Hydrological Status Monitoring • Forecasting of Environment Damaging • Emergency Messages • Collection of In-Situ Measurements & Distribution	• Use of GEO Weather S/C • Hydrosat LEO, Tropical Regions, Arid Regions		- VISSR (e.g. MSG) - ATSR, MIMR, "SAR", AVHRR - Direct User Comms Practicable
Agrisat	• Operational Mission - Soil Humidity & Temperature - In-Situ Measurements - Deforestation - Ice & Snow Coverage - Vegetation Identification etc.	• One S/C in LEO, not Sun Synch. • Inclination 55 deg		- MOMS - SAR - Direct User Comms Pakcage
Complementary EO Satellite	• Provision of Complementary, Short Preparation Flight Opportunities for EO Instruments	• Small Standard S/C Bus in LEO		e.g. - AMAS, DCP - MIMR, SAR, AUHRR - MOMS - Direct User Comms Package
Airguide	• Improve Airline Safety, Fuel Savings, Delays by Monitoring of - Jet Streams - Volcanic Clouds - Severe Storms	• Three Small GEO S/C for Global Coverage		- GEO-TOMS - Cloud Top Radiometer - Comms Package for direct Crew/Airplane Connection
URM	• An Eccliptic Reference Ulysses • Forecast of Solar Weather (Preoperational System)	• One Small S/C in HEO		- Angas - Magnet - Cospin - Dust - Taus
Lunar Mapping	• Global High Resolution Lunar Mapping • Precursor for Future Exploration & Utilization	• Small S/C in Lunar Polar Orbit (100 km)		- High Resolution Camera

Others Under Consideration are e.g. Optical Data Relay Satellite, Environment Law Enforcement/Monitoring System, Adv. Global Ozone Mapping S/C,
MAPSAT, Solid, Cube, etc.

SMALL SATELLITES SYSTEMS AND SERVICES, ARCACHON, FRANCE, 29. JUNE - 03. JULY 1992

Fig. 3-4: Potential Model Missions

ESA / ESTEC / FSD Dornier Deutsche Aerospace	**I A T - F S D** **MODEL MISSION & ADVANCED TECHNOLOGIES**	DATE: 01.07.92 PAGE: 09

Model Mission	Potential Application of Advanced Technologies	Advanced Technology for the Payload
• Complementary E/O Satellite (CEOS)/ Hydrosat	- Adv. Solargenerator & Battery Technology - Adv. Power Electronics - Adv. Data Processing Technology - Adv. Data Storage Devices - Adv. Microwave Telecomunication - Adv. Thermal Control - Adv. Mission Ops & S/C Autonomy - Adv. Management and Engineering Approach	- Adv. On-board P/L data processing - Adv. On-board Data Storage
Airguide	- Adv. Solar Generator (& Battery) - Adv. Power Electronics - Adv. Processor Technology - Adv. Microwave Telecommunication - Adv. Antenna Technology - Adv. Mission OPS & S/C Accuracy - Propulsion for Tranfer to GEO - Adv. Management and Engineering Approach	- Adv. On-board Image Processing - Adv. On-board Data Storage - Adv. TM/TC Concept
Ulysses Reference Mission (URM)	- Adv. Solar Generator & Battery Technology - Adv. Processing - Adv. Management and Engineering Approach	- Use of Ulysses H/W
General Tendency	Less Mass Less Volume Less Power	Higher Performance

SMALL SATELLITES SYSTEMS AND SERVICES, ARCACHON, FRANCE, 29. JUNE - 03. JULY 1992

Fig. 3-5: Model Missions, Advanced Technologies and Impact on Satellite Characteristics

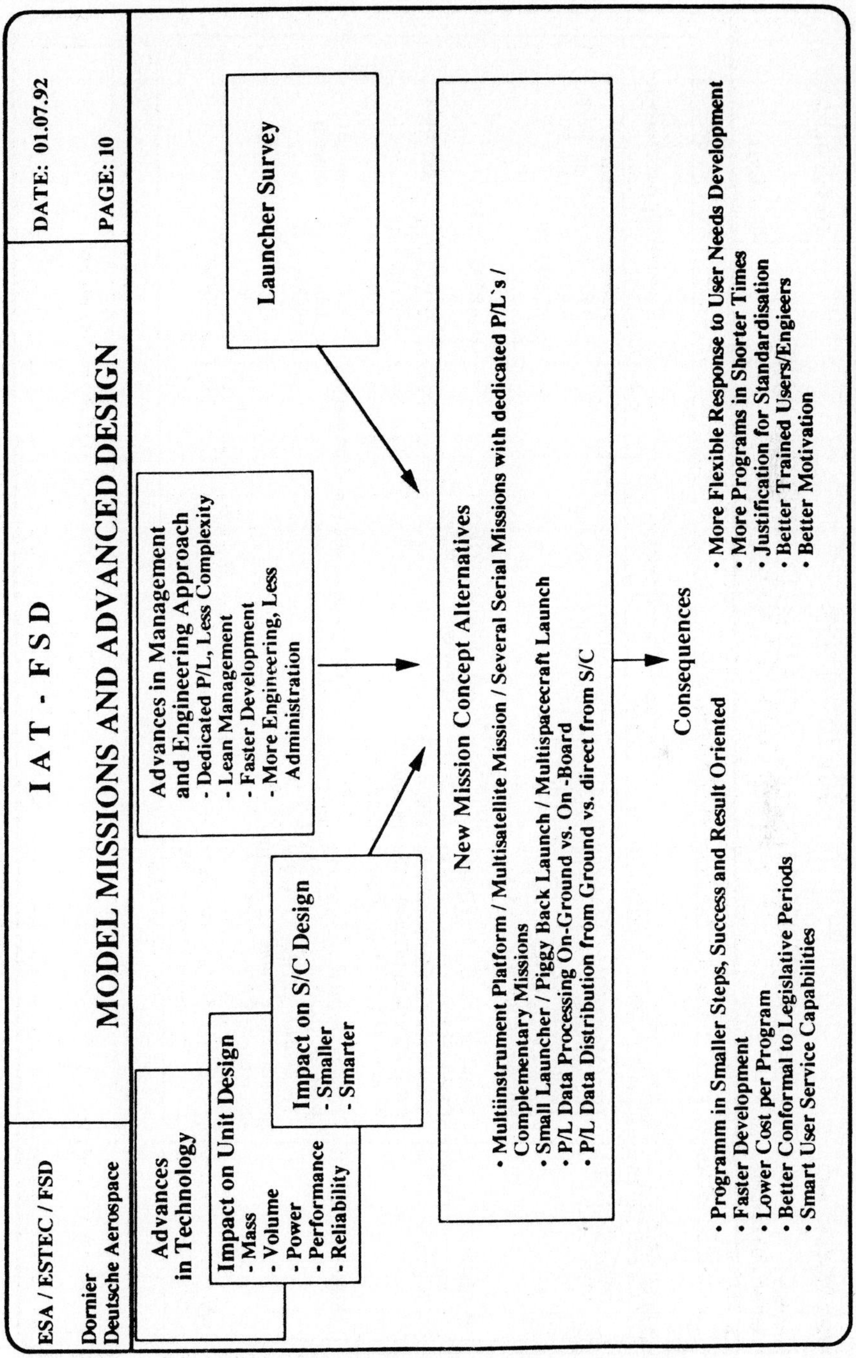
ESA / ESTEC / FSD
Dornier
Deutsche Aerospace
I A T - F S D
MODEL MISSIONS AND ADVANCED DESIGN
DATE: 01.07.92
PAGE: 10
Advances in Technology
Impact on Unit Design
- Mass
- Volume
- Power
- Performance
- Reliability
Impact on S/C Design
- Smaller
- Smarter
Advances in Management and Engineering Approach
- Dedicated P/L, Less Complexity
- Lean Management
- Faster Development
- More Engineering, Less Administration
Launcher Survey
New Mission Concept Alternatives
• Multiinstrument Platform / Multisatellite Mission / Several Serial Missions with dedicated P/L`s / Complementary Missions
• Small Launcher / Piggy Back Launch / Multispacecraft Launch
• P/L Data Processing On-Ground vs. On-Board
• P/L Data Distribution from Ground vs. direct from S/C
Consequences
• Programm in Smaller Steps, Success and Result Oriented
• Faster Development
• Lower Cost per Program
• Better Conformal to Legislative Periods
• Smart User Service Capabilities
• More Flexible Response to User Needs Development
• More Programs in Shorter Times
• Justification for Standardisation
• Better Trained Users/Engieers
• Better Motivation
SMALL SATELLITES SYSTEMS AND SERVICES, ARCACHON, FRANCE, 29. JUNE - 03. JULY 1992

Fig. 3-6: Model Missions, Advanced Technologies and Impact on Design

ESA / ESTEC / FSD	I A T - F S D	DATE: 01.07.92
Dornier Deutsche Aerospace	MODEL MISSION CHARACTERISTICS AND LAUNCH OPPORTUNITIES	PAGE: 11

Model Mission	Satellite Characteristics	Orbit Caracteristics	Launch Opportunities
• CEOS- Hydrosat	• Total Mass (BOL) : 300 kg (Goal) • Payload Mass : < 80 kg (TBC) • Total Power (EOL) : < 500 W (TBC) • Comms Data Rates : TBD • Number of S/C's : 1-3	Orbit Altitude: 250 km (TBC) Inclination: 55 deg	ARIANE IV (shared) ARIANE V Piggy Back DELTA II (shared) PEGASUS
• Airguide	• Total Mass (BOL) : 300 kg • Payload Mass : 40 kg • Total Power (EOL) : 500 W (TBC) • Comms Data Rates : 1 Mbps (Rasdata) • Number of S/C's : 3	Orbit Altitude: GEO Inclination: 0 deg	ARIANE IV ARIANE V Piggy Back DELTA II
• URM	• Total Mass (BOL) : 150 kg • Payload Mass : 24 kg • Total Power (EOL) : 120 W • Comms Data Rates : 10 Kbps • Number of S/C's : 1	Orbit Altitude: 400 km x 200 000 km Inclination: low	ARIANE IV (shared) DELTA II (shared) SCOUT II Molniya (shared)

Fig. 3-7: Model Mission Characteristics and Launch Opportunities

ESA / ESTEC / FSD	I A T - F S D	DATE: 01.07.92
Dornier Deutsche Aerospace	ADVANCED GROUND SEGMENT APPROACH	PAGE: 12

Advanced

- **Small Master Control Station, High Degree of Automatization**

- **Extensive Use of Small / Low Cost In-Situ Measurement Stations for EO**

- **Improved On-Board Data Collection and Processing Capabilities**

  Goal: "Direct" - Level 4 Data Products Delivery

- **Advanced Small and Low Cost User Terminals**

Fig. 3-8: Advanced Technologies and Ground Segment Approach

ESA / ESTEC / FSD

Dornier
Deutsche Aerospace

I A T - F S D

MODEL MISSION AND COMMERCIAL APPROACH

DATE: 01.07.92

PAGE: 13

Model Mission	Program Approach	Potential Customers	Typical Contractual Procedure
LEOS / HYDROSAT AGRISAT	• Demo Mission - 1 S/C - 1+2 Years • Complementary EO Missions 1+2 Years • Pre-Operational Model 1+2 Years - Improved Ground Infrastructure Build up - Improved Space Segment - User Familiarisation • Operational Model No. 1 3-5 Years • Operational Model No. 2 3-5 Years - improved P/L and Services	- ESA, Nat. Agencies - Environmental Agencies - UN - EUMETSAT etc. - Regional, multi-national Authorities e.g. - Middle East - North Africa	- Techn. Requirements Service Requirements Document - Typical Payment Plan • 30 % fee after successful launch • 30 % fee after 0.5 Year successfull operation • Specific amount of "national contributions" by interested states / organisations
AIRGUIDE	• Demo Mission - 1 S/C - 1+2 Years • Operational Mission No. 1 3-5 Years - 3 S/C • Operational Mission No. 2 3-5 Years - improved P/L and Services	- ESA, Industry - Airlines, Shipping Agencies - Possible US Cooperation	
URM	• Reference Mission to Ulysses and preoperational mission • Operational Program - 1 S/C - improved User Services	- ESA, Nat. Agencies - Power Companies, Insurance Companies Health Organization - Possible Russian Cooperation	

SMALL SATELLITES SYSTEMS AND SERVICES, ARCACHON, FRANCE, 29. JUNE - 03. JULY 1992

Fig. 3-9: Advanced Commercial Approach

4. Outlook of the Study

After a detailed Model Missions Requirements Analysis two of the three Model Missions are finally selected as Reference Missions for distinct case studies. For three Reference Missions Potential New Services are identified being followed by an analysis of the payload characteristics.

Finally this allows to establish an elaborate set of Reference Mission Requirements for the case studies.

Two case studies on conceptual design level will be performed and extensions to other missions will be analyzed. The study will be finalized after programmatic analysis. The outlook is summarized in Fig. 4-1.

ESA / ESTEC / FSD Dornier Deutsche Aerospace	IAT - FSD OUTLOOK OF STUDY	DATE: 01.07.92 PAGE: 14

A What are the Most Important Technologies which make a Satellite and its Payload really "Small-and-Smart"?

- Data Processing and Storage
- Power Generation and Storage
- Telecommunications, Antenna Technology
- Management and Engineering Approach

B New Services by combining "Classical Services" ----> Hydrosat
New Specific, Selfstanding Services Tailored to Customer Requirements
----> Airguide

C Major Task of Next Phase: Conceptual Design of two Selected Model Missions

D What is the Adequate Approach Applicable to "Small-and-Smart" Satellites and the Corresponding Ground Infrastructure

SMALL SATELLITES SYSTEMS AND SERVICES, ARCACHON, FRANCE, 29. JUNE - 03. JULY 1992

Fig. 4-1: Study Outlook

S-80 : UN SATELLITE A MOINS DE 50 MF

par
A. LAMOTHE

AEROSPATIALE - CANNES

RESUME

Le système S-80 est un système de localisation de mobiles proposé par le CNES, utilisant une constellation de satellites défilants en orbite basse.

AEROSPATIALE, associé à son partenaire ALCATEL ESPACE, est en charge de l'étude de définition du segment spatial S-80. L'objectif majeur de cette étude est la définition d'un satellite S-80 à un coût récurrent nettement **inférieur à 50 MF**.

Cet objectif a été atteint par une approche technique spécifique.

Par ailleurs, le satellite proposé offre une **large capacité de mission**.

ABSTRACT

The S-80 system is a localization system for mobiles, proposed by CNES, using a constellation of small low earth orbit satellites.

AEROSPATIALE, associated with ALCATEL ESPACE, was in charge of the definition study of the S-80 space segment. The main objective of this study is the definition of the S-80 satellite at a recurring cost **below 50 MF** (about 8 M$).

This objective has been achieved by a specific technical approach.

Furthermore the proposed satellite offers a **wide mission capacity**.

1 - PRINCIPALES SPECIFICATIONS DU SATELLITE S-80

Caractéristiques de la constellation (Walker 5/5/3) :

- cinq satellites sur cinq plans orbitaux équirépartis,

- chaque satellite est décalé en phase par rapport au précédent de $3 \times 2\pi/5$,

- la position relative des satellites doit être contrôlée, ce qui nécessite un système de contrôle d'orbite.

- Altitude 1248 Km : faibles perturbations orbitales, radiations importantes (ions lourds)

- Inclinaison 57,1° : pas de direction solaire privilégiée.

Constellation S-80

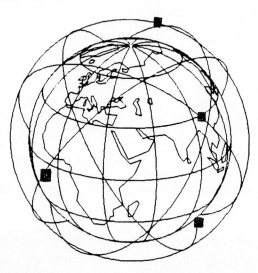

Charge utile :
- Bandes VHF / UHF, ce qui implique de grands aériens.
- Puissance consommée jour et nuit : 100 Watts - c'est essentiellement cette puissance qui distingue S-80 d'un micro-satellite amélioré.
- Besoins en pointage : 5° en tangage et roulis.

Calendrier :
- Première constellation mise à poste de 96 à 98.
- Durée de vie du satellite : 5 à 7 ans.
- Durée de vie du système : 20 ans.

Moyen de lancement :
- Injection directe par PEGASUS, SCOUT, ou équivalent.

2 - OBJECTIF 50 MF

Le satellite S-80 est beaucoup plus petit mais comprend les mêmes fonctions qu'un gros satellite, dont le coût récurrent est dans un rapport 10 par rapport à l'objectif fixé ici. Atteindre cet objectif a donc nécessité d'appliquer un certain nombre de principes de base :

* **Technologie simple**, éprouvée et adaptée :
- structure métallique, générateur solaire Silicium, pas de mécanismes d'entraînement, batterie NiCd...

* **Electronique** adaptée à l'objectif de coût et compatible de la durée de vie du système :
    - politique composants adaptée et souple,
    - utilisation de composants intégrés ASIC et FPGA

* **Maîtrise des coûts dès la prédéfinition** :
    - utilisation de l'analyse fonctionnelle pour réaliser le satellite juste nécessaire,
    - utilisation de l'analyse de la valeur,
    - chaque concept technique envisagé est associé à une estimation de coût.

* Travail en **groupe intégré pluri-disciplinaire** :
    - permet de limiter les risques d'erreurs sur les grands choix programme,
    - le satellite le moins cher n'est pas la somme des équipements les moins chers,
    - prise de conscience des impacts des solutions choisies sur les autres sous-ensembles ou activités,
    - importance de la production, de l'AIT et des achats dès la conception initiale.

* **Remise en cause des habitudes** acquises sur les "satellites lourds"
    - remise en cause de la notion de "sous-système",
    - simplification du formalisme interne et externe,
    - pas de luxe inutile : "juste nécessaire" seulement

* Politique **qualité adaptée** basée sur la **maîtrise des risques** :
    - analyse de risque comme base du plan de développement et de la politique qualité,
    - efforts qualité ciblés, en évitant le saupoudrage,
    - importance de la qualité dès la conception préliminaire,
    - qualité "courante" par la motivation et la formation à l'auto-qualité des intervenants.

* Prise en compte de l'effet **"petite série"** :
    - efforts en développement pour éviter les modifications sur les modèles récurrents,
    - production en série de certains éléments (structure, générateur solaire),
    - limitation des temps d'attente en AIT.

3 - L'HERITAGE

L'héritage EOLE :

La mission d'EOLE était du même type que celle de S-80 (localisation de balises), mais avec des performances très différentes.

Le satellite S-80 a principalement hérité d'EOLE un faux air de famille, l'expérience d'anciens et quelques anecdotes. Par contre, la stabilisation par gradient de gravité étudiée en détail sur EOLE n'a finalement pas été retenue pour le satellite S-80.

L'héritage ARSENE :

ARSENE est un satellite radio-amateur dont la structure, l'assemblage et les tests sont réalisés par AEROSPATIALE-CANNES. Ce satellite doit être prochainement lancé par ARIANE pour une orbite 20000 x 36000 Km.

L'expérience ARSENE a été particulièrement utile par la présence au sein de l'équipe S-80 à Cannes des principaux responsables AEROSPATIALE d'ARSENE qui ont apporté leur expérience concrète d'un satellite à coût réduit et un certain nombre d'idées techniques.

Autres héritages :

AEROSPATIALE a bien sûr mis à profit toute son expérience de concepteur, réalisateur et maître d'oeuvre de satellites, mais également son expérience de la production en série de cases à équipements de missiles, ainsi que l'expérience cannoise et société en matière de composants électroniques intégrés.

4 - COMBIEN LE KILO ?

Le satellite S-80 est essentiellement dimensionné par la puissance de la charge-utile (100W) et non par sa masse.

Toutefois, cette puissance charge utile se traduit directement en kilogrammes de satellite.

L'objectif de coût récurrent d'un satellite S-80 de 150 kg serait donc d'être **nettement inférieur à 300 KF/kg**, valeur très comparable à ce que pourrait être un objectif de coût de gros satellite.

Une certaine réserve doit néanmoins être observée :

- Il est facile de diminuer la masse du satellite (utilisation de structures carbone) au prix d'une augmentation du coût du satellite;

- par ailleurs, le prix du lancement de petits satellites en orbite basse est plus lié au volume du satellite qu'à sa masse.

5 - LA PLATE FORME S-80

Description d'ensemble

Configuration de lancement

Configuration déployée

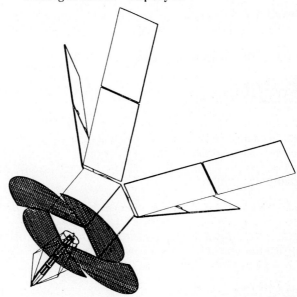

Le satellite S-80 est constitué :

- d'un générateur solaire omnidirectionnel,

- d'une stabilisation géocentrique 3 axes,

- d'un contrôle d'orbite,

- d'un contrôle thermique passif,

- d'une alimentation électrique semi-régulée,

- d'une gestion bord centralisée.

Ce satellite peut être lancé par PEGASUS, SCOUT, ou équivalent.

Performances

L'architecture proposée est adaptée aux besoins de S-80, mais perme
néanmoins une grande polyvalence de missions et de charges utiles :

capacité charge-utile :

30 à 60 kg maximum - 10 à 30 litres environ dans la plate-forme + 300
400 litres en face terre (lié au moyen de lancement)

environ **100 watts moyens**

plage orbitale :

- altitude 500 à 1500 km

- inclinaison : > 30° - Une orbite équatoriale peut être envisagée égalemen
avec des adaptations de la plate-forme.

capacité de pointage :

- nominalement 2 à 3° à 3σ pour le besoin S-80;

- peut être facilement portée à **quelques dizièmes de degré** san
modification majeure, et pour un coût réduit.

CONCLUSION

AEROSPATIALE dispose d'un concept de mini-plate-forme polyvalente pou
orbite basse à un coût très attractif largement compatible de l'objecti
initialement fixé.

De plus, l'approche utilisée et les sous-ensembles définis pour ce programme
peuvent facilement être utilisés ou adaptés pour d'autres besoins.

SMALL SATELLITE MODULAR DESIGN AND APPLICATION PROSPECT

Yuan Jie and Chen Jin Jun

805 Institute Shanghai Bureau of
Astronautics Ministry of Aeronautics
& Astronautics ------SHANGHAI CHINA

Abstract:
This paper systemically analysising the subsystem's functions of smallsatellites, imagine a kinds of configuration methods of small satellites modular design, that divided a wholespacecraft into three modules: payload module, common service module and attitude control module.Selecting proper modules,the customer could integrate a small satellite as their requirement.At last , the paper probes the possiblity of using Chinese launch vehicle to launch this kind of modular small satellites,and prospects small satellite's application.

1.Background

In the last few years, the small satellites range of application are expanding widely along with the vigorous development of satellite's technology, especially the microelectronics and microminiaturization developing, which enhancedcap ability of small satellites greatly.

Nowadays, small satellites will be attracted by military department and civil user of notable features, such aslow cost, short production period and launching perpare essily,etc. But recently, small satellite manufacture period more longer and cost still very expensive.

This paper systemically analysising functions of small satellites, discussing modules design possibility of small satellites which have different functions. The objective is carrying small satellite design towards standard oriented developing, reducing work load and production period, to achieve small satellite standard manufacture batch processing,reduced cost greatly, and make the small satellite's application widely.

2.Modular design concept

We known ,every satellite is comprised of several subsystems,so is small satellite. These subsystems could be divided into two groups: payload system and support systems(also called ensure systems).The different kinds of satellite, its payload system more different. But the support systems Which ensured satellite itself and payload system to operate normally in orbit are simular or even the same. So it is possibility that design a kinds of general common service bus which carried all support or ensure systems of satellite, to offer payload usingby all kinds of small satellites.

What is called modular design is a method that under foundation of common bus concept, through systemically analysising spacecraft subsystems functions, at last divided into several efficient and simple modular indepentive bus to design. According to the the different kinds of small satellite, each module designed several standard bus for customer selecting. So the modules are brought together to complete thesatellite with minimun additional engineering and cost.

3.Modular small satellite capability

(1) satellite gross mass: 200--400 kg;

(2) payload mass: 50--150 kg;

(3) structure form : boxed dimensions, 500mm x 500mmx H mm

(H ;hight)

(4) satellite useful life : 2--5 years ;

(5) attitude control mothods ;three options.

Gravity gradient model

Spin stablized model

Three axis stabilization model

(6) power system : 2--4 boards of solar panels .

gross power :180---360 w-hs

(7) TT&C.system: telemetry transmitor,dual frequency transmitor,

S--band received antenna, etc.

(8) Onboard computer and Data storage:

--general purpose 16 bit microprocessor;

--16 Megabytes data storage;

--Data rates up to 2.0 mega-bits per second

4.Modular design construction

Analysising spacecraft construction and capabilities, we relized that a whole satellite could be divided into several subsystems: payload, structure attitude control ,TT&C., power ,propulsion and thermal system, etc . Except payload system ,the others are small

satellite's common service segments. So the small satellite
subsystem could be designed available off-the-shelf
components. The result is small satellite designed three
modules:payload module , common service module and attitude
control module. A basic small satellite should be composedof
the three modules. The different small satellite could be
comprised of different standard modules option by mission
requirements.

These modules are designed independently . Each
module has standard electric and mechanical joints that
makes a convenience of modules integration.

4.1 Payload Module

The payload module buses the customer payloads.
Its boxed dimensions of module bus depended on specific
payload requirements.There are three versions to selsect.

(1) payloads mass under 50 kg:
boxed dimensions: 500mm x 500mm x H mm (H = 300mm) ;

(2) payload mass from 50 to 100 kg:
boxed dimensions: 500mm x 500mm x H mm (H = 400mm);

(3) payload mass from 100 to 150 kg:
boxed dimensions: 500mm x 500mm x H mm (H = 500mm):
These standard modules aft frame mounted with the
fore frame of common service module's , and have general
electric and mechanical joints .

Certainly, the customer also can prepare their
unatantard payload bus independently to the other module.
But theelectric and mechanical joints must be stantard , and
connected to the common service stantard module. Therefore,
could make the payload module design flexibly.

4.2 Attitude Control Module

The attitude control module provides the small
satellite with the means to control the spacecraft attitude
in all. The attitude control subsystem option
is determined by specific requirement accuracy of payload
spaceflight mission.The module option directly influenced
module' complication. There are four versions to select.

(1) Gravity gradient modules.

The module boxed dimensions: 500mm x 500mm x H mm(H=
250mm)

Adotping a gradient stabilitial boom, attitude
determination sensors and damper libration. The gravity
graient stabilization boom is aretractable rod. Before
operation the boom retracted.Full lengeth of boom is about
2. 0 m. This module could achieve stability control
accurate within 5.0 degrees.

(2) Spin stabilized Module

The module boxed dimension:500mm x 500mm x H(H =250mm)

This module adopted magnetix torquer, 2 horizon scanner,2 sun sensors, nutation damper and anhydrous hydrazine propulsion system.

this module could achieve attitude stability accuracy within 1.0 degrees.

(3)Three axis stabilization Module I

The module boxed dimensions :500mm x 500mm x H mm(H=250mm)

This module offers customer high accurate of attitude stabilization. Adopting deviation momentum wheel system. The system is comprised of a reaction wheel ,a ststional earth horizon scanner,and a couple of magnetic torquing with mounted crosscut position. Although called deviation momentum wheel system, actually the system belongs toa double spin stabilization system.

Spin body not satellite but momentum wheel. So it had features of high accurate ,simple and relization. Attitude control module controled by common service module through general joints. The onboard computer received the attitude message to dual data with preposed attitude algorithm, convenience to catching initial attitudes, nutation damping and momentum wheel discharging load,to achieve the attitude control. The attitude accurate within 0.5 degrees. This module I could not select propulsion system.

(4) Three axis stabilization module II

Simplar to Module I. The boxed dimensions:

500mm x 500mm x H mm (H= 500mm);

This module add a anhydrous hydrazine propulsion system. A variety of application as requirements, such as :orbit munevour and adjust or three axis attitude control. The propulsion system is comprised of surface tension tank ,12 thrusters and so on. The tank could hold 20 to 60 kg as selected. Thrusters are available in three sizes: 1 N, 2N, 5N of thrust.The impulse up to 2971 m/s. The system could offer about 700 m/s delta V to satellites. The propulsion system controled by common service module.and the alternate ACS altered operation controled by ground ststion.

Attitude control module fore frame connected with common service module, also has standard electric and methanial joints.

4.3 Common Service Module

Common service module is small satellite control centre. Spacecraft's subsystems including: onboard computer,power system ,TT&C. system, and thermal system ,all located in the module. Most electrical equipments mounted in structure shell of the module.

The module boxed dimensions: 500mm x 500mm x Hmm (H=250mm);

Module bus aft and fore frame connected with attitude controlmodule and payload module. Both have standard electric and mechanial joints.

The subsystems inside common service module detailsas follow:

(1) control system

satellite control system adopted two general proposed 16 bit microprocessor,alternate each other. data storge upto 16 megabytes, and its data rates up to 2.0 mega-bit per second. System adopted "onboardstantard general control software" which offered by shanghai bureau ofastronautics MAI.P.R.C.

the system offer payload a variety range of capabilities suchas data dual, program control and elemetry data transfers.

(2) Power system

This system is conprised of solar array panels , Ni--Cd battarys, power wastager,shunting distributer and voltagedivider, etc.

a. solar panels. adopting 2 or 4 boards of panels. The solar panels folding beside bus shell. The power system could offer 180 or 360 w--hs power. Such power capabilty is sufficient to support the satellite and payload and Ni--Cd restorged batterys .

b.Ni--Cd batteries

Ensuring adequate reserve, long useful life and highrelization, adopted teo groups Ni--Cd batteries with parallel design to alternate operation. Discharged depth down to 12 percent.

Base board of solar panel is made of carbon fibre boards for preeing aluminium honeycomb glued together. and theframe material alsousing carbon fibre to reduce panel's mass.

(3) TT&C. system

TT& C. system is comprised of received antenna, telemetry receiver,commanding decipherer and dual frequency transmiter. It performs processing tasks as follows:

* take off the folding solar panels;
* control onboard subsystem opening or shutting;
* change the alternate subsystem equipments and alter operation situation.
* control spacecraft orbit maneuver or orbit adjust.

TT&C. system transmit message with two mothods: actually telemetry and delay telemetry. The program--control by onboard computer.

Common service module is small satellite's centre bus. customer could adjust several optional equipments accoding to requirements.

4.4 Structure design

Small satellite's form selected hexahedron version. The resason as follow:

* structure shell simple, install equipments conveniently ;
* speciafic suited to install folding solar panels.
* structure symmetrizable,easily control movement inertia and centre of mass.
* inherit past versions of satellites design and manufacture abundantly experiments .

Structure material general uses Alum-alloy and carbon fibre compound which stronger intensive.

The spacecraft structure shell and subsystem component are designed to endures that worst of all known launch environments, and will be compatible with Chinese or the others country's launch vehicles.

4.5 Thermal Design

Adopting passive temperature control subsystem , module designed isothermly. The objective is to keep the spacecraft inside range of temperatures from −5 to +35 C. degrees. This thermal subsystem minimizes power and mass.

5. Small satellite basic modules configuration

According to conception of small satellite modular design,offers several basic modules configuration as follow:

5.1 Gravity gradient model

Fig.1 shows the model.

Adopting two boards of non-steerable solar panels. The attitude control accurates within 5.0 degrees. This small satellite model more likely to operate at about 1000 km circular orbit or mini-elliptic orbit.

5.2 Spin stabilized model

fig.2 shows the spin stabilized model.

Adopting four boards of steerable solar panels.
Attitude control accurate within 1.0 degrees. For
this version of model ,the more higher orbital altittude is ,
the more exact spin stabilized attitude within.

5.3 Three axis stabilization model I, II

Fig.3 shows the three axis stabilization model.

Adopting Four boards of steerable solar panels.
Version II adding a propulsion system , so offers great

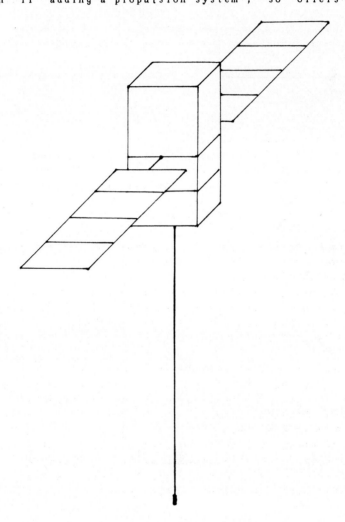

Fig. 1 Gravity gradient model

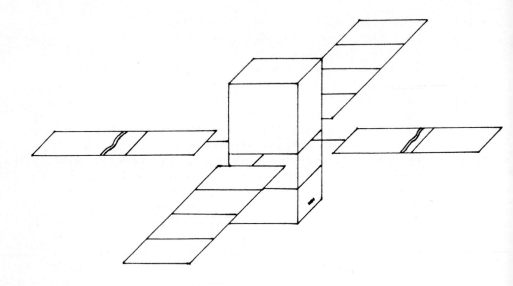

Fig. 2 Spin stabilized model

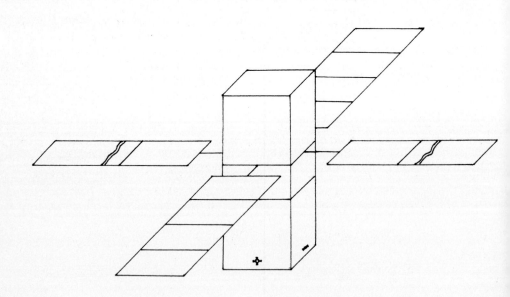

Fig.3 Three axis stabilization model

capiability of orbit adjustment and manuvourment.
Attitude control accurate within 0.5 degrees.

* According to a variety range of payload mass from 50 to 150 kg, The payload module's height dimensions could be selected .

6. Launch Services

The P.R.china has capability to support launching small satellites. The Chinese launch vehicle versions might be LM--2, LM--3 and LM--4 .The launching methods could be adopted two kinds: piggyback launching and Multi--satellites simultaneous launching. The Long Match 4 maybe suit for the modular small satellite launching.

Long Match 4 is a three stages launch vehicle with N_2O_4 / UDMH propellant combination, with good performance, hign reliability and reasonable launch service price.

Fig.4 shows the payload capability of LM--4.

According to requirements of customers, LM--4 could also offer multi-satellites simultaneous Launching services. By limited fairing volume, five modlar small satellites stacked together could be launched into orbit. The LM--4 launch vehicle could distribute these satellites into their demanded location on the same orbit.

7. Application Prospect

It is a variety range of application for small satellites . Many countries such as United States, U.K., Janpan, France and the fore Soviet union have been using small satellites to research and application in military , civil user and science fields, such as:Uosat plan university of surrey U.K., iridium system motolar company U.S., coscon system fore Soviet union ,and so on.

According to Chinese situation ,we estimate that the

Payload mass

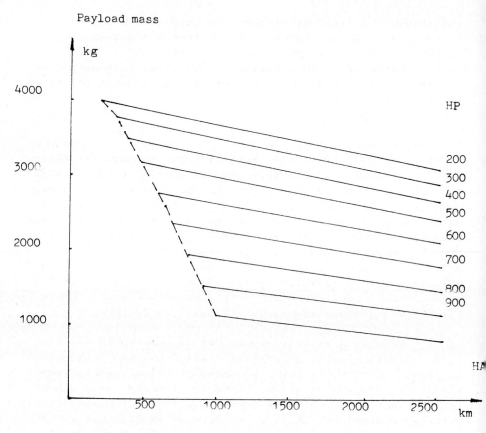

HA: Apogee height   HP: Perigee height

Fig. 4 Payload Capability

requirement of application would be steaibly increased in follow fields: In military field, an urgent needs of deploy a kinds of special purposed advanced small satellites for telecommination, navigative location and commanding deploying to suit with future modern wars. In civil user fields : telecommination, telepost, education, natural disaster prediction and relief,etc , small satellites also be very useful. In addition, a small satellite system suits for a wide range of space scientific reseach and experiment applications , such as: sun monite including sunspot group, solar flare eruption and sun active level monite, atmosphere density measurement, and space enviorment measurement , test, spericially about space radiation enviorment and effects which influenced spacecraft operation useful life. Certainly,small satellites would also be used in other sides.

8.Conclusion

Small satellites are useful.But a low cost , simple engneering and suitable to launching of small satellite could be accepted by customers, this is a developing orient ion and existence premiss of The small satellite .

This paper introduces a kinds of small satellite modular architecture, which is based on systemically analy- sising function of small satellites, utilizing the modules, the customer can select the capability required for a specific application. We believes modular design and produce adopted this methods ,will greatly reduce the total small satellite system price,and also offer the customers a change, the application prospect is bright.#

SYNTHESE DE LA SESSION
ARCHITECTURE SATELLITE

Pas de concept d'architecture révolutionnaire, mais intérêt d'une architecture modulaire et adaptable.

Besoins d'une méthodologie de conception appropriée pour satisfaire un objectif fondamental qui est la maîtrise des coûts :

– utilisation des techniques d'analyse de la valeur dès le début du programme,

– équipe projet intégrée et pluridisciplinaire travaillant en un lieu unique,

– durée du programme limitée (environ 2 ans),

– aspects contractuels pas trop rigides.

Choix techniques appropriés :

– technologies simples, éprouvées,

– politique qualité adaptée, basée sur la maîtrise des risques : qualité juste nécessaire,

– standards d'interfaces simples et adaptés.

SYNTHESIS OF THE SESSION
SATELLITE ARCHITECTURE

No revolutionary architectural concept but interest of modular, adaptable architecture.

Need for suitable design methods to meet a fundamental objective – keeping costs under control:

– *use of value analysis techniques from the start of the programme;*
– *integrated, multidisciplinary project team working at a single location;*
– *limited programme duration (about 2 years);*
– *contractual aspects not too inflexible.*

Appropriate technical choices:

– *simple, proven technologies;*
– *right quality policy based on risk control: just sufficient quality;*
– *simple, appropriate interface standards.*

SESSION VIII

TECHNOLOGIE
DES SOUS-SYSTEMES

SUBSYSTEMS TECHNOLOGY

ARSENE GaAs SOLAR ARRAY

L. BRAMBILLA, A. CAON, R.CONTINI, G. D'ACCOLTI, E. ROSSI,
G. VERZENI   - FIAR Spa -
B. BOLLANI, C. FLORES, F. PALETTA, D. PASSONI, A. TOSONI,
- CISE Spa -
E. RAPP - CNES -
F. VIOLA - ASI -

ABSTRACT

This paper presents the GaAs solar array of ARSENE, a radio-amateur spin stabilized spacecraft, made by CNES, that will be
placed in an equatorial orbit (20000-36000 Km) by ARIANE 4
launcher, in September 1992.
The solar array was electrically designed and manufactured by
FIAR utilizing the typical LPE GaAs solar cells, produced by
CISE; the above mentioned activities were coordinated and funded
by ASI.
The solar array consists of 6 body mounted solar panels providing a BOL electrical output of 183W at the conditions of AMØ
and 25°C, with an overall active area of 0.8 m^2; each panel
structure, manufactured by AEROSPATIALE, comprises of an Aluminum honeycomb substrate with Aluminum skins, insulated on the active area.
A wide testing activity was carried out for the qualification
and acceptance of the ARSENE solar array.
An engineering solar panel was successfully submitted to the
qualification tests including thermal vacuum, thermal shocks and
acoustic noise.
The flight units were successfully submitted to the thermal vacuum test; the acceptance tests will conclude with the rotational,
acoustic and vibration tests to be performed at satellite level.

1. INTRODUCTION

The ARSENE satellite represents an important novelty from a technological point of view: it is the first satellite entirely powered by an European GaAs solar array. The electrical network,
mainly composed by 986 2x4 cm^2 GaAs solar cells and 58 2x2
cm^2 planar Silicon blocking diodes, was designed and assembled
by FIAR on the six Aluminum honeycomb panels manufactured by
Aerospatiale.
About 1350 2x4 cm^2 GaAs solar cells, having an average AMØ
efficiency of 17.5%, dedicated to the ARSENE flight and engineering panels, were manufactured by CISE, in a very short time period, using a high capacity Liquid Phase Epitaxy (LPE) system.
The above mentioned activities as well as the GaAs solar panels
qualification and acceptance tests were successfully carried out
in the period August '91-February '92.
The GaAs solar array of ARSENE allows to demonstrate two important points:

- the CISE solar cells and FIAR module technology constitute realistic space approved material and technology applications;
- the FIAR and CISE production capability is good enough to satisfy any feasibility requirements concerning the main power generating solar array of mini satellites.

The achievement of these goals should contribute to win the general reticence in switching from Si to GaAs, taking into account that the intrinsic advantages of GaAs over Si solar cells (higher efficiency and greater thermal and electron/proton radiation resistance) are well known.

2. SPACECRAFT DESIGN SUMMARY

A summary of the main spacecraft design features is shown in Table 1.
The shape of ARSENE is hexaedric with 6 solar panels mounted on its body (see fig. 1).
The main payload is formed by radio-amateur repeaters operating in VHF, UHF and 2,4 GHz bands during the 5 years mission.
The launch is foreseen by September 1992 on ARIANE 4 carrier.

TABLE 1

- Stabilization	:	Spin - 60 Rpm
- Attitude control	:	Active - with cold gas
- Lift-off mass	:	150 Kg
- Final orbit	:	elliptic-equatorial
		perigee : 20000 Km
		apogee : 36000 Km
		period : 17h 30'
		inclination : $0°$
- Life duration	:	5 years
- Power requirement	:	GaAs body-mounted panels
		42W EOL at 25.5V
- Launch	:	ARIANE 4 - September '92

3. SOLAR ARRAY DESIGN & PREDICTED POWER OUTPUT

The solar array is composed by 6 body mounted solar panels with the following dimensions:
- 5 panels 612 x 352 mm^2
  (available area for solar module : 588 x 328 mm^2)
- 1 panel 612 x 272 mm^2
  (available area for solar module : 588 x 272 mm^2)
The mechanical structure of each panel comprises of a 14.6 mm thick aluminum honeycomb substrate with 0.4 mm thick aluminum skins; the active face sheet is covered with a 50 um thick dielectric insulating (KAPTON) material.
Each panel includes the holes dedicated to the panel fixing to the satellite, the protection cover fixing and the wiring feed through.
The solar array electrical design was carried out taking into account the mission characteristics, the electrical requirements and on the basis of the CISE GaAs solar cells characteristics detailed in the next chapter.
The solar array electrical requirements are summarized herebelow:

- EOL EQX power   : 42W at 25.5
- Bus voltage   : 25.5 - 26.4V obtained by a shunt regu-
                           lator, using a linear (dissipative)
                           concept.
- Each string protected by blocking diode.
- Each panel grounded through bleeder resistors.
- Maximum difference of the number of strings assembled on sub-
  strate panels: 1 string

On the basis of the mission parameters and GaAs cell characteristics, the following sizing and degradation factors were considered:

- Illumination intensity : autumn EQX
- Sun pointing offset   : 5°
- Radiation   : 1 MeV equivalent fluence of about
                            $2E14$ c/cm^2
- UV/Micrometeorites
- EOL operative temperat. : 8°C
- Non operating temperat. : 18°C
- Calibration
- Assembly/mismatch
- Configuration control   : $1/\pi$
- Cosine deviation law
- Random failure
- Panel wiring/blocking diode voltage losses.

Concerning the above described factors, the I-V characteristics
of an ARSENE typical LPE GaAs solar cells (efficiency of 17.5%
with an area of 8.1 cm^2) were predicted for the B.O.L. in orbit conditions and the EOL mission conditions by means of a design computer tool.
In fig. 2, the I-V predicted characteristics of the GaAs cell
has been plotted; the maximum power and working points have been
specified.
As shown in fig. 2 the EOL cell working point was chosen at 780
mV corresponding to the load current of 181 mA.
In this hypothesis the solar array electrical requirements were
met with an electrical network composed by 29 parallel connected
strings of 34 series connected GaAs solar cells: each large panel (GS1 .... GS5) embodies 5 strings and the small one 4 strings.

4. GaAs SOLAR CELLS MANUFACTURING

The basic structure of the GaAs cells is reported in figure 3.
It is a simplified structure in which only a GaAlAs layer, beryl-
lium-doped is deposited on a high quality GaAs substrate n- type
using a high-capacity LPE (Liquuid Phase Epitaxy) system.
The p-n junction is obtained by diffusion of beryllium from the
GaAlAs layar directly in the GaAs substrate underneath.
From this structure, the following simplified fabrication se-
quence was adopted:
* Epitaxial growth
* anti-reflection coating (ARC) evaporation
* AuGe back contact evaporation and alloying
* grid definition using photolithography
* ARC etching
* GaAlAs etching
* Palladium deposition

* Ag thickening
* Cell cutting.
About 1600 cells were produced and 1340 cells were selected according to the procurement specification.
The cells showing cosmetic defects, cracks and poor electrical
performances represented less than 20% of the whole production.
The yield was considered quite accetable.
The efficiencies of all cells are in the range 17-19%, the
avarage efficiency is 17.7% (AM0). Figg. 4,5,6 show the distribution of short circuit current, open circuit voltage and efficiencies of one thousand cells.

5. SOLAR PANELS ASSEMBLY AND TESTING

5.1 Components and Technology

The solar array was realized by FIAR by means of soldering technology using silver out of plane stress relief loop interconnec-
tor and bus bar for the cell and string connections.
The GaAs solar cells were protected with 125 μm thick CMX
coverglasses using the RTVS695 gluing resine.
The photovoltaic module was laid down onto the panel substrate
by means of the RTVS691 resin; each string was protected by two
2 x 2 cm^2 silicon planar blocking diodes.
Different thermistors for the temperature control and bleeder resistors for the panel grounding were fixed to the flight units.

5.2 E.M. Panel Assembly & Testing

The E.M. was realized assembling 72 GaAs solar cells, 5 diodes
and 1 thermistor, onto the dielectric insulating layer (Kapton)
covering the Aluminum skin, in such a way to test all the critical positions of the integration on the panel.
In particular the cells were disposed in 3 strings, one of which
perfectly representative of those composing the flight panels.
The layout of the panel is shown in fig. 7.
Electrical measurements of the complete strings were performed
at ESTEC laboratory using the MBB solar simulator calibrated for
AMØ conditions, 25°C.
The E.M. panel so assembled was submitted to the following tests:
- insulation resistance at 100 V
- acoustic test (qualification level of ARIANE 4 launch)
- thermal vacuum test (10 cycles; -50/+30°C)
- thermal shock test (1200 cycles; -80/+30°C)
in order to verify the suitability of the electrical design and
the good panel performance for the ARSENE environmental conditions.
Before and after each environmental test, the E.M. panel was
electrically measured at AMØ, 25°C conditions and visual inspected without showing any significative electrical and mechanical degradation.

5.3 F.M. Panel Assembly & Testing

986 GaAs solar cells were dressed, and electrically characterized for the integration of the ARSENE solar array.

A screening activity was carried out in order to minimize the electrical mismatch among the cells composing the same strings; this selection was performed at the EOL voltage working point foreseen for the ARSENE mission (780 mV).
A dedicated jig was used for the string forming: 34 solar cells and 2 blocking diodes were in series connected.
Five strings of this type were integrated on each panel except for the smaller one composed by 4 strings.
The electrical network comprising of the bleeder resistors and the thermistors was connected to the main connector /RAYCHEM MTC100) of each panel.
The 6 flight panels (GS1...GS6) are shown in fig. 8.
The electrical characterization was performed using the FIAR flasher, calibrated at AMØ conditions and 25°C.
The IV curves for the small panel (GS6) and for 1 large panel (GS1) are shown in fig. 9 and fig. 10.
The electrical output of the solar array (sum of the six panels) is reported herebelow for the main parameters:
- Isc   = 6.9 A
- Voc   = 33.9 V
- Pm   = 182.6 W
- Pl(25.5V) = 171.5 W

Considering the above mentioned results and the predicted degradation in orbit (20%) as well as the $1/\pi$ geometric factor, the computed EOL power is 43.7 watt complying with the minimum requirement of 42 watt at the bus voltage of 25.5V.
The flight panels were successfully submitted to the acceptance tests at FIAR laboratories.
The panel insulation resistance was tested at 100V showing a resistance values higher than 10 GOhm.
The flight units were submitted to 5 thermal vacuum cycles between +30°C and -50°C at a pressure better than 1E-6 TORR.
The electrical measurements and visual inspections performed before and after each tests showed neither electrical nor mechanical degradation.

6. CONCLUSION

The design and manufacturing activities carried out for the realization of ARSENE GaAs solar array showed the significative production capability level achieved by FIAR and CISE.
The experience and know how gained with this project will facilitate the selection of the GaAs technology for the next space project.
In particular considering small satellites, in which the photovoltaic collection area constraints are defined by the shroud dimensions, the adoption of GaAs solar cells make available more electrical power to be delivered to the payload.

ACKNOWLEDGEMENTS

The authors wish to thank Mrs. H. Mengs and J.C. Larue from ESTEC for the support on the acoustic and electrical tests.

Fig. 1: ARSENE SATELLITE.

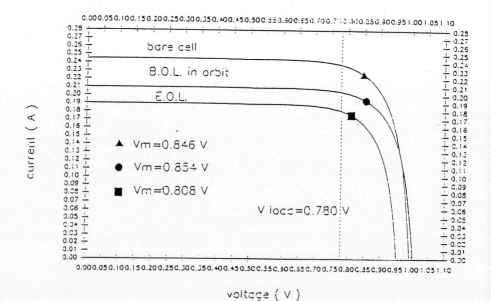

Fig. 2: GaAs CELL PREDICTED I-V CHARACTERISTIC:

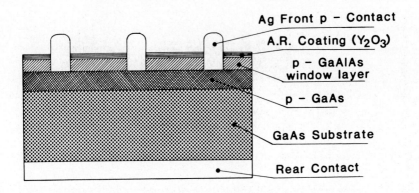

Ag Front p – Contact

A.R. Coating (Y_2O_3)

p – GaAlAs
window layer

p – GaAs

GaAs Substrate

Rear Contact

Fig. 3: GaAs SOLAR CELL STRUCTURE.

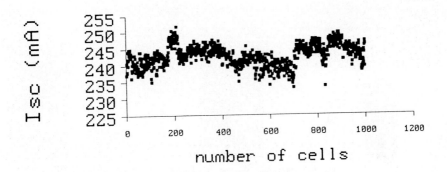

Fig. 4: Isc DISTRIBUTION FOR 1000 CELLS SAMPLE.

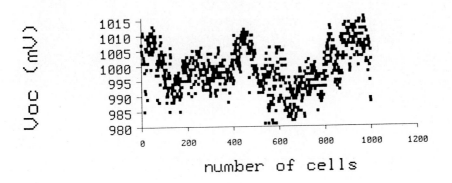

Fig. 5: Voc DISTRIBUTION FOR 1000 CELLS SAMPLE.

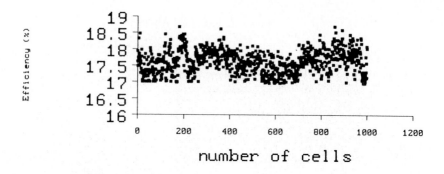

Fig. 6: EFF. DISTRIBUTION FOR 1000 CELLS SAMPLE.

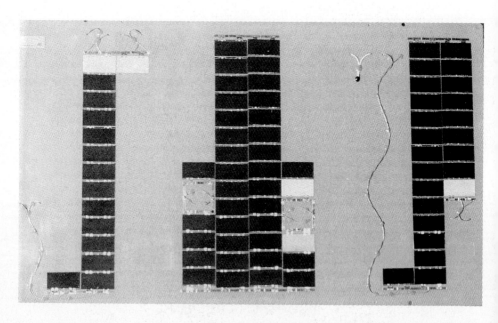

Fig. 7: E.M. ELECTRICAL LAYOUT.

Fig. 3: ARSENE FLIGHT SOLAR PANELS.

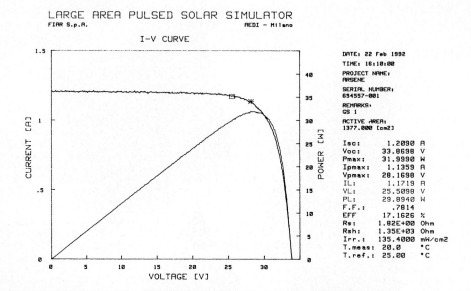

Fig. 9: GS1 LARGE PANEL ELECTRICAL MEASUREMENT.

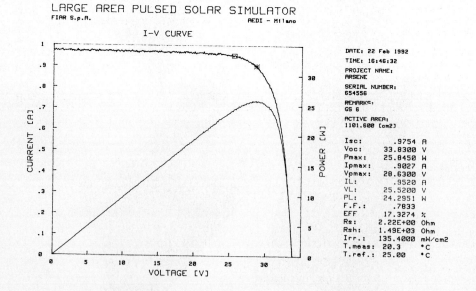

Fig. 10: GS6 SMALL PANEL ELECTRICAL MEASUREMENT.

Small Satellite Nickel-Hydrogen and Nickel-Metal Hydride Power Applications

William Dean Cook and Dwaine Coates

Eagle Picher Industries, Inc.
Joplin, Missouri, USA

ABSTRACT

Recent growth in Small Satellite technology has prompted the development of Nickel-Hydrogen (Ni-H$_2$) batteries to support this expanding market. Past development of Nickel-Hydrogen batteries has been primarily suited for the higher cost Aerospace industry and as a result has been overlooked by the Small Satellite market. This is primarily due to the cost and availability of small capacity cells. Eagle-Picher, the leader in Nickel-Hydrogen battery technology for the past 18 years, saw the need to support this market and has developed Nickel-Hydrogen batteries in the 2AH-20AH capacity range at a competitive cost, while still maintaining the long cycle life and high reliability required for this application. Development of this product has lead to a joint venture with **Orbital Sciences Corporation** to deliver a 6AH, 25 volt battery for use in the **APEX** (Advance Photovoltaic and electronic Experiment for U.S.A.F. System Command) and the **Sea Star** small satellite programs. These satellites are slated for three (3) and five (5) year LEO missions.

Nickel and silver-metal hydride batteries are being developed for aerospace applications by Eagle-Picher. Metal hydride batteries offer a number of advantages over other aerospace battery systems. Nickel-metal hydride batteries have twice the gravimetric energy density of nickel-cadmium and twice the volumetric energy density of nickel-hydrogen. Silver-metal hydride batteries have the potential of three times the energy density of nickel-metal hydride and exhibit superior charge retention characteristics. Aerospace metal hydride batteries are hermetically sealed, operate at low pressure and are prismatic in geometry. They exhibit excellent overcharge and overdischarge capability. Preliminary calorimetry data indicates superior thermal performance as compared to nickel-cadmium and nickel-hydrogen batteries. Some initial AC impedance spectroscopy work has been completed on both metal-hydrogen and metal-hydride battery systems. The objective of current programs at Eagle-Picher is to develop high energy density, long cycle life metal-hydride batteries for the aerospace market and to establish a testing database to support future applications.

1.0 INTRODUCTION

It is possible Small Satellites may become the majority rather than the minority in aerospace applications. Candidates for single purpose satellites include communications, surveillance, meteorology, and store and forward data transfer to name a few. Assuming a mission from 3-5 years in length (5840 cycles per year LEO) 17,520 cycles to a possible 29,200 cycles are required to support these systems. To date only Ni-H$_2$ battery systems can reliably support these stringent requirements and maintain an efficient depth-of-discharge (DOD).

Small Satellite producers have typically used Ni-Cd batteries with a sacrifice in DOD and cycle life. The Small Satellite market clearly expressed a need for a battery technology that could provide long cycle life, a reasonable DOD and a competitive price.

Eagle Picher, recognizing this need, started development of a 6.4 cm (2.5 inch) diameter Ni-H$_2$ cell in a capacity range from 2-20 AH to support the Small Satellite market. Along with this design, the concept of Common Pressure Vessel, "CPV", was also introduced to further enhance the cell specifications. These activities, in addition to major cost reductions, have lead to a proven design with over 100 modules built and tested to date. Part of these 100 modules were qualified and delivered to Orbital Sciences Corporation for system testing with 40 additional flight cells in process for the **APEX** and **Sea Star** small satellite programs.

2.0 CELL DESIGN

The cell design **RNHC-6-1** consists of a standard off the shelf stainless steel vessel (304L) with a dual stack assembly (CPV). See Figure 1 for cell drawing. The dual stack assembly is configured in a familiar ''pineapple stack'' configuration consisting of positive plates made of nickel slurry and the negative plates manufactured with a photo etched nickel substrate coated with a thin layer of platinum/teflon slurry. The separator utilized is Zircar with alternate separators under investigation for added cost reduction. The plate leads are directed through the cell via slots in the center core and are connected to each terminal via TIG welding. The

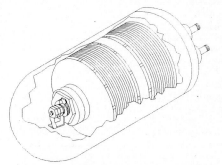

Figure 1. Cutaway illustration of an RNHC-6-1 Common Pressure Vessel (CPV) Nickel-Hydrogen Cell.

cell interconnect is also routed through the center core and TIG welded at the end. All cell terminals are routed through the bottom end plate thus allowing all intricate machining to be contained in the base plate. The terminals have compression seals similar to present Ni-H$_2$ cells but utilize a proven, cost effective boss design.

3.0 CELL DESIGN VERIFICATION

3.1 Proof Pressure

All cells are pressurized to 1.5 times the MEOP per MIL-STD-1522A with helium while submerged in water to detect any signs of leaks. Test results also indicate the cell structure remains in specification with no significant deformation of the vessel.

3.2 Cycle Test

Additional tests were performed to verify the vessel's ability to support the required large number of cycles. A sample vessel, less the cell stack, was filled with oil and then subjected to the pressure extremes expected during normal cycle operation. Testing was successfully conducted for more than 40K cycles. Future design features will be incorporated to further improvements to this capability.

3.3 Burst Test

To insure an adequate vessel safety factor, burst pressure tests were conducted utilizing vessel and the design detailed in Figure 1 (less the stack). The vessel was filled with oil and pressure applied until a rupture occurred. Test results indicate the vessel is capable of handling pressure up to 3,500 psi. This provides ample safety factor assuming a cell working pressure of 500 PSI. This test may also be conducted after completion of the cycle test. For the Orbital Sciences program 27,000 pressure cycles were completed on the vessel and then the burst test conducted. The test results indicate the vessel is capable of 2,600 PSIG after 27,000 cycles.

3.4 Vibration Test

Vibration tests were conducted on a single cell to the levels shown in Figure 2 with no anomalies demonstrated during or after the test.

3.5 Fracture Mechanics Analysis:

This analysis was performed by Aerospace Corporation to insure a leak before burst design to satisfy MIL-STD-1522A.

3.6 Performance Test:

Performance tests were conducted at 0°, 10°, and 20°C at the cell level (C/10 charge and a C/2 discharge). The results are detailed in Figures 3 and 4.

Technical Data for RNHC-6-1:

Rated Capacity	6 AH
Nominal Voltage	2.5 Volts
Cell Mass	633 Grams
Diameter	6.48 cm
Length	17.15 cm
Capacity to 2.0 v @ 10°C	7.1 AH
Specific Energy	28 WH/KG
Energy Density	39.2 WH/L
Operating Pressure	400 PSI
Safety Factor	5/1 Ratio
Cell Case	304L SS
Separator	Zircar
Positive Electrode	Slurry
Energy Density	39.2 WH/L
Operating Pressure	400 PSI
Safety Factor	5/1 Ratio
Cell Case	304L SS
Separator	Zircar
Positive Electrode	Slurry

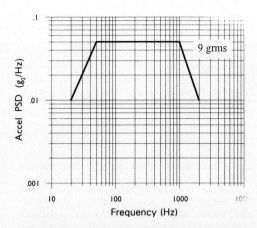

Figure 2. Component Level Random Vibration Levels

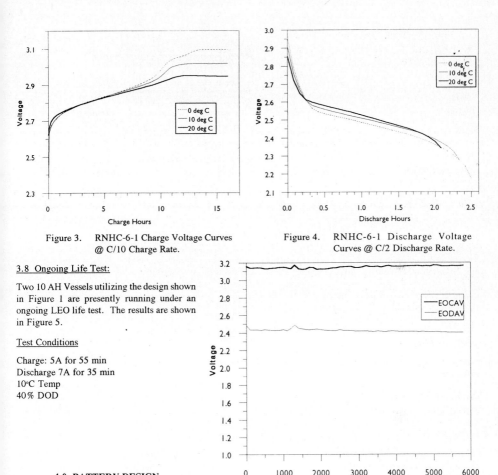

Figure 3.   RNHC-6-1 Charge Voltage Curves @ C/10 Charge Rate.

Figure 4.   RNHC-6-1 Discharge Voltage Curves @ C/2 Discharge Rate.

3.8 Ongoing Life Test:

Two 10 AH Vessels utilizing the design shown in Figure 1 are presently running under an ongoing LEO life test. The results are shown in Figure 5.

Test Conditions

Charge: 5A for 55 min
Discharge 7A for 35 min
10°C Temp
40% DOD

Figure 5.   RNHC-10-1 LEO Life Test Chart.

4.0 BATTERY DESIGN

The SAR-10027 battery consists of 10 vessels mounted to an aluminum base plate via a two piece aluminum sleeve positioned directly over the stack area (see Figure 6). This sleeve not only provides physical mounting support but also provides the thermal path for heat removal. The cell is isolated from the sleeve with a Chotherm insulator to provide a first degree of isolation protection. The sleeves are mounted to a thin aluminum base plate. This base plate is mounted to the mechanical structure located in the satellite. Utilizing heaters and satellite position, the battery temperature is maintained between -5°C to 20°C.

This battery design utilizes two strain gauge circuits mounted directly to the cell outside wall. The gages are utilized to provide a direct indication of the pressure inside the cell. Due to the unique property associated with Ni-H$_2$ cells, pressure at the end of charge levels off when a cell reaches full capacity. This provides an excellent indicator for state of charge.

The battery also contains heater strips affixed to the bottom of the battery base plate and thermistors attached to the cell casing.

All connections to the battery are made via two connectors.

4.1 Battery Qualification Testing

In addition to the normal capacity and electrical checks, all batteries are vibrated to the levels shown in Figure 2. Thermal/ Vacuum testing is also preformed on each battery for 120 hours at temperature cycles from -5°C to 20°C. Battery testing results were not available at the time of this writing.

Technical Data for SAR-10027 Battery

Rated Capacity .... 6 AH
Nominal Capacity .... 25.0 Volts
Battery Mass 8467g
Length .... 40.6 cm
Width .... 39.4 cm
Height .... 8.3 cm
Capacity to 2.0 V @ 10°C .... 7.1 AH
Specific Energy .... 21.20 Wh/Kg
Energy Density .... 13.5 Wh/l
Vibration .... 9.0 Grms
Thermal/Vacuum .... 120 hr
Thermistors .... 2 each
Heaters .... 2 each
Electrical Isolation .... Two level

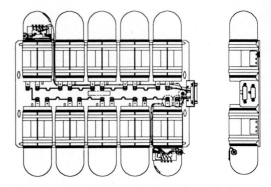

Figure 6.   SAR-10027 Nickel-Hydrogen Battery Outline

5.0 NICKEL-METAL HYDRIDE BATTERIES

Nickel-hydrogen (Ni-H$_2$) batteries have almost exclusively replaced aerospace nickel-cadmium (Ni-Cd) batteries in geosynchronous (GEO) and low-earth-orbit (LEO) communications and surveillance satellites. There is a growing market for smaller, lower cost satellites which require higher energy density power sources than aerospace Ni-Cd at a lower cost than Ni-H$_2$. These include small LEO satellites with scientific payloads, tactical military satellites and satellite constellation programs such as Iridium and Brilliant Pebbles. Small satellites typically do not have the spacecraft volume or the budget required for Ni-H$_2$ batteries. Ni-Cd's do not have adequate energy density and have other problems such as overcharge capability and memory effect. Metal hydride batteries provide the ideal solution for these applications. Some preliminary information regarding the development of Ni-MH batteries for aerospace applications has been previously published jointly by Eagle- Picher Industries, Inc. (EPI) and Ovonic Battery Company (OBC) (1).

Nickel-metal hydride (Ni-MH) batteries provide twice the gravimetric energy density of aerospace Ni-Cd's and twice the volumetric energy density of space Ni-H$_2$. Projected cost is less than aerospace Ni-Cd and much less than Ni-H$_2$. Silver-metal hydride (Ag-MH) batteries offer the potential of three times the energy density of Ni-MH. Metal hydride batteries are hermetically sealed, operate at low pressure and are prismatic in geometry. They have excellent overcharge and overdischarge characteristics. Several companies are currently entering the commercial Ni-MH market but cells are not yet generally available.

6.0 HYDRIDE ELECTRODE MATERIALS

Hydrides are a large class of chemical compounds including both metallic and non-metallic species. Metallic hydrides are of primary interest as potential rechargeable battery electrode materials. Various metals and alloys are known to reversibly store relatively large quantities of hydrogen under a variety of conditions. There are two basic hydrogen storage systems currently under study for battery application. These are the AB2 type alloys such as iron-titanium and nickel-titanium and the AB5 type compounds such as lanthanum-nickel and mischmetal-nickel. The nickel-titanium system has undergone extensive development by the Ovonic Battery Company (2, 3). Additional elements such as zirconium, vanadium and chromium are used as modifiers to enhance the performance and cycle life of the basic nickel-titanium alloy. Most of this work has been done in the context of commercial batteries such as "C" and "AA" size cells.

The AB5 type rare earth containing alloys have been extensively investigated. These compounds are of the basic CaCu$_5$ structure. The study of LaNi$_5$ for battery applications goes back to the early seventies. The material was studied both as a possible hydride electrode material (4,5) and as a means of hydrogen storage to reduce the operating pressure in a standard nickel-hydrogen cell (6,7). It was determined that modification of the basic rare earth-nickel alloys by partially substituting other elements provided materials with greatly enhanced performance as a reversible battery electrode. A great deal of work has been done in this area (8) and many patents have been issued (9,10,11,12). There has also been considerable interest in using mischmetal-nickel alloys as battery electrode materials (13,14).

Mischmetal is an indeterminate mixture of rare earth elements containing primarily lanthanum, cerium, neodymium and praseodymium. Other rare earths typically make up less than 5 per cent of the total. The relative composition is dependent on the source of the ore.

Figure 7 shows comparative energy density data for three different materials. One material is a nickel-titanium based alloy (Ni-Ti), one is a rare earth based custom alloy (RE) and the third is a mischmetal-nickel alloy (MM-Ni). The nickel-titanium material was obtained from Ovonics, the mischmetal-nickel alloy was procured from Treibacher-Austria and the custom alloy was prepared by the Fine Inorganic Chemicals Division of Rhone-Poulenc. All three are in the 200-250 milliampere-hour per gram energy density range.

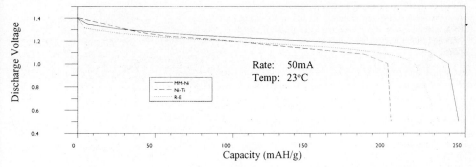

Figure 7.   Metal Hydride Energy Density

6.1 Electrode Preparation

Electrodes can be prepared by a variety of methods such as sintering, pasting, screening, pressing and combinations thereof. Binders may or may not be used depending on the fabrication method. Suitable binders for hydride electrodes include polytetrafluoroethylene (PTFE), latex, poly M, polyethylene-oxide, methylcellulose and others. Potential substrates include nickel wire mesh, non-woven nickel fiber, expanded nickel metal, microperforated nickel foil and nickel foam. Variables, such as thickness and porosity, within each type of substrate can also be considered. Sintering conditions such as time, temperature and atmosphere composition can be varied. Treatment of the powder prior to electrode fabrication can also be important. Parameters such as mesh size and powder additives can affect electrode performance. Alloy composition may also interact with the electrode fabrication variables to affect relative performance. Evaluation of all possible combinations of all the possible variables is virtually intractable. However, suitable electrodes can be prepared by judicious selection of the appropriate variables based on past experience.

7.0 CELL DESIGN

A conservative approach to cell design is necessary to meet the rigorous requirements of the aerospace industry and to minimize potential technical risk. Metal hydride aerospace cell designs have been based primarily on existing flight-proven aerospace Ni-Cd cell designs. The low pressure operation of the metal hydride system allows cells to be constructed using prismatic geometry cell containers. This method of construction is an enormous advantage over the nickel-hydrogen system which has a large number of complex internal parts. The prismatic metal hydride cell contains only electrodes, separation, electrolyte, tabs and terminals. This simplicity of design makes the cell more cost effective to produce and more reliable in operation. Aerospace applications require abusive environmental testing such as shock and random and sinusoidal vibration. This testing simulates the rigors of the launch environment. A flat-plate, prismatic cell has exceptional resistance to these types of stress compared to a flight Ni-H$_2$ cell. The flat- plate design also offers thermal advantages over a cylindrical cell. Heat is transferred to the cell case from the electrode stack in a more efficient manner in a prismatic cell. This heat can then be removed from the battery through conduction to a radiator plate. A typical aerospace design prismatic cell is shown in Figure 8.

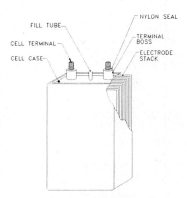

Figure 8.   Prismatic Aerospace Nickel-Metal Hydride Cell Design.

Prismatic cells have been built and tested ranging from 4 ampere-hours to 180 ampere-hours. Commercial or aerospace nickel electrodes can be used in the cell depending on the application and the cycle life required. Cells have been built and tested using both as well as fiber nickel electrodes. The hydride electrode can be a nickel-titanium based alloy such as that patented by OBC or a variety of other hydride-forming materials such as mischmetal or other rare earth alloys. A number of commercial Ni-Cd type separators are compatible with the system. Separator selection depends on application and cycle life. Aerospace Ni-Cd and Ni-H$_2$ separators can be used in premium applications.

8.0 BATTERY DESIGN

A nickel-metal hydride cell develops about 1.25 volts at the midpoint of discharge which is the same as Ni-Cd or Ni-H$_2$. Most applications require higher voltages which necessitates connecting multiple cells electrically in series. Normally the cells are sized to satisfy the ampere-hour requirement of the battery to eliminate the problems associated with connecting multiple cells in parallel. A prototype aerospace Ni-MH battery is shown in Figure 9. This battery has been built and tested at Eagle-Picher. The battery contains ten cells connected in series. Each cell is a nominal 10.0 AH. Battery output is therefore 10 AH at a nominal 12.0 volts. Battery construction is straightforward and simple. Connectors, wiring, instrumentation and on-board electronics are usually dictated by the application and can be integrated into the design as required.

Another potential Ni-MH battery design for aerospace applications is shown in Figure 10. This battery was integrated and tested for potential small satellite applications. In this design several commercial cylindrical "C" size Ni-MH cells have been packaged into a flight configuration aerospace battery. The cells are potted together using silicone RTV and may be further restrained by endplates if the application requires. This type of battery has utility in the small satellite industry where the cost and/or life expectancy of the spacecraft does not warrant the cost of full-fledged aerospace batteries. There are currently several small satellites flying commercial Ni-Cd cells including two Defense Advanced Research Projects Agency (DARPA) Lightsats (15).

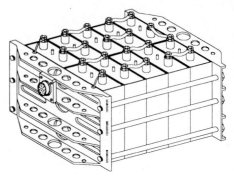

Figure 9. Prototype Nickel-Metal Hydride Aerospace Battery Design.

9.0 CELL TESTING

Prismatic aerospace quality cells have been built and tested ranging in size from 4.0 ampere-hours (AH) to 180 AH. Other designs have also been built including a 250 milliampere-hour button cell. Cells have been built containing both Ovonics material and other hydrogen storage materials. Some initial prototype prismatic aerospace cells were constructed using existing flight Ni-Cd hardware. Two different types of cells were built. One type contained heavy-loaded commercial nickel electrodes and the other contained lighter-loaded aerospace nickel electrodes manufactured on an aerospace nickel-hydrogen production line. Both cell types used Ovonics-manufactured hydrogen storage electrodes. Figure 11 shows comparative discharge profiles for these two cells as compared with a normal production aerospace Ni-Cd. The Ni-Cd cell is a nominal 2.5 AH design. Replacing the cadmium with hydride yields just over 4.0 AH for the same weight and volume. Replacing the aerospace nickel electrodes with the heavier loaded commercial electrodes brings the cell capacity above 5.0 AH in the hydride version. This direct comparison of prismatic Ni-Cd and Ni-MH shows the substantial gains in energy density possible with metal hydride batteries.

Figure 10. Nickel-Metal Hydride Alternative Battery Design.

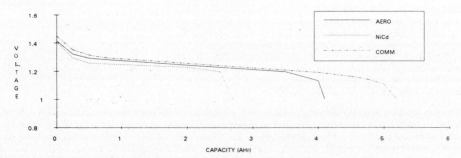

Figure 11. Nickel-Metal Hydride vs Nickel Cadmium Energy Density

Figure 12 shows the rate capability of a group of 10.0 AH prismatic aerospace cells which were subsequently integrated into a prototype aerospace battery (Figure 9). Aqueous electrochemically impregnated aerospace nickel electrodes and Ovonics alloy hydride electrodes were used in construction. Pellon 2506 aerospace grade battery separator was used. 31% aqueous potassium hydroxide with no additives was used as the electrolyte. The cells were discharged at rates from 1.0 ampere up to 30.0 amperes at room temperature. All charges were done at the 0.1C rate (1.0 ampere). Even at 30.0 amperes (a 3C rate) the cells are still achieving better than nameplate capacity. There is only 1.5 AH difference (about 12%) between

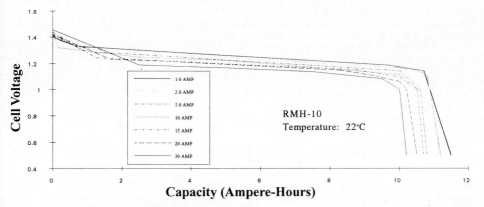

Figure 12. Nickel-Metal Hydride Aerospace Cells

the capacity obtained at 0.1C and 3.0C. There is less than a 100 mV voltage drop (about 7%) in the discharge plateau voltage between the 0.1C and the 3.0C rate. All of the discharges were done at room temperature without active cooling. Some of the observed difference in the plateau voltages is probably due to the much warmer temperatures experienced at the higher rates. The internal impedance of the entire group of cells varied from 1.8 to 1.9 milliohms measured at 1000 Hertz.

There are several cells currently on cycle life test. The test is set up on a ninety minute low-earth-orbit (LEO) cycle regime. The charge time is fixed at 55 minutes and the discharge is 35 minutes. There are about 25 cells currently on test representing several different designs and cell capacities. The discharge rate is fixed at 2.55±0.05 amperes so the depth-of-discharge (DOD) for any given cell is determined by its ampere-hour capacity. The cells are at room temperature with no active cooling. Figure 13 shows a comparison of an early cycle with a later cycle for a 4.0 AH aerospace cell. The cell contains EPI aerospace nickel electrodes and Ovonic hydride electrodes. The cell is operat-

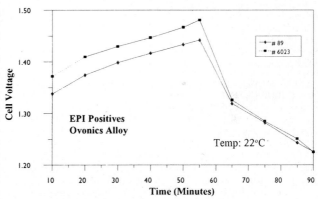

Figure 13. Nickel-Metal Hydride LEO Life Test.

ing at 37% DOD with a charge return factor of about 1.6%. This factor would be about 10% for a space nickel-hydrogen cell operating at the same DOD which attests to the greater charge efficiency of Ni-MH over Ni-H₂. The cells have completed over 6000 cycles and are performing very well. There is very little depression in the end-of-discharge voltage.

Calorimetry testing of prismatic aerospace Ni-MH cells is currently being done jointly with Boeing Aerospace in Seattle, Washington (16,17). Data has previously been generated by Boeing on Ovonics Ni-MH cylindrical "C" size cells. Preliminary results indicate that thermal performance of the Ni-MH system is much better than either Ni-Cd or Ni-H₂. The thermal data generated so far agrees well with the improved charge efficiency observed in the Ni-MH system. Figure 14 shows the heat flow characteristics and cell voltage during a charge/discharge cycle. This data was supplied by Boeing Aerospace on a cell constructed by EPI. During charging the hydride electrode material is electrochemically charged with hydrogen to form a metal hydride and there is little net heat flow at the cell level. When 100% state-of-charge is reached and oxygen evolution at the nickel electrode becomes predominant, the heat being generated by the cell increases rapidly. During discharge the hydride alloy is endothermic which decreases the net heat flow generated by the cell. The endothermic nature of the metal hydride alloy during discharge will allow a reduction in the size and weight of the spacecraft power system cooling radiators thereby increasing the overall power system energy density.

Some preliminary AC impedance spectroscopy work has been carried out on both aerospace and commercial nickel-metal hydride cells jointly between EPI and Texas Research Institute-Austin (TRI). The program also included study of the space nickel-hydrogen battery system. The study was carried out under the sponsorship of the U.S. Air Force Phillips Laboratories at Edwards Air Force Base under topic number AF91-149. A Phase I summary report has been issued (18). The primary conclusion of the study was that AC impedance spectroscopy was a valuable tool in characterizing metal hydride cells, particularly in the low frequency region below 1 Hertz. There is a systematic decrease in the Warburg (diffusion controlled) impedance at low frequencies with cell aging. Figure 15 is an Argand diagram for two similar nickel-metal hydride cells, one having 10 charge/discharge cycles and the other having 2000 cycles. There is a pronounced frequency shift of the transition point between the diffusion controlled and capacitive regions that occurs with cell aging. This effect may be due to electrode growth and changes in electrode structure that occur during cycling. Data analysis and equivalent circuit modeling is currently underway to interpret the large amount of data gathered.

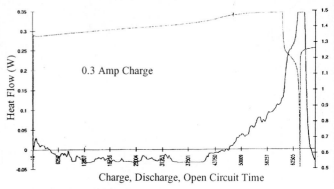

Figure 14.   Heat Flow and Voltage during 0.3 Amp Charge, 2.5 Amp Discharge and Open Circuit.

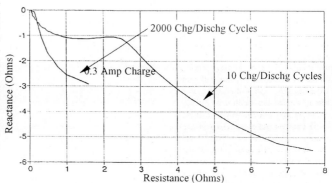

Figure 15.   ARGAND Diagram from 3 mHz to 10 Hz for two Nickel-Metal Hydride "C" Cells.

10.0 SILVER-METAL HYDRIDE BATTERIES

Testing of prismatic aerospace silver-metal hydride cells is still in the initial stages. Preliminary results indicate that a considerable increase in energy density is possible over the corresponding nickel cell. Figure 16 shows a direct comparison of the nickel and silver-hydride systems on a milliampere-hour per gram basis. Both cells were discharged at the C/4 rate at room temperature. This data reflects the inherent higher energy density of the silver electrode over the nickel electrode. The silver cell yields about three times the electrical capacity of the nickel cell. The plateau voltage is also slightly lower with the silver-hydride mid-point discharge voltage occurring at about 1.0 volt. The increase in capacity more than makes up for this decreased voltage on a watt-hour per kilogram energy density basis. Current aerospace silver-zinc cells have a cycle life of about 200 to 300 cycles. Silver-hydride would be expected to exceed this figure based on the replacement of the zinc electrode with the more stable hydride electrode. Battery wet life for aerospace silver-zinc cells is about 6 months. The wet life should also significantly increase by replacing the zinc electrode with a hydride electrode. Charge retention of the silver-metal hydride system is much better than that of the nickel-metal hydride system. Capacity retention data for open-circuit stands of up to 30 days is indicated in Figure 17. The sealed silver-metal hydride aerospace cell retains almost 80% of its original capacity even after a 30 day open-circuit stand. This is superior to the current aerospace nickel-metal hydride system. Continuing development work is planned to evaluate and improve the cycle life of the silver-metal hydride system. Silver migration is expected to be the major failure mechanism and work will be focused on developing an optimum separator system to maximize cycle life.

11.0 CONCLUSION

The **APEX** and **Sea Star** satellites both utilize two (2) SAR-10027 Batteries supplied by Eagle Picher and configure them in parallel. The anticipated depth of discharge is 30% with a wide variety of charge/discharge schemes anticipated. The **APEX** satellite has a one (1) year mission with a goal of three (3) years. The **Sea Star** satellite has a three (3) year mission with a goal of (5) five years. Both satellites will be operating in a LEO orbit at temperatures from -5°C to 20°C.

Testing of prismatic aerospace design metal hydride cells is still underway. The results to date are very promising. It is anticipated that the metal hydride chemistry will function well in aerospace applications including the more demanding

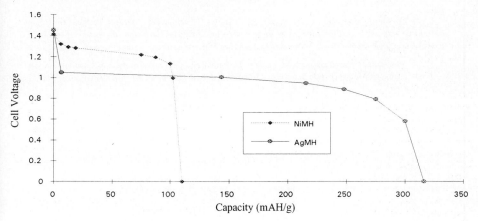

Figure 16.   Silver vs Nickel Hydride

low-earth-orbit missions. The system is ideal for the new generation of small satellites being developed for communications, surveillance and SDI programs. The Iridium and Brilliant Pebbles satellite constellation programs are prime examples. The system promises excellent performance and cycle life at a reasonable cost as compared to other aerospace systems. The metal hydride chemistry also has a much broader application base as a potential replacement for other nickel-based and sealed lead acid batteries in a variety of commercial, military and aerospace applications. The metal hydride system contains no toxic materials such as lead, cadmium or mercury. This provides enormous environmental benefits over other battery systems in terms of manufacture, disposal and recycling of spent batteries. The increased energy density of the silver-hydride system may also prove useful in premium commercial and military applications. The nickel-metal hydride system is currently being commercialized by a number of companies and is readily adaptable to military and aerospace markets as well.

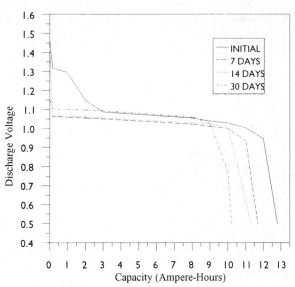

Figure 17.   Silver-Metal Hydride Capacity Retention

ACKNOWLEDGMENTS

The authors would like to thank Chris Fox for editing, desktop publishing and preparation of the manuscript. The authors would also like to thank Chris Johnson at Boeing for the nickel-metal hydride calorimetry data and Lowell Smith at Texas Research Institute-Austin for the AC impedance spectroscopy work. The authors would also like to thank Captain Alex Webster, USAF and acknowledge support of the impedance spectroscopy work by the U.S. Air Force Phillips Laboratories.

REFERENCES

(1)   J. Brill, D. Coates, P. Bemis, S. Venkatesan, M. A. Fetcenko, S. R. Ovshinsky, "Sealed Nickel-Metal Hydride Batteries for Small Satellite Applications", Fourth AIAA/USU Conference on Small Satellites, Logan, Utah August 1990

(2)   S. Venkatesan, M. Fetcenko, B. Reichman, K. C. Hong "Development of Ovonic Rechargeable Metal Hydride Batteries", Proceedings of the 24th Intersociety Energy Conversion Engineering Conference (IECEC), Washington, D.C., August 1989, pp. 1659-1664.

(3)   M. A. Fetcenko, S. Venkatesan, K. C. Hong, B. Reichman "Hydrogen Storage Materials for use in Rechargeable Ni-Metal Hydride Batteries", Proceedings of the 16th International Power Sources Symposium, 1988.

(4)   H. Ewe, E. W. Justi, K. Stephan, Energy Conversion 13, 109 (1973).

(5)   G. Bronoel, J. Sarradin, M. Bonnemay, A. Percheron, J. C. Achard, L. Schalpbach, International Journal of Hydrogen Energy 1, 251 (1976).

(6)   M. W. Earl and J. D. Dunlop, Proceedings of the 26th Power Sources Symposium, Atlantic City, N.J., June 1974.

(7)   J. D. Dunlop, M. W. Earl, G. van Ommering, U.S. Patent 3,959,018 (May 1976).

(8)   J. J. G. Willems, Phillips Journal of Research, 39, Supplement No. 1 (1984).

(9)   P. Boter, U. S. Patent 4,004,943 (January 1977).

(10)   A. Percheron, J. Achard, J. Loriers, M. Bonnemay, G. Bronoel, J. Sarradin, L. Schalpbach, U.S. Patent 4,107,405 (August 1978).

(11)   J. Willems, J. van Beek, K. Buschow, U.S. Patent 4,487,817 (December 1984).

(12)   A. Percheron, J. Achard, J. Sarradin, U.S. Patent 4,609,599 (September 1986).

(13)   U.S. Patent 4,152,145 (May 1979).

(14)   U.S. Patent 4,096,639 (June 1978).

(15)   T. Darone, P. Stiffler, R. Bonometti, B. Carter, E. Eng "Utilization of Small Commercial Grade Nickel Cadmium (Ni-Cd) Cells in Low Earth Orbit (LEO) Applications" Fourth AIAA/USU Conference on Small Satellites Logan, Utah August 1990.

(16)   D. K. Coates, C. J. Johnson, R. D. Wright, S. Venkatesan, S. Dhar, M. Fetcenko "Thermal Properties of Nickel-Metal Hydride Batteries" Fifth AIAA/USU Conference on Small Satellites, Logan, Utah August 1991.

(17)   D. Coates, 1991 NASA Aerospace Battery Workshop, Marshall Space Flight Center, Huntsville, Alabama October 1991.

(18)   R. L. Smith, A. V. Bray, D. Coates "Development of an Accelerated Life Test for Nickel Hydrogen and Nickel-Metal Hydride Batteries", USAF PL-TR-91-3105 Final Report, Phillips Laboratories, Edwards Air Force Base, January 1991.

A Power System for a Micro-satellite

Dan Olsson

Power Conditioning Section, ESTeC, Noordwijk

ABSTRACT

The European Space Agency's technical center, ESTeC, has together with Surrey Satellite Technology (SST), designed a power system for a micro-satellite.
The satellite, Space Technology Research Vehicle (STRV-1), a project of the Royal Aerospace Establishment (GB), mainly aimed at technology demonstration experiments and studies of radiation effects, is planned to be launched into Geostationary Transfer Orbit (GTO), as a Ariane ASAP passenger in 1993.
The low average solar array power (25 W) and the small volume allocation of the Power System electronics (2.8 dm^3) formed a challenge when trying to produce a failure tolerant power system.
As a result of several simplification iterations, it has been possible to accommodate a modular power electronics system, with a high degree of failure tolerance, having a mass of less than 2.6 kg and an internal power consumption of less than 3 Watt.

1. INTRODUCTION

In recent years most micro-sat's have been built by universities or companies with little or no large satellite design background.
While this has had many positive effects, certainly in the the reduction of heavy management and lower cost, it has also meant a large variety in system design with big differences in performance.
When designing the STRV-1 Power System, ESTeC wanted to take advantage of it's long experience of Power System design, especially in the areas of protection and failure propagation, since we felt that this had been a somewhat neglected feature in many small satellite power systems up to now.
Maintaining the security features of a large satellite power system and still keeping a low component count proved to be a difficult task. It was necessary to go through several reviews of the electrical design in order to reduce the component count, whilst maintaining reliability as the prime objective.

2. SYSTEM TRADE-OFFS

When selecting the building blocks for a spacecraft power system, the most important criteria are failure propagation and reliability.
To achieve the reliability, there is a choice between hot or cold redundancy. For a micro-satellite where space, mass, power and orbital visibility are limited, the obvious choice is to implement hot redundancy since it utilizes the hardware more efficiently. (However, some degradation of performance in case of failure may have to be accepted in order to avoid over-dimensioning of the system).
To avoid failure propagation, it is necessary have a fail-safe approach, which isolates the fault to the defect unit without overloading the rest of system.
With this in mind, it is preferable to use converter topologies that lend themselves to input current limitation and therefore the buck (step-down) converter has been chosen as building block for all DC-DC converters, since it also offers an easy control approach.

Another area where a trade-off is necessary is the selection of voltages to be distributed to the users.

Some users prefer to receive a fixed set of voltages like +5 and +/- 12 Volt in order to avoid designing any DC-DC converter, while others prefer to get one voltage and make their own conversion to the voltages they actually need.

Also the Power System designers are divided to two camps, tho ones who want to keep their system as simple as possible, only charging the battery and dumping excess power and the others who want to deliver a well defined bus voltage during all operational phases, thus making user converter design easier.

There is no trivial answer to these selections, but the following facts tend to drive the design;
- To distribute several voltages to each user leads to a complex power system interface, harness and a large number of power switches.
- Modular redundancy means current sharing, which implies current control of the DC-DC regulators.
- A high bus voltage has less distribution losses than a lower voltage one.

In the GTO orbit, where for more than 90 % of the time the spacecraft is in sunlight, it was clear that STRV-1 would benefit from a efficient converter for the sun-lit phase.

For this reason, a switching shunt regulator was selected, combining the highest possible efficiency with simple drive and control.

Due to requirements on high peak power, modularity and use of a standard distribution voltage ,it was decided to have a fully regulated 28 Volt bus, with Battery Discharge Regulators (BDR) and Battery Charge Regulators (BCR) implemented as redundant units.

The 28 Volt regulated bus was selected for the reasons of being a "de facto" standard and having growth capability from the STRV-1 level up to several hundred watts.

3.   MISSION REQUIREMENTS

Environment

- Orbit	GTO (200 x 36000 km) , 10.6 hour orbit
- Maximum eclipse	125 minutes
- Radiation dose	20 krad for the electronics (estimated)

Summary of Initial Power System requirements

- Life	1 year
- Mass	2.5 kg
- Volume	400 x 160 x 45 mm
- Modularity	Suitable for STRV-1a and STRV-1b
- Bus regulation	28 Volt +/-2% at user level
- Power capability	80 Watt peak (all phases), 30 Watt average
- BCR, BDR efficiency	>85 %
- Reliability	0.97 , No single point failure (if possible)

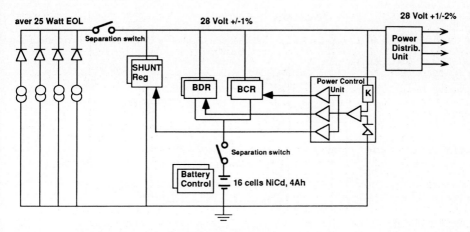

Fig. 1   STRV Power System block diagram

4.   DESCRIPTION OF THE POWER SYSTEM

4.1   Power Conditioning

4.1.1 Control and Operation

As shown in Fig. 1, the quadrant arranged solar array sections have been diode-ORed together, with Shottky-diodes, forming the 28 Volt power bus.
The bus voltage is controlled by a majority voting (one failure tolerant) error amplifier. The output from this amplifier is used to determine which one of the modules, Shunt Regulator, Battery Charge Regulator (BCR) or Battery Discharge Regulator (BDR), should control the bus voltage.
The BCR's and the BDR's have been implemented as conductance controlled hot redundant units, while the Shunt regulators are effectively in hot standby.
The power system is designed to work autonomously, without any intervention from the Data Handling System of the spacecraft, in order to avoid operational constraints and assure interruption-free energy delivery.
(The only parameter which may have to be changed during the mission is the temperature compensated battery end-of-charge voltage level, adjusting to battery ageing effects.)

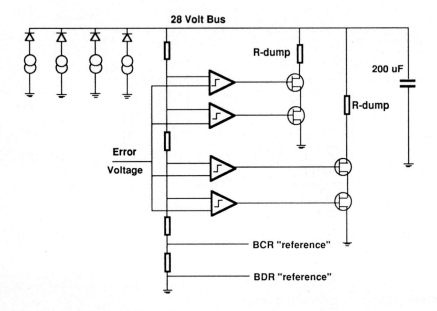

Fig 2   Shunt regulator

4.1.2 Shunt regulator

In sunlight, when available solar array power is greater than the sum of load power and charge
power, the bus voltage will be controlled by a switching Shunt Regulator, fig 2.
Under switch mode control, this regulator will dump excess solar array power into a 20 Ohm
resistor connected across the bus. Due to the digital nature of this control, a triangular ripple
on the 28 V bus will occur, with a magnitude of about 100 milliVolt peak-peak.
This simple method, mainly suitable for low power spacecrafts,which offers a array/spacecraft
power transfer efficiency of 98.5 %, needs only one series diode per solar array string
compared to two for an array section clamping shunt regulator (S^3R).
The frequency at which the Shunt Regulator will operate is dependant upon the the amount of
excess power, however the maximum frequency is in the order of 15 kHz.
The shunt regulator also houses the bus capacitor bank (200 µF), made from self-healing
MKU-capacitors
In case of open-circuit failure of the operating shunt regulator, the redundant one will take over
automatically.

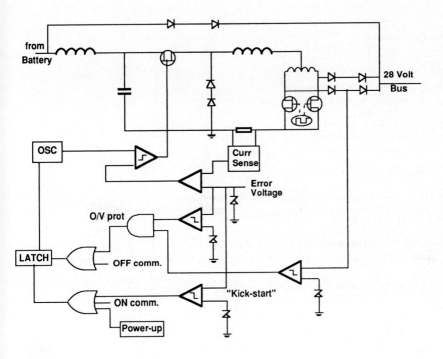

Fig 3   Battery Discharge Regulator

4.1.3 Battery Discharge Regulator (BDR)

For eclipse operation and peak power demands, the NiCd-battery is supplying the 28 V bus by means of two hot redundant Battery Discharge Regulators (BDR's), fig 3.
The topology used is a conductance controlled buck converter, switching at 100 kHz, followed by a push-pull converter having an auto-transformer configuration. The push-pull converter, being free-running, doubles it's input voltage, thus enforcing the buck converter to provide about half the bus voltage (14 V), at the transformer centertap location.
Because the BDR's are not powerful enough to provide fuse blowing energy, there are by-pass diodes directly connecting the battery with the bus in case of uncontrolled undervoltage events. With this configuration the battery voltage may vary between approx. 15-28 V in order to produce a 28 V Bus. (This corresponds to 15 - 18 NiCd battery cells in series.)
Each BDR module has a peak power capability of 50 Watt, giving a total power capability of 100 Watt in eclipse.
The BDR conversion efficiency is greater than 90 %.
The BDR is protected from overcurrent by the limiting the centertap current and from overvoltage by sensing of both the error voltage and output voltage followed by switch-off of the push-pull stage.

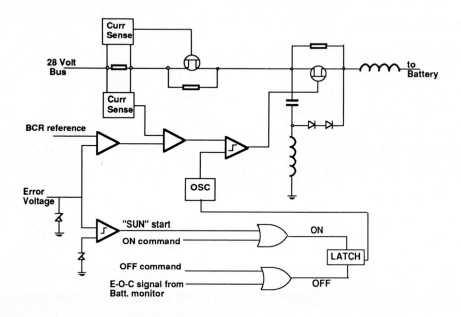

Fig 4   Battery Charge regulator

4.2   Battery Charging and Management

The charge power is taken from the bus by means of two, hot redundant, Battery Charge Regulators (BCR's), fig 4, implemented as conductance controlled buck converters, switching at 100 kHz.
Each BCR has a maximum charge power of 7 Watt, corresponding to C/13 at battery level, thus giving a total maximum charge rate of C/6.5.
Charging starts as soon as solar array power exceeds the demand from the load and terminates when a end-of charge signal is received from the Battery Monitor.

Each BCR is connected to a separate Battery Monitor module, which provides end-of-charge signals.
These signals can either come from comparing the battery voltage with one out of four temperature compensated voltage levels or from the Battery Recharge Experiment, carried on STRV-1a.
(The Battery Recharge Experiment utilizes a technique which is based on the detection of the temperature rise of the battery cells at the end-of-charge.)
The Battery Monitor also has a battery undervoltage detection which disconnects non-essential loads in case the battery voltage goes below 16 Volt .
The overall battery voltage is sensed to determine end-of-charge and compared with a telecommand selectable voltage level.

After charge termination a trickle charge of 25 milliAmp (C/150) is maintained into the battery, via resistors, from the bus.
The BCR is protected from short circuit from bus to battery by an electronic series switch.
The conversion efficiency of the BCR is higher than 90 %.

4.3   Power Distribution

The interface between the bus and the users is the power distribution module, containing the 16 payload/subsystem switches, which all have overcurrent protection.
The non-essential systems and the payloads are connected via commandable latching switches, while all essential systems simply have foldback limiters.
All latching switches receive a battery undervoltage signal from the Battery Monitor, which turns off all non-essential loads until the battery voltage has recovered. (This undervoltage signal can be disabled by ground command.)
Due to the small volume allocated, the switches have to use a low number of components. A compromise was found between performance and size, using switches consisting of a current sensor and a P-channel MOSFET
(The selected design uses a PCB area of about 10 cm^2 per switch.)

4.4   The Solar Array

The solar array of STRV-1a is made out of four GaAs-panels (50 cm x 40 cm), three of which are covered with 2x4 cm EEV cells and one covered with FIAR/CISE cells, (2 strings of 40 cells, 3.9x3.9 cm 290 μm LPE GaAs with 500 μm CMG cover-glass), providing 25 W end-of-life (18% eff).
Due to the spacecraft shape (cubical) and the spin stabilization, the maximum available solar array power (BOL) will fluctuate between 25 and 35 Watt in a sinusoidal manner.
Due to the high radiation dose in GTO, the output power is predicted to decay by about 10 % within the one year life.

4.5   The Battery

The single battery consists of 16 commercial NiCd cells in series, Gates Goldtop
(GH-4300D), with a nominal capacity of 4 Amperehours.
These cylindrical cells are divided into two battery packs with 8 cells each for mass balance reasons.
The cells are mounted laying down, inserted into holes milled out of a solid aluminium block.
The battery packs also contain thermistors necessary for the charge control of the battery.
The mass of each battery pack is 2.2 kg and the maximum expected Depth of Discharge is 60 %, this level only occurring during the infrequent 2.2 hour eclipses.

4.6   Housekeeping

The power system provides the following analogue telemetries:
Bus Current
Charge Current
Discharge current
Solar Array current
Battery voltage

In addition it also provides status signals for all on-off command functions.

4.7   Protection

To protect the power system electronics from internal failures, the following measures have been taken:

4.7.1 System:
Error Amplifier, Shunts, BDR's, BCR's and Battery Monitors have been implemented as hot redundant, where one module can perform the whole task, with only some degradation of performance. This approach has resulted in a single failure tolerant system.
The power system is designed to be autonomous, operating without intervention from any other on-board subsystems.
Solid state protection has been used to a maximum extent in order not to disturb the bus, should a failure occur.

4.7.2 Shunt Regulator:
The Shunt switch is implemented with N-channel MOSFET's arranged in a quad configuration tolerate both a single short-circuit or open-circuit of one transistor.
The lines connecting the external shunt dump resistors to the power bus are protected by fuses.

4.7.3 The BDR's:
The output current is limited to 1.7 Amp per module, giving protection against thermal stress of the components and short-circuits in the push-pull converter.
In case of short circuit of the buck switch, where an overvoltage failure case would result, the push-pull converter will be turned off, thus preventing such an event.
Also, there is an automatic inhibit installed which prevents inadvertent commanding off both BDR's.

4.7.4 The BCR's:
The charge current is limited to 250 milliAmpere into the charger module.
A additional series switch will shut the BCR module down, in the event that the current limiter transistor goes short circuit.

4.7.5 Battery management:
A battery undervoltage signal has been implemented (equivalent to 1 Volt / cell), which result in disconnection of spacecraft non-essential loads. (This signal can be disabled by telecommand.)
Although a failure of the end-of-charge detection electronics may lead to permanent charge current from one BCR, since this is limited to C/13 rate it has been assumed that the spacecraft battery can accept this condition at least up to the next ground visibility period.

For the protection against events external to the power system, the following has been implemented :

4.7.6 Power Distribution:
To protect against spacecraft load short-circuits the power system has:
Four switches connected to the essential subsystems, implemented with a foldback characteristic, giving a dissipation of about 1 watt in a failed condition.
Twelve switches implemented as reset-able overcurrent trip-off switches connected to the non-essential subsystems and the payloads.
This fast current limiting feature of these switches assures that the bus will stay within specification also during user short-circuit events.

5.   BUDGETS

Submodule	PCB Area	PCB Mass	Power
BDR module	200 x2	300 x2	750x2
BCR module	120 x2	200 x2	180x2
Shunt module	20 x2	30 x2	25x2
Battery management module	75 x2	90 x2	150x2
Power distribution module	200	300	600
Main error amplifier	30	50	160
TOTAL	1060cm^2	1590g	2910 mW

The complete power electronics has been built by Surrey Satellite Technology into a single unit, with a total mass of 2.6 kg.

6.   POWER SYSTEM PERFORMANCE

The STRV-1 power system features:

A regulated 28 Volt bus, (+1/-2 % at the user interface)
Source DC regulation of less than 1 milliVolt
An bus output impedance of 250 milliOhm (peak)
A peak power capability of 100 Watt
Bus voltage ripple of less than 100 milliVolt peak-peak
Solid State protection of all user power outlets
Hot redundant regulators and error amplifiers
Battery charge control either by temperature compensated voltage limit or (on STRV1-a only)
by the temperature derivative technique of the Battery Recharge Experiment .
Bus overvoltage protection
Automatic load disconnection at battery undervoltage (equivalent to 1 Volt / cell)
Short-circuit protection of all switching transistors
Self-healing bus capacitors
Protection against switching both BDR's off simultaneously
Gallium-Arsenide solar array (4 panels)
Nickel-Cadmium battery (16 cells, 4 Amperehours), Mass 4.4 kg
Charger/Discharger conversion efficiencies of more than 90 %
Power electronics mass of 2.6 kg
Standby power consumption of 2.9 Watt

7.   GROWTH POTENTIAL

The present design can accommodate spacecraft power of up to about 100 Watt without major modifications.
With higher power the method of dumping excess power in resistors may become unpractical and should probably be substituted for a shunt regulator with shunting across array sections, like the S^{3}R.

Also, as current increases, the use of MOSFET P-channel switches lead to high losses and if paralleling becomes unpractical, N-channel devices must be used.

This means that isolated FET drivers must be used, causing an increase in design complexity. The battery management is mainly designed for GTO or GEO environment and can supply a maximum charge current of 1 Amp. For LEO applications, where the charge rates are higher some redesign will be necessary and the battery monitoring may have to be refined.

It should be concluded that this is a power system designed for mini- and micro-satellites in GTO or GEO application, but adopting it for higher power or LEO application could be readily achieved. It mainly involves re-sizing the power components.

Going in the other direction, shrinking the system, is also a possibility. The first possibility that comes to mind is to delete the BDR's. This saves 1 Watt and 0.5 kg to the price of having a sunlight regulated bus and placing more design concerns onto the power users.

The ultimate saving is to delete the battery, having an operational spacecraft only in sunlight . This might be an option for spin stabilized GTO missions, which spend more than 90 % of their life in the sun, but of course, such a power system will have no peak power capability, but could consume less than 1 Watt and weigh about 0.5 kg (excluding solar arrays).

8.   CONCLUSIONS

It has been shown that a "classical" power system can be implemented also in a very small satellite, without consuming a lot of mass or power whilst maintaining most of the failure tolerance that is required for large satellites.

The performance of this design is, in terms of sunlight efficiency and reliability, higher than most small satellite power systems used up to now.

9.   ACKNOWLEDGEMENTS

The author wishes to thank Mr J. Haines for his system design, Mr K. Burrows for his excellent breadboarding and Mr V. van der Zel of Surrey Satellite Technology for his contribution of the mechanical definition and manufacture of the power system electronics described in this paper.

10.   REFERENCES

The Space Technology Research Vehicle,
K.A. Ryden,
Proceedings of the Royal Aeronautical Society Conference on Small Satellites, 24 Jan 1991,
pp 4.1-4.11

The Sequential Switching Shunt Regulator, S^3R,
D. O'Sullivan, A. Weinberg,
Proceedings of the third Estec Spacecraft Power Conditioning Seminar 1977, ESA SP-126,
pp. 123-131

Protection Concepts used in Spacecraft Power Systems,
D. Levins,
Proceedings of the European Space Power conference 1991, ESA SP-320,
pp 157-162

DATA HANDLING STRATEGY FOR THE SPANISH SMALL SATELLITE PROGRAM (MINISAT)

X. Lobao, L. Pina

INISEL ESPACIO - Barcelona (SPAIN)

ABSTRACT

This paper describes the data handling approach that has been considered for the Spanish program of small satellites. The program is aimed at the development of a general-purpose platform to cover a wide range of missions, varying from digital communications to astronomy and Earth observation. The different characteristics of the missions force very stringent system requirements being set up in order to maintain the versatility of the platform.

The fact that most of the foreseen missions must be operated in Low-Earth orbits and that the ground infrastructure must in some cases be very limited leads to intermittent ground coverage with long periods of time without ground support. Therefore, large capacity for data storage must be provided on board for both engineering and mission data, and high data rates must be used for downloading the stored information during contact periods. Additionally, a high degree of autonomy is needed for the spacecraft, and procedures have to be provided for the autonomous operation and for failure detection and recovery of the different elements during the intervals without ground coverage.

On the other hand, a small satellite has important constraints on mass, size and power, and especially on cost. Consequently, simplicity is one of the most important driving requirements.

The approach that has been taken consists of the centralization of the platform intelligence in the data handling computer. Thus, the computer is devoted to several mission-dependent functions besides its normal data handling functions: attitude determination and control, thermal control, power distribution control and processing of payload mission data. A powerful microprocessor is used to cope with the high processing power required.

Solid-state memory devices are used to allow the high data capacity foreseen for the missions while keeping reasonable mass, size and power budgets.

1. MINISAT OVERVIEW

The aim of the Minisat program is the design and development of a general purpose spacecraft and associated ground infrastructure suitable for a wide range of missions, varying from astronomy and Earth observation to digital communications [Ref.1].

The typical mission profile corresponds to operation from Low-Earth Orbits (LEO) (between 500 and 900 Km) in equatorial ($0 < i < 40$) or polar ($70 < i < 100$) planes. These orbits will be achieved by means of dedicated launch using Pegasus or Scout.

The kind of missions planned will require different stabilization approaches, although 3-axis stabilization is the most likely scenario.

The overall mass has to be between 200 and 450 Kg, and the average power consumption per orbit around 120 W.

The ground infrastructure is also conceived with flexibility as a driving factor. Thus, depending upon the mission needs, one or more Earth Stations will be setup for satellite operations.

From the point of view of the spacecraft design, a worst case scenario must be considered, in which a single Earth Station is used for telemetry, tracking and command and for mission data reception.

In consequence, a limited number of contact periods (1-2 per day) with short duration (5-12 minutes) is foreseen. Therefore, the spacecraft must be provided with large on-board data storage and a high degree of autonomy of operation. The spacecraft must also be provided with mechanisms for the transmission in a fraction of the visibility period of all the data stored during the periods without ground support.

2. DATA HANDLING SYSTEM

The data handling subsystem of a spacecraft takes care of the management of the spacecraft resources by means of telecommands uplinked from ground and telemetry data that is sent to ground for health management and performance evaluation.

The telecommands result in control commands being distributed at a predefined time to their destination, where they are executed.

The telemetry data, consisting of measurements and status, are gathered from the different on-board elements and correspond to engineering data necessary for the housekeeping of the spacecraft, and mission data.

In cases in which a high degree of autonomy is required, the data handling subsystem monitors the housekeeping data and takes corrective actions in case of malfunction.

Additionally, depending upon the mission needs, the data handling subsystem acquires, stores, processes and/or transmits the mission data.

The particular case of a small satellite is still more stringent and requires the maximum number of functions to be concentrated in a single unit. Thus, frequently, the data handling subsystem, which contains processing capabilities, is assigned additional tasks.

Correspondingly, the data handling subsystem of the Minisat program, besides the normal data management functions, is responsible for attitude determination and control, power distribution control, thermal control, and in some cases mission data processing.

The functions of the Minisat data handling subsystem are [Ref. 2]:

- Telecommand reception, decoding and distribution to their destination.
- Time-tagged and delayed command scheduling.
- Macro command expansion.
- Interface with the different on-board elements for monitoring and control.
- Data acquisition from the different on-board elements (housekeeping and mission data).
- Monitoring of the different on-board elements (status, extreme values monitoring, out-of-limit checking).
- Initiate predefined recovery actions upon a failure detection.
- Telemetry data formatting according to packet TM standard.
- Multiplexing of the different telemetry data channels into the downlink stream.
- Telemetry data encoding (Reed-Solomon and convolutional encoding).
- Telemetry data transmission to the TT&C subsystem during periods of ground support.
- Data storage (housekeeping and mission data) during non-coverage periods.
- On-board time management.
- Housekeeping and data management for the payload.
- Attitude determination and control implementation.
- Power distribution control implementation.
- Active thermal control implementation.
- Mission dependent data processing.

2.1. DRIVING FACTORS

In a small satellite bus the driving factors, besides cost and turnaround time, are volume, size and power consumption [Ref.3].

In order to meet these requirements, the number of units must be minimized. Therefore, redundancy must be limited and the maximum integration of functions within units pursued.

The use of low-power technologies (such as CMOS) for electronic devices is dictated by the need to minimize power consumption.

In a system with limited redundancy, special measures have to be taken to assure sufficient reliability. In space, and especially in Low Earth orbits, the spacecraft has to cope with a harsh radiation environment.

Electronic devices are susceptible to single event upsets (SEU) caused by energetic ions and secondary particle radiation, and to latchup caused by single heavy ions [Ref.4]. The errors produced by SEU affect especially memory devices, and as a consequence, cause software errors. Therefore, in order to increase reliability, hardware implementation of functions is preferred to software implementation, which leads to the use of ASIC devices wherever possible.

In order to provide tolerance to failure while taking into account the above mentioned constraints, a subsystem-level redundancy approach has been considered in order to avoid single point failures.

Therefore, a unit, termed emergency box, has been defined to take over the functions of the other units in case a failure is detected. The design has been done modularly, so that single functions can be setup without modifying the operation of the remaining functions.

2.2. BASIC CHARACTERISTICS

In order to meet the stringent requirements regarding on-board autonomy derived from the reduced ground infrastructure, a large amount of data storage must be provided in the data handling subsystem. Thus, 32 Mbytes of mass-storage are provided to record spacecraft and mission data between contacts with the ground station, which can be up to 24 hours apart.

All the data contained on-board must be dumped to ground during the contact periods, which can last between 5 and 10 minutes. Therefore, a high data rate must be provided in the downlink. The baseline is 1 Mbps. To achieve a low bit error rate at this data rate with limited use of on-board power in the transmission equipment, a safe protocol and data encoding techniques must be used. The new ESA packet telemetry standard is used for telemetry data formatting together with Reed-Solomon and convolutional encoding techniques, that are used to provide further error protection and to cope with bursts of errors in the link.

During the contact periods commands must be uplinked for immediate and delayed execution. Provision for time-tagged commands must be provided due to the long periods without ground support. The uplink uses a data rate of 1 Kbps. The efficiency required to transfer the large amount of commands needed can only be achieved through the use of high-efficiency and reliable protocols. Therefore, the new ESA packet telecommand standard is used for telecommand transmission.

A powerful microprocessor is used in the on-board computer to allow the data handling system to offer processing services to the payload in addition to the data handling functions. Therefore, processing power must be reserved for mission data processing (e.g. data compression, feature extraction, geometric and sensor corrections). A minimum of 1 MIPS (millions of instructions per second) is required. Besides the data handling and the mission data processing functions, the on-board computer will be devoted to control law execution for attitude determination and control, thermal control and power distribution control.

2.3. SUBSYSTEM DESCRIPTION

The structure of the data handling subsystem is shown in figure 2.3-1. The subsystem consists of the following elements:

- Telecommand decoder (TCD)
- Telemetry format generator (TMFG)
- Virtual Channel Multiplexer (VCM)
- Telemetry encoder (TME)
- Emergency box (EB)
- On-Board Computer (OBC)
- Remote Terminal Units (RTU)

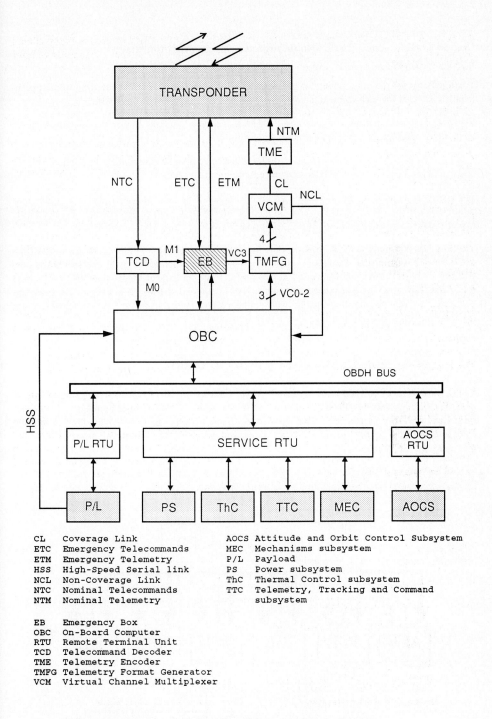

CL   Coverage Link   AOCS Attitude and Orbit Control Subsystem
ETC   Emergency Telecommands   MEC   Mechanisms subsystem
ETM   Emergency Telemetry   P/L   Payload
HSS   High-Speed Serial link   PS   Power subsystem
NCL   Non-Coverage Link   ThC   Thermal Control subsystem
NTC   Nominal Telecommands   TTC   Telemetry, Tracking and Command
NTM   Nominal Telemetry   subsystem

EB   Emergency Box
OBC   On-Board Computer
RTU   Remote Terminal Unit
TCD   Telecommand Decoder
TME   Telemetry Encoder
TMFG Telemetry Format Generator
VCM   Virtual Channel Multiplexer

Figure 2.3-1. Data Handling Subsystem block diagram.

571

The telecommand (TC) decoder is responsible for decoding the command packets to be sent to the OBC or the EB for further distribution and to decode, interpret and distribute the commands to be sent directly to the users.

The telemetry (TM) format generator is responsible for organizing the data according to the packet telemetry format for each of the telemetry channels and to interface with the VCM.

The virtual channel multiplexer generates the TM data stream by taking in turn the formatted data at its inputs according to a predefined scanning algorithm.

The TM encoder adds the symbols that correspond to Reed-Solomon encoding in the adequate places and generates the convolutional codes for the continuous data stream.

The emergency box is the backup to the different data handling units provided to avoid single point failures. It can be setup to take over individually any of its functions (emergency TC decoding, essential data acquisition and monitoring, emergency TM formatting and transmission).

The on-board computer is the core of the data handling subsystem and is responsible for most of the data handling functions, as explained below. The OBC is connected to the users via the OBDH bus, which is a single-master bus controlled by the central terminal located within the OBC, and which uses a simple protocol to distribute commands to and to acquire data from remote terminals. Users are connected to remote terminals using well-defined signal types and the remote terminals are responsible for timing, multiplexing and analog to digital conversion.

2.3.1. CONNECTION TO THE DATA HANDLING USERS

The connection with the data handling users is done via the ESA OBDH bus (interrogation/response bus). The bus controller is located within the OBC and three RTUs have been considered: Payload RTU (P/L RTU) for connection to the mission equipment, AOCS RTU for connection to attitude determination and control sensors and actuators, and Service RTU for transmission to/from the remaining satellite equipment.

The RTUs are responsible for the distribution of commands (on/off pulses or digital commands) and for data acquisition (analog and digital parameters) to/from the different users connected to them.

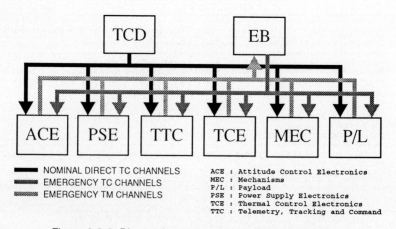

Figure 2.3-2. Direct telecommand and telemetry channels.

572

The data rate on the OBDH bus has been setup at 512 kbps. This data rate must be sufficient to cope with the housekeeping data acquisition and commanding needs and to support mission data transmission for an average payload.

For demanding payloads generating bursts of data at rates higher than the OBDH bus can manage a direct link to the OBC is provided supporting data rates up to 1 Mbps.

Besides the connection via the OBDH bus, some discrete command lines have been provided for high-priority telecommands, which are distributed directly by the TC decoder, and which can also cope with a failure in the bus or the remote terminals. Figure 2.3-2 shows these direct command lines together with the discrete lines associated with the emergency box.

2.3.2. ON-BOARD COMPUTER STRUCTURE

The on-board computer consists of the following elements as displayed in figure 2.3-3: central processing module, mass-memory and OBDH bus communications controller. Figure 2.3-3 shows also the interface of the OBC with the rest of data handling units.

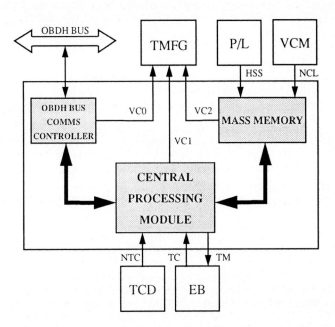

Figure 2.3-3. On-Board Computer structure and interfaces.

The mass storage device is based on solid-state memory, using high-density static CMOS RAM devices, in order to achieve the needed capacity whilst maintaining reasonable budgets for volume, mass and power consumption. The susceptibility to radiation, derived by the fact that rad-hard devices of such density are not available, is compensated by the use of error detection and correction codes.

Some approaches are being considered in order to relieve the microprocessor of the on-board computer of the burdensome synchronous operations.

The regular telemetry data acquisition is carried out autonomously by the OBDH bus communications controller. An ASIC is being designed to carry out the tasks of autonomous data acquisition and generation of the OBDH bus protocol.

Another task that is autonomously executed is telemetry data formatting and multiplexing according to the packet TM standard definition. As a result of this process a continuous data stream of TM frames is generated from the different data sources. This data stream is directed either to the mass-memory during non-coverage periods or to the transmission equipment after being encoded for error protection.

The data stored in the mass-memory are dumped to ground during coverage periods through one of the multiplexed channels, so that data generated in real time can be concurrently transmitted. Even though the data stored in the mass-memory are already formatted, they undergo again the formatting process to keep synchronization of the TM data stream.

Different microprocessors are being considered to form the core of the OBC. Although Intel 80386/80387 has been considered as baseline due to the high processing power and the capabilities for direct memory addressing, some other alternatives are being contemplated, such as the use of the rad-hard version of the MIL-STD-1750 instruction set architecture processor, and particularly the new powerful version, MA31750. This being a 16-bit processor requires the use of memory paging mechanisms to be applied in order to achieve the size of the mass-memory needed.

2.3.3. EMERGENCY BOX CONCEPT

The redundancy approach implemented consists of the use of a single box to take over in a degraded operational mode most of the functions that are normally carried out by the different units.

Thus, there is the possibility of some emergency commanding by using a subset of commands addressed directly to the emergency box, though formatted according to the packet TC standard. The commands received can be distributed to the on-board users using either the normal path through the OBDH bus via the OBC or directly by means of a set of discrete command lines (high-power pulses, discrete on/off and serial channels), as shown in figure 2.3-2. There is also the possibility of connecting one of the multiplexer access points of the TC decoder to the emergency box to cope with the case in which the link between the OBC and the TC decoder fails.

The emergency box is also provided with some essential TM acquisition capabilities from the on-board users. Therefore, a set of discrete lines are considered (for digital and analog TM data gathering) (see figure 2.3-2). The data thus acquired are formatted according to the packet TM standard. These data can be either sent to the nominal TM processing chain using one of the virtual channels or directly transferred to the transmission equipment. In this last case a lower data rate will be used in the downlink so that no data encoding is needed to achieve the specified bit error rate.

The data acquired from the different on-board elements are also monitored in the emergency box. Status parameters are checked for unexpected values, and measurements checked for out-of-limit situations. In case any anomaly is detected, corrective actions are undertaken.

The emergency box is normally in standby mode, monitoring the data handling system. In case a failure is detected in one of the data handling units (by itself or by the OBC), the emergency box is configured to undertake the corresponding function.

3. REFERENCES

[Ref.1]   MSAT-ESP-230-001-SEN
Especificacion de sistema de minisatelites
issue 1, Sept. 1991

[Ref.2]   MSAT-ESP-360-001-INL
Especificacion subsistema Gestion de Datos (OBDH)
issue 1, rev. A, Sept. 1991

[Ref.3]   Wertz, J.R., Larson, W.J. (editors)
Space Mission Analysis and Design
Kluwer Academic Publishers, 1991

[Ref.4]   Srour, J.R., McGarrity, J.M.
Radiation Effects on Microelectronics in Space
Proceedings of the IEEE, vol. 76, no. 11, Nov. 1988, pp. 1443-1469

The STRV On Board Data Handling (OBDH) System.

An Introduction   by H G Andrews

INTRODUCTION.

This note outlines the operation of the Space Technology Research Vehicle (STRV) On Board Data Handling system (OBDH). STRV is a 50kg satellite designed to research and demonstrate, new and improved technologies during a one year GTO mission. It aims to improve the performance, lifetime and cost effectiveness of future space systems by using new processes, techniques & components as part of both platform and payload design. The OBDH system supports the data processing and control requirements of each STRV equipment.

OBDH DESCRIPTION

The OBDH system has been designed within Space Sector to operate for one year in GTO where it will receive an estimated total dose of 25krads. It is implemented using a range of Silicon on Sapphire (SoS) and other radiation tolerant technologies including Application Specific ICs (ASICs) and Field Programmable Gate Arrays (FPGAs). These improve reliability, volume, mass and power consumption with further mass savings gained by extensive use of surface mount packaging. Low cost, personal computer based ground support equipment has also been designed to enable testing of the OBDH and other STRV equipments throughout the assembly integration and test phases.

The OBDH system consists of six functionally separate units (see below) and three main busses. The architecture is flexible to allow efficient support of equipments which range in complexity and provides alternative control paths and redundancy to improve reliability.

THE STRV OBDH ARCHITECTURE

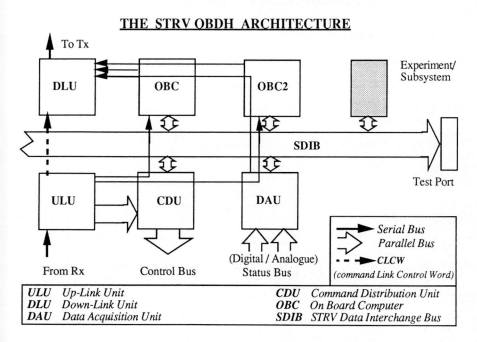

ULU	Up-Link Unit	CDU	Command Distribution Unit
DLU	Down-Link Unit	OBC	On Board Computer
DAU	Data Acquisition Unit	SDIB	STRV Data Interchange Bus

The Up-Link Unit (ULU) receives and disseminates ESA Packet Standard Telecommand packets and provides the On Board Computers with source packets. It provides the Command Distribution Unit (CDU) with an eight bit parallel word and the Down-Link Unit (DLU) with the Command Link Control Word (CLCW). The ULU design is based on the SAAB telecommand decoder .

The On Board Computer (OBC) is based on the radiation tolerant (SoS) 16 bit Mil-Std 1750 microprocessor chip set and includes 64K words of rad-hard RAM and 32K words of ROM. It supports the 8-bit parallel STRV Data Interchange Bus (SDIB) and serial uplink and downlink interfaces. The OBC receives commands from the ground via the ULU and produces source packets of data for transmission to ground via the DLU or for storage pending later execution. Commands are executed immediately upon receipt or are stored to operate autonomous 'time tagged' routines. OBC2 is a spare 'slot' for demonstrating new single board computers. A test port is also included with SDIB and OBDH serial I/O interfaces to allow testing of the OBDH and other equipments operation throughout. assembly integration and test.

The Command Distribution Unit (CDU) provides 128 single bit logic outputs by decoding the eight bit parallel word supplied by the ULU. These outputs form the Control bus and are used for simple control such as power or mode switching . The CDU may be controlled directly from the ground (via the ULU and the eight bit parallel word) or by the OBC (via the SDIB) implementing immediate or autonomous 'time tagged' commands.

The Data Acquisition Unit (DAU) 'reads' the status bus of 128 digital, 56 analogue and 16 temperature inputs. The DAU may operate autonomously by collecting a complete status field, which is inserted into a source packet and transfered to the Down-Link Unit. The DAU may also be computer controlled (via the SDIB), allowing single inputs to be selected and inspected in any order.

The Down-Link Unit (DLU) arbitrates between and accepts source packets of data from the OBC, OBC2 and the DAU, it appends appropriate headers, includes the Command Link Control Word (CLCW) and presents a completed transfer frame to the transmitter for transmission to ground.

TECHNICAL SUMMARY:

MASS:	2.5kg (inc OBC2).
DIMENSIONS:	400 * 160 * 66 mm.
POWER CONSUMPTION:	6.3 W (maximum power mode, inc OBC2).
RADIATION TOLERANCE:	40krads (softest component).
NEW TECHNOLOGIES USED:	First use of the UK manufactured (SoS) MAS 281/Mil Std µprocessor. The SAAB Telecommand decoder (a rad-hard ASIC), FPGAs.
S/W LANGUAGE:	ADA.
MEMORY:	64K words RAM, 32k words ROM.
COMMUNICATIONS PROTOCOL	ESA Packet Telemetry Std ESA PSS - 04 -106 ESA Packet Telecommand Std ESA PSS - 04 -107

For more information contact: H G Andrews, Space sector, DRA (AD), RAE Farnborough Hants GU146TD (UK). Tel 0252 24461 Ext 4166, Fax 0252 515518.

SYNTHESE DE LA SESSION
TECHNOLOGIE DES SOUS-SYSTEMES

L'émergence des minisatellites est principalement due au grossissement continuel des satellites « traditionnels » et ceci dans tous les thèmes du domaine spatial.

Cette évolution « naturelle » a eu pour immédiate conséquence l'augmentation du coût du kilogramme en orbite et donc, corrélativement, la difficulté à obtenir des décisions de programme.

C'est ainsi qu'au fur et à mesure de cette augmentation en masse, on a vu une diminution corrélative du nombre de satellites lancés. Par conséquent, les opportunités de vol étant de plus en plus rares, la communauté spatiale des utilisateurs se tourne progressivement vers la filière des minisatellites.

Si minisatellite est souvent synonyme de coûts faibles, mini-satellite est toujours synonyme de masse faible, ce qui signifie que cette évolution est largement conditionnée par la disponibilité des technologies qui permettent d'atteindre cet objectif.

Évolution technologique pour les minisatellites veut donc dire intégration plus grande (miniaturisation) et améliorations des performances (rendements). Ces progrès technologiques ont naturellement été les plus rapides dans le domaine de l'électronique bord, mais les domaines mécaniques et chimiques n'ont pas encore connu, ces dernières années, la même forte évolution.

Toutefois, on a pu noter de nets progrès (en cours) notamment dans le domaine de l'énergie bord (cellules solaires et batteries).

Le succès à venir des minisatellites passera à coup sûr par des progrès substantiels dans ces deux domaines, appliqués notamment aux sous-systèmes :

– contrôle d'attitude,

– pointage,

– propulsion,

– antenne.

Il serait donc important à l'avenir de renforcer ces axes de recherche et si possible d'en présenter les résultats lors de notre prochain colloque, en élargissant les types de sous-systèmes traités et la description des équipement et des technologies associées.

Notons enfin en guise de conclusion finale, que ces évolutions technologiques dynamisées par les minisatellites, auront à coup sûr des retombées directes sur la technologie et donc les performances de toute l'activité spatiale.

SYNTHESIS OF THE SESSION
SUBSYSTEMS TECHNOLOGY

The emergence of mini-satellites is mainly due to the continual increase in the size of "conventional" satellites, which is occurring for all themes in the space field.

This "natural" development has had the immediate consequence of increasing the cost per kilogram in orbit and, as a corollary, the difficulty of obtaining programme decisions.

With increasing mass, we have therefore seen a correlated decrease in the number of satellites launched. Consequently, as launch opportunities have become rarer, the space user community has gradually turned towards mini-satellites.

If the term mini-satellite is often synonymous with low costs, it is always synonymous with low mass, which means that this development is very dependent on the availability of technologies that allow the mass objective to be met.

For mini-satellites, technological evolution thus signifies greater integration (miniaturization) and improvements in performance (efficiency). This technological progress has naturally been fast in the field of on-board electronics but mechanics and chemistry have not kept pace in recent years.

Notable progress has, however, been made in on-board power (solar cells and batteries).

The future success of mini-satellites will certainly come through substantial progress in these two domains, particularly as applied to the following subsystems:

– attitude control;

– pointing;

– propulsion;

– antennas.

It is thus important to strengthen these lines of research in the future and, if possible, present the results at our next symposium, whilst widening the types of subsystems dealt with and the description of the associated equipment and technologies.

As a final conclusion, it is worth noting that these technological developments encouraged by mini-satellites, are sure to have direct spin off on the technology and thus the effectiveness of all space activity.

SESSION IX

ACCES
A LA TECHNOLOGIE SPATIALE

ACCESS TO SPACE TECHNOLOGY

UN MINI SATELLITE NOMME ARSENE
COMMENT LE REALISER A COUT MINIMUM

Jean-Paul RIHET
Chef du Projet Arsène

Jean-Pierre REDON
Chef du Projet Arsène

Aérospatiale
Cannes

Centre National d'Etudes Spatiales
Toulouse

1 - INTRODUCTION

L'objectif de cette publication est de présenter le système Arsène (bord, sol) en mettant en avant les caractéristiques qui font son originalité et qui le rendent particulièrement adapté au développement de mini satellites de la classe 100-250 kg.

Avant d'aborder le plan technique (définition, réalisation, intégration) et contractuel (financier) qui est l'objet de notre communication, nous allons essayer de replacer ce projet Arsène dans son contexte.

Ce contexte quelque peu marginal, en regard des projets classiques de satellite, fait ressortir le caractère particulier de ce projet par son extraordinaire aventure humaine et technique qui a marqué son développement.

Malgré les péripéties et les rebondissements divers de ce "gentleman satellite", dont les tribulations ont débuté il y a près de 13 ans, il a atteint l'âge adulte et est entré, de plein pied dans sa phase finale qui se concluera par son lancement si les Dieux des "gentlemen satellite" qui ont veillé sur lui jusqu'à maintenant continuent à le soutenir.

2 - LE PROJET ARSENE

Une poignée de radio-amateurs du Centre National d'Etudes Spatiales décident en 1979 de créer une association nommée RACE (Radio Amateur Club de l'Espace).

Cette association, type loi de 1901, a pour objectifs principaux :

- Favoriser l'étude

- Etudier

- Réaliser

- Mettre en oeuvre

- Exploiter en orbite

un satellite de télécommunications du service amateurs

- Contribuer

- Favoriser

- Soutenir

l'effort d'éducation dans le domaine spatial en associant les établissements d'enseignement secondaires et supérieurs.

Ces passionnés de l'Espace et de la Communication décident d'initier un programme de réalisation d'un mini satellite auquel ils donneront le nom d'ARSENE (Ariane Radioamateur Satellite ENseignement et Espace).

Deux idées maîtresses guident la définition du projet :

- Mettre à la disposition de la communauté mondiale des radio-amateurs, de plus d'un million de pratiquants, un satellite dédié, car il constituera un noeud essentiel pour l'interconnexion de réseau de transmissions "par paquets", que les radio-amateurs ont installés sur tout le globe terrestre.

- Contribuer à l'effort d'éducation dans le domaine spatial en associant les établissements d'enseignement tant secondaires que supérieurs, dans les phases déterminantes du développement du projet :

. définition

. conception

. réalisation

. gestion

. suivi en orbite.

Il faut se féliciter de l'impact pédagogique du projet Arsène qui a vu plus de 300 étudiants, lycéens, collégiens participer au programme et récompensés par deux médailles d'or au Congrés de l'IAF à Rome et Tokyo, une thèse de docteur ingénieur et un mémoire d'ingénieur CNAM.

Mais et c'est la partie la moins visible de l'iceberg, le projet Arsène au travers de son développement à caractère industriel a permis un remarquable rapprochement entre le monde industriel du domaine spatial et l'enseignement.

Il a induit un respect mutuel entre l'industrie et l'enseignement, une sensibilisation avérée du monde de l'éducation aux contraintes de délais, modes de fonctionnement, organisation du travail, critères de qualité, financement qui sont les fondements essentiels à mettre en oeuvre pour délivrer dans les délais prévus un produit performant dans le respect des spécifications qui lui étaint imposées.

L'association de ces compétences diverses (industrielles et didactiques) a permis une large diffusion à partir des établissements industriels (SEP, Aérospatiale, Sextant, Dassault...) ou etatiques (CNES, ENSAE, DGE...) de la culture scientifique et technique du domaine spatial.

3 - LE PROJET ARSENE ET LE CNES

C'est naturellement, et compte tenu de sa compétence dans le domaine spatial, que le CNES a participé et participe d'une manière particulièrement active au développement du programme Arsène.

Le projet est articulé sur le RACE Maître d'ouvrage, le CNES comme maître d'oeuvre et l'Ecole Nationale Supérieure de l'Aéronautique et de l'Espace responsable du segment sol.

3.1 - Le CNES a mis à la disposition du RACE :

- les moyens humains par la nomination d'une équipe de projet qui peut faire appel aux différents experts CNES dans les domaines aussi divers que la thermique, les mécanismes, l'énergie bord, la télémesure, la télécommande, les structures, les télécommunications, la stabilisation.

Cette équipe de projet peut également s'appuyer sur des spécialistes extérieurs au CNES.

3.2 - les moyens techniques en autorisant :

. l'utilisation de ses laboratoires

- base d'antennes
- pneumatique
- peinture
- environnement
- dessin
- orbitographie
- calcul
- fiabilité
- ...

3.3 - la cession, ou prêt longue durée de composants et matériels divers restant de programmes antérieurs et devenus sans emploi comme :

- composants électroniques
- panneaux solaires
- petite mécanique diverse en titane
- appareils de mesure

Depuis prés de treize années, le projet a avancé plus ou moins rapidement, au gré des disponibilités des matériels, des hommes, de l'argent, nerf oh combien sensible, mais toujours avec le soutien du CNES.

Le satellite Arsène existe et il est l'objet de la présente communication.

4- LE SATELLITE ARSENE

4.1 - L'idée - Le concept

- Un club de passionnés de communication et d'Espace, le RACE , dans leur grande majorité professionnels de l'Espace ont voulu un satellite dédié pour les Radio-amateurs.

- Le satellite est d'accés libre et gratuit à toute personne possédant outre la licence de radio-amateur, le matériel émission réception indispensable

- Arsène n'est l'objet d'aucun enjeu économique

- Il permet d'évaluer des technologies et des concepts nouveaux, de faire participer :

  • Le monde didactique avec les universités et les écoles d'ingénieurs à la définition, la réalisation d'un système spatial incluant le segment spatial avec un satellite unique, Arsène, et le segment sol avec une station de télémesure et télécommande, servant également de station d'intégration du satellite chez l'industriel.

  • Le monde industriel (Aérospatiale Cannes) à l'assemblage final, les essais d'environnement et la campagne de lancement.

  • Le monde étatique (DGE, CNES) au financement partiel et à la maîtrise d'oeuvre.

Ce triumvirat, d'idées à priori divergentes, prouve par la réalisation de notre "gentleman satellite" la faisabilité de ce type de coopération.

4.2 - Les spécifications

Les spécifications du satellite ont été dictées par les buts du système qui sont :

- Mettre à la disposition de la communauté mondiale des radio-amateurs un nouveau satellite.

- Contribuer à l'effort d'éducation dans le domaine spatial.

Les spécifications et exigences associées sont :

- Orbite élevée non géostationnaire : visibilité longue pour tous les radioamateurs

- Zone de visibilité -60° Latitude Sud à 60° Latitude Nord

- Fréquences :

> . tenant compte du parc radio-amateurs (maximum d'utilisateurs potentiels)
>
> . évitant le brouillage intra-systèmes
>
> . utilisant pour les radio-amateurs du matériel sur catalogue

- Mission Télécommunications

> . Etre un noeud supplémentaire du réseau radio-amateur
>
> . Utiliser les modes packet radio, BLU, TTY, phonie
>
> . Mettre en oeuvre la bande S

- Véhicule

> . Poids (interface lanceur) < 210 kg
>
> . Embarquement compatible Ariane
>
> . Dimensions inscrites dans un volume O = 900 mm H = 1110 mm
>
> . Conception modulaire liée au découpage des tâches
>
> . Utilisation des matériels développés : coût minimum
>
> . Solutions techniques simples, rustiques, fiables, de mise en oeuvre aisée
>
> . Contrôle thermique passif
>
> . Energie régulée jour et éclipse
>
> . Stabilisé par rotation
>
> . Satellite autonome : se met en position sauvegarde seul
>
> . Station de contrôle sol unique pour intégration/Mise à poste/Suivi en orbite
>
> . Coût réduit
>
> . Réalisation de mini satellites de même concept à coût récurrent faible
>
> . Confirmation du savoir faire de mini satellites à défilement ou géostationnaires
>
> . Validation du concept de lancement
>
> . Confirmation de la possibilité d'emport de charges utiles diverses.

4.3 - L'Architecture Mécanique et Electrique

De forme hexagonale inscrite dans un cylindre de 900mm de diamètre et d'une hauteur de 1110mm, Arsène se compose :

- D'un plateau central en NIDA de 61mm, appelé plateau porte-équipements sur lequel est installé le système gaz froid de contrôle d'attitude associé aux tuyères de spin/despin et basculement

- De deux cônes carbone montés de part et d'autre du plateau central

- Du plateau inférieur sur lequel est fixée la jupe conique interface avec la sangle de séparation

- Du plateau supérieur sur lequel sont installés sur une face les aériens et de l'autre l'électronique charge utile

- De six murs fixés sur le plateau central

- De six générateurs solaires équipés de cellules solaires en Arseniure de Gallium (étudiés, développés, réalisés par l'industrie Italienne sous contrat ASI)

- D'un moteur d'apogée à tuyère intégrée et corps principal en carbone (structure bobinée)

- Des équipements du véhicule (énergie bord, pyrotechnie, électronique de mesure d'attitude, télémesure, télécommande) fixés sur les murs et le plateau central

- D'un senseur Galliléo (senseurs terrestres et solaires).

4.4 - Orbite finale - Mise et maintien à poste

- L'orbite finale choisie est

périgée	- 20 000 km
apogée	- 36 000 km
inclinaison	- 0°

- Arsène sera injecté sur l'orbite de transfert par le lanceur Ariane (200/36000 km/7°) l'axe X du satellite situé dans le plan de l'orbite GTO

- Les manoeuvres pour atteindre l'orbite finale seront réalisées par la station de contrôle et de télécommande STELA installée à l'ENSAE à Toulouse avec le support d'une station aval de télémesure uniquement,   mise en place sur l'île de la Réunion.

- Ces manoeuvres se décomposeront :

  - Orbite Transfert n°2

    . Vérification état satellite

    . Restitution attitude

. Manoeuvres correction si nécessaire

. Mise en configuration pour préparer l'allumage du moteur

- Orbite Transfert n°4

  . Vérification état satellite

  . Restitution d'attitude

  . Mise en spin à 90t/mn (obtention d'un bonne raideur gyroscopique)

  . Mise à feu du moteur d'apogée (Back-up sur le 6ième ou 13ième apogée)

- Orbite finale

  . Vérification (bulletin NORAD) des paramètres de l'orbite finale

  . Despin à _ 60t/mn

  . Basculement de l'axe X jusqu'à sa perpendicularité sur le plan de l'orbite

  . Vérification de l'état du satellite

  . Recette en vol et autorisation de trafic via la charge utile

Le maintien à poste ne devrait imposer qu'une seule manoeuvre annuelle, les diagrammes toroïdaux des antennes autorisant un dépointage de l'axe X de 6° (angle au sommet du cône).

4.5 - Le financement

Le projet étudié et développé sous maîtrise d'ouvrage du RACE (Association type loi de 1901) a trouvé ses financements sous les formes les plus diverses :

- Subventions de la part du Ministère de l'Industrie à l'initialisation du projet

- Taxe d'apprentissage qui était versée par les industriels à l'ENSAE pour le projet Arsène.

- Mecenat des industriels de l'espace français (Aérospatiale, Dassault, SEP, SEXTANT, Arianespace, SNPE... pour ne citer que les plus importants).

- Mecenat des agences spatiales nationales et internationales :

  . CNES : par la mise en place d'une équipe projet, la donation de matériels vol et sol, le soutien logistique durant l'avancement du projet

  . ESA : par la mise à disposition gracieuse d'équipements vol et de moyens d'essais

  . ASI : par l'étude, la définition, la réalisation à titre gracieux des six panneaux solaires AsGa.

- Subventions d'organismes etatiques

. Ministère de la Défense dans le cadre de l'étude du moteur Mars

. Ministère de l'Espace dans le cadre de l'assemblage, l'intégration, les essais et la campagne de lancement Arsène.

- Bénévolat des hommes, radio-amateurs
  qui ont assuré les maquettages, modules, essais, qualification des différents sous-systèmes électroniques du satellite.

5 - COMMENT A T-ON REALISE ARSENE A COUT MINIMAL ?

5.1 - Réalisation mécanique, solutions

La structure a été pensée en fonction de la tenue aux vibrations suivant les spécifications ARIANE, mais aussi en fonction des critères de tenue du moteur MARS et d'une réalisation simple et peu couteuse.

De plus cette structure doit être susceptible avec son interface de pouvoir s'adapter à d'autres configuration et d'avoir comme objectif de ne pas créer de soucis aux autres passagers du vol ARIANE.

Pour être simple la structure est basée sur des panneaux de réalisation facile avec inserts rapportés collés à froid. De même pour les générateurs solaires et les plateaux supérieurs ou plateau charge utile et inférieur ou plateau arrière.

Les liaisons et reprise des efforts se font par cornières en alliage léger boulonnées.

La liasse de structure a fait l'objet d'un balayage en faisabilité, analyse de la valeur simple mais efficace, étude des assemblages, revue des dessins et cotations. Le résultat est probant sur la rapidité de réalisation mais encore plus sur le nombre d'anomalies rencontrées : trois anomalies dont une venant d'une erreur de définition d'un équipement.

Masse de la structure environ 20 Kgs

Durée de réalisation moins de six mois.

5.2 - Méthode d'intégration

La méthodologie projet est expliquée dans le paragraphe suivant.

L'intégration est donc faite en fonction de cette méthodologie, c'est-à-dire une petite équipe intégrée, avec temps de réaction court.

L'équipe d'intégration comporte un ingénieur généraliste, un ingénieur électronicien, un agent technique mécanicien. A la demande un spécialiste RF, un cableur ou un spécialiste des systèmes de commande AOCS.

L'intégration se fait sur un seul lieu avec les stations de contrôle à base de calculateurs personnels utilisables pour la station sol.

La suite des opérations est la suivante :

- Intégration mécanique à blanc, puis démontage.

- Intégration équipement par équipement pour les alimentations de la gestion bord. Utilisation du cablage de vol pour les connections.

- Mesures des divers paramètres

- Intégration de la charge utile

- Essais avec télémesure et télécommande, étalonnages et vérifications.

- Essais de la partie Packet et linéaire

- Essais du système de pilotage et de commande

- Essais de la pyrotechnie

- Essai final aprés remontage de la structure et du système de largage.

- Essai de rotation et pesée/centrage/inertie

- Essais de vibrations sinus et acoustique

- Essai final et départ en campagne de lancement.

Tous les essais, toutes les procédures, toutes les anomalies sont disponibles pour consultation sur des livres de bord, mais sans formalisme.

Toutes les procédures et tous les compte-rendus d'essais sont décrits sur des documents réalisés de façon formelle.

5.3 - *Gestion du projet chez l'industriel*

La gestion d'un tel projet chez l'industriel nécessite une mise en oeuvre particulière, et les recommandations habituelles de base ont été suivies, c'est-à-dire :

- application de la loi de Pareto : 80% des coûts sont le résultat de 20% du temps passé en définition au départ : porter son effort sur l'analyse de la valeur et de risques. En particulier la liasse fabrication a fait l'objet d'une analyse serrée.

- faire dés le départ un organigramme technique en fonction des choix, le choix fondamental était : ARSENE ne doit donner aucune inquiétude mécanique aux autres passager durant le lancement. Ce choix s'est révélé exact pour les modifications de la définition initiale.

- travailler en groupe dés le départ avec la production, l'AIT, le bureau d'études, la qualité produit si nécessaire, les spécialistes, et bien sûr le responsable programme.

- suivre les recommandations sur le travail en groupe : ordre du jour, compte-rendu, courrier rapide (même porté à la main), communication des informations à tous les participants en temps réel, motivation.

- décider et réaliser si nécessaire, mais ne jamais laisser traîner les affaires; La durée de décision sur quelques modifications et leur réalisation n'a pas dépassé deux heures dans certains cas.

- tenir des réunions courtes avec le client et avec peu de participants.

- les dépenses et leur contrôle, les modifications, l'avancement du projet sont dans les mains d'une seule personne. Le contrôle des coûts se fait chaque mois dès que le fichier informatique de suivi des coûts est disponible.

- essayer de prévenir les anomalies plutôt que de passer du temps à les réparer. Ne pas faire d'essais que l'on ne saura pas exploiter!

L'équipe est composée selon les moments entre quatre/cinq personnes et sept au maximum.

5.4 - La rigueur, la qualité, les coûts

5.4.1 - La rigueur et la qualité

Dés le départ réalisation d'un organigramme technique qui permet de définir les tâches, qui fait quoi, ainsi que les lots de travaux et les fiches de tâches.

Ecriture des spécifications aussi rapidement puis revue de tout ce qui est nécessaire pour bien travailler : c'est la revue de structuration.

Ensuite application de la prévention :

- revue de liasse y compris par le responsable programme

- revue des points critiques chaque fois que cela est nécessaire

- analyse des solutions sur les plans fonctionnels ; de la valeur ; des risques.

Tout ceci de façon naturelle et non formelle.

La qualité est une qualité produit qui fonctionne à la demande une grande partie des actions étant menées par les participants et le responsable programme. L'appel au spécialiste ne se fait que pour les cas ou le projet a besoin d'informations ou d'un jugement particulier.

La rigueur a été un des objectifs :

- pas de réunion sans ordre du jour

- pas de fin de réunion sans compte-rendu et actions listées répondant à la question : qui et pour quand ?

- liste d'actions entre projet et industriel tenue à jour

- gestion permanente en temps quasi réel de :

  • suivi des modifications

  • du logiciel

  • des opérations de contrôle et de mise en oeuvre

  • de remontée vers la liasse des modifications.

5.4.2 - Les coûts

Les méthodes exposées vont dans le sens de la réduction des coûts, mais pour mieux cerner ceux-ci il faut travailler aux justes spécifications, rechercher les ratio de prix favorables avec analyse des risques chez les sous-traitants.

Par exemple le choix du sous-traitant pour le plateau 1920mm n'a demandé qu'une dizaine de jours pour décider.

Les procédures sont simplifiées.

Les évolutions des coûts sont suivies en permanence, ainsi que engagements, pointages, dépenses diverses.

Résultat : plateforme nue, y compris panneaux GS mais sans cônes carbone aux environs de 1, 5 MF.

5.5 - Les expériences à en tirer

5.5.1 - Sur le management du projet

Les expériences acquises montrent que la loi de Pareto ou des 80/20 s'applique à plein et que la bataille des coûts se gagne dés le départ d'un programme. Des efforts importants doivent être consentis au départ sur l'organisation, les choix, l'organigramme technique, la définition des tâches et des produits simples ou composites.

Le travail en groupe est la base et le groupe doit être motivé naturellement, si la motivation et l'appropriation du projet est bonne le travail se fait "presque tout seul!"

La gestion des coûts et des travaux doit se faire de la même façon que le suivi des objectifs techniques.

Pour un petit programme comme celui-ci les coûts réduits passent par un responsable unique et si possible pluri-disciplinaire qui suive aussi bien les liasses, que les modifications, que les engagements etc...

5.5.2 - Pour l'industriel

Une des questions de fond est : faut-il faire une PME spécifique pour un petit programme ou pas ? Je pensais au départ que oui, dans la réalité si ce programme est marginal par rapport aux autres produits on peut travailler avec une structure traditionnelle en acceptant certaines contraintes.

Je pense cependant qu'il faudrait plus d'ouverture sur les méthodes de travail dans certains cas, et je reconnais que toute structure sans valeur ajoutée directe a été contournée, cela ne veut pas forcément dire que cette structure n'est pas nécessaire pour d'autres programmes.

Le tout est de définir simple et de savoir décider vite en fonction de l'expérience.

5.5.3 - Pour le client

Les relations client/industriel doivent être bonnes et bien définies. Il faut de plus que le client s'adapte à ses propres exigences, c'est-à-dire qu'il accepte pour un programme à faible coûts d'avoir une équipe réduite.

Une équipe forte et nombreuse chez le client n'est pas compatible avec une équipe réduite chez l'industriel.

Les réunions doivent être peu nombreuses et avec la participation juste nécessaire. Une réunion avec de nombreux participants entraîne mathématiquement beaucoup de questions, beaucoup de remise en cause par le sentiment de chacun des spécialistes d'où beaucoup d'heures consommées. Cela ne veut pas dire qu'il ne faut pas utiliser les experts, bien au contraire, mais il faut les utiliser comme pour initialiser des données d'intelligence artificielle!

Il faut donc une remise en cause fondamentale et réelle des habitudes et des relations client/industriel.

CONCLUSION

Le mini-satellite ARSENE est une réalité. Il existe à l'Etablissement de l'Aérospatiale Cannes où il a subi avec succés les essais d'environnement. Il a même fait quelques liaisons d'essai au sol dans son fonctionnement nominal et dans tous ses modes ; il n'attend donc plus que le lancement où il pourra prouver en orbite que malgré toutes les péripéties de sa vie agitée il est bien vivant...

Il a eu en effet a subir des tribulations techniques, des attaques de sceptiques qui disaient le projet non-viable, des renoncements devant les difficultés ; mais heureusement pour lui certains de ses pères ont fait preuve de détermination et même de passion pour mener à bien la fin de sa réalisation et lui donner la parole en orbite.

Son histoire peut se résumer par des mots :

- tribulations techniques et humaines

- attaques

- lassitude

- renoncement

- oubli, indifférence

- embuches

- hétérogénéité

- astuce

- intelligence

- détermination

- passion

Dans quel ordre les écrire, quels verbes utiliser pour condenser l'histoire d'Arsène au travers de ces mots ? Vraisemblablement tout ordre choisi pourrait résumer Arsène.

Il ne faut pas aussi oublier que ce programme a permis à de nombreux étudiants de se faire la main sur les techniques spatiales et aussi de valider in situ des travaux pour mener à bien ce genre de réalisation. Il permettra en orbite encore à d'autres étudiants de mieux comprendre ce qu'est un contrôle d'attitude ou une télécommande/télémesure.

Il va aussi permettre au-delà des frontières et des océans de faire communiquer tout un monde de passionnés que sont les radio-amateurs et dans des conditions expérimentales aujourd'hui et pourquoi pas professionnelles demain ?

Nous plagions, sans remords, mais avec leur accord, un intervenant majeur du projet Arsène l'ENSAE :

L'histoire d'Arsène est un conte.

"La formule utilisée pour la fin d'un conte est traditionnelle :"il vécurent heureux...". En fait, est-ce bien la fin d'un conte, ou le début d'une nouvelle histoire ? Car enfin, oserait-on laisser se perdre un tel retour d'expérience, les concepts d'Arsène, petit satellite simple et robuste, de la classe des 150 kg, pourvu d'un moteur d'apogée, du lancement sur Ariane en troisième passager, d'une station de développement et de contrôle évolutive utilisant au maximum des éléments banalisés et peu coûteux, le rapprochement productif des milieux industriels et de l'enseignement, la diffusion de la culture de l'espace. Aucun doute, c'est le début d'une nouvelle histoire."

Alors pour finir de façon plus poétique disons qu'ARSENE est une belle histoire de la technique, et de l'amitié et qu'elle mérite un "happy-end" où il faut espérer que comme dans tous les contes "il vivra heureux et aura beaucoup d'enfants".

Mais ceci est une autre histoire trés proche de nous ; mais ne sommes nous pas là pour en parler ?

Peut-être lors d'un prochain séminaire ?

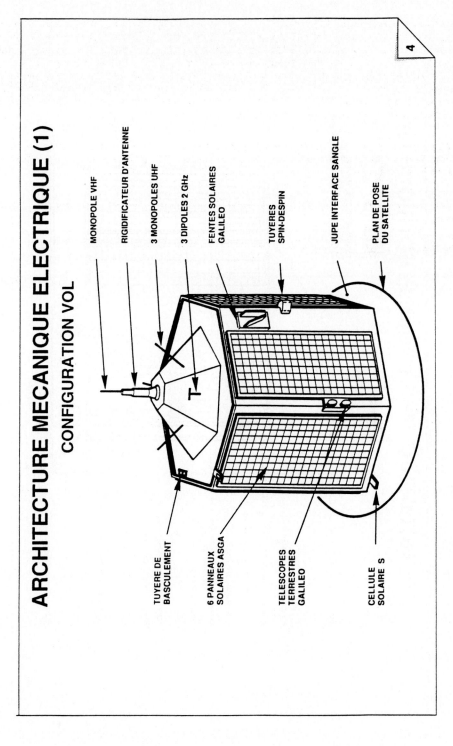

ARCHITECTURE MECANIQUE ELECTRIQUE (1)

CONFIGURATION VOL

MONOPOLE VHF

RIGIDIFICATEUR D'ANTENNE

3 MONOPOLES UHF

3 DIPOLES 2 GHz

FENTES SOLAIRES
GALILEO

TUYERES
SPIN-DESPIN

JUPE INTERFACE SANGLE

PLAN DE POSE
DU SATELLITE

TUYERE DE
BASCULEMENT

6 PANNEAUX
SOLAIRES ASGA

TELESCOPES
TERRESTRES
GALILEO

CELLULE
SOLAIRE S

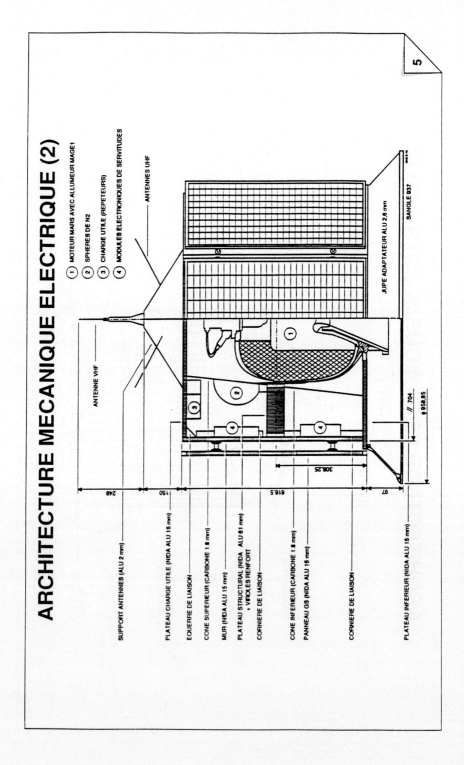

ARCHITECTURE MECANIQUE ELECTRIQUE (2)

1 MOTEUR MARS AVEC ALLUMEUR MAGE1
2 SPHERES DE N2
3 CHARGE UTILE (REPETEURS)
4 MODULES ELECTRONIQUES DE SERVITUDES

ANTENNES UHF

ANTENNE VHF

SUPPORT ANTENNES (ALU 2 mm)

PLATEAU CHARGE UTILE (NIDA ALU 15 mm)

EQUERRE DE LIAISON

CONE SUPERIEUR (CARBONE 1.8 mm)

MUR (NIDA ALU 15 mm)

PLATEAU STRUCTURAL (NIDA ALU 81 mm)
+ VIROLES RENFORT

CORNIERE DE LIAISON

CONE INFERIEUR (CARBONE 1.8 mm)

PANNEAU GS (NIDA ALU 15 mm)

CORNIERE DE LIAISON

PLATEAU INFERIEUR (NIDA ALU 15 mm)

JUPE ADAPTATEUR ALU 2.6 mm

SANGLE 937

248
150
618.5
97

308.25

// 704

ⵁ 958.85

5

ORBITE FINALE - MISE ET MAINTIEN A POSTE

1 - INJECTION SUR L'ORBITE DE TRANSFERT
- SEPARATION D'ARSENE
- VITESSE DE SPIN $W_0 \leqslant 5$ tr / mn

2 - MISE EN ROTATION JUSQU'A $W_1 \simeq 60$ tr / mn
3 - MESURE ET CORRECTION FINE DE L'ATTITUDE
4 - REMISE EN SPIN JUSQU'A $W_2 = 90$ tr / mn

5 - MISE A FEU DU MOTEUR D'APOGEE
::::> INJECTION SUR L'ORBITE FINALE

ORBITE FINALE
(20 000 Km / 36 000 Km / 0 DEGRE)

ARSENE

ORBITE DE TRANSFERT
(200 Km / 36 000 Km / 07 DEGRES)

TERRE
KOUROU

CNES 153

6 - DESPIN JUSQU'A $W_3 \simeq 60$ tr / mn
7 - BASCULEMENT DE L'AXE X DE 98 DEGRES (90° SUR L'EQUATEUR)
8 - MESURE DE L'ATTITUDE AVANT ET APRES LE BASCULEMENT

9 - AJUSTEMENT DE LA VITESSE DE SPIN A $W_4 \simeq 60$ tr / mn
10 - MAINTIEN D'ATTITUDE ET DE VITESSE DE SPIN

W_1 X W_2 X W_0 X W_3 X W_4 X

DIAGRAMME FONCTIONNEL ARSENE

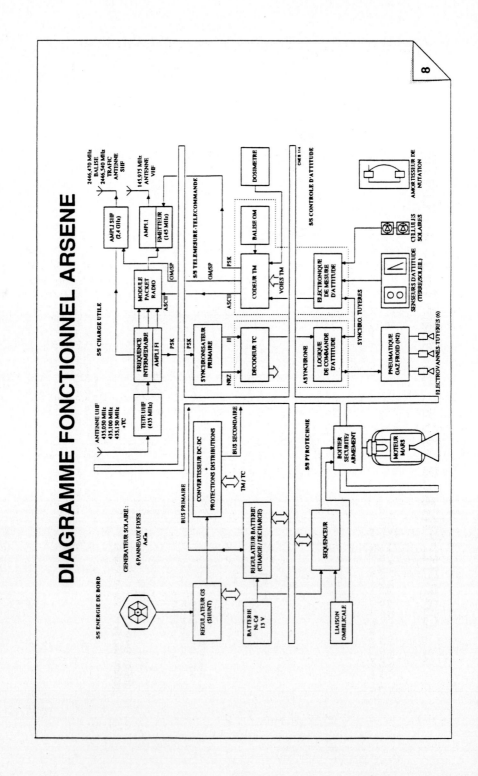

TUBSAT, Low Cost Access to Space Technology

U. Renner, B. Lübke-Ossenbeck, P. Butz

Technical University of Berlin, Germany

Abstract

Low cost access to space technology is based on the balance between low cost experiments, low cost launch opportunities (secondary payloads) and low cost space platforms. This paper describes the TUBSAT design philosophy that provides at affordable cost conditions all necessary services to the customer: volume, mass, electrical power, data transmission, thermal control and last not least high accuracy attitude control to any desired direction.

1. Design Concept

Space technology is beginning to become conservative in comparison with terrestrial developments. This reflects the lack of low cost test opportunities in orbit. "Low Cost" is a reasonable percentage of the development cost of a particular space technology experiment, as for example electric propulsion devices, star trackers, GaAs-Solar arrays, inflatable structures or surface tension tanks.

The development cost of each device is in the 10 Mio dollar ball park. The customer would be prepared to pay up to 1 additional Mio dollar for in orbit qualification. In average, 3 experiments can be integrated on a single experimental platform. Hence we are talking about available funding in the order of 3 Mio dollar to be evenly shared between the experiments, the spacecraft and the launch services.

Launch services for less than 1 Mio dollar are only available for secondary passengers who accept the rules of the game:

1. late notice of launch opportunity
   (typically 1 year in advance)

2. pre-definded orbit

3. severe mass and volume restrictions

4. no mercy in case of late delivery.

To comply with these requirements, the spacecraft has to be extremely simple and adaptable a) to the mass, volume and orbit constraints of the launcher and b) to the mass, volume and field of view expectations of the experimentors.

2 . Launch Opportunity

The most regular launch opportunity for secondary payloads is presently provided by Arianespace within the ASAP programme. As shown in Fig.1, up to 4 passengers can ride on a narrow platform into low earth orbit or elliptical GEO transfer orbits. The size of each passenger is limited to less than 0.5 m in each direction, the mass to less than 50kg. The launch cost for each passenger is in the order of 0.5 Mio dollar. The ejection mechanism has to be provided by the customer, only the ejection signal to the pyrotechnical bolt cutter will be transmitted by Arianespace.

Fig. 1:   ARIANE V44/ASAP Launch Opportunity

Comparable opportunities on a case by case basis are made available by NASA on the STS-GAS programme, by Mc Donnel Douglas on Delta, by OSC on Pegasus and by the Russian space agency on MIR and a number of low orbiting launchers. The constraints are similar, but never exactly the same.

3. Structure, Power Supply, Thermal Control

Fig. 2 shows the primary structure of TUBSAT-A (Technical University of Berlin Satellite) that has been launched on Ariane V44/ASAP on 17 July 1991. The frame of aluminium profiles is adapted to the available ASAP volume (38 x 38 x 38 cm). As much of this volume as possible shall be made available to the experiments. For this reason, the battery cells (NiCd) are spread flat on the bottom and sandwiched between two 5 mm thick aluminium plates to provide favourable thermal conditions.

Fig. 2:   Primary Structure of TUBSAT-A

Once the experiments are integrated, the frame is covered by 3 mm thick aluminium plates. TUBSAT-A is not attitude controlled. Hence every surface that is not needed for experiments (Fig. 3) is covered with solar cells. If attitude control is available, as on future TUBSAT models, only one panel needs to be covered with solar cells and the remaining 5 surfaces can be given to the experiments.

Since the inner volume of TUBSAT-A was not required by the experimentors, it was convenient to implement the ejection spring inside the spacecraft (Fig. 4). For future missions where more demanding experiments (propellant tanks, inflatable structures) may require the inner volume, an external ejection mechanism is envisaged.

Fig. 3: TUBSAT-A

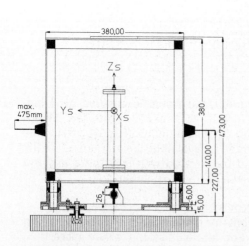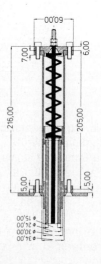

Fig. 4: Ejection Mechanism inside TUBSAT-A

This structure is rather compact and stiff (natural frequency at180 Hz), provides sufficient mechanical protection, thermal capacity and conductivity and some shielding against space radiation. The mass of 10 kg is not eccessive in comparison with the total mass envelope of 50kg. Typically, secondary payloads (that fly instead of ballast mass) are more volume than mass constraint.

Thermal control is achieved by black painting or black anodizing. The average temperature in orbit is 0°C which is acceptable to the battery and convenient for the electronics and in particular for the CCD sensors. If the spacecraft is controlable, the average temperature can be raised by 20°C by pointing a corner of the cube constantly towards the sun or lowered by 20°C by pointing a face to the sun.

4. TTC and Data Handling

The TTC and data handling unit used on TUBSAT-A (Fig. 5) consists of a standard handheld transceiver (Yaesu FT-23R) that transmits and receives at VHF two audio frequencies (1200 and 1800 Hz). It is augmented by a printed circuit containing the FFSK modem (upper right) and a single chip processor (lower left). This unit communicates with the ground station at a rate of 1200 baud and is responsible for the health of the spacecraft and the experiments, in particular for the battery charge control. TUBSAT-B will provide additional high speed data transmission capacity at 19.200 baud (GMSK modulation) and extended data storage capacity (4 M byte).

Fig. 5: TTC and Data Handling Unit

The TTC antenna on board consists of a single λ/4 monopole antenna (Fig. 3, the second antenna is redundant). The ground station uses a steerable circular polarized Yagi antenna.

5. Attitude Control

Attitude control is not necessary for space radiation or communication experiments at lower frequencies, e.g. at VHF since the on board antenna characteristic is omnidirectional.

Attitude control is not strictly neccessary but convenient for power supply (only one solar array) and thermal control as discussed before.

Attitude control is mandatory for the majority of space technology experiments, i. e. communication experiments at higher frequencies, solar cell experiments , earth, sun and star sensors, propulsion experiments, microgravity research, inflatable structures, tethered satellites or rendezvous manoeuvers. In particular, when the relative orbital position within a chain of satellites has to be maintained, attitude control is a must.

The target for this control is, depending on the experiment, the sun, a star, a second satellite or a dedicated point on the earth, i.e. a variable fixed or slowly moving target.

The TUBSAT attitude control system is based on 3 reaction wheels (Fig.6). The reaction torques are sufficient to re-orient the spacecraft

Fig. 6:   Reaction Wheel Assembly

to any desired orientation within 1 minute. The total mass of the reaction wheel assembly including 3 reaction wheels, the associated wheel drive electronics and the attitude control electronics is 2.5 kg. The overall dimensions are 10 x 10 x 15 cm.

3 axis information is provided by a star sensor (Fig. 7) with the dimensions 12 x 10 x 3 cm and a mass of 0.5 kg. The pointing accuracy depends on the selection of the focal length of the optics. In the present design, a focal length of 18 mm is implemented, the associated field of view is 20 x 30 degrees and the accuracy in the arc min ball park.

Fig. 7:   3 Axis Star Sensor

This star sensor is presently being qualified on board TUBSAT-A. Fig. 8 shows a typical test result that has been obtained on 1 June 1992, i.e. almost 1 year into the orbital life time; 16 consecutive exposures at 0.5 min intervals show a number of traces (i.e. stars) plus a few single spots (i.e. noise). The signal is separated from the noise in Fig. 9 and the centre of rotation is established. 7 different objects are visible. Any one of them deliveres sufficient information on the centre, the rate and the sense of rotation, i.e. the same information as 3 rate gyros. In this case, a sector of 60° is achieved in 7 sec i.e. a full rotation in 7 x 6 = 42 sec (1.4 rpm).

Star identification via brightness and geometrical configuration is the next step: Fig. 10 shows that the bright star no. 1 (Fig. 9) with saturated signal is Jupiter (magnitude - 2) and that the weak signal of star no. 7 that hardly exceeds the noise background is a star of magnitude 4.6. This picture demonstrates the dynamic range of the sensor and its sensitivity even at reasonably high rates of rotation.

The on board control loop is based on a further data reduction: only one pair of stars is selected, and relative angles α, β, γ are measured as shown in Fig. 11. These angles are used as targets for 3 individual reaction wheel control loops. If $\alpha = \beta = \gamma = 0$, the spacecraft remains where it is (without any drift). If the targets are biased, the spacecraft can be directed to any desired direction.

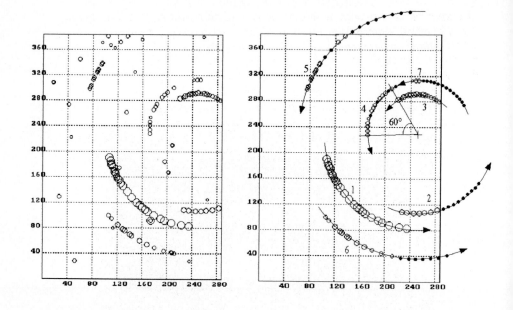

Fig. 8:   Raw Sensor Data

Fig. 9:   Filtering and Extrapolation
of Star Tracks

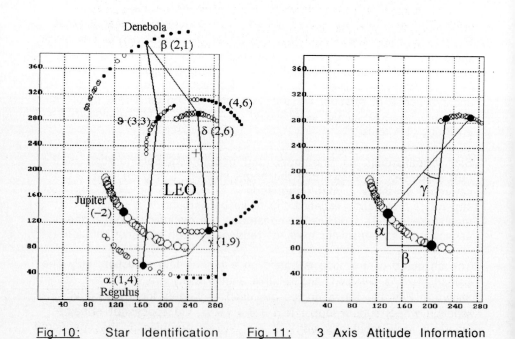

Fig. 10:   Star Identification

Fig. 11:   3 Axis Attitude Information

The validity of the design has been verified on a 3 axis air bearing (Fig.12) where a dynamically representative model of TUBSAT-B (same inertia distribution) has been locked via 3 reaction wheel control loops to the star background of Berlin at night. The test set-up was on top of the university building.

Fig. 12:   3 Axis Air Bearing Test

Reaction wheels are unable to compensate external disturbance torques. At reasonably low orbits these torques are mainly due to residual magnetic dipols on board interacting with the magnetic field of the earth. The most straight forward method for compensation is a switchable dipol, i.e. a copper or aluminium coil wrapped around the spacecraft (say 100 times or less). A single coil is sufficient since the attitude control system can provide any desired orientation.

6. Summary

The appealing aspect of a microsatellite is that it can be dedicated to a single (or a few) experiment, in comparison with e.g. spacelab where 80 experiments are flown together. However, to achieve this goal, the cost of the platform and the launch cost have to be balanced with the cost of the experiment.

In addition, the microplatform should provide similar resources (mass, volume, power, data transmission, thermal and attitude control) as a large platform like spacelab or EURECA.

TUBSAT-A is a prototype that verifies the design concept, qualifies data transmission and data handling and in particular the 3 axis star sensor.

TUBSAT-B (to be launched next year) and future models will provide a structure that is adaptable to the individual launch opportunity and leaves as much room as possible to the experiments. It deliveres all neccessary servies and in particular 3 axis attitude control with arc min accuracy to any desired direction. The total cost for the spacecraft will remain within the 1 Mio dollar target.

Plate-formes standards pour petits satellites.

Marc SCHAEFER

EREMIS, Paris, FRANCE

L'expérience d'un projet tel que SARA permet à une équipe de proposer des plate-formes utilisables pour des missions variées. Des solutions classiques sont étudiées dans l'objectif de s'adapter à des interfaces lanceurs particulières. L'originalité de la démarche consiste à adapter la plate-forme à la mission tout en s'adaptant aux moyens de lancement. L'augmentation des opportunités de lancements tant à l'est qu'à l'ouest vont permettre de concrétiser ces projets.

Introduction

Une expérience de plusieurs années.

SARA (Satellite Amateur de Radio Astronomie) est un petit satellite mis en orbite par Ariane en juillet 1991 (vol 44). SARA a permis à une équipe compétente d'assimiler et de rationnaliser à l'échelle des petits projets spatiaux les techniques spatiales.

Cette expérience est un atout important pour augmenter les chances de succès d'une mission orbitale. En effet quelques soient les choix qui ont été fait pour SARA ils ont conduit une équipe à aller jusqu'au bout d'un projet spatial, ce qui n'est pas si fréquent.

Un environnement adapté.

Cette équipe a souhaité se regrouper pour former une société capable de mener à bien des projet non plus dans le cadre amateur mais dans un cadre professionnel.

C'est ainsi qu'EREMIS (Etude et REalisation de MIcroSatellites) propose plusieurs structures orbitales capables d'embarquer les missions les plus variées.

L' exemple suivant illustre la simplicité de ces réalisations et les possibilités de microsatellites rapidement disponibles à faible coût. Ils ne sont pas restrictifs. Il est essentiel de comprendre que ces projets peuvent s'adapter rapidement à la mission choisie. C'est cette adaptabilité qui est la principale caratéristique des missions légères.

Une plateforme stabilisée trois axes.

Le châssis.

Le satellite est un parallélépidède très allongé: sa longueur est de 900 mm alors que sa section n'est que de 300 * 300 mm. Il est réalisé en alliage d'aluminium. Sa masse avec l'adaptateur et les équipements est de 40 à 50 kg.

La tenue mécanique est assurée par une cheminée centrale courant sur les 900 mm, de section 230 * 230 mm, constituée de quatre tôles usinées en treillis et assemblées par soudure. La cheminée se termine à chaque extrémité par une pièce soudée de 300 * 300 mm ouverte au centre sur 210 * 210 mm. Tous les équipements se fixent sur cette cheminée (à l'extérieur pour les cartes électroniques, à l'intérieur pour les objets volumineux). Le satellite est fixé sur le lanceur par ses deux pièces d'extrémité, la séparation est obtenue par une chaîne pyrotechnique expansible.

L'une des petites faces est orientée au Nadir. C'est elle qui stabilise thermiquement le satellite, grâce à un revêtement à forte émissivité infra-rouge recouvrant la pièce d'extrémité inférieure et son bouchon: ce revêtement met le satellite à l'équilibre avec la Terre. Cette face nadir supporte les antennes et les instruments de télédétection.

L'autre petite face, orientée au Zénith, est recouverte d'un isolant thermique, à l'exception des mécanismes de contrôle thermique qui découvrent plus ou moins des surfaces à haute émissivité.

Les quatre panneaux solaires forment les grandes faces du satellite. Ils se fixent sur les pièces d'extrémité par des liaisons qui les isolent thermiquement de la cheminée. Ils sont réalisés en aluminium et leurs grands côtés sont reliés mécaniquement (ce qui donne la raideur à l'ensemble des panneaux) et thermiquement (ceci permet de gagner 40 % de puissance électrique en refroidissant le panneau éclairé).

On notera qu'il n'est nécessaire de déployer aucune antenne, aucune perche de gradient de gravité ni aucun panneau solaire, ce qui est très favorable à la fiabilité du satellite.

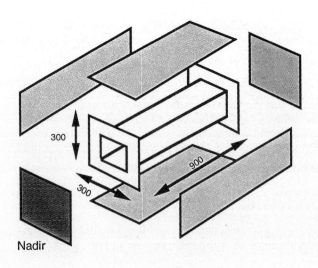

Le contrôle d'attitude.

La stabilisation en tangage et roulis est obtenue par gradient de gravité. La forme allongée du châssis évite de recourir à une perche. Deux capteurs situés sur les petites faces du satellite, constitués d'une surface absorbant les infra-rouges mais pas la lumière visible, détectent la présence de la Terre par la chaleur qu'elle rayonne: si le satellite s'est stabilisé tête en bas, une roue à inertie fait un nombre de tours prédéterminé, ce qui fait réaliser un demi-tour au satellite.

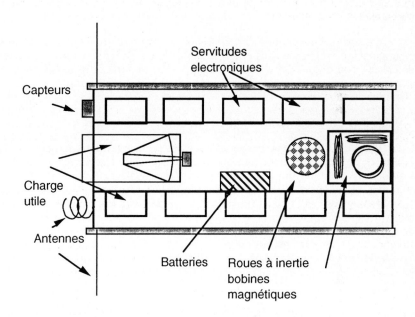

Nestor est stabilisé sur trois axes: une petite face est au Nadir, l'autre au Zénith, les grandes faces sont respectivement devant, derrière, à droite et à gauche dans le sens de la marche.

La stabilisation en lacet est dûe à l'effet gyroscopique de la même roue à inertie en rotation lente. Le satellite étant stabilisé en position verticale, il fait un tour sur lui-même à chaque orbite. L'axe de la roue est orienté droite-gauche: en présence d'un angle de lacet non nul, cet axe bascule sur lui-même d'un tour en 100 mn, ce qui crée un couple gyroscopique annulant le lacet.

Il convient encore d'amortir les oscillations du satellite autour des axes de tangage, roulis et lacet: on utilise à cet effet le champ magnétique terrestre, qui induit des courants de Foucault dans des bobines. On donne à ces bobines une résistance artificiellement faible (inférieure à ce que permet le cuivre) en forçant par une alimentation externe le courant à y circuler pour annuler les variations de flux magnétique dans la bobine.

Tous ces couples stabilisateurs sont largement supérieurs à ceux créés par la traînée aérodynamique (à 800 km d'altitude) et la pression de rayonnement. En revanche, il faut prendre garde aux couples magnétiques: les boucles de courant et les aimants permanents ne doivent pas excéder 10-2 A.m2 (les bobines amortisseuses seront parcourues par un courant permanent pour compenser les fuites magnétiques des moteurs électriques), et il faut utiliser des matériaux amagnétiques pour les grandes pièces (c'est d'ailleurs le nickel des accumulateurs qui limite la précision du pointage).

On arrive finalement à une précision de pointage de l'ordre de 2°. On notera que le pointage est obtenu sans que le satellite ait à mesurer son attitude et déduire par des calculs compliqués la correction à apporter, et sans faire usage de tuyères de contrôle d'attitude avec leur tuyauterie associée: là encore, la simplicité est favorable à la fiabilité du satellite.

Les ressources de la charge utile.

Plusieurs emplacements sont disponibles pour loger des équipements. Les faces extérieures de la cheminée offrent quatre emplacements fractionnables de 900 * 230 * 15 mm, qui accueilleront typiquement des cartes électroniques. L'intérieur de la cheminée , qui peut communiquer avec le Nadir et le Zénith, autorise un encombrement de 160 * 160 * 900 mm à partager avec les accumulateurs, la roue à inertie et les bobines amortisseuses: c'est suffisant pour un téléscope de télédétection, par exemple. La face Nadir, qui reste accessible lorsque le satellite est monté sur l'adaptateur du lanceur, est un endroit privilégié pour monter les capteurs qui feront face à la Terre. La face Zénith peut accueillir les capteurs qui ne doivent pas observer la Terre, ou les expériences fonctionnant à très basse température par refroidissement radiatif.

Tous ces emplacement offrent des températures clémentes, entre -5 et +15 °C. Les capteurs et composants qui supportent entre -50 et +90 °C pourront être montés sur les panneaux solaires; la stabilisation du satellite en lacet permet de distinguer les faces avant et arrière, par exemple pour les mesures d'impacts.

La masse maximum embarquable est de l'ordre de 10 kg. On remarquera l'accessibilité de tous les sites.

La puissance électrique à partager entre les expériences et les émetteurs radio est de 8 W (en moyenne sur une orbite). Elle peut augmenter de 40% si on utilise des photopiles à l'arséniure de gallium.

La mémoire est constituée de puces de silicium de 1 Mbit chacune. La place et la puissance disponibles permettent d'envisager une capacité de 1,5 Gbit, soit un peu plus qu'une image de 6000 * 6000 pixels de 32 bits chacun.

C'est surtout la complexité de la station terrestre qui détermine le débit des transmissions descendantes. Si le récepteur au sol traite et mémorise les messages en temps réel et dispose d'une antenne de gain 23 dBi (soit quatre hélices couplées), on peut transmettre en UHF avec 10 W et une modulation de phase à quatre états jusqu'à 128 kbit/s, soit 1,5 Gbit en 3 jours à raison de 6 passages de 10 mn par jour. Si on veut mémoriser le signal reçu sur une cassette audio et le décoder en temps différé, un débit de 9600 bit/s est possible en VHF ou UHF avec une petite antenne. Enfin, on pourrait même imaginer de transmettre 500 caractères par passage en utilisant la balise modulée en Morse, recevoir avec une antenne non pointée et décoder les messages à l'oreille...Pour ce qui concerne la liaison montante, un débit de 9600 bit/s permet de transférer 5,8 Mbit à chaque passage.

Les applications.

Sur une orbite quasi-polaire à 800km d'altitude, la durée de vie n'est limitée que par la santé du satellite. Lancé à coté d'un satellite placé sur une trajectoire héliosynchrone, un petit satellite sans contrôle d'orbite dérive lentement. Les applications sont très larges; la liste n'est pas exhaustive:

-test de composants en orbite: la capacité d'emporter sur une même plateforme un grand nombre de composants et de tester en vraie grandeur les contraintes orbitales, justifient cette méthode par rapport aux tests au sol.

-observation de la terre: même sur une petite plateforme, il est possible d'atteindre des performances intéressantes (résolutions de quelques dizaines de mètres et champs de quelques dizianes de kilomètres).

-messageries.

-suivi des phénomènes naturels, comme, par exemple, les volcans. Ce suivi peut comporter une partie imagerie embarquée et une partie écoute et retransmission des messages de balises au sol.

-tous les sujets ci-dessus peuvent être exploités dans un cadre scolaire avec un but pédagogique dominant les aspects opérationnels

Coûts et délais.

L'intérêt des petites structure est de parvenir à des prix de revient très bas. Le coût de ces plateformes hors charge utile se situe aux alentours des 7MF. Ces prix se justifient aisément lorsqu'on observe la durée de développement (<2ans) et le petit nombre de personnes qui y travaillent (<5).

Les opportunités de lancement

Les possibilités de lancement à l'est comme à l'ouest sont multiples. L'adaptation des gros lanceurs est quasi-universelle et chaque constructeur prévois une plate-forme du même type que celui développé par Arianespace.

L'expérience du projet SARA nous permet de bien appréhender les problèmes spécifiques soulévés par ces projets. Les possibilités du plateau ASAP sont certainement plus grandes que celles annoncées et il est toujours possible de dégager des compromis pour des utilisations spécifiques.

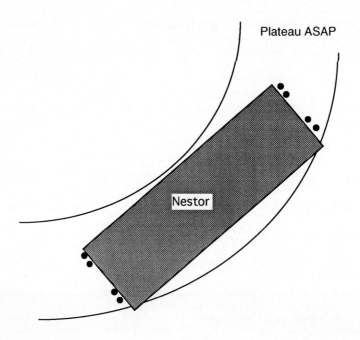

Plateau ASAP

Nestor

Les lanceurs Russes sont porteurs de grands espoirs dans ce domaine. Les prix et les fréquences de lancement sont hautement intéressants. Des programmes de démonstration doivent être menés pour en prouver la fiabilité et en évaluer les possibilités opérationnelles.

conclusion.

La réalisation de systèmes spatiaux utilisables pour des applications scientifiques ou civiles n'est plus le seul privilège des grosses structures. Le coût de ces projets et désormais à la dimension de petites sociétés dynamiques. Les petites plateformes ne doivent pas se limiter à des produits du type plateformes à gradients de gravité. Certes ces satellites réunissent des caractéristiques de simplicité et de pérénnités séduisantes cependant leurs performances sont limités. Les possibilités de miniaturisations ainsi que la disponibilité de composants civils utlisables permet la réalisation de plate-formes évoluées atteignant les performances de pointage et de contrôle d'orbites nécessaires aux projets ambitieux. L'accès aux orbites geostationnaires ne doit pas être non plus négligée. Ainsi on pourra assister à une rationalisation de l'accès à l'espace.

MINISAT PROGRAMME

Dr. José M. Dorado

Instituto Nacional de Técnica Aeroespacial
MADRID. SPAIN

ABSTRACT.

The interest of exploring the potentiality of small satellites is high for any country that wants to improve the means to perform operations in space. By this reason INTA has initiated the development of the MINISAT Programme.

The objective of the MINISAT Programme is to obtain the necessary elements to perform space missions in a way that, when compared with a "normal" mission, offers:

- similar payload support capabilities
- shorter program delays
- lower program costs

The basic programme approach aims to obtain, as a first step, a system composed of a space platform and a ground segment for orbit and mission control, both with a high degree of standardisation in their:

- contents and
- interfaces with payloads and launch vehicles

A MINISAT mission is normally based on a dedicated launch. Launch vehicles being considered in the design are: SCOUT 1, SCOUT SM and PEGASUS. Attention is also being paid to use other transport modes (A4 piggyback, shared launch)

The MINISAT design takes into consideration

- the own Spanish experience in this matter
- the market study performed by ESA (call for ideas, June 18, 1990)
- the NASA's SMEX program approach and proposals received
- ISAS scientific program experience
- typical application missions requirements (communications, observation)

The programme Phase C has started in March 1992, with company CASA, as prime contractor for the development of the system (platform + ground segment) reporting to INTA.

REASONS FOR THE INTEREST OF SMALL SYSTEMS.

Three main and new facts have modified the scenario of the space industry:

- advances in the field of materials, that have led to higher functional integration, higher process speeds and storage capacity of electronis data and to more sensitive detectors. As a result, **more reliable, economic and performing systems** have, respectively, been made possible.

- improved knowledge of the space systems and technologies
  As a result, **more reliable systems** can be designed and manufactured

- improved design and engineering tools (CAD, CAM, etc) that have permitted the design of **more reliable and economic systems**

The overall result of these changes is that more performing and reliable systems are now possible and that lower costs should be associated to this improvement. Alternatively, that competitive small systems are a feasible possibility.

Some constraints also exist that limit the benefits of these possibilities. They are a consequence of the fact that not all the equipments in a space system have evolved at the same pace. In this respect the most limiting aspects are:

- large size of electrical generators
- large mass of electrical batteries
- low specific impulse of propulsion systems
- increased demands of users

It is clear that potentialities of small systems can be used at their best in those cases in which the impact of these constraints can be minimised, i.e. full sun orbit, LEO and no propulsion requirement.

Finally, an added advantage of these small systems is the feasibility to provide a full service package (from payload to orbit data reception) at competitive rates and within affordable budgets

DESIGN OBJECTIVES OF THE MINISAT PLATFORM

The main requirement on the design of the MINISAT Platform is to obtain a product that be **attractive** and **affordable** to the user.

To be **attractive** the following requirements have been placed on the platform design:

- to offer the user a service as integrated as possible or the possibility of a hands-on operation
  This may take the form of a package including from payload integration to delivery of received data, or the form of direct satellite utilisation by the user
- to provide the payload with functional characteristics equivalent to the ones

that can be obtained in any large platform
- a "solo" flight to orbit, a "solo" use of the platform
- 2 years from program start to launch
- standard, simple and user-friendly interfaces to the payload
- flexibility to accomodate a wide range of payloads

To be **affordable** an approach has to be taken to protect costs. This approach considers:

- an integrated service package
- a design lifetime of three years around
- standard and simple interfaces between the different systems
- a modular platform concept with a high degree of standardisation
- a coherent industrial approach (team size, lot manufacture, user office)
- platform functional capabilities easily matched to mission needs
- additionally, the possibility of piggyback or shared flight.

CONCEPT OF THE MINISAT PLATFORM

The **first driver** in selecting an approach for the platform concept has been to achieve a **maximum of standardization**. This is not only a decission but almost a forced requirement as a result of the design objectives mentioned above. In consequence the problems associated with the standardisation of a space platform are being faced and must be solved in the best manner. These problems can be summarised in one: the risk to build-in a system functional overcapacity to cope with the requirements of the most demanding mission.

The selected concept is mainly a result of the approach taken to solve this trade-off between standardisation and efficiency. These are the main elements of this approach:

1-a division of the equipments into two groups

The first group contains those elements which are required in all missions
They are defined as **basic equipment**

The second group contains the payload equipment and other equipments that are needed for a particular mission.
They are defined as **specific equipment** and constitute the **real payload** of that particular mission.
Some of the equipments in this group are similar to the basic equipment (i.e momentum wheels)

2-a second division of the basic equipment into two new groups.

The first group contains the equipments that do not require any change or that requiring a change they can be used "as they are" because the penalty associated to this decission (i.e. the use of an "overdimensioned" equipment) can be accepted when considering other benefits

The second group contains the equipments that require a change for every mission and this is a not minor change. Within this group most the equipments accept a modular solution (i.e. storage batteries, solar panels) and in consequence most of the equipment in this group is quasi-basic equipment.

3-a grouping of the equipments by platform modules, in agreement with their individual nature: basic, quasi-basic and specific. A three modules physical configuration is so derived.

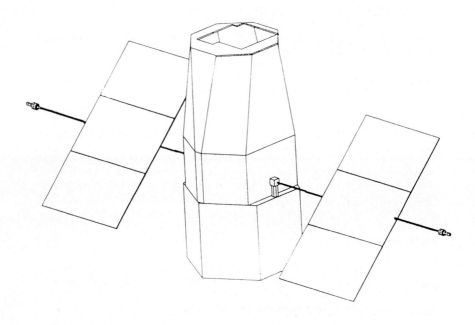

FIGURE 1. PHYSICAL CONFIGURATION

A **second driver** when defining the concept approach has been to **make full use of those advances that have made competitive the small systems**. These advances, already mentioned above, are: use of advanced IC´s, use of a maximum degree of functional integration, use of proven solutions and technologies, use of advanced engineering and design tools.

A **third driver** has been to adopt a **full system approach** including in the trade-off between standardisation and efficiency not only the platform elements but also the launch vehicle and the ground stations.

As an addition to this, an office has been created to initiate and maintain a close contact with all potential users since now. From this, important data on interface definition is expected.

Finally attention has also been given to analyse the **interest of different manufacture approaches**: lot manufacture at tbd level (equipment, subsystem, platform module) and to **limit the expensive activities** associated to an independent oversight of the work, relying instead in selected key personnel.

SITUATION OF THE MINISAT PROGRAMME

Phase A of this programme was completed by INTA within 1990 with the participation of AGUSTA (Italy) and SENER (Spain).

Phase B was completed within 1991 and was carried out by INTA with the support of Spanish companies: CASA, SENER and INISEL.

The programme was submitted to the approval of the Spanish Interministerial Comission for Science and Technology early in 1992. Final approval to perform **Phase C** was given in March 1992 with a budget of US $17 M.

The planned **Phase C Milestones** are as follows:

March 16th   1992   Start preparations for Phase C
May   4th   1992   KOM with prime contractor
June   1st   1992   KOM Phase C
Sept   14th   1992   SRR
Nov   30th   1992   PDR
Nov   1st   1993   CDR
March 31st   1994   Phase C completion.

Start of **Phase D** is planned for the end of 1993, overlapping the end of Phase C.

MAIN CHARACTERISTICS OF THE MINISAT PLATFORM

ORBIT
: L.E.O
300 Km minimum perigee
2000 Km maximum apogee
Inclinations from 0° to 100°
Optimised for circular orbits between 400 and 900 Km of altitude

LAUNCHERS
: SCOUT 1
SM SCOUT
PEGASUS
Also secondary ARIANE 4 P/L

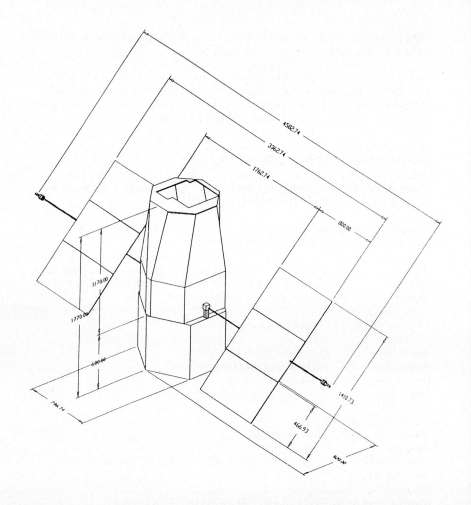

FIGURE 2

APLICATIONS	Scientific
	Technology demonstration
	Communications
	Earth Observation

DIMENSIONS   See Figure 2

MASS
Basic Modules	120 Kg
Specific equipment	70 Kg (up to)
Total for design	500 Kg
Avail for P/L	380 Kg (up to, theoretical pending on mission requirements and launcher capability)

ELECTRICAL POWER
Basic equipment	60 w
Specific equipment	20 w (up to)
Payload	150 w (up to, max eclipse)
Bus	28 V unregulated
Battery	NI-CD
Solar Generator	36 w EOL/panel
	6 to 12 panels

PAYLOAD DATA
Storage	20 Mbytes (basic)
Data Rate	1 Mbps
Telemetry	S band

STABILIZATION
| Basic | 1 axis, 0,5° |
| Optional | 3 axis, 0,1° |

PROPULSION
Optional, N2/N2H4
| Delta V | 100 m/s |

THE SPACE TECHNOLOGY RESEARCH VEHICLE: DEVELOPMENT STATUS

K.A.RYDEN

Space Sector, Defence Research Agency, Farnborough,UK.

ABSTRACT

The Space Technology Research Vehicles (STRVs) currently under development at the Defence Research Agency, UK, are briefly described and the up-to-date technical status is detailed.

The two STRVs are planned for launch in late 1993 and will carry into orbit a range of new technology which requires in-orbit evaluation prior to its application to much larger and more expensive missions. The new technologies include radiation-resistant microelectronics, radiation monitoring instruments, advanced structural materials, electrostatic hazard measuring instruments and alleviation techniques and new power system components.
Many of the research results of the mission are obtained during the satellites development phase, some of which are briefly summarized here.

1. INTRODUCTION

The STRV mission has been fully described in Reference 1: the information given there remains essentially accurate. A brief summary of the mission is given below.

Two 50kg satellites are to be launched into geostationary transfer orbit (GTO) as auxilliary payloads on an Ariane 4. Their mission is to enable research into the performance of a range of new on-board technologies over a one year period. GTO offers a number of important features for the research programme:

   a) A radiation dose equivalent to ten years in geostationary orbit is obtained in just one year, so enabling excellent radiation-tolerance tests to be performed.
   b) High altitudes are achieved at which the satellite is potentially subject to electrostatic charging and hence a proper study of this hazard is possible.
   c) Very low altitudes are also reached (200km) thus enabling a study of the atomic oxygen erosion of spacecraft surfaces to be performed.

The basic characteristics of the satellites are listed in Table 1 below. The two satellites, designated 1a and 1b, are very similar with regard to the platform design but carry different payloads.The technology experiments themselves have been contributed by a number of organizations including ESA and JPL as well as DRA.

The STRV orbit is highly elliptical and since only one ground station is to be used visibility is restricted to about 20% of each day on average. This therefore requires that the satellites have a considerable degree of on-board autonomy to operate experiments and also attitude control manouvres out of contact.

Table 1   STRV   Spacecraft Summary

Orbit	GTO (36 000km x 200km, i=7 deg.)
Launch	Ariane 4
Mass	50kg
Dimensions	40x50x50 cm (box)
Power	30W GaAs arrays
	28V regulated bus
Structure	Carbon-fibre PEEK
Attitude sensing	Sun angle (1a & 1b) Earth angle (1a)
Attitude control	Spin stabilization (5/10 rpm)
	Magnetorquer precession to maintain
	90+/-20 deg. sun angle
Communications	ESA TM/TC Packet standard
	1kb/s downlink at S-band
Ground Station	12m dish Lasham UK
On-board computers	Mil-std 1750 Silicon-on-sapphire
Software	ADA
Lifetime	1 year max.

In the paragraphs below a short summary of the status of each *engineering model* subsystem is provided. The qualification programme calls for one engineering model satellite which preceeds the two flight model spacecraft.

2. STRUCTURE

The concept of the structural design has been established for some time and manufacture and delivery of the EM structure is now completed. Some further drilling of the structure will be needed but the current task is the vibrational qualification of the structure using dummy masses (see Fig.1). So far, a resonance search has been performed to establish the major resonant modes of the structure. These tests have yet to be completed but have already given pointers to where local stiffening is required.

Fig.1 STRV Vibration Test

The use of carbon-fibre PEEK materials (employing aluminium honeycomb) for the bulk of the structure has proved to be successful so far except in the area of solar panels where sufficient surface flatness could not be achieved for the fragile gallium arsenide solar cells. Conventional aluminium panels are now being investigated as the safest and quickest alternative. Both STRV1a and STRV1b will now use carbon-PEEK structures.

Thermal tests on a structural and thermal model (prior to the EM) have also been completed (Fig. 2) and are being used to verify the finite element computer thermal model.

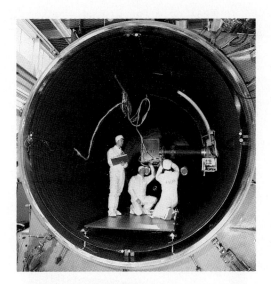

Fig 2. STRV Thermal Vacuum Test

3.POWER SYSTEM

The power system consists of solar arrays, power conditioning, batteries and electrical ground support equipment (EGSE).

Solar panel cell layouts have been finalized and an engineering model carbon-PEEK solar panel has been prepared with a variety of cells arranged in strings. However, in the light of the problem mentioned above a new aluminium EM solar panel will be required.

Low-cost batteries have been specified and procured and both thermal-vacuum and vibration tests have been completed.

The EGSE consists of a solar array simulator, a prototype power conditioning unit and a 'switching box'. The switching box is a bench version of the spacecraft's power switching and distribution unit which therefore enables manual control of the switches for ground checkout purposes. Individual incoming units are now undergoing compatibility tests with the switching box prior to acceptance.

The power conditioning subsystem design and EM development has been virtually completed and delivery of the EM unit itself is imminent. Environmental tests will then be carried out.

4. RF SYSTEM

The requirements on the RF system have been fixed and the EM transmitters and RFDU (Radio Frequency Distribution Unit) have been delivered and environmentally tested. Delivery of the EM receivers is still awaited. Power system compatibility tests with the transmitter highlighted an undesireble EMC interaction which has since been corrected by adding additional filtering in the transmiter power input stage.

A set of RF EGSE is available for ground checkout purposes which includes a test receiver and test transmitter which forms a 'mini-ground station' (see Fig.3).

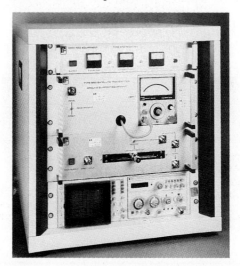

Fig 3. RF System EGSE

Antenna patterns have now been measured using both an aluminium model 'tin-sat' and a cabon-PEEK model satellite. The differences between the patterns in the two cases has been found to be relatively small, although the potential effect of the carbon-fibre structure was previously a cause for concern.

RF system to ground segment compatibility tests are now planned for the summer of 1992.

5. OBDH SYSTEM

The on-board data handling (OBDH) system employs the ESA packet telemetry and telecommand standard which allows a flexible approach to link utilization especially with regard to the use of the on-board computers. The OBDH system consists of an 'up-link unit' (or telecommand packet decoder) a 'command distribution unit', a 'data acquisition unit' and a 'downlink unit' (or telemetry frame assembler). In addition there are two on-board computers which employ the Mil-Std 1750. At the time of

writing all the above units have been designed and simulated on
CAD systems. In most cases preliminary prototypes have been
produced and successfully tested and 'second prototypes' are
under construction. The next stage is the EM model construction
where all pcbs are integrated into one OBDH box. The use of
prorgammable gate arrays has proved to be extremely useful in
reducing the board area of the circuitry so leading to a compact
design.

Fig. 4 MAS281 Mil Std 1750 Microprocessor

The on-board software (being written in ADA) is divided into the
two areas of the 'operating system' (essential to any functions)
and the 'applications software' (applicable to specific user
applications). The operating system design is now complete and
it has been coded into ADA, compiled into Mil-std 1750 code and
run on a prototype OBC. Initial worries the the ADA code might
generate an excessivley high overhead and so rapidly use up the
relativley small memory have been overcome. Requirements
definition on the applications software is still proceeding in
advance of detailed coding.

Ground support equipment in the form of 'simulator' cards which
plug into PCs and simulate the interfaces of the OBDH system
(ULU,CDU,DAU,DLU) are now available. These are used to perform
compatibility checks on delivered subsystems and to assist later
in spacecraft level tests.

6. ATTITUDE CONTROL SYSTEM

The two most complex units within the attitude control system
are well advanced having already completed EM environmental
testing: these are the actuator electronics unit and the fan-
beam electronics unit (STRV1a only). They share a unit of EGSE
which enables their performance to be verified. Prototype
magnetorquers have been produced and the engineering model is
now in preparation. A problem has occured on the fan-beam
sensors in that they are too sensitive to temperature variation
- this is now under investigation. The EM analogue sun sunsor
and nutation damper assemblies are at the final stages of
construction.
An on-board software algorithm which performs a simple hill-
climbing function to control solar aspect angle bas been
developed and coded into ADA. It has yet to be coded and run on
the OBC.

629

7. EXPERIMENTS

The experimental payload has been well described in Ref and with regard to development status the situation varies considerably. There is insufficient room here for a worthwhile report on experiment status.

8. GROUND SEGMENT

The requirements on the ground segment have been finalized and work to install the necessary hardware and software is underway. The 12m antenna at Lasham is being refurbished with a new tracking system and feed assembly (Fig. 5): the tracking system has been demonstrated on a low-earth orbiting satellite. Once the S-band feed is installed the Hipparcos satellite will be tracked as an test case since it is in a similar orbit to that planned for STRV. Compatibility tests with the spacecraft RF system are planned for the summer of 1992 and will include a 20km line of sight test. In due course this will allow a complete communications loop test to be performed using the assembled satellite.

Fig. 5 12m Diameter Antenna, Lasham

9. CONCLUSIONS

The STRV mission is now well under way and the definition of the satellite and ground segment design is now, in large part complete. Of course the results from engineering model tests are liable to cause certain areas to undergo changes if their performance proves unsatisfactory. Spacecraft level testing of the EM is expected to be completed in the autumn of 1992.

10. REFERENCE

D G Fearn, R D Gould, K.A.Ryden 'The Development Status of the Space Technology Research Vehicle (Oct 1991)',IAF-91-008, 1991 Montreal, Canada.

PROJET D'EXPERIENCE SCIENTIFIQUE SPATIALE EMBARQUEE SUR

"PETIT SATELLITE"

par

I. H. KEROUB
TECHNION - ISRAEL INSTITUTE OF TECHNOLOGY
NORMAN AND HELEN ASHER SPACE RESEARH INSTITUTE
TECHNION,32000 Haifa   Fax: 972 4 230956

RESUME

Toute expérience spatiale embarquée sur "petit satellite" doit satisfaire à des limitations draconniennes de masse et de consommation d'énergie. Dans le cadre du futur lancement du "TECHSAT" petit satellite conçu et réalisé par le technion de Haifa, la présente étude a pour objet la préparation d'un projet de recherche spatiale universitaire et technique compatible avec:

*   * Les limitations sévères de masse et de consommation d'énergie

*   * La simplicité d'accès et de participation de tout laboratoire de recherche y intéressé

*   * L'adoption ou l'adaptation éventuelle des expériences proposées par d'autres concepteurs de "petits satellites".

Le schemma directeur de l'implémentation comporte trois segments:
1) Le segment satellite, sous la responsabilité du promoteur du "petit satellite",
2) Le segment "réception", implémenté dans les stations d'écoute au sol participant a l'expérience,
3) Le segment "exploitation", basé sur l'adoption d'algorithmes dérivés à partir des nouvelles méthodes de calcul des Contenus Totaux Electroniques (C.T.E).

1 - *INTRODUCTION*

La présente étude a pour objet la préparation d'un projet de recherche spatiale universitaire et technique, compatible avec les limitations sévères de masse et de consommation d'énergie d'un petit satellite. De plus, il convient d'assurer la simplicité d'accès et de participation active a tout laboratoire de recherche qui le désire. Cette proposition n'est pas exclusive a TECHSAT, petit satellite conçu et réalisé par l'Institut Polytechnique de Haifa - le Technion - , mais peut etre adaptée par tout concepteur de "petit satellite" y intéressé.

Le but de l'expérience proposée est dans une contribution au domaine de la modélisation ionosphérique.

Son succès conduirait a une modélisation de la variation longitudinale des gradients latitudinaux des C.T.E ionosphériques.

Nous évoquons les divers segments de l'implémentation:
* le segment satellite,
* le segment réception,
* le segment exploitation,
avant de conclure avec l'évocation des applications technologiques,en sus de l'intérêt scientifique géophysique intrinsèque de l'expérience proposée.

2 - *LE SEGMENT SATELLITE;*

Il est sous la responsabilite directe du promoteur du satellite. Celui-ci fixe une enveloppe "masse", "encombrement", "consommation d'énergie", à ne pas dépasser pour l'expérience proposée.

En principe, une masse d'un kilogramme et une consommation d'énergie d'un watt sont des objectifs a portée de la technique actuelle pour les balises radio embarquées pour les besoins de l'expérience.

Des antennes "ruban" linéaires sont utilisées dans la bande "hautes fréquences". Elles allient légèreté et efficacité.

3 - *LE SEGMENT RECEPTION.*

La chaine de réception décrite ici est la plus simple possible. Cette simplicité a pour but de faciliter l'accès de l'expérience à tout laboratoire. Nous en détaillons ci-après les éléments.

3.1 Les antennes

Elles sont prévues pour fonctionner aux fréquences émises par les balises spatiales embarquées sur le satellite. Elles doivent avoir une polarisation linéaire afin de détecter les oscillations de l'amplitude dues a l'effet Faraday avec le contraste maximum, et de plus, doivent avoir un diagramme de rayonnement connu. La solution généralement adoptée consiste en l'emploi d'antennes dipoles érigées horizontalement à une hauteur du sol égale au quart de la longueur d'onde du signal reçu.

3.2 Le récepteur

Suivant la fréquence de travail, le signal reçu par l'antenne est soit injecté directement dans un récepteur de trafic, soit soumis a un changement de fréquence préalable qui abaisse la fréquence du signal.

Le récepteur de trafic (par exemple R.Collins R 390/URR) est un équipement de hautes performances et de grande stabilite de fréquence. La bande passante du récepteur varie par valeurs discrètes entre 100 Hz et 16 KHz.

3.3 Filtrage et détection

Le signal basse fréquence amplifié prélevé à la sortie du récepteur passe par un filtre passe bas externe et un détecteur qui fournit un signal continu dont l'amplitude varie proportionnellement à l'amplitude du signal haute fréquence.

3.4 Enregistreur

On utilise un enregistreur multi-voies comportant des amplificateurs a courant continu qui amplifient le signal redressé avant de l'enregistrer. Une des voies est généralement utilisée pour l'enregistrement d'un signal horaire.

4 – LE SEGMENT EXPLOITATION

En possession d'enregistrements d'effet Faraday sur une ou plusieurs fréquences dans la bande des hautes fréquences HF, il nous faut passer a leur exploitation.

L'application des méthodes de dépouillement classiques disponibles pose des problèmes aigus pour les passages de jour de satellites défilants: en effet, les résultats donnent des gradients exagérés de CTE, totalement incompatibles avic ceux déterminés à partir de sondages ionosphériques par contre-haut, qui présentent des gradients modérés, pour des stations de latitudes géomagnétiques comparables à celle de Haifa.

Afin de surmonter ces difficultés, nous suggérons d'utiliser de nouvelles méthodes de calcul des CTE, décrites et référencées dans Kéroub (1991). Ces méthodes présentent une grande souplesse d'application et sont fiables.

4.1 Intérêt scientifique

4.1.1 La mise en application des nouvelles méthodes pour des stations de latitude géomagnétique modérée passe par l'utilisation des concepts de la propagation transionosphérique transversale des ondes électomagnétiques considérées.

4.1.2 La vérification des concepts intervenant dans la mise au point fait appel a des travaux d'ellipsometrie dans le domaine des hautes fréquences. Par exemple, le dispositif d'antennes de réception au sol suggéré ci-dessus est facilemnt extensible a un système de trois antennes utile pour l'étude détaillée de la propagation des ondes électromagnétiques dans la zone de propagation transverse (schématisee sur la figure 1). La figure 2 présente l'allure des enregistrements de la zone transverse par trois antennes distinctes.

4.1.3 L'accès à des données fiables de CTE sur un large intervalle latitudinal en temps réel ou différé, permet la calibration d'expériences de détermination des CTE par d'autres méthodes (Keroub, 1991).

4.1.4 Contribution a l'étude phénoménologique des perturbations ionosphériques itinérantes.

4.1.5 Contribution à l'élaboration d'un modèle adéquat du CTE (amélioration des performances de systèmes de navigation, d'orbitographie, etc...).

4.1.6 Etude des propagations trans-horizon des ondes radio: par exemple, les systèmes de gestion des fréquences tels que le "JINDALEE frequency management system" (Earl & Ward, 1986,1987) sont incapables de modéliser l'ionosphère,en presence d'une couche E sporadique occultante. Dans ce cas,l'information fournie en temps réel par les gradients de CTE complète notre connaissance sur le comportement global de l'ionosphère, a l'échelle régionale.

4.1.7 L'existance d'universités et de groupes de recherche internationaux intéressés par ce domaine est de prime importance pour l'extention de la couverture régionale fournie par chaque station à une couverture plus étendue résultant de l'ensemble des stations participant a l'expérience, et ce faisant, améliorant la fiabilité et le domaine de validité des modèles ionosphériques qui en seraient dérivés.

5 - CONCLUSION

Une expérience d'utilisation des petits satellites à des fins de recherches géophysiques et appliquées est proposée.

Elle concerne la modélisation de la variation longitudinale des gradients latitudinaux de CTE.

Les résultats espérés sont essentiellement:

* Une contribution a la modélisation ionosphérique en temps réel et en temps différé;

* Des progrès dans notre connaissance des applications des mécanismes de la propagation transverse ionosphérique;

* Une contribution aux domaines de la propagation transhorizon transionosphérique.

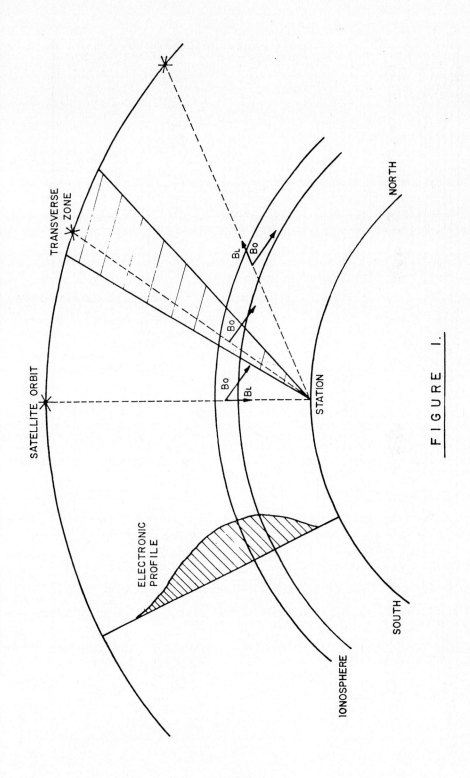

SATELLITE ORBIT

TRANSVERSE ZONE

ELECTRONIC PROFILE

IONOSPHERE

STATION

SOUTH

NORTH

B_L

B_0

B_0

B_0

B_L

F I G U R E   I.

635

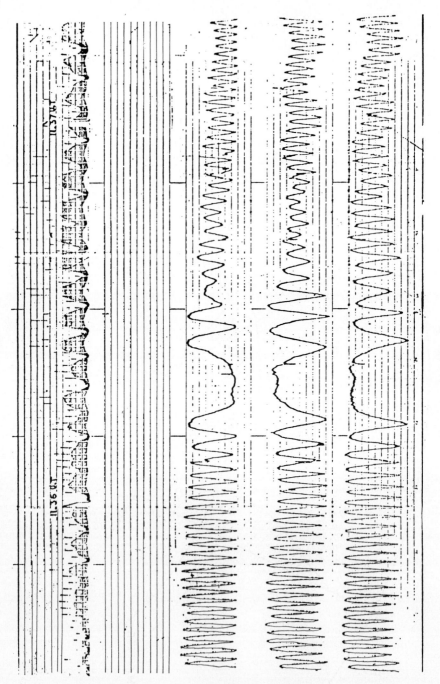

FIGURE 2

* L'ensemble constituant une plate forme idéale pour la collaboration spatiale internationale.

6 - REFERENCES

EARL, G.F. AND WARD, B.D.,
"FREQUENCY MANAGEMENT SUPPORT FOR REMOTE SEA-STATE SENSING USING THE JINDALEE SKYWAVE RADAR",
IEEE J. OF OCEANEC ENG., VOL. OE-11, NO. 2, PP. 164-174, APRIL 1986.

EARL, G.F. AND WARD , B.D.,
"THE FREQUENCY MANAGEMENT SYSTEM OF THE JINDALEE OVER-THE-HORIZON BACKSCATTER HF RADAR",
RADIO SCIENCE, VOL. 22, NO. 2, PP. 275-291, MARCH-APRIL 1987.

KEROUB I.H.,
"SYNERGETIC PROGRESS OBTAINABLE IN THE TEC REGIONAL MODELING BY THE COMBINED USE OF LOW-ALTITUDE POLAR ORBITING SATELLITE BEACONS AND G.P.S TRANSMISSIONS",
PROCEEDINGS OF THE INTERNATIONAL COMMSPHERE SYMPOSIUM, PP W 1.3.1-5, DECEMBER 16-19, 1991, HERZLIYA, ISRAEL.

ALEXIS and HETE:
Two Small, Low Cost, Scientific Satellite Systems

François Martel, Rick Fleeter
AeroAstro *

Introduction: Low Cost Spacecraft for Space Science

Real progress in reducing the costs and time to develop, launch and operate satellites expands the range of practical applications for space systems. In particular more scientific space experiments become accessible within the budgets and schedules of research organizations. AeroAstro has been built on the premise that by reducing costs, the number of space systems developed and deployed will grow because more organizations will be able to afford space activities.

The cost of a project includes not only the development of a space platform and its instruments, but also launch, and ground system development and operations. It is also often important for a small research group to be as fully independent and self reliant as possible, in order to have maximum operative flexibility, and to avoid the costs and delays of interactions with larger organizations having different priorities and methods. To meet those needs AeroAstro provides integrated space and ground station systems and operation support. ALEXIS and HETE are two examples of such systems, designed for independent use by research institutions.

ALEXIS - Designed for Low Cost

ALEXIS, Array of Low Energy X-ray Imaging Sensors, is a space platform carrying six new imaging telescopes in the ultra low energy X-ray range (ref 1). The telescopes are used for technology testing and astrophysical observations. The experiment is conducted by the US Los Alamos National Laboratory, and funded by the Department of Energy (DOE). The launch of ALEXIS is to be performed by the US Air Force using a PEGASUS rocket.

The ALEXIS spacecraft is shown in the figure next page in its flight configuration during radio tests in an anechoic chamber. The spacecraft is physically small - less than 1 meter tall with mass below 120 kg. About 65% of the satellite mass and volume are payload - the actual spacecraft bus weighs less than 45 kg.

ALEXIS in flight configuration is shown during RF tests in anechoic chamber.

ALEXIS' small size resulted partly from reduction in the system requirements. There is limited redundancy, commercial parts were admitted for some components where the equivalent military part was quite large or heavy (e.g. NiCd batteries) and parts were employed which had not previously been used in space, including, for example, a dense packaging of a commercial static RAM memory chip. The benefits of the small package ripple throughout the program. There is only 1 structural element which doubles as the housing for all of the digital electronics (cpu, I/O, memory, analogue and RF interfaces etc.). The cost to fabricate this small assembly was low due to its simplicity and small size. During assembly and test, no complex fixtures were required and minor repositioning of the spacecraft could be done by hand. Excepting the solar panels (manufactured by IAI using their already established processes), all construction was from 6061 aluminum and almost no additional mass above that required for ease of fabrication was necessary for structural strength.

In many cases the cost, power consumption mass and / or volume of commercially available components would force the satellite design to violate the budget and cost envelopes of the program. In these cases AeroAstro developed custom components including radios, sun sensors, torque coils and charge controllers which fit the ALEXIS design constraints. We sometimes modified existing equipment or requested modifications of commercial devices to make them suitable for space application. To do this at low cost requires an organization streamlined to do product development quickly and inexpensively, and the program philosophy to admit application of new designs in the spacecraft.

The resulting spacecraft is shown schematically next page along with a brief table of capabilities. Built for about $3M, the satellite provides 0.2° attitude determination, buffering of almost 1Gbit of data, a downlink of 750 kbit/s and it provides continuous power to the payload of 50 watts. Thus, despite it's low cost, the spacecraft provides performance in some ways better than 1-ton class spacecraft of only a few years ago.

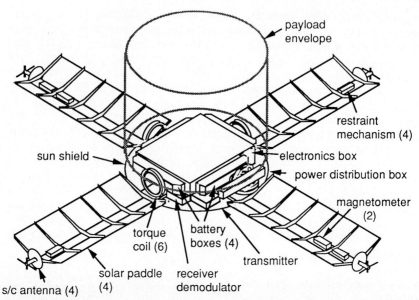

payload envelope

restraint mechanism (4)

sun shield

electronics box

power distribution box

magnetometer (2)

torque coil (6)

battery boxes (4)

transmitter

s/c antenna (4)

solar paddle (4)

receiver demodulator

The ALEXIS Spacecraft employs a central electronics box which also serves as the primary structure. The spacecraft is shown in the flight configuration (solar panels fold upward for storage and launch). Each solar panel is about 80 cm in length

Specification	Value	Unit	Comments
Payload Power	50	W	continuous, unregulated
Pointing	± 2.0	deg	knowledge to ±0.2°
Roll Angle	±0.25	deg	Knowledge of roll angle
Payload Mass	80	kg	Bus 45; payload up to 150
Diameter	60	cm	
Height	15	cm	
Data Storage	112	Mbyte	
Data Downlink Rate	750	kbit /s	
Data Downlink / Day	112	Mbyte	
Data Uplink / Day	4	Mbyte	allows software uploads
Data Error Rate	<2e-8	bit/ bit	
Spacecraft Lifetime	>18	months	Nothing precludes 36 months
Reliability	>95	%	
Quality			Mil 883-B / some commercial

Another element of the ALEXIS cost strategy was the ground station design. While ALEXIS was developed within a 2 year period, ground operations can last even longer and could be even more costly than the spacecraft itself. To reduce these costs, a ground station was developed which could be housed within the offices of the user group at Los Alamos National Lab (LANL), and whose software enabled independent management of the spacecraft by users themselves. The scientific teams operating ALEXIS have in effect full control of the spacecraft operations, and depend on external institutions only for orbital updates to be regularly provided by NORAD.

The ALEXIS ground station uses a 1.8 meter diameter dish installed on the roof at LANL. An IBM PC supports the antenna pointing and tracking, and an Apple Mac II fx handles all satellite links including commanding, data uplink and downlink, and archiving.

ALEXIS Status

ALEXIS was conceived as a quick, low cost program to launch an array of 6 ultra soft X-ray sensors to acquire experience with their new technology and to map the ultra soft X-ray sky. The program was lengthened due to integration of a secondary payload for radio propagation experiments, and then again, due to the value of the combined payloads, to upgrade the hardware quality specifications and to modify the program approach to include more documentation and traceability. Nonetheless, ALEXIS was completed within about 2 years and the testing program was spread over an additional several months. The spacecraft is now ready to launch and is in storage waiting for the Pegasus launch vehicle. The reliance of the US Air Force and NASA programs on Pegasus has at least provided us with a single launch vehicle, but it has also made these programs vulnerable to any problems with the vehicle. Just as a robust small satellite industry requires multiple vendors servicing a large number of programs, there will be a need for the market to include multiple small launch vehicles, as well as a larger number of piggyback accommodations like the Ariane ASAP. ALEXIS launch is expected in September, pending the outcome of Pegasus developmental tests.

HETE: The Next Generation

Description

The original concept of using a small, low cost anti-sun pointing spacecraft for astrophysics research was initiated by MIT's Center for Space Research (CSR) in a 1987 proposal to NASA, described in reference 2.   The principal mission of HETE (High Energy Transient Experiment) is the detection and precise location of the sources of gamma ray bursts, using an array of gamma ray detectors, built by CESR in France under CNES funding, an imaging X-ray telescope, developed with ISAS funding by RIKEN in Japan, and four   UV telescopes built for NASA by MIT-CSR.

The project was fully funded by NASA in Spring 1992 as a management experiment and a pilot project for "Small University Satellites". NASA management involvement in the project is kept to a minimum, chiefly high level progress monitoring, and   launcher interface and safety supervision. The project is defined   by its scientific goals and has a fixed budget and a tight schedule. MIT is responsible for design, manufacturing, testing and operations of the whole HETE system. If difficulties arise affecting budget and/or schedule, they are to be handled if need be by "descoping" the goals. The project is a NASA Class D operation, for which few restrictive specifications apply, except concerning safety. As a consequence the projected costs for the HETE program are very low compared to similar "classical' programs.

AeroAstro has worked cooperatively with MIT since 1989 to define the design and the actual spacecraft is now in development at AeroAstro. Launch is planned aboard Pegasus in late 1994. An early model of the spacecraft is shown in the figure next page. That model includes an inert (vaporizing liquid) propulsion system to raise the orbit from the expected STS deployment at 300 km to the operational orbit at 550 km. The system now under development does not carry that propulsion system, since Pegasus will inject HETE at its nominal altitude. Many of the HETE system requirements are similar to ALEXIS except that the spacecraft is not spinning and is   stabilized   using   a   single   momentum   wheel.

Early HETE model shows gamma, X-ray and UV telescopes pointing in the anti-sun direction.

HETE takes the concept of user independence developed for ALEXIS several steps further. The HETE ground system consists of three major ground stations, nominally at 120° longitude intervals near latitude 40°, and over 20 receive-only ground stations located at observatories around the world (see illustration next page).

The three major stations will have full capability for command uploading to the platform and data downloading. They will be remotely controlled by MIT using the Internet communication network. In addition HETE will broadcast warning and status signal at low data rates to the small receive-only stations. That will allow the possibility for astronomical observatories around the world to rapidly observe the sky in the direction of bursts detected and located by HETE. This ground station network is in effect a very sophisticated system allowing full control of a powerful astrophysics experiment by an educational and research institution, and permitting extensive international cooperation within research laboratories in many countries.

After HETE is deployed in its operational orbit, navigation and timing information will be independently acquired by accurate ranging from the three major ground stations, as well as an on-board GPS receiver.

HETE benefits from many of the technical and organizational lessons learned in the ALEXIS program. We have found several avenues to providing "graceful degradation" as an intermediate between no redundancy and fully redundant designs. And thanks to increasingly miniaturized components, HETE can support, in about the same mass, volume and power envelope, a higher degree of redundancy. The HETE bus is much more highly integrated with the payload in order to maintain small size and mass with increased capability. This advantage comes with the disadvantage that each payload interface is mechanically more complex. However, electrically each payload element is thought of as a discrete device supported by bus carrier. Thus each experimenter (HETE supports 4 experiment development groups) is supplied with a simple emulator of the HETE digital and power interface, including software, so that most of the development can be completed without the need to travel to the integration facility at AeroAstro.

HETE Groundstation System

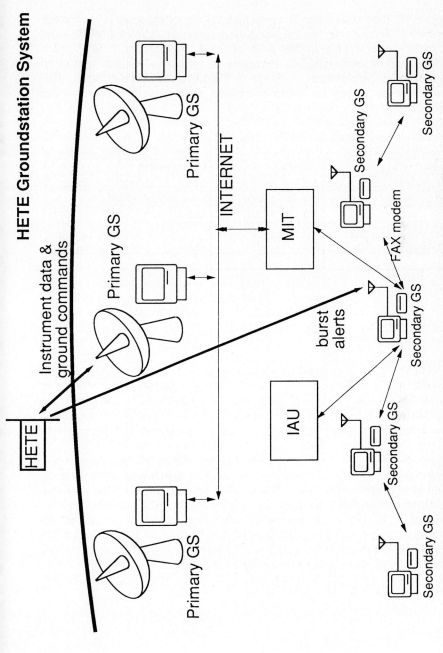

HETE primary groundstations receive instrument data via a high speed satellite downlink. This information is relayed to MIT via Internet. Secondary groundstations receive burst alerts via a low speed satellite downlink. This information is relayed to MIT, IAU and the neighboring secondary GS via fax.

The HETE processor uses 3 cpus (a total of 12 processors on board) combined to provide the equivalent power of 80 VAX-MIPS, and supports an on-board memory of about 1 Gbit using 1 Mbit static SRAM. Uplink and downlink capability is similar to ALEXIS and code uploading is supported. There is also a low data rate, VHF transmitter on board for communications to the receive only ground stations.

General specifications for HETE are shown in the table below.

Specification	Value	Unit	Comments
S/C Power	60	W	37 W to payload
Pointing	± 2.0	deg	knowledge to ±0.2°
Drift rates	5"/sec	deg	Orbit night (goal 1.8"/sec)
Total Mass	<109	kg	
Diameter	60	cm	Appr. (TV screen shape)
Height	90	cm	
Data Storage	96	Mbyte	
Data Downlink Rate	230	kbit /s	
Data Uplink / Day	7.5	kbit /s	Software uploads
Data Error Rate	<2e-8	bit /bit	
Spacecraft Lifetime	6	months	Nothing precludes 18 months
Reliability	>95	%	
Workmanship			Best Commercial Practice Mil-P-55110 as a guide
Quality	10	krad	SEU tolerant design, latch-up protection.

Begun in earnest in 1991, HETE is due for launch in December 1994 aboard a NASA Pegasus in a tandem launch with the Argentine solar research satellite, SAC-B. The HETE spacecraft bus design and development team, including spacecraft and ground station developers, program management and support staff, consists of 15 individuals working at a level of about 10 full time equivalent people. The development budget, including the master ground station and 20 receive only ground stations, is about $3.5M

Summary:

ALEXIS and HETE are part of a continuing evolution of small, relatively simple, low cost spacecraft. In these cases, small means that a small group of engineers can develop the system without needing a large, complex support infrastructure. Also, complexity is low enough that acceptable reliability can be achieved without the highest quality parts and without highly redundant architectures. The design process includes interactive decision making to balance mission goals/ costs / complexity / and system reliability.

ALEXIS and HETE are the most advanced small satellites in their price and performance class in the US, combining powerful information storage and processing capability with moderately high data rate telemetry systems, moderate power availability to the payload and sophisticated attitude determination and control systems.

References:

1. Priedhorsky, W.C. 1990, in High Energy Astrophysics in the 21st Century, ed. P.C.Joss (American Institute of Physics, NY), pp.359-364

2. Ricker, G.R. et al 1992, in Gamma-Ray Bursts: Observations, Analyses, and Theories; eds, C.Ho, R.I.Epskin, and E.F.Fenimore (Cambridge University Press, Cambridge UK), pp. 288-296

* AeroAstro Inc., 520 Huntmar Park Drive, Herndon ,VA 22070, (703) 709 2240

TITUS - A Micro-satellite for Technology Demonstration

M. Morelière, THARSYS

R. Bertrand, THARSYS

presented by M. Morelière

ABSTRACT

TITUS is the first representative of a small satellite family developed by EuroAstro, subsidiary of the French company THARSYS and the US company AeroAstro. Designed as a micro-satellite of 50 kg for ASAP or Pegasus launch, its mission is to offer cheap and rapid commercial flight opportunities for technology demonstration in earth orbit.

Depending on the available launch slots, TITUS will be injected into GTO or SSO so that he will cross the Polar Horn, the South Atlantic Anomaly or the Van Allen Belts with each revolution. Both orbits offer an interesting particle and radiation environment to demonstrate or to qualify space equipment such as electrical and electronic components and assemblies, solar cells, batteries, sensors, microwave components, material test experiments or mechanical equipment.

TITUS' design philosophy is based on simplicity and reliability using classical and well demonstrated sub-system technology and a modular bus design. Mission life time is at least 1 year.

This article describes the TITUS mission aspects and mission analysis. Furthermore it explains the design philosophy and the TITUS platform with an example of a gravity gradient stabilized platform for Low Earth Orbits.

Introduction

Space missions have traditionally consumed large budgets and taken nearly a decade to progress from conception to orbit. These constraints have limited access to space, especially for technology demonstration missions, which require a rapid cycle from design to launch and, due to their experimental character, imply a certain risk for the carrier.

In this scope THARSYS develops a satellite family offering cheap, adequate and rapid commercial flight facilities for technology demonstration and qualification. The first representative of this satellite family will be TITUS. To meet the requirements of rapidity and low cost, the major design criteria for TITUS are

- simple sub-system design resulting in high system reliability
- use of classic and well demonstrated technology for the satellite bus.
- modular bus structure without imposing a bus architecture to the customer

TITUS will also profit from THARSYS' small and flexible company's structure and an innovative system design methodology including a interdisciplinary work team, advanced design tools and direct contact to the customers during the satellite design, manufacturing and integration phases.

TITUS family mission

TITUS will bring technology demonstration and qualification payloads into Geostationary transfer orbit (GTO) or sun-synchronous orbit (SSO) depending on the available launch slots.

Geostationary Transfer Orbit (ARIANE only)	
Apogee height [km]	36000
Perigee height [km]	200
Inclination [degrees]	7
Orbit period [hours]	10,5
Sunsynchronous Orbit (ARIANE or PEGASUS)	
Orbit height [km]	700 - 850
inclination [degrees]	98,2 - 98,8
Orbit period [minutes]	98,7 - 101,8

Table 1: Orbit data

Both orbits offer an interesting space environment for demonstration and qualification purposes: Apart from the galactic and solar radiation, on SSO the satellite will regularly cross the South Atlantic Anomaly and the polar regions with higher particle concentration due to the 'polar horn' of the magnetic field of the earth, whereas on GTO TITUS will run through the Van-Allen-Belts with each revolution. The total absorbed doses have been estimated 1-2 MRad per year on GTO and 8-11 KRad per year on SSO (mean values for silicon and 1 mm of aluminium shielding).

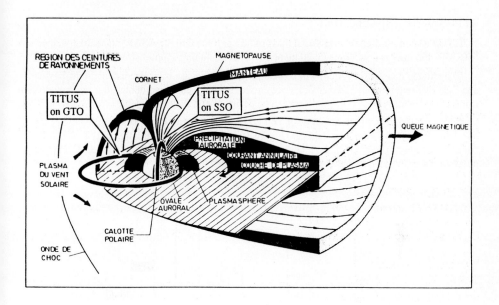

Figure 1: TITUS orbit scenarios[1]

To profit from the new low-cost launch facilities for small satellites, it will be compatible with the ARIANE 4 and PEGASUS launchers. Once in orbit, TITUS' tasks are to activate and to keep on running the payloads, to supply them with new instructions from the ground and to report all sorts of payload events (e.g. SEU, Latch-up, burn out) or performance variations.

Who is getting on ?

TITUS will be able to transport and to operate various technology demonstration experiments in form of electronic boards or discrete assemblies which have to be tested in earth orbit environment. Possible payloads are for instance:

- all sorts of electronic boards, electrical or electronic components or assemblies
- solar cells
- batteries
- power electronics
- sensors
- microwave components
- micro accelerometers
- material test experiments or mechanical equipment

Payloads are not recoverable.

---

1. source: C.E.S.R

TITUS System specification

TITUS is a microsatellite with a total mass of 50 kg. It fits into the ASAP[1] standard envelope of 450x450x450 mm³ and will contain 20 kg of payloads (including support structures and harness).

The attitude control subsystem will be defined on case by case basis dependent on the payload and customer requirements. In many cases of environmental technology demonstration, attitude control is not mandatory so that the platform can be designed as a floater.

Since the feasibility of the floater design on GTO is not evident, it has been verified by means of our Attitude Control Simulation Package (Figure 3): In spite of the important perturbation torques in the perigee regions of the orbit, the modulus of the angular velocities remains limited. Occurring nutation can be attenuated with a simple viscosity damper.

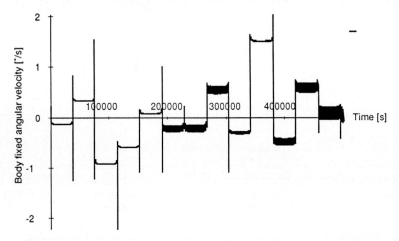

Figure 2: Angular velocities of a floater satellite on GTO for 14 perigee passes

The payloads will dispose of 10 W continuous power (BOL on GTO) or 17,5 W peak power. The guaranteed thermal environment will be between -35°C and 80°C.

The TITUS On-Board-Computer manages and stocks max. 2 Mbits of payload telemetry data per day. This data are transmitted within the platform telemetry data stream to the TITUS ground station in Toulouse / France, where they are converted into a directly readable data format and delivered immediately to the customers. The mission duration is at least one year.

---

1. ARIANE Structure for Auxiliary Payloads

Example of a gravity gradient stabilized platform

In the following we present a sample design of a gravity gradient stabilized platform which has been customized to the specifications of the client. It shows the possible synergetic effects between the customer's payload and the platform since the telecommunication payload performs also telemetry and telecommand functions for the platform.

As a true ASAP microsatellite with 50 kg total mass, it fits into the ASAP standard envelope of $450\times450\times450$ mm^3. The satellite shape is a cone covered with silicon or GaAs solar cells. The conical shape ensures good illumination of the solar arrays in all orbital phases.

The mean solar array generated power (worst case, EOL) has been evaluated with an in orbit simulation (Figure 4) to 17,5 W, so that the payload may consume 8,3 W permanent power. Figure 5 shows the power budget for a max. eclipse ratio of 35% and a minimum operational life time of 3 years.

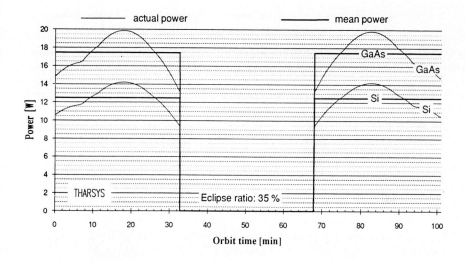

Figure 3: In orbit solar array power and mean solar array power (GaAs cells, EOL)

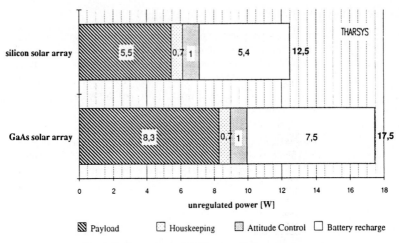

Figure 5: Power budget (silicon or GaAs solar arrays)

The platform has its own on board computer for housekeeping functions. Since the mission is telecommunication, the platform uses the payload's RF link and modem for telemetry and telecommand. The platform is stabilized by means of a 6 m gravity gradient boom. Three magnetorquers assure the attitude acquisition before boom deployment and damping of attitude oscillations in the operational configuration.

Total mass budgets for this platform with optionally silicon or GaAs solar arrays are given in Figure 6 permitting a max. payload mass envelope of 24,2 kg.

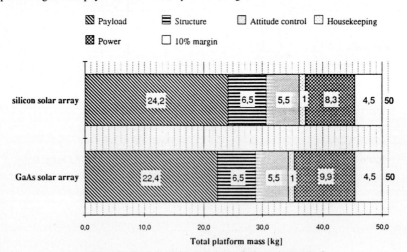

Figure 6: Mass budget (silicon or GaAs solar arrays)

656

TITUS project summary

PLATFORM	
Mass:	50 kg
Size [mm]:	450x450x450
Launch:	compatible to ASAP and PEGASUS launching systems
Power (Solar arrays)	20-26 W (BOL, GaAs cells)
Communications	S-Band downlink 2000 bps uplink 500 bps
PAYLOAD	
Total payload mass	20-25 kg max.
Payload power (continuous):	8-10 W (BOL)
Payload telemetry data	2 Mbits per day
Price (including launch)	500-600 kF/kg 80-100 k$/kg

SYNTHESE DE LA SESSION
ACCES A LA TECHNOLOGIE SPATIALE

1 - Les utilisateurs et concepteurs des micro et minisatellites

La technologie spatiale a été rendue plus accessible par le biais des petits satellites principalement aux universitaires, aux chercheurs des grandes écoles scientifiques et aux organismes étatiques :

Au cours de cette session nous avons eu des exposés de :

- l'Université technique de Berlin (satellites TUBSAT),
- de scientifiques (Institut Polytechnique TECHNION de HAIFA),
- d'association d'élèves ingénieurs (ENSAE, ESIEESPACE), ainsi que des présentations de :
  - l'Institut National des Techniques Aérospatiales (INTA) espagnol et,
  - de l'Agence de Recherche de la Défense Britannique (Defence Research Agency : DRA).

2 - Les missions

L'accès à la technologie spatiale s'effectue principalement à travers des missions à caractère technologique comme :

- la tenue aux radiations (cellules solaires, composants, revêtement thermique...),
- la qualification en vol d'un équipement (senseur d'étoile sur TUBSAT, équipement pour la RAE),
- la connaissance de l'environnement spatial, comme la propagation des ondes électromagnétiques dans l'ionosphère présenté par l'Institut Polytechnique TECHNION et HAIFA.

Sur un même satellite, ces missions peuvent être partagées entre plusieurs organismes, comme par exemple l'ASE, le JPL et la Defence Research Agency pour le microsatellite de la DRA. Ces satellites sont généralement réalisés avec le concours des industriels et le support d'établissement étatiques.

3 - Le satellite type

Aujourd'hui le satellite type pour accéder à la technologie spatiale est principalement le satellite compatible avec la plate-forme ASAP montée sur ARIANE. C'est donc un satellite de 50 kg maximum, de volume limité. Il est possible de le réaliser avec des objectifs de coût réduit et une durée de développement courte (2 ans environ).

Suivant sa mission, ce satellite est lancé sur l'orbite de transfert vers l'orbite des satellites géostationnaires ou sur une orbite polaire. Les satellites de ce type différent principalement par le type de stabilisation choisie, elle caractérise généralement la complexité du satellite et la puissance allouable à la mission (de quelques watts à une dizaine de watts).

Il nous a été présenté des satellites qui flottent dans l'espace, comme SARA, des satellites spinnés, comme ceux développés par la Defence Research Agency Britannique, des satellites stabilisés par gradient de gravité ou des satellites stabilisés trois axes comme TUBSAT B.

4 - Les autres satellites

Au-dessus de la gamme des satellites de 50 kg, il nous a été présenté des satellites réalisés avec des moyens étatiques plus importants, comme le satellite MINISAT de l'INTA. C'est un satellite de la classe SCOUT, PEGASUS de quelques centaines de kilogrammes et pouvant délivrer 150 watts à la charge utile. Il ne s'agit plus d'un satellite universitaire, mais d'un satellite réalisé dans un cadre national.

Notons enfin le cas où la mission impose un satellite lourd (200 kg), comme c'est le cas du satellite ARSENE réalisé pour un club de radio-amateurs (RACE).

5 - Les nouvelles sociétés

L'accès à la technologie spatiale, comme nous l'avons vu à travers ces « petits satellites » a donné naissance à côté des principaux maîtres d'œuvres de satellites à des sociétés bien plus modestes, mais susceptibles de construire des petits satellites pour un coût faible. Au cours de cette session nous avons eu des présentations de la société AEROASTRO (satellites ALEXIS et HETE), de THARSYS ainsi que de toutes jeunes sociétés comme ASAC, EREMIS.

SYNTHESIS OF THE SESSION
ACCESS TO SPACE TECHNOLOGY

1. Users and designers of micro and mini-satellites

Space technology has been made more accessible, particularly to Universities, researchers in the scientific Grandes Ecoles, and state bodies, thanks to small satellites.

During this session, we heard talks from:

- BERLIN Technical University (TUBSAT satellites),
- scientists (TECHNION Polytechnic Institute in Haïfa),
- student engineers' associations (ENSAE, ESIEESPACE);

and presentations from:

- the Spanish National Institute for Aerospace Techniques (INTA),
- and the British Defence Research Agency (DRA).

2. Missions

Access to space technology is usually through technological missions such as:

- radiation tolerance (solar cells, components, thermal coating, etc.);
- in-flight qualification of equipment (star sensor on TUBSAT, equipment for the RAE);
- understanding of the space environment, e.g. the propagation of electromagnetic waves in the ionosphere presented by the TECHNION Polytechnic Institute of Haïfa.

These missions may be shared among several organizations on the same satellite like, for instance, ESA, JPL and the Defence Research Agency for the DRA's micro satellite. The satellites are generally made with the cooperation of industry and support from state establishments.

3. The typical satellite

Today, the typical satellite for access to space technology is mainly a satellite compatible with the ASAP platform mounted on ARIANE. It is therefore a satellite weighing 50 kg at most and having a limited volume. It can be made on a low budget with a short development time (about 2 years).

Depending on its mission, the satellite is placed in a transfer orbit for geostationary satellites or in a polar orbit. Satellites of this type differ principally in the type of stabilization chosen, which is generally characteristic of the satellite's complexity and the power that can be allocated to the mission (from a few watts to ten watts or so).

We were introduced to satellites that float in space, like SARA, spun satellites, like those developed by the British Defence Research Agency, satellites stabilized by gravity gradient and satellites stabilized on three axes, like TUBSAT B.

4. Other satellites

Above the 50 kg range of satellites we were told about satellites made with greater, state means like INTA's MINISAT. This is a satellite in the SCOUT or PEGASUS range with a mass of a few hundred kilograms and able to deliver 150 watts to the payload. This can no longer be a university satellite but a satellite built in a national framework.

We should also note the case where the mission makes a heavy satellite (200 kg) indispensable, as was the case of the ARSENE satellite built for an amateur radio club (RACE).

5. New companies

As we have seen through these "small satellites", access to space technology has encouraged the founding of companies much smaller than the principal prime contractors for satellites, who can make small satellites at low cost. During the session, we had presentations from AEROASTRO (ALEXIS and HETE satellites), THARSYS, and very young companies such as ASAC and EREMIS.

SESSION X

ASPECTS ECONOMIQUES

ECONOMICS

BIG RESULTS WITH SMALL SPACE SYSTEMS
What Small Systems Are Doing Today

Gilbert D. Rye and Henry F. LeMieux

Orbital Sciences Corporation
Fairfax, Virginia, USA

ABSTRACT

Small space systems have received considerable attention in recent years due to the prospects that they could dramatically simplify and reduce the cost of conducting missions in space. Doubters, however, have questioned whether any meaningful space activity could ever be conducted with such "small" platforms. The majority of space users today remain uncommitted: many still ask, "What can really be done with small spacecraft?" This paper addresses that question by showing what is actually being done with small space systems today. It first reviews emerging customer needs for small systems and the capabilities that have evolved in response to those needs. It is then shown that the state of the art in small systems is quite sophisticated and capable, and demonstrates that significant benefits are being realized in space research, remote sensing and communications programs through the exploitation of these systems. It then presents a representative sample of small space products produced by Orbital Sciences Corporation.

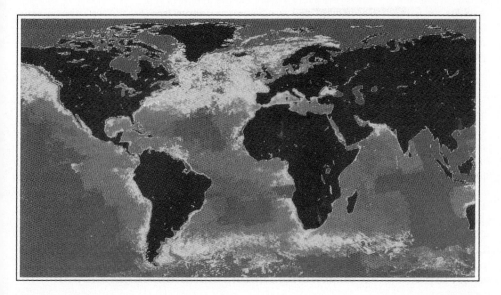

Figure 1. *A Small Spacecraft is Being Built Today to Generate Daily, Worldwide, Ocean Color Data Sets Similar to this One, Enabling the World's First Commercially Owned and Operated Remote Sensing System.*

INTRODUCTION

The world's first fully commercial remote sensing system; affordable global, uninterrupted, two way communications; regularly repeating, recoverable, dedicated microgravity research missions; these are some of the advanced space services being constructed today utilizing modern small space systems.

Demanding missions? Yes, but today's small space systems are up to the task. tenth of a degree attitude control; Half a kilowatt peak power; ten year goal lifetimes; launch of seven satellites simultaneously on a *small* launch vehicle; these capabilities are being produced in Small Space Systems *today*.

Small space systems, encompassing spacecraft weighing less than 700 kg, the mission specific instruments that can be accommodated on such platforms, and launchers (ELVs) capable of delivering up to 2200 kg to Low Earth Orbit (LEO), have existed since the very first satellites were placed in orbit. But these spacecraft historically offered minimal functionality and through time, spacecraft designers tended to produce ever larger, more expensive systems. Recently that trend reversed. Miniaturization technologies evolved to the point where for many missions *modern* Small Space Systems can deliver a significant amount of performance at a fraction of the cost of their larger brethren.

Small space systems have matured greatly in recent years, and today offer an impressive menu of sophisticated capabilities. This is enabling a broad array of new space applications. What has caused this maturation process? And how far has it progressed? What can Small Space Systems do for user's *today*?

This paper will describe the recent evolution of space user's requirements which have necessitated more capable, cost-effective small space systems. It will then review the new technologies that have developed which allow small systems to achieve high performance-to-cost ratios, and discuss the resulting cost, reliability, operational, and development time advantages. Significant focus will then be devoted to what is presently being done on existing small spacecraft programs in the communications, remote sensing and space research fields. Finally, an overview will be given of the small space products and services available from Orbital Sciences Corporation (OSC).

EVOLVING CAPABILITIES FOR EMERGING CUSTOMER REQUIREMENTS

Three classic motivations stimulated the drive to advance and exploit the capabilities of small space systems: reduce costs; improve responsiveness to the end user, and; address new threats and opportunities which outstrip the capabilities of existing systems. Adding intensity to this push was an increasingly dynamic and demanding global operating environment, which established an acute need for innovative new technological solutions to evolving customer requirements.

For instance, the incentive to reduce system costs was enhanced by persistent U.S. budget deficits, a weakened economy and reduced East-West tensions, which combined to necessitate severe U.S. Government budget cutbacks. In order to continue to be able to achieve their objectives, the US Department of Defense (DoD), The National Aeronautics and Space Administration (NASA) and the other civil agencies are finding it more important than ever to reduce mission costs. This translates directly into increased demand for lower cost alternatives to the expensive large space systems of the past.

In the commercial sector, most potential ventures simply are not financially feasible with the traditional cost of doing business in space. The expense of building and launching historically large spacecraft requires prohibitively high initial investment by most would-be commercial space venturers. However, there are spacecraft and ELV cost thresholds below which some commercial applications become commercially viable. Thus, there exists added incentives for space systems designers to innovate lower cost approaches.

Significant challenges also exist in improving responsiveness to end users. In the military world, the experiences of Desert Storm validated previous studies which identified the need for improved direct satellite support of field units. Many, if not most of our current space assets presently support top level decision makers, meaning that in many cases the tactical needs of field commanders may not receive high priority. The solution requires the development of new, dedicated systems which can be deployed in support of tactical forces. Such systems will not need all of the advanced capabilities of strategic support systems — communications capacity may be reduced, imaging resolution may be coarser. But they must be capable of launch-on-demand, in multiple units, and be cost effective. Traditional large space systems cannot always satisfy these requirements.

Global change research presents another challenge in improving the responsiveness of space systems to end users' needs. Scientists must have near term data from space remote sensing platforms in order to understand changes in the global environment and recommend policy responses to emerging environmental challenges before the end of the decade. A traditional, large remote sensing spacecraft would require ten to fifteen years to design, build and launch. Clearly a more time-responsive alternative system must be found.

Communications is another space application where improved responsiveness to the needs of end users is necessary. Systems have been designed which could offer affordable, hand portable, worldwide mobile satellite communications. In order to reduce the size and power of the handset, such systems necessitate multiple satellites orbiting nearer to the earth than do traditional geosynchronous communications satellites. To make such a capability financially feasible, the spacecraft will have to be inexpensive and capable of being launched several at a time on a reasonably priced ELV. Additionally, it must be possible to replace an individual spacecraft rapidly if it fails. Here again, traditional, large spacecraft and launchers cannot satisfy all of these requirements.

In parallel with these evolving cost and responsiveness requirements is the recent dramatic shift in geopolitical international security threats. In the case of the United States and the NATO alliance, the monumental threat shift from a single, predictable, centralized source to multiple, unpredictable, distributed sources necessitates space assets which can respond rapidly and effectively in support of contingencies anywhere on the globe. Present capabilities are not well-suited for this threat environment.

The Evolution of Small Systems' Capabilities

Technological developments in the 1980s and early 1990s enabled dramatic improvements in the functionality achievable with Small Space Systems. The successful miniaturization and weight reduction of electronic, optical and structural components and the introduction of support infrastructures and new operating procedures significantly increased the performance-to-weight and performance-to-volume ratios of most mission payload, spacecraft bus, launch vehicle and ground segment subsystems.

The most significant advances were made in spacecraft computing capacity and data storage. Very Large Scale Integration (VLSI) chips can now perform complex communications and logic functions at a fraction of the weight and power of previous technology. This enables greater spacecraft autonomy and allows large amounts of error correcting data storage (EDAC) to be carried on board. The development of efficient gallium arsenide and indium phosphide solar cells facilitates greater power output with smaller arrays. Advanced composite materials provide strong, lightweight structural materials. The launch of the Global Positioning System (GPS) allows precise orbit determination to be accomplished with small, lightweight GPS receivers. Advanced optical technologies such as wedge spectrometers and smart retinas have reduced the size and mass of space sensors. And advanced operating approaches such as air launch have increased the flexibility and reduced the costs and response time of the launch segment.

These developments have had several significant impacts on space system design. First and foremost, miniaturized components allow very capable space systems to be constructed at a fraction of the size and weight that has historically been required to achieve comparable functionality. This in turn reduces materials, assembly and testing costs. Second, the fusion into single, solid state components of functions that previously required multiple, interacting modules reduces the complexity and increases the reliability of space systems. This lowers engineering, assembly and test costs, allows greater modularity of design, shortens development times and facilitates the mass producibility necessary for building spacecraft constellations. In combination with the greater spacecraft autonomy afforded by increased on-board computing power, the simplicity also reduces the level of expertise required to operate such systems, thus broadening the range of users who can exploit the benefits of space.

Perhaps the most substantial benefit of miniaturization is that it reduces launch costs. The launch segment typically accounts for half of all mission expenditures. Small spacecraft can split costs with other users and share rides on traditional large ELVs. Or they can exploit the benefits of a dedicated launch on lower cost, small ELVs. New small launchers in particular offer considerable cost savings, in addition to shorter lead times and launch-on-demand capabilities.

These new technological capabilities allow small space systems to uniquely satisfy the emerging requirements outlined above. Figure 2 illustrates this. Government agencies can exploit small systems' modest costs to meet the demands of declining budgets. Commercial space ventures can employ similar cost savings to produce financially viable business plans. The military will be able to draw on small systems to field cost-effective, simple, launch-on-demand tactical space assets. NASA plans to take advantage of small systems' short lead times to conduct near-term environmental research missions. LEO mobile communications operators can exploit the low cost, producibility, multiple launch and replacement-on-demand capability of these systems to facilitate LEO constellations. And the US DoD and NATO can utilize these same features to develop space support systems capable of optimal response through launch-on-demand to a wide variety of global contingencies.

In summary, the present market demands cost-effectiveness, simplicity, responsiveness, and launch flexibility from space systems. *Small* Space Systems potential to deliver these attributes for many space applications is clear. But what has been done to validate these claims? Have these advantages been tested in actual demonstration programs? Has a mission yet realized actual benefits through utilization of small space systems? The answer is "yes."

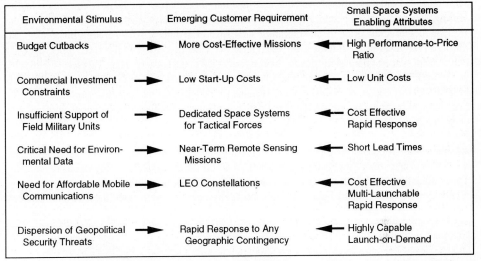

Environmental Stimulus	Emerging Customer Requirement	Small Space Systems Enabling Attributes
Budget Cutbacks	More Cost-Effective Missions	High Performance-to-Price Ratio
Commercial Investment Constraints	Low Start-Up Costs	Low Unit Costs
Insufficient Support of Field Military Units	Dedicated Space Systems for Tactical Forces	Cost Effective Rapid Response
Critical Need for Environmental Data	Near-Term Remote Sensing Missions	Short Lead Times
Need for Affordable Mobile Communications	LEO Constellations	Cost Effective Multi-Launchable Rapid Response
Dispersion of Geopolitical Security Threats	Rapid Response to Any Geographic Contingency	Highly Capable Launch-on-Demand

Figure 2. The Advantageous Match Between Emerging Customers Needs and Small Space Systems Capabilities.

SMALL SPACE SYSTEMS IN ACTION

Several recent demonstration programs have validated the advantageous match between the capabilities of small space systems and the new requirements facing space users. And indeed, a second wave of programs is presently underway which will employ small systems in full operational support of military missions, global change research, commercial business ventures and scientific experimentation.

Small space systems have been employed in a significant number of recent programs. Since 1980, 24 modern small spacecraft have been placed in orbit (excluding amateur spacecraft). Several of these were carried on one of the 15 launches of small ELVs during the same period.

In reviewing this activity, one can identify three major milestones in the development of modern small space systems. First, the space community recognized the ability of these systems to perform meaningful space missions. Second, operators in specific space application areas began to test these systems' suitability for delivering cost-effective results in their particular field. Initially, they were assessed as testbeds for space technology, science and research experimentation and shortly thereafter, they were evaluated for use in LEO communications missions.

As these two milestones were successfully achieved, space users began to incorporate small systems into their core missions. This important third milestone, a litmus test of whether small systems would be vigorously accepted by the space community, was achieved in the space research area two decades ago in the Air Force's Space Test Program (STP). More recently, this milestone was achieved in the communications arena, with the selection of small satellites and launchers for the ORBCOMM program and most of the many other recently proposed LEO communication constellations.

Most recently, small satellites have been accepted into a third space application area, earth remote sensing. It is notable that operators in this arena chose not to conduct precursor demonstration missions with small spacecraft prior to incorporating such spacecraft into actual operating missions. This illustrates the level of confidence with small space systems that exists in the U.S., based upon the multitude of successful missions that have been conducted in the last ten years. This fact is reinforced by Figure 3. The percentage of small spacecraft missions devoted to "proof of utility" increased briefly in 1990-1991 as operators evaluated these systems for new LEO communications applications. But beginning this year, no further testing or validation is planned. Small systems are now entrusted with operating missions.

As small systems technology progressed from proof-of-concept and evaluation of capabilities during the 1980's to operational application in the 1990's their functional capabilities improved dramatically. Today's small spacecraft offer a remarkable array of sophisticated capabilities. Figure 4 sets forth the "state of the art" that is being built into small spacecraft today. In some cases, these capabilities have

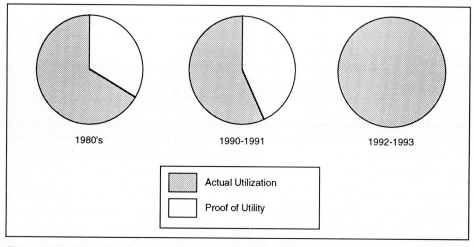

Figure 3. *Trend Toward Greater Operational Utilization of Small Spacecraft.*

already been demonstrated by small spacecraft on orbit. In others, spacecraft are under contract to launch and perform these functions by the end of 1993. In combination with the advanced capabilities and efficiencies of today's small sensors, transmitters and receivers, this level of performance enables a broad range of cost-effective research, communications, and remote sensing applications. To demonstrate how these technologies are being applied and to present a clear picture of the state of the art in small systems today, the next three sections will provide representative examples of recent or ongoing small satellite missions in each of the three major application areas.

Function	Capabilities Being Built Today
Pointing Control	0.2°
Power (Total Peak, BOL)	500 w
Design Life (Goal)	5 (10) Years
Data Memory Storage	1.25 Gigabits
Downlink Data Rate	2 Mbps
Orbit Determination	Within 100m
Mass Available for Experiment	150 lbm

Figure 4. *"State of the Art" in Small Space Systems.*

Communications

LEO communications has been the most active application of small satellites in the past decade, accounting for 14 spacecraft, about 60% of all small satellites launched (excluding amateur spacecraft). The first missions to demonstrate the usefulness of modern small systems for communications applications were the OSCAR amateur radio satellites, which initially carried simple bent-pipe communications payloads.

But the US Defense Advanced Research Projects Agency (DARPA) became interested in small spacecraft for communications purposes in the early 1980's. DARPA sponsored a mission that is widely regarded as the father of the modern small satellite era, the Global Low Orbit Message Relay (GLOMR) spacecraft. GLOMR delivered only modest capabilities as delineated in Figure 5. But when it was launched in 1985 and accomplished its mission after being built in less than a year for an initial contract price of approximately $1 million, it generated considerable enthusiasm for the potential of small space systems.

This success convinced DARPA, the US Navy and the US Air Force's Space Test Program to fund one follow-on spacecraft and initiate three new communications related small satellite evaluation programs representing a total of 12 additional small communications spacecraft. Two of these subsequent programs, the Multiple, Autonomous Communications Satellites (MACSats), and the MicroSats, launched in 1990 and 1991, respectively, validated the specific utility of small spacecraft for LEO communications.

The two MACSats are significantly more capable than their predecessors, offering an encrypted store and forward capability with 2.4 MegaBytes (MB) of memory. Their capabilities are shown in Figure 5. During

	Launched			Proposed
Spacecraft	GLOMR	MACSATS	MICROSATS	IRIDIUM
Launch Year	1985	1990	1991	1996
Mass	68 kg	62 kg	22 kg	500 kg
Power (Orb. Avg. BOL)	5w	9w	3-8w	1200w
Attitude Control	None	Grav. Grad.	Spin	3 Axis 0.1°
Transmitters	2 UHF	2 UHF	UHF	TBD
Propulsion	None	None	N_2	N_2H_4
Orbit Determination	None On Board	None On Board	None On Board	Unknown
Lifetime	3 Month Design	3 Year Goal	3 Year Goal	6-8 Years
Approximate Bus Cost	$1M	$2M	<$2M	<$10
Notes		2 Produced, Multiple-Launch	7 Produced, Multiple-Launch	

Figure 5. Capabilities of Small Communications Spacecraft.

Operations Desert Shield and Desert Storm the MACSats performed the first known operational functions of modern small satellites by relaying routine logistics messages between a deployed Marine Amphibious Unit and its home base in the US.

The MicroSats advanced these capabilities several steps further, to become the most capable small communications spacecraft built to date. Figure 6 shows them attached to their carriage structure on the Pegasus® ELV prior to launch. MicroSats provided bent-pipe and store & forward communications for secure analog voice, digital voice and digital data relay. Figure 5 shows their ground breaking attributes. The 741 km circular, polar constellation of seven MicroSats was designed to offer near continuous-in-plane push-to-talk tactical military communications. All seven were launched on Pegasus® in July of 1991, though into a lower orbit than was planned. The spacecraft met all program technical objectives before reentering in late January of 1992.

The accomplishments of this mission were of great import to the LEO mobile communications field. MicroSats demonstrated the capability to achieve near-continuous communications coverage using a space segment composed of LEO small satellites and a ground segment of simple, portable, hand-held transceivers. The utility of such a system was demonstrated in a number of exercises by the services and defense agencies. According to DARPA, these uses included: "Using MicroSats to extend communications beyond the line of sight from ships; using hand held Marine radios and MicroSats to communicate between headquarters and Marines in the field; high quality voice communications from mobile terminals; high quality communications for the Army over a distance of 2,000 miles; and using MicroSats to relay messages from a two watt transmitter to the Navy's Geosynchronous Fleet Satellite Communications (FLTSATCOM), thus allowing the small transmitter to send messages to about one-

Figure 6. MicroSats Attached to Carriage Structure on Pegasus.

third of the Earth's surface." The system's ability to support lightweight, highly mobile ground transceivers was particularly useful during the disaster relief efforts in the Philippines following the Mount Pinatubo eruption.

Although this mission provided coverage within only one orbital plane, global coverage could be achieved with three of these planes. Also noteworthy was the ability to deploy such a system through the launch of only one, inexpensive small launcher. This kept total mission costs below $16 million, and, with Pegasus®' rapid-response capability, illustrated that the technology exists today to field a launch-on-demand space support system in response to rapidly developing contingencies.

Due to the success of the MicroSats missions, a number of programs are moving forward today which will result in the deployment of operating, small communication satellite systems as early as 1993. The US Navy ArcticSat program plans to deploy a polar constellation of small spacecraft for communicating with units inside the Arctic circle, which are beyond the line of sight of existing geosynchronous spacecraft. But the great majority of activity is within the commercial arena, with no less than eight separate organizations planning to launch constellations of small spacecraft to provide global, mobile commercial voice communications and/or data messaging services. Spacecraft are already under design for several of these missions which are an order of magnitude more capable than the MicroSats.

One example is the satellite being designed by Lockheed for the Iridium constellation. These capabilities of this bus are presented in Figure 5. The communications payloads of 77 of these spacecraft will offer continuous-coverage, mobile voice communications worldwide. Iridium intends for its spacecraft to be compatible with a large ELV (for multiple satellite launches) and a small ELV (for a dedicated, rapid replacement launch).

Small systems are also being considered for geosynchronous missions. DARPA is planning a geosynchronous small spacecraft with an Extremely High Frequency (EHF) Communications payload, and several commercial satellite communications firms are interested in purchasing 450 kg, 12 transponder class geosynchronous satellites for capacity supplementation and gap-filler missions.

Clearly, small spacecraft have been accepted into the world of communications, and are evolving rapidly to meet ever more challenging requirements. The bottom line: with LEO applications, communications providers can only deliver a cost effective, uninterrupted service to their customers by exploiting the operational and cost advantages offered by small space systems.

Observation and Remote Sensing

A more recent application of small satellite technology has been in the field of remote sensing. Interest in earth observation from small satellites developed rapidly during the 1990's. At the beginning of 1991, there were no known small remote sensing spacecraft under contract. By the end of 1992, seven are expected to be in fabrication for DoD, NASA and the commercial sector. The reasons for this explosion of activity, as shall be shown, are the dramatic cost, schedule and operational benefits achievable through smaller systems.

The amateur radio community deserves credit for conducting the first known earth observations from modern small spacecraft. Oscar 9 carried a crude earth imaging payload in 1981, and this was followed by similar experiments on Oscars 11, 15 and 18, which produced rough photos of Earth's surface with 2 to 5 km resolution.

In 1991, NASA initiated two programs which will produce a new generation of vastly more capable small remote sensing spacecraft. Early in the year, NASA signed a contract with OSC to design, build, launch, operate and provide ocean color data from what will be one of the most capable small satellites known to have been built, SeaStar. Later in the year, NASA contracted with TRW to build another very capable small spacecraft to carry the Total Ozone Mapping Spectrometer (TOMS). Both of these programs will gather critical data for scientists studying the global environment, and both are using small space systems for the launch and space segments.

As SeaStar represents the leading edge in small space systems, it is worth examining in greater detail. SeaStar, shown in Figure 7, will be the world's first commercially developed, owned and operated remote sensing spacecraft. As such, the spacecraft serves as the foundation of a complete business venture. Such a venture would not have been possible with the high initial capitalization requirements of traditional large space systems. Only by using a small sensor, spacecraft and launcher was it possible to craft a viable business plan. It should be noted that NASA, acting in its role as anchor customer for the data generated by SeaStar, is providing $43.5 million toward the system's construction. But the cost to NASA of procuring and integrating a sensor, spacecraft, launch vehicle and ground control hardware and operating the system for five years would have been much higher without OSC's commercial approach based on small space systems.

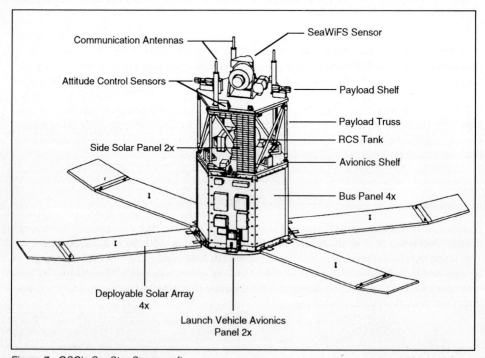

Figure 7. OSC's SeaStar Spacecraft.

The SeaStar satellite itself utilizes OSC's unique PegaStar™ spacecraft bus design, which is further described below, and will be launched on Pegasus®. Its capabilities are summarized in Figure 8.

SeaStar will carry the Sea-Viewing Wide Field Sensor (SeaWiFS) shown in Figure 9, which is being manufactured by Hughes Santa Barbara Research Center. SeaWiFS is an imaging, scanning, visible and near infrared 8 band radiometer optimized for sensing ocean color. It employs a filter spectrometer, and achieves 4% relative radiometric accuracy. From an orbit of 750 km, it will provide a 1.13 km Instantaneous Field Of View (IFOV) with a 1500 km swath width. SeaWiFS weighs only 45 kg and requires approximately 70 watts orbit average power.

It is this small sensor's ability to generate meaningful scientific data, and OSC's ability to utilize Pegasus® and PegaStar™ to cost-effectively place SeaWiFS into orbit that enable the first viable business plan for a commercially-owned remote sensing system. Beginning in 1994, OSC will be commercially providing direct downlinks of ocean color data sets to government and commercial customers around the globe. Small space systems make this possible.

Not surprisingly, other remote sensing groups are rapidly moving to exploit the benefits of small systems on their own programs. The US Navy will soon award a contract for one or more GeoSat Follow-on (GFO) spacecraft. It will be a 230 to 450 kg spacecraft, launched on a small ELV, and will carry a radar altimeter to map sea surface height worldwide. The Strategic Defense Initiative Organization (SDIO) will soon select two contractors to build a total of four "Brilliant Eyes" spacecraft as forerunners of a possible constellation of ballistic missile launch sensing spacecraft. And NASA is evaluating the possibility of gathering additional critical near-term environmental data for its global change research program (EOS) by contracting for an advanced Earth observing small satellite which would launch before 1996.

	In Fabrication	Proposed
Spacecraft	SeaStar	EOS
Launch Year	1993	1995
Mass	245 kg	300 kg
Power (Orb. Avg. BOL)	200w	200-300w
Attitude Control	3 Axis, 0.5° 1.23 mrad Knowledge	3 Axis, 0.1°
Transmitters	2 S Band 2 L Band	2 S Band
Propulsion	N_2H_4	N_2H_4
Orbit Determination	Autonomous GPS to w/in 100m	GPS
Lifetime	5 Year Design, 10 Year Goal	3-5 Year
Approximate Bus Cost	$7-11M	TBD
Notes	Fully Redundant 1.25 GBit Data Recorder 2.6 Mbps Downlink	All Specs TBD

Figure 8. Capabilities of Small Remote Sensing Spacecraft.

A number of commercial companies are investigating SeaStar-like commercial remote sensing businesses based on small systems. Small sensor technology exists today to produce a wide range of commercially attractive data products from small spacecraft. As an example, at least one company is presently marketing a sensor which will provide better than 5 m ground resolution from 750 km, but which weighs only 77 kg and consumes approximately 100 w.

The speed with which small space systems have been accepted within the remote sensing community and incorporated into operating missions has been surprising. But the reasons are again clear. Without the cost and operational advantages of small systems, the SeaWiFS, TOMS, GFO and Brilliant Eyes programs likely would not have been fiscally viable. Remote sensing is an example of where small systems offer an enabling capability to investment-conscious commercial and budget-conscious government users.

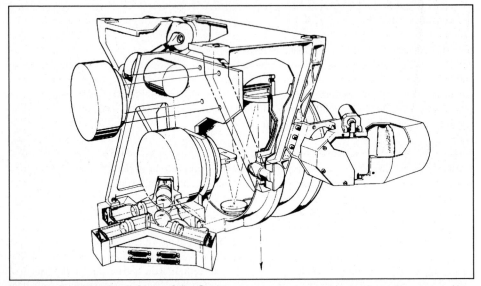

Figure 9. SeaWIFS Small Ocean Color Sensor.

Space Research and Experimentation

Space experimenters and researchers were the first space users to exploit small spacecraft in their core missions. The role of small systems in space research has grown significantly, owing primarily to the lower cost of conducting research with small platforms.

The US Air Force's Space Test Program (STP) began launching experiments on dedicated small spacecraft during the 1960's. Recent efforts included the Polar Beacon Experiment and Auroral Research (Polar BEAR), Polar Orbiting Geomagnetic Survey Satellite (POGS) and the Radiation Experiment (REX), among others. These missions combined with the success of SDIO small spacecraft experiments to demonstrate the utility of small satellites in performing rapid, cost effective missions for the space research and experimentation community.

A series of ambitious small satellite-based space research programs were then initiated. Los Alamos National Laboratory (LANL) procured a small spacecraft to carry its Array of Low Energy X-ray Imaging Sensors experiment (ALEXIS). ALEXIS, shown in Figure 10, is a very capable small spacecraft, as verified by the attributes set forth in Figure 11. It's payload of six wide field, low energy X-Ray telescopes will provide the first continuous low energy X-ray mapping of the sky and deliver unprecedented mapping resolution.

These are impressive capabilities, but NASA, SDIO and the Air Force went several steps further and established full-up, repetitive, long-term programs to exploit the advantages of small spacecraft and launchers for space experimentation. These programs will result in even more sophisticated spacecraft than ALEXIS. In the late 1980's NASA initiated the Small Explorer program, which will conduct one to two launches annually of small scientific satellites built by NASA's Goddard Space Flight Center. The first of this series, the Solar, Anomalous, and Magnetospheric Particle Explorer (SAMPEX) will launch on NASA's final Scout small ELV this year and study solar energetic particles, anomalous

Figure 10. The Los Alamos National Laboratory's ALEXIS Spacecraft.

cosmic rays, galactic cosmic rays and magnetospheric electrons. NASA has procured up to ten Pegasus® launches to carry ensuing missions. The first two of these are the Fast Auroral Snapshot Explorer (FAST), which will launch in 1994 to investigate the processes operating within the auroral region, and the Submillimeter Wave Astronomy satellite (SWAS), which will launch in 1995 to study how molecular clouds collapse to form stars and planetary systems.

SDIO is using small spacecraft in its Miniature Seeker Technology Integration (MSTI) program. These spacecraft will evaluate advanced small sensors' abilities to detect, track, and guide interceptors against ballistic missile threats. More than seven MSTI spacecraft are planned for suborbital and orbital missions. The MSTI and SMEX programs chose small spacecraft to allow them to achieve important space research and experimentation within budgetary constraints and with reasonable development timelines.

The Air Force used similar rationale when it established the Space Test Experiments Platform (STEP) to support the STP program. Through this contract, the service procured three small satellites with options for nine more, and has contracted for up to 40 Pegasus® vehicles to launch them, in addition to other small payloads. The first two STEP busses will be much more capable than ALEXIS, as shown in Figure 11. A third STEP is presently in design.

The most capable space research satellite presently under contract was also procured by the Air Force to carry the Advanced Photovoltaic and Electronics Experiment (APEX). Like SeaStar, the most sophisticated small spacecraft in the remote sensing arena, APEX is being built by OSC and exploits the advantages of OSC's PegaStar™ spacecraft bus. Figure 11 displays APEX's capabilities. Its avionics are radiation hardened to enable a three year lifetime goal in an orbit which passes through the Van Allen belts. Indeed, the primary objective of this mission is to evaluate the effects of single event upsets and total dose radiation exposure on the performance of advanced solar cells and other test devices.

	Launched	Awaiting Launch	In Fabrication		Proposed
Spacecraft	POGS	ALEXIS	STEP	APEX	SEI
Launch Year	1990	1992	1993	1993	1997
Mass	68 kg	113 kg	270-370 kg	246 kg	70 kg
Power (Orb. Avg. BOL)	9w	57w	100-200w	210w	100w
Attitude Control	Grav. Grad.	Spin	3 Axis, 0.5°	3 Axis, 0.5°	3 Axis, 1-5°
Transmitters	1 UHF	S-Band	S-Band SGLS	S-Band SGLS	2 S or X Band GDSN
Propulsion	None	None	N_2H_4	N_2H_4	Bi-Prop
Orbit Determination	None On Board	Unknown	Unknown	Autonomous GPS to w/in 100M	TBD
Lifetime	1 Year	3 Year Goal	6 Month Design	1 Year Design, 3 Year Goal	1-3 Year
Approximate Bus Cost	~$2M	~$2M	$5-6M	$8-9M	TBD
Notes		96 MB RAM	2 in Production	64 MB EDAC SRAM 155 lbm for Payload	Representative Lunar Mission

Figure 11. Capabilities of Small Space Research Satellites.

Potential future applications of small satellites in the space research category include NASA's Commercial Experiment Transporter (COMET), and precursor planetary survey missions as part of the NASA's Space Exploration Initiative. (SEI). COMET is intended to provide regularly scheduled 30 to 60 day recoverable and 100 day non-recoverable missions to LEO for microgravity research beginning in 1993. SEI would use small spacecraft to survey landing sites and environments on the Moon and Mars in advance of more ambitious, surface landing spacecraft.

SMEX, MSTI, STEP and APEX represent vigorous core programs based on small space systems. The clear lure of small systems for space research and experimentation are both the low threshold cost of conducting missions, and the rapid timelines within which research results can be generated. Small systems enable these programs to conduct more research in less time, thus allowing space experimentation as a whole to progress at a faster, more productive pace.

Trends

An obvious trend in each of these application areas is the consistent, aggressive expansion in what can actually be accomplished with small space systems. The capabilities and sophistication of small satellites have dramatically increased over the last several years and are continuing to do so. Figure 12 illustrates this graphically. The chart shows a dot for all industry-manufactured small spacecraft programs that OSC is aware of. The position of the dot is based on the contract date and a measure of spacecraft capability which is derived by an OSC quantitative model. It should be noted that some dots represent programs which produced more than one spacecraft of identical capability. This chart illustrates the clear and continuing trend toward more capable small systems. This is a direct result of more space users incorporating small systems into more challenging and meaningful programs.

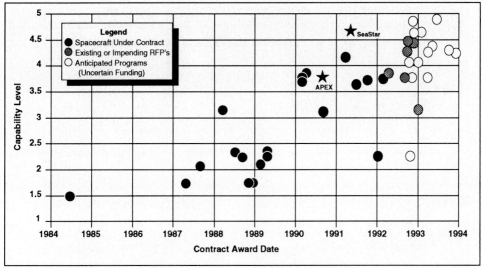

Figure 12. The Trend Toward Greater Capability in Small Spacecraft.

Concurrent with this trend, not surprisingly, has been a parallel increase in small spacecraft mass. It is tempting to infer from such a trend that small spacecraft designers have fallen prey to the historic "bigger is better" philosophy which resulted in today's expensive behemoth spacecraft. That is not so. As an example, the MicroSats, launched in 1991 at less than 23 kg each, were each more capable than were the MACSats, launched in 1990 at 62 kg, which in turn were more capable than was GLOMR, launched in 1985 at 68 kg. So the performance-to-mass ratio continues to improve. In fact, what has caused small spacecraft to grow is that they are being accepted into ever more demanding space application areas. Many space research missions inherently require greater capabilities from the spacecraft bus than do simple bent-pipe communication missions. Similarly, remote sensing typically requires higher bus performance than does space research. More capabilities generally do necessitate more bus mass. But the important point is that capabilities are being produced today with much less cost, mass, and development time than was required even five years ago. Affordable new communications, remote sensing and space research missions are now possible — through small space systems.

OSC'S SMALL SPACE PRODUCTS AND SERVICES

Orbital Sciences Corporation offers a very capable line of small spacecraft and launchers in addition to complete turn-key systems and space-based services to allow space users to benefit from the developments described above. OSC produces the Pegasus® and Taurus™ space boosters, the PegaStar™ spacecraft bus, and in 1994 is planning to provide initial ORBCOMM worldwide data messaging services and SeaStar ocean color data sets.

Pegasus®

Pegasus®, the "launch vehicle of choice" in the international small launch services market, is shown in Figure 13. The world's most advanced small space launch vehicle, it has been developed and is now being produced and launched by OSC, Hercules Aerospace Corporation and our industrial partners to meet the launch needs of defense, civil, commercial and international small satellite missions. To date,

Figure 13. Pegasus in Flight.

Pegasus® has been selected for over sixty launches and options by DARPA, the USAF, NASA, commercial and international customers.

Pegasus® is a winged, three stage solid rocket space booster which offers low cost, dedicated launches for payloads in the less than 540 kg class. It is lifted by a carrier aircraft to a level flight condition of about 12,500 m and Mach 0.8 prior to release for launch. Pegasus® exploits this imparted altitude and velocity to achieve significant cost and performance savings.

This unique air-launched approach additionally affords numerous operational advantages. Pegasus® is independent of fixed launch sites, which expands its range of achievable launch inclinations, reduces weather constraints, and improves system survivability and security during launch preparation and operations. This also eliminates the need for pad refurbishment, which allows rapid mission call-up and quick turnaround. Pegasus®' simple design and operational approach accommodates "hot" or "cold" storage for long periods, enabling launch-on-demand and high sustained launch rates.

Figure 14 illustrates Pegasus®' performance to circular, polar orbits. In response to the trend toward increased mass in small satellites (described above), OSC has designed an enhanced version of Pegasus® designated the Pegasus® XL. The XL uses a simple lengthening of the Stage 1 and Stage 2 motors to increase the propellant load by 24% and 30% respectively. This straightforward enhancement maintains conservative design margins and provides a significant improvement in available performance, as displayed by Figure 14. Pegasus® XL will be available for launches in 1993. For missions requiring slightly more performance than the standard Pegasus® versions, and/or greater injection precision, OSC offers the Hydrazine Auxiliary Propulsion System (HAPS). HAPS boosts performance to higher orbits and improves injection accuracy by an order of magnitude.

Pegasus® has completed two missions to date, and the next is scheduled to occur this summer. Its most recent flight was on July 17, 1991 (F-2). This mission successfully placed seven small communications

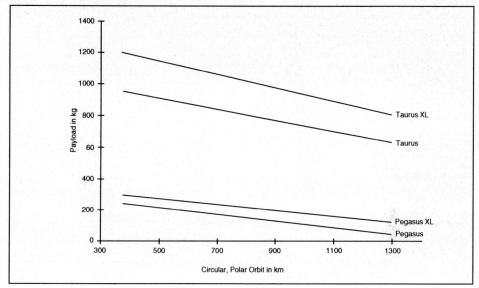

Figure 14. Approximate Payload Performance of OSC Launch Vehicles.

satellites into low Earth orbit, demonstrating Pegasus'® ability to deploy multiple satellites into orbital constellations with one launch. The flight also demonstrated the use of HAPS as a liquid fourth stage. Pegasus'® maiden flight occurred on April 5, 1990. This launch successfully achieved mission objectives, validating the vehicle's unique design and air-launched concept. Pegasus® is currently available to international customers at a nominal 12 to 18 month lead time.

Taurus™

For missions requiring greater performance, OSC offers the Taurus™ ground launched vehicle, shown in Figure 15. Taurus™ is a low cost, 1400 kg class ELV which is currently in development under contract to DARPA for launch in the first half of government FY 1993.

Taurus™ is composed of the three Pegasus® motors stacked on top of a Peacekeeper-class Stage 0 and exploits assembly, avionics and software technologies developed on the Pegasus® program. As part of the DARPA contact, Taurus™ will demonstrate a rapid response capability to establish a launch pad on an unimproved site within 5 days of call-up. From this "ready" condition, Taurus™ will launch within 72 hours after receiving its payload. Taurus™ can also be launched into a wide variety of inclinations from NASA's Wallops Flight Facility in Virginia for customers which do not require mobile launch siting.

Taurus™' performance capability into a circular, polar orbit is shown in Figure 14. The enhanced Taurus™ XL achieves greater performance by using an improved first stage and the XL motors in place of the standard Pegasus® motors for the upper stages. This configuration will be available in 1993. Taurus™ and Taurus™ XL can inject payloads of 480 and 580 kg, respectively, into a Geosynchronous Transfer Orbit (GTO). The HAPS system may also be used with Taurus™ for payloads with precise orbital injection requirements.

Figure 15. OSC's Taurus Launch Vehicle.

In addition to the first flight, DARPA holds four contract options for Taurus™ launches. The vehicle is currently available to international customers with a nominal 18 month lead time.

PegaStar™

PegaStar™ is the most capable and cost-effective small spacecraft bus being built today. Its combination of high performance, low cost, short lead times, and compatibility with flexible, cost effective small ELVs enables a wide range of civil, military and commercial missions. Specifically, it has been chosen to perform the most challenging small satellite-based space experimentation remote sensing missions undertaken to date.

PegaStar™ is a unique spacecraft bus design which exploits certain commonalities between spacecraft and launch vehicle structures and avionics to achieve an efficient integrated spacecraft-to-launch vehicle design. This eliminates unnecessary, mass and volume wasting redundancy between the spacecraft and the launch vehicle and allows PegaStar™ to provide greater mass, volume, and/or subsystem support to the experiment payload. Figure 16 describes the performance capabilities of the current PegaStar™ design. These capabilities are designed for each mission, so that for a particular program, PegaStar™ may provide more or less capability in a given category. Though PegaStar™ is optimized for launch on Pegasus®, it is also compatible with OSC's Taurus™, or can be adapted for use on other launch vehicles.

The integrated spacecraft/launch vehicle approach provides programmatic benefits as well. It simplifies the customer-to-contractor interface, lowers schedule risk by simplifying the traditional programmatic interface between the ELV and spacecraft suppliers and reduces costs by eliminating unnecessary hardware duplicity between the spacecraft and the launch vehicle.

Currently OSC has two PegaStar™ spacecraft in production. The first was chosen by NASA to carry the important Sea-viewing Wide Field Sensor (SeaWiFS) on a five year mission to provide Ocean Color

Data Sets beginning in late 1993 (SeaStar). PegaStar™ also was selected by the US Air Force's Space Test Program to carry the Advanced Photovoltaic and Electronics Experiment (APEX) on a three year mission through the Van Allen belts beginning in FY1993. The APEX engineering model is shown in Figure 17. The selection of PegaStar™ for these missions was strongly driven by its unique ability to provide the greatest experiment mass and volume achievable on a Pegasus® launch vehicle, at the most cost-effective price; benefits which are being validated through the successful execution of these two programs. PegaStar™ is available for international customers with a nominal 18 to 24 month lead time.

Spacecraft Capability	PegaStar
Payload Accommodation	Up to 16 ft³, 200 lbm
Power (Peak, BOL)	500 w (300 for Payload)
Attitude Control	3 Axis Better Than 0.1°
Telemetry	2.6 Mbps
Data Storage	1.25 Gbit (EDAC SRAM)
Position Determination	Better Than 100m (GPS)
Orbit Adjust/Maintenance	N_2H_4 Propulsion (125 lbm)
Mission Duration	5 Year Design Life (10 Year Goal)
Development Time	18-24 Months
Approximate Cost	$6-15 Million

* Note That All Data is Representative of Performance Capabilities Achievable with a Typical PegaStar Design. Mission Specific Designs May Produce More Capable or More Modest Performance.

Figure 16. Representative Capabilities of PegaStar.

Figure 17. OSC Engineers with the Engineering Model of APEX.

Turn-key Services

In addition to stand-alone launch vehicles and spacecraft, OSC can offer complete, turn-key systems. For instance, on the SeaStar mission, OSC is procuring the mission specific payload (SeaWiFS), and providing the spacecraft, launch vehicle, integration, launch operations, on-orbit check-out, operations and system management, and data delivery to NASA for five years. NASA is, in fact, buying only data.

Space-Based Services

OSC will soon be offering two space-based services which exploit small space technology. The SeaStar program, introduced above, will begin commercially marketing ocean color data sets in 1994. Licenses are currently available which will enable customers to receive direct downlinks from the satellite with local area coverage in 1.13 km resolution (at nadir) at least once per day. Global data sets in 4.5 km resolution will be available from Virginia every 48 hours.

The ORBCOMM system also will exploit OSC's small space products to offer global, ubiquitous, two-way data messaging and position locating using inexpensive, pocket portable, hand-held terminals. A

Figure 18. Prototype ORBCOMM Ground Terminal.

prototype terminal is shown in Figure 18. This service will be ideal for emergency alerts and position reporting, remote asset monitoring and data acquisition, tracking of property and animals and personal business messaging. Initial operational capability is planned for 1994.

CONCLUSIONS

This paper has described what is being done with small space systems today. The intent is to demonstrate what can be done and will be done tomorrow and in the coming decades. The intrinsic value of these systems to perform cost effective, meaningful space missions has been repeatedly validated, and they are presently being entrusted with communications, remote sensing and space research core missions.

REFERENCES

The MicroSpace Revolution. *D. W. Thompson, Orbital Sciences Corporation, April 1992.*

"Memorandum for Correspondents." No. 49-M. *Defense Advanced Research Projects Agency, February, 1992.*

Pegasus® Dedicated and Multiple Launch Capabilities for Low Earth Orbit Communications Satellite Constellations. *M. Mosier, Orbital Sciences Corporation, January, 1992.*

The Taurus™ Space Booster Payload Interfaces, Processing Procedures and Launch Operations for Low Earth Orbit Communications Satellites. *J. Padavano, S. Frazier, and E. Rutkowski, Orbital Sciences Corporation, January, 1992.*

US Civilian Government Expendable Launch Vehicle Payload Compendium. *Sixth Edition, National Aeronautics and Space Administration, Code ML, Washington, DC., December 1991.*

Pegasus® Payload User's Guide. *Release 2.00, Orbital Sciences Corporation, May, 1991.*

Pegasus® Launch Services and the PegaStar™ Integrated Spacecraft Bus. *M. Mosier, Orbital Sciences Corporation, May, 1991.*

The Pegasus® Air Launched Space Booster Payload Interfaces and Processing Procedures For Small Optical Payloads. *M. Mosier, G. Harris and C. Whitmeyer, Orbital Sciences Corporation, March, 1991.*

L'ASSURANCE PRODUIT DES PETITS SATELLITES

J.L. De MONTLIVAULT - BUREAU VERITAS
J. CADELEC - CALIREAL

1. INTRODUCTION

Alors que la taille des satellites de télécommunications ne fait que croître, que le budget des grands programmes spatiaux atteint des proportions énormes, on assiste à un regain d'intérêt pour les petits satellites. Ce symposium en est la meilleure démonstration.

Certains esprits perspicaces ont en effet noté que l'argent du contribuable pourrait être mieux employé à financer une dizaine de petits projets qu'un seul gros satellite dont l'échec est alors catastrophique[1]. Tout le monde a en tête le drame de Challenger et l'échec du Hubble Space Telescope.

Par ailleurs on assiste dans le domaine des télécommunications à une redécouverte de l'orbite basse. Plusieurs projets de systèmes de communications avec les mobiles envisagent des dizaines de satellites à défilement. Il est bien évident que la faisabilité de tels projets dépend essentiellement de la possibilité de réduire les coûts des satellites.

Des satellites encore plus modestes sont proposés pour assurer une messagerie électronique, avec des possibilités d'applications militaires. Dans ce domaine on pense bien sûr aux "brilliant pebbles" de l'Initiative de Défense Stratégique, mais aussi à l'intérêt de déployer un grand nombre de satellites d'écoute en orbite basse.

Enfin dans le domaine scientifique, même si là aussi la tendance est vers des missions de plus en plus complexes, il reste néanmoins un grand nombre d'expérimentations intéressantes qui peuvent être réalisées avec des moyens modestes tout en bénéficiant des progrès que permet la miniaturisation des systèmes embarqués de traitement de l'information.

Cependant tous ces projets de petits satellites n'ont d'intérêt que si leur coût est vraiment très réduit. La modestie des budgets doit compenser la nécessaire limitation de performance.

Par ailleurs comme le fait remarquer Mr. Parkinson [1], il faut gagner un facteur 4 à 5 sur le coût par kilogramme d'un satellite en orbite basse par rapport à celui d'un satellite en orbite géostationnaire pour conserver l'optimisation de la répartition entre coût de lancement et coût de réalisation.

Mais comment réduire ces coûts ? Si la mission du petit satellite est moins critique que celle du gros engin, on devrait pouvoir économiser sur les tâches d'assurance produit, c'est à dire la somme des activités de sûreté de fonctionnement et d'assurance de la qualité.

---

1. Organizational impediments to the reduction of costs of space programmes, R.C. PARKINSON. Paper presented at the 42nd Congress of the IAF, ref. IAA-91-639.

La qualité n'est-elle pas de répondre au juste besoin! Or le coût relatif de l'assurance produit d'un projet spatial ne représente que 8 à 10 % du total, soit donc pas plus que dans n'importe quel autre projet. Une économie dans ce domaine n'aurait donc qu'un impact limité.

En fait il faut distinguer entre les coûts liés au fonctionnement du système qualité, qui sont relativement faibles, et les coûts induits par les exigences qualité qui eux peuvent être très élevés. Ainsi il est bien connu que le coût d'un kilo de matériel est quelque dix fois plus élevé en spatial qu'en aéronautique. Il semble qu'il y ait de la marge pour faire des économies substantielles même si le matériel spatial souffre de la contrainte liée à l'impossibilité de maintenance et de l'absence de tout effet de série.

C'est donc l'ensemble du cycle industriel (conception, développement, fabrication, essais) qu'il faut revoir afin de déterminer les possibilités d'économies réellement significatives. Mais pour cela il est nécessaire de faire des distinctions entre les divers petits satellites. Il est clair qu'on ne suivra pas la même approche pour un petit satellite scientifique que pour une série de satellites de télécommunications.

2.   DIFFERENTS TYPES DE PETITS SATELLITES ET RISQUES ASSOCIES

Quand on examine les divers projets de petits satellites, il semble utile de les classer en trois grandes catégories:

Catégorie I : Les satellites à mission expérimentale.

> Exemples: les satellites scientifiques
> les satellites technologiques
> les satellites amateurs
> les capsules récupérables utilisées en micro-gravité

Il s'agit en général de satellites, ayant une relativement faible durée de vie (6 mois à 2 ans) et dont l'échec a des conséquences limitées.

Etant donnée la spécificité de leur mission, ces satellites sont généralement réalisés à un seul exemplaire. Toutefois la même plate-forme peut être ré-utilisée par plusieurs satellites. De même des expériences de micro-gravité très diverses peuvent faire appel à la même capsule récupérable.

Catégorie II : Les satellites opérationnels réalisés en petites séries.

> Exemples: les satellites de télécommunications en orbite basse
> les satellites de navigation
> les satellites militaires d'écoute

Pour ces satellites les exigences de durée de vie peuvent être aussi sévères que pour les satellites géostationnaires de télécommunications, soit 10 à 13 ans actuellement.

Ces satellites peuvent par contre faire l'objet de petites séries tels les projets Iridium (77 satellites) ou GPS (24 satellites) qui toutefois sont probablement trop gros pour rentrer dans la catégorie des petits satellites. Un effort d'"industrialisation" pour diminuer les coûts de fabrication est d'autant plus nécessaire qu'autrement le coût du système devient prohibitif.

Pour ces programmes, ce qui compte, c'est la fiabilité du système. La mort accidentelle d'un satellite est acceptable, car on peut espérer qu'il y aura toujours quelques satellites de rechange en orbite. Par contre un défaut de conception ou une dérive de composant se révélant après 1 à 2 ans en orbite aurait des conséquences catastrophiques.

On peut cependant limiter ce risque en effectuant une mise en place progressive du système permettant ainsi de tester valablement la fiabilité en orbite des premiers satellites avant de mettre en place le système complet. La qualité de la fabrication doit également bénéficier de l'effort d'industrialisation lié à la mise en place d'une petite série.

Catégorie III : Les satellites opérationnels réalisés en quelques exemplaires seulement.

Exemples: les satellites de retransmission de messages en temps différé
les satellites d'observation à moyenne résolution

Il s'agit là de satellites opérationnels, donc à durée de vie assez longue mais réalisés seulement à quelques exemplaires. La panne d'un satellite affecte donc directement la mission et oblige à refaire un lancement pour reconstituer la capacité en orbite.

Pour chacune de ces catégories, on peut donc définir un risque :

- modéré pour le satellite expérimental,
- contrôlable pour le satellite opérationnel en petite série,
- significatif pour le satellite opérationnel réalisé à quelques exemplaires seulement.

L'effort qualité requis est donc croissant quand on passe de la catégorie I à la catégorie II et de la II à la III.

Le tableau 1 synthétise notre appréciation des niveaux de risque et des efforts de qualité requis pour chacune des trois catégories de mission.

Il est intéressant de noter que la NASA dans le document intitulé "Guidelines for Standard Payload Assurance Requirements" identifie 4 catégories d'exigences: renforcées, de référence, réduites pour une augmentation acceptable des risques, enfin correspondant à un programme restreint d'assurance produit.

Tableau 1 - Tableau des diverses catégories de petits satellites				
CATEGORIE	DUREE DE VIE	RECURRENCE	RISQUES	NIVEAU DE QUALITE
I satellites expérimentaux	courte	un seul exemplaire	X	X
II satellites opérationnels de petites séries	longue	petite série	X	XX
III satellites opérationnels en quelques exemplaires	longue	quelques exemplaires	XX	XXX

3. REVUE DES DIFFERENTES EXIGENCES EN MATIERE D'ASSURANCE PRODUIT

3.1 Caractéristiques générales de l'approche spatiale

Qui dit spatial, dit salle blanche et gants blancs. Depuis le début, la réalisation de satellites a impliqué le maximum de précautions pour assurer la réussite de la mission. Rien ne semble devoir être négligé, qu'il s'agisse de la conception du produit, de la qualification des opérateurs ou de la propreté.

Toute cette activité s'inscrit dans un système de management dit d'Assurance Produit. Pour les très grands programmes, la moindre absence de rigueur peut avoir des conséquences catastrophiques, comme l'a révélé l'échec de la navette spatiale Challenger. Mais pour les projets plus modestes, sans sacrifier le système d'Assurance Produit et en particulier le contrôle des non-conformités, est-il possible d'adapter certaines exigences? La réussite de bon nombre de projets scientifiques est là pour prouver qu'une approche pragmatique, qui respecte les contraintes de budget, permet d'adapter les exigences sans trop de risques.

De façon plus précise, nous nous proposons d'analyser les différentes disciplines de l'Assurance Produit pour identifier les aménagements qui seraient acceptables pour certaines catégories de missions.

3.2 Fiabilité

La fiabilité, assurance produit à la conception, qui se situe à l'intérieur du concept de sûreté de fonctionnement regroupe :

- le calcul de fiabilité prévisionnelle,
- l'analyse des taux de charges des composants,
- l'analyse des Modes et Effets des Défaillances et de leur Criticité (AMDEC),
- l'analyse dite "pire cas".

Le calcul de la fiabilité prévisionnelle apparaît indispensable lorsque l'équipement ou le système doit répondre à une exigence contractuelle de fiabilité. Cependant, quelle est l'efficacité réelle de ce calcul ? Son résultat permettra-t-il d'adapter le niveau de qualité des composants électroniques ou de redonder les fonctions? Le niveau de qualité des composants, qui peut dépendre, et c'est souvent le cas, du budget disponible n'est pas obligatoirement négociable. Il est plus difficile de nier l'intérêt de redonder des fonctions, mais ne peut-on pas accéder à ces besoins via l'AMDEC. Malgré son intérêt, nous proposons de classer le calcul de fiabilité dans la catégorie des exigences souhaitables, mais non indispensables pour les applications scientifiques.

Une illustration de cette réalité se rencontre dans le projet du Centre National d'Etudes Spatiales (CNES) SIGMA[2], où pour un objectif de fiabilité de 0,75, on obtient 0,83 avec des composants de niveau ESA/SCC C et 0,60 avec des composants de niveau B, MIL-STD-883C. La logique conduirait au choix du niveau C ESA/SCC, on a cependant choisi des composants de niveau de qualité inférieur, en les soumettant à des essais additionnels.

---

2. Synthèse des activités composants du projet SIGMA, F.LINDER, document interne CNES RA/DP/QA/D/90-90/395, 1990.

Bien que l'analyse des taux de charges des composants soit liée au calcul de fiabilité prévisionnelle, puisque les taux de défaillances individuelles dépendent des charges réelles appliquées, il présente un intérêt propre car, l'utilisation de composants électroniques ou mécaniques au delà de leurs possibilités physiques reste une faute majeure. Le respect des exigences de taux de charges de l'ESA, du CNES ou de la NASA est donc une exigence minimum à prendre en compte lors de la conception, même si les missions de courte durée ne nécessitent pas des réductions de charges aussi importantes.

L'AMDEC qui requiert beaucoup d'efforts est utile à l'identification des défaillances critiques ou catastrophiques potentielles. La question qui se pose en fonction de la mission est de choisir le niveau de détail de cette analyse. Doit-elle être effectuée pour toutes les fonctions et doit-elle descendre au niveau des composants élémentaires? La réponse est certainement, que pour toute fonction critique, il faut descendre jusqu'au niveau de détail qui permet d'évaluer les risques potentiels réels et donc de déclencher les actions correctives palliatives (changement de conception, mise en place d'une redondance active ou passive, suivi particulier du composant critique, etc). L'AMDEC est aussi un bon outil pour identifier les erreurs de conception et reste indispensable pour toutes les fonctions critiques au succès de la mission. On retiendra aussi, que les nouveaux composants doivent faire l'objet d'une attention particulière. Pour les projets des catégories I et II, on peut choisir de n'effectuer cette analyse que sur les fonctions critiques. Mieux vaut faire un effort complet sur un volume moindre, que de n'approfondir aucune fonction.

Quant à l'analyse pire cas, qui consiste rappelons-le, à vérifier le maintien de fonctionnalité lorsque le vieillissement des composants génère une dérive des paramètres (voir, par exemple, la norme de l'Agence Spatiale Européenne ESA PSS-01-301), nous n'hésiterons pas à la classer dans la catégorie facultative. Un bon concepteur doit avant tout s'assurer que la fonctionnalité est maintenue à l'intérieur des limites extrêmes des paramètres des composants utilisés. Il sera avisé d'y ajouter une marge de sécurité. Seule la catégorie III nous paraît requérir le maintien de cette analyse.

Le cas des dérives dues à l'effet des rayonnements ionisants doit être traité à part. Il est évident que si certains composants parfois indiqués comme critiques (quartz, transistors bipolaires) ne le sont pas toujours, certains composants et matériaux sont très sensibles. Des produits MOS non durcis "standards" peuvent ainsi ne pas survivre à des doses supérieures à 2 kRAD.Si. Cela convient à des applications en orbite basse d'une durée de un à deux ans, mais n'est pas compatible avec des applications de 10 à 13 ans mentionnées auparavant pour la catégorie II. Les composants les plus récents, du fait de la réduction des géométries sont aussi de plus en plus sensibles aux effets des ions lourds et des rayons cosmiques. Il faut donc aussi prévoir des palliatifs aux changements d'états qui peuvent en résulter. Pour résumer, la fiabilité dans certain cas doit intégrer l'analyse et l'identification des composants et matériaux critiques ou incompatibles avec les niveaux de rayonnement prévus et les contraintes d'exploitation.

Si les besoins en maintenabilité et disponibilité ne peuvent être totalement négligés pendant la conception, il s'agira plus d'un état d'esprit que de réalisation d'analyses approfondies. Cependant, des applications peuvent avoir des exigences prévisionnelles à démontrer dans ces domaines. Ainsi la disponibilité d'un système reposant sur plusieurs satellites d'applications dépendra de la fiabilité de chaque satellite et la maintenabilité d'équipement embarqués sur des plate-formes récupérables est à prendre en compte. Il est bien évident aussi que les analyses de risques liées à la sauvegarde du champ de tir sont indispensables.

Le tableau 2, résume nos propositions.

Tableau 2 - fiabilité		
CATEGORIE I	CATEGORIE II	CATEGORIE III
* AMDEC (fonctions critiques) * Taux de charge * Effets des radiations	* Calcul de fiabilité * AMDEC (fonctions critiques) * Taux de charge * Effets des radiations	* Calcul de fiabilité * AMDEC général * Taux de charge * Effets des radiations * Analyse pire cas

3.3 Composants électroniques

Sélection, approvisionnement et maîtrise des composants électroniques, tel est le titre des normes applicables à ce domaine. On retrouve bien là les exigences d'assurance qualité classiques liées à la fois au choix de produits adaptés et "qualifiés" provenant de sources "qualifiées", aux inspections techniques et à l'organisation assurant la maîtrise de la qualité, du délai et du coût. Autrement dit, trois composantes sont à considérer dans la constitution du coût: le prix des composants, le prix des inspections, le prix du management. Cela peut représenter environ 15% du coût d'un système et 30% du coût d'un équipement.

De nombreuses études existent à ce propos qui butent toutes sur le rapport de prix existant entre les composants produits selon les exigences spatiales et les prix des produits CECC ou US-MIL satisfaisant des exigences minimum de fonctionnement en température et de sélection. Cela conduit souvent, comme nous l'avons déjà vu à choisir des niveaux de qualité différents de ceux qui seraient normalement nécessaires. Les systèmes ESA/SCC B ou C en Europe ou MIL-S aux Etats-Unis conduisent en effet, indépendamment de la sévérité des essais de sélection, à des coûts liés aux petites quantités, à la documentation nécessaire (spécification, "flow" de production, traçabilité, enregistrement des mesures, etc.), à la gestion des essais de lots, à l'existence d'équipes spécialisées. Ces coûts sont difficilement compressibles[3].

Le choix de produits qualifiés, même pour applications non-spatiales, chez des fabricants eux-mêmes homologués augmente considérablement le niveau de confiance dans la qualité des composants obtenus[4].

Il est difficile dans le cadre de cet article de faire des propositions pour l'ensemble des composants électroniques, aussi à titre d'exemple le tableau 3 résume ce qui est proposé dans le cas des dispositifs semi-conducteurs discrets.

---

3. Niveaux de qualité et d'essais de lots des composants électroniques pour applications scientifiques, J.CADELEC, Etude CNES, Rapport final, Volume 1, Octobre 1991.

4. Upscrening of components for space applications, R.FIDLER, ESA electronic components conference, Noordwijk, Novembre 1990.

Tableau 3 - composants semi-conducteurs discrets		
CATEGORIE I	CATEGORIE II	CATEGORIE III
* Source qualifiée	* Source qualifiée	* Source qualifiée
* Niveaux de qualité CECC 50000, niveau A ou MIL 19500, JANTXV	* Niveaux de qualité ESA/SCC niveau C	* Niveaux de qualité ESA/SCC niveau B ou MIL JANS
* Essais de lots Mesures électriques	* Essais de lots LAT 3 allégé	* Essais de lots LAT 3 ou 2
* Essais complémentaires PIND test	* Essais complémentaires Aucun	Essais complémentaires Aucun
* Inspections Recette en usine avec DPA allégée	* Inspections Inspection d'entrée à la carte	* Inspections Recette en usine ou inspection d'entrée DPA
* Remarques Assemblage et/ou tests en Europe préféré	* Remarques Pas de "precap" client	* Remarques "Precap" client

Pour les autres composants, on peut de la même façon optimiser les coûts provenant des niveaux de qualité et des inspections diverses effectuées par l'acheteur. Quant au coût provenant du management de l'approvisionnement, le gain obtenu pour les coûts non-récurrents et l'assurance d'un management homogène plaident en faveur d'un système centralisé[5].

3.4 Matériaux et Procédés

De quoi s'agit-il ? De sélectionner, spécifier et vérifier la conformité ou la validité des matériaux et procédés utilisés, et de disposer d'un management adapté. Il s'agit bien là du respect des règles de l'art.

Il n'est pas pensable d'utiliser un matériau dont le taux de dégazage sera tel qu'une contamination des optiques du satellite est assurée avant la fin de la mission. Il n'est pas pensable d'effectuer l'assemblage par soudure des composants électroniques dans des conditions d'environnement inadaptées et par du personnel non formé.

Dans le cas d'utilisation de lignes non formellement qualifiées, il est sans doute possible au moyen d'audit et d'inspections "point-clés" d'éviter une procédure lourde de qualification formelle tout en maintenant une assurance qualité minimum. Au contraire dans le cas d'une ligne qualifiée, on limitera les inspections clients. Un cas particulier est celui d'un équipement qui développé par exemple, pour des applications militaires ou aéronautiques utiliserait des circuits imprimés ne répondant pas exactement aux spécifications spatiales. Ne faudrait-il pas dans la catégorie I, envisager une dérogation?

---

5. Coordinated Parts Procurement for ISO - A contribution to Cost-Effectiveness, M.VON HOEGEN, J.MINNEE & F.J.ZIEGLER, ESA Bulletin 67, 1991.

3.5 Assurance de la qualité

Rappelons qu'il s'agit de l'ensemble des actions préétablies et systématiques nécessaires pour donner la confiance appropriée en ce qu'un produit ou service satisfasse les exigences relatives à la qualité. Pour les activités spatiales, cela revient à être conforme à une norme telle que le document ESA PSS-01-20 ou aux normes internationales ISO 9001 ou 9002.

S'agissant d'exigences à la conception, le modèle applicable est celui de la norme 9001 dont nous pouvons dire que nous avons déjà vu les aspects qualité en définition et conception, en approvisionnement (composants et matériaux) et en production (procédés). Les aspects management et documentation seront traités plus loin.

Les thèmes à considérer sont donc :
- gestion de configuration et traçabilité,
- inspections et essais,
- maîtrise des équipements de mesurage et d'essai,
- gestion des non-conformités,
- actions correctives,
- enregistrements relatifs à la qualité,
- manutention, stockage, conditionnement et expédition,
- audit du système qualité,
- formation du personnel.

La discussion ne peut qu'être brève, car on ne voit pas de quelle discipline, on peut faire l'économie, si ce n'est, peut-être, des audits qualité internes, qui dans le cadre d'un projet spatial peuvent être remplacés par des audits et inspections de produits, ainsi que par les revues de projets.

Bien entendu, aucun système ne dispense de la préparation d'un plan qualité chargé de garantir les exigences spécifiques au projet telles que prise en compte des niveaux de radiations ionisantes, de la propreté exigée, de définir le plan d'inspection et d'essais, etc.. Nous sommes d'ailleurs partisan d'intégrer ce plan qualité au plan de management du projet. On pourrait même parler comme le fait le CNES d'un plan "Assurance Mission" ou comme le fait la NASA d'un "Assurance Implementation Plan"[6].

Le tableau 4 résume pour les trois catégories de risques définis quelle peut être la norme de référence exigible pour l'assurance qualité.

Tableau 4: assurance de la qualité		
CATEGORIE I	CATEGORIE II	CATEGORIE III
* *Niveau* Démarche ISO 9000	* *Niveau* ISO 9001	* *Niveau* ISO 9001 ou ESA PSS-01-0 ou CNES SM-50
* *Plan qualité* oui	* *Plan qualité* oui	* *Plan qualité* oui

---

6. Guidelines for Standard Payload Assurance Requirements for GSFC orbital projects, SPAR-3, March 1990.

3.6 Documentation

Il est intéressant à ce propos de considérer l'approche NASA. En nous reportant au SPAR[6], nous constatons que pour les instruments, c'est à dire les charges utiles de satellites, la NASA exige 50 documents différents dans le cas nominal. Ce nombre est réduit à 45 pour la catégorie immédiatement inférieure, dont 5 doivent simplement être disponibles pour revue chez le contractant. Enfin dans la catégorie où la NASA est prête à prendre le plus de risques, elle n'exige plus que 29 documents dont 8 seulement disponibles pour revue. C'est donc dans ce dernier cas une réduction du coût de la documentation d'environ 50%. Une telle économie doit être faisable, au moins pour notre catégorie I des satellites expérimentaux (Cf. Tableau 1).

3.7 Tests et essais

Dans la mesure où sur un petit satellite on peut être amené à faire des analyses de fiabilité moins approfondies que pour un satellite plus complexe, il importe de ne pas réduire la séquence de test, au moins sur les premiers modèles de vol. Par contre dans le cas d'une petite série (catégorie II), on pourrait envisager d'alléger le plan de test si le retour d'expérience en orbite est satisfaisant pour les premiers modèles de vol et si le nombre d'anomalies décelées durant certains tests est suffisamment faible.

3.8 Management

Le coût des programmes spatiaux est fortement aggravé par la lourdeur des organisations. En Europe tout particulièrement, les obligations du retour géographique entraînent une parcellisation des tâches et donc une gestion des interfaces complexe. Un programme de petit satellite doit obligatoirement échapper à ce type de contrainte et donc ne doit faire intervenir qu'un nombre très limité de partenaires.

A l'intérieur de l'entreprise, il est également souhaitable que le petit satellite échappe à la lourdeur des structures mises en place pour les grands programmes. Il vaut mieux une organisation projet très intégrée, plutôt qu'une organisation matricielle. En particulier l'Assurance Produit ne doit pas être l'affaire exclusive d'un service spécialisé, mais la responsabilité de chacun des membres de l'équipe de projet. Ce n'est qu'ainsi qu'il sera possible de mettre en oeuvre les principes de l'ingénierie simultanée ("concurrent engineering").

Il faut aussi pouvoir faire des économies sur toutes les tâches de contrôle en confiant la conception et la réalisation des petits satellites à des techniciens expérimentés pour lesquels l'auto-contrôle serait systématique. En fait c'est le principe même de la qualité totale qu'il s'agit de mettre en oeuvre (Total Quality Management), ce qui devrait être d'autant plus facile à réussir que le travail aura été assigné à une petite équipe intégrée.

En fait ce que nous suggérons n'est ni plus ni moins que de revenir aux types d'organisations qui ont fait le succès des tout premiers projets de satellite. L'expérience acquise depuis permet d'être beaucoup plus efficace sans que pour autant l'enthousiasme des équipes en soit nécessairement réduit.

4. CONCLUSION

Comme nous le disions dans l'introduction, les projets de petits satellites n'ont d'intérêt que si leurs coûts sont réduits de manière significative. C'est possible sans prendre de risques inacceptables, en allégeant les exigences en matière de composants, en faisant des analyses de fiabilité moins poussées et en réduisant les exigences en matière de documentation.

Mais en aucun cas, il ne faut sacrifier la rigueur générée par un système d'assurance qualité dont l'efficacité sera d'autant plus grande qu'il sera mieux intégré aux diverses fonctions d'ingénierie. Comme le souligne Mr. Giudicelli[7], le coût des actions qualité décroît en fonction même de la capacité des ingénieurs à les incorporer dans les tâches de conception et à les exécuter au moment voulu. Le système d'Assurance Produit idéal est celui qui intègre complètement les équipes qualité à l'ingénierie, ce qui suppose que tout participant au projet ait reçu une solide formation qualité.

En fait, l'essentiel est de mettre sur pied une organisation très ramassée échappant par là même à la lourdeur habituelle des structures industrielles. C'est la meilleure façon de pouvoir faire à la fois de l'ingénierie simultanée et de la Qualité Totale. Les actions qualité, loin d'être réduites, sont alors prises en compte par chacun des acteurs.

---

7. Study of Cost Effectiveness of Product Assurance for Space Applications, Final Study Report, Ph.GIUDICELLI, ESA Contract N° 6322/85/NL/AB, October 1987.

ESSAIS D'ENVIRONNEMENT DES MINI SATELLITES

Gérard BOURES - Joseph MERLET
INTESPACE - Toulouse

1 - INTRODUCTION

Les études de marché font apparaître un très grand développement des mini satellites dans les années futures.

Une des caractéristiques de certains des programmes est le grand nombre de modèles identiques ce qui doit changer fondamentalement la philosophie d'intégration et d'essais par rapports aux séries de 2 à 5 satellites réalisées habituellement.

Comme dans tous les programmes de satellites, une analyse du profil de vie doit être effectuée. Elle conduira à la réalisation d'essais de qualification et de recette strictement nécessaires, car concevoir pour ces nouveaux projets un programme d'essais dérivé de ceux des années 60, que l'on appliquait sur des satellites de masses similaires, les rendraient non compétitifs.

Nous proposons une démarche qui, sans remettre en cause les objectifs du projet, intégrera -dès la conception- les méthodes, moyens d'essais et capteurs de mesure afin de réduire les coûts et délais en essais (Figure 1).

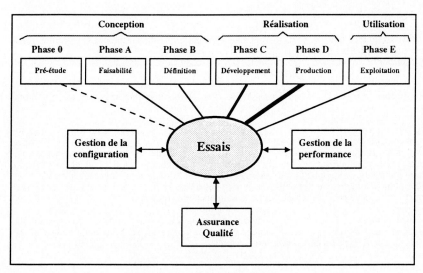

Figure 1 - Essais et déroulement d'un projet

2 - PROFIL DE VIE ET ESSAIS

Le programme d'essais d'un micro ou mini satellite doit être établi à l'issue d'une démarche logique de personnalisation -Figure 2- (MIL-STD. 810 E - GAM EG 13 D) et non extrapolé des spécifications d'essais existantes pour les satellites actuels (1 tonne - 4,5 tonnes).

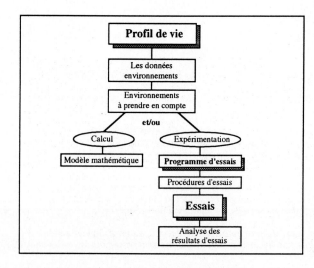

- Identifier toutes les situations pendant la vie du satellite.

- Valoriser l'environnement de chaque situation.

- Analyse des données, Décision

- Elaboration programme et procédure (RG Aéro 00011)

- Réalisation des essais

- Exploitation des résultats d'essais pour retour à conception, intégration, modification programme ou procédure d'essai

Figure 2 : Du profil de vie aux essais

Par exemple :

1- L'environnement vibro-acoustique pendant les opérations de lancement (opérations juste avant le tir) diffèrent notamment en fonction du type lanceur :
   - Lanceur conventionnel : environnement vibro-acoustique : quasi nul, le lanceur étant sur sa table de lancement.

   - Lanceur aéroporté : environnement vibro-acoustique important, le lanceur étant arrimé sous son avion porteur.

2- La prise en compte des données techniques dérivées de la stratégie marketing de prise de parts de marché ou des compensations : par exemple intégration initiale en Europe, intégration finale et essais en Asie, Amérique ou Afrique, qui ajoute un "environnement de transport" ; actuellement, les satellites sont isolés de ces contraintes liées à cette situation, à l'aide de containers sophistiqués (pressurisation, contrôle de température, amortisseur de vibrations). Compte tenu des objectifs de coût des micro ou mini satellites et leur cadence de production, on ne peut penser utiliser de containers aussi coûteux.

Il y aura donc lieu de caractériser chaque situation avec ses données d'environnement correspondantes (Figure 3) et de ne s'engager dans un processus d'expérimentation que si les dossiers de calcul, expérience, ... sont insuffisants.

SITUATION	ENVIRONNEMENTS		
	Mécanique	**Thermique**	**Electrique**
Réalisation Intégration 			
Essais 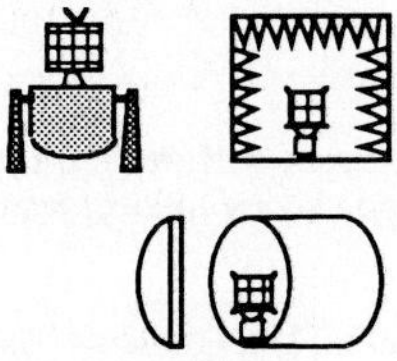			
Transport	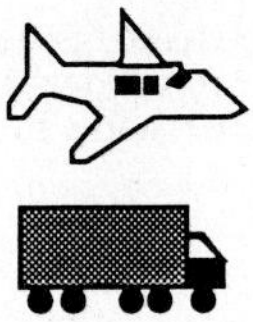 -Vibrations -Chocs -Secousses	-Température -Humidité -Dépression -Brouillard salin	
Opérations de lancement	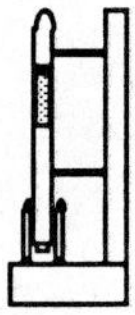 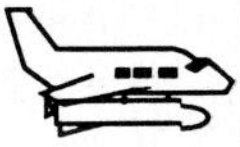 Négligeable **OU** -Vibrations -Chocs pyro. -Bruit acoustique -Accélération	-Température -Humidité -Dépression	-EMI -Orages
Lancement	 -Vibrations -Chocs pyro. -Bruit acoustique -Accélération	-Température -Humidité -Dépression	-EMI
Vie Orbitale	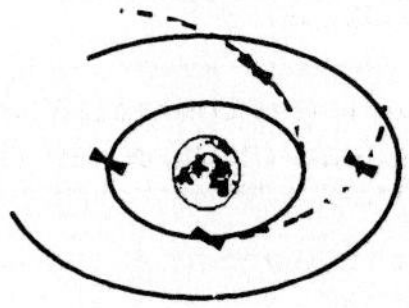 -Micro-vibrations	-Vide -Température -Rayonnements	-EMI -Décharges électrostatiques -Magnétisme

Figure 3 : Situation et agents d'environnement d'un mini satellite

3 - DEMARCHE INTEGREE CONCEPTION - INTEGRATION - ESSAI

La grosseur des équipes projet, la complexité des missions envisagées pour les satellites classiques, ont souvent conduits par le passé à trouver des démarches parallèles conception - intégration.

Il faut dire que les compétences des équipes sont, en général, assez éloignées. Cependant, dans le cas des mini satellites, il est possible d'envisager une nouvelle démarche qui, en étant intégrée -c'est à dire en prenant globalement les problèmes- réussira à diminuer les coûts et les délais en optimisant chaque étape.

Nous allons, dans ce paragraphe, proposer des pistes de recherche. Celles-ci sont liées à deux phénomènes :

- Le premier : amélioration de la demande d'ensemble.
 Cette amélioration, en simplifiant les concepts, en réduisant l'effort de travail, en diminuant les distances entre les équipes, devrait inévitablement réduire les coûts et les délais.

- Le second est lié au marché.
 En effet, les mini satellites sont apparus avec l'apparition d'Université en tant que concepteur de produit. Les coûts de conception et de réalisation, dans ce cadre non industriel, sont indubitablement plus faibles que sur le marché classique.
 Ces types de micro satellites sont un défi économique lancé aux industriels, si ceux-ci veulent rester compétitifs. De plus, la stratégie marketing risque de compliquer la situation en faisant intervenir des partenaires moins sophistiqués que ceux de notre monde traditionnel de l'Espace.

3.1 AMELIORATION DE LA DEMARCHE D'ENSEMBLE

Ainsi plusieurs pistes sont à défricher :

1- Utiliser un plan de développement qui réduit au minimum les essais de recette.
 Ce point est surtout valable en mécanique.

2- Concevoir une famille de micro satellites dont la signature mécanique et thermique sera aisément identifiable et interprétable.
 La structure ne devrait pas subir de changement important nécessitant une re-qualification ou même une caractérisation.
 De même du point de vue thermique, les matériaux utilisés ainsi que les formes extérieures doivent rester identiques du moins pour les surfaces qui ont de forts coefficients d'échange.

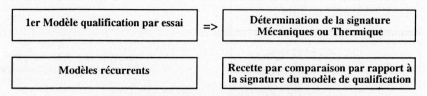

Figure 4 : Recette en environnement par comparaison

3- Renforcer les liens essais-conception, c'est à dire améliorer le retour d'information entre les essais et la conception en :

- réduisant le nombre d'informations à exploiter dans les essais de recette ;

- développant de manière important les moyens d'analyse de résultats d'essai. Actuellement, à part quelques tentatives, les moyens sont frustes et conduisent donc à des coûts très élevés. Ceci est en plus amplifié par le grand nombre de voies de mesure, donc de résultats à étudier ;

- créant des liaisons informatiques entre ces moyens d'analyse et les moyens de conception (Figure 5).
L'information, en grande quantité, n'est en fait disponible que sur support papier. La difficulté du transfert d'information entraîne une quantité faible de résultat exploité par les concepteurs
En ce sens, le résultat technico-économique des essais est faible et doit être largement améliorée pour les micro satellites.
Une situation intéressante pourrait être créée en livrant directement les résultats de l'analyse par une liaison informatique centre d'essai - industriel client. Une autre situation favorable serait la présence de l'équipe de conception pendant les essais. Cette équipe ayant des moyens de calcul permettant le recalage de modèle en thermique, par exemple.
On voit que cette liaison communément appelé calcul-essai a de nombreuses possibilités d'amélioration.
Ainsi, l'amélioration de la démarche d'ensemble doit contribuer à une démarche de plus en plus intégrée conception-essai.

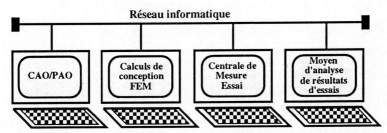

Figure 5 : Liaisons informatiques

3.2 SIMPLIFICATION DE LA TACHE AIT

Les petits satellites, s'ils seront un lien de concurrence exacerbée, pourront être moteur dans l'optimisation de certaines tâches.

Plusieurs pistes sont là aussi à défricher (Figure 6) :

1- La conception robuste du chariot d'intégration qui doit être capable de servir pour partie comme adaptateur d'essai.

699

Par exemple : en mécanique, les essais réclamés par le Manuel Utilisateur ASAP, font que ceux-ci peuvent être réalisés sur des moyens standards disponibles chez bon nombre d'industriels.

La marge de masse est telle que la partie supérieure du chariot d'intégration peut très bien être conçue comme l'adaptateur de vibration du satellite.

2- En thermique la conception et la réalisation des essais est à remettre en cause. Les essais vide-soleil sont réputés coûteux et sophistiqués. Il y a lieu d'envisager de les remplacer par d'autre moyen.

Une suggestion : nous proposons d'utiliser un nouveau moyen d'essai basé sur la technique Infra-Rouge.

La méthode d'essai repose sur un modèle spécifique basé sur les coefficients thermo-optiques en Infra-Rouge. Le moyen d'essai est constitué de panneaux qui forment une boîte entourant totalement le satellite. A chaque panneau I.R. est associé une face ou une partie de face du satellite. Par ce moyen, on peut donc simuler chaque phase de la vie du satellite, ceci d'un point de vue thermique et sans modifier quoi que ce soit dans l'arrangement des panneaux, mais simplement en affichant des consignes de température sur chaque panneau correspondant à un flux donné.

Ce moyen permet, à peu de frais, de faire une simulation complète ; il est composé d'un caisson à vide et de générations thermiques associées aux panneaux. On voit, dans cette suggestion, tout l'intérêt d'une démarche intégrée conception-essai.

3- La notion de prise diagnostic en essai. Cette notion repose sur plusieurs points :

• le faible nombre de points de mesure comme déjà suggéré précédemment,

• la répétitivité des conceptions, donc la simplicité des analyses,

• la notion de capteurs "perdus" -la structure est instrumentée une fois pour toute- ce qui diminue d'autant les efforts de main d'œuvre d'intégration associés au démontage, au décollage des capteurs et de leurs câbles, au remontage du satellite.

La prise diagnostic aurait l'avantage de standardiser l'essai de même que la mesure, ce qui est encore facteur de réduction des coûts.

D'autres pistes sont également possibles, nos propositions ne sont pas exhaustives, mais il est certain que les micro satellites sont un challenge pour l'industrie spatiale face aux nouveaux intervenants.

4 - CONCLUSIONS

Les différentes propositions mentionnées :

- démarche de personnalisation pour établir le programme d'essai,
- prise en compte de moyens d'essais "rustiques" dans la conception du satellite,
- recette des modèles récurrents par comparaison à la signature du modèle de qualification,
- réseau informatique et station de travail conception, intégration, essais, exploitation,
- capteurs de mesures "perdus" et prise diagnostic,

concourent à une optimisation des durées et du coût des essais dans le nouveau contexte de production de série de satellite (dont la réalisation devra être accélérée et le coût réduit).

Reste néanmoins posé le problème des "essais contractuels" qui devraient être analysés dans une réflexion :
        "Comment prononcer la qualification et la recette de séries de mini satellites ?"

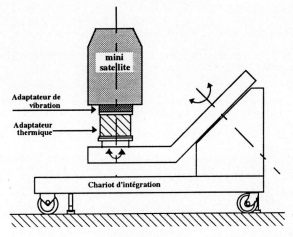

Chariot d'intégration

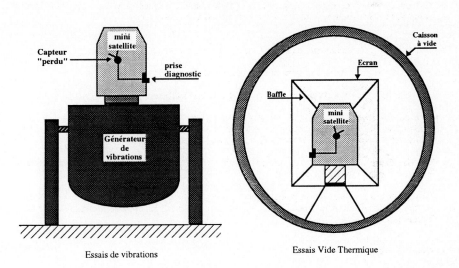

Essais de vibrations

Essais Vide Thermique

Figure 6 : Moyens d'intégration et d'essais

Cost drivers - why do conventional satellites cost so much?

Dr Chris Elliott, Smith System Engineering, UK

Introduction

There has been an evolution in the space projects carried out in the USA and Europe from the early days of simple, dedicated and inexpensive missions through to the present position where most missions are complex, multi-purpose and expensive. Even as late as 1970, major national programmes were based on small satellites and launchers. For example, in 1971, the UK successfully launched a satellite using the Black Arrow launch vehicle. The total cost of the Black Arrow development programme, including ground facilities and four vehicles, was approximately $35M (adjusted for inflation to 1990).

The analysis presented in this paper has emerged from discussions with US and European specialists and concludes that there is a positive feedback mechanism which systematically forces space missions to become more expensive, take longer to execute and fail to satisfy the needs of their users. This mechanism is described and an approach to mission planning and execution is proposed in which the positive feedback should cause the costs to spiral down instead of up.

The vicious spiral

The positive feedback mechanism starts with the belief that space projects are expensive. The consequence of this belief is that there will not be many projects. Few projects mean that:

- they must be planned carefully to get the best out of them;

- they must be reliable;

- they need to be large to achieve a lot from each project;

- there will be little competition (not only commercial competition between suppliers but there is also little competition of ideas if there is only one project every few years).

Each of these brings consequences for the conduct of the projects.

Planning causes delays. High reliability when not building many systems means that integrity must achieved by design. This precludes the use of the latest, unproven technology and, taken with the planning delays, means that spacecraft are built with obsolete components.

Large projects need large launch vehicles which, when combined with the lack of competition and the need for high reliability, means that launch is expensive.

Large projects also require large payloads and justify a large (and expensive) ground infrastructure. Large payloads bring a twist of their own. The space systems are too big to be built by a single contractor and it is necessary to invoke a complex (and expensive) management structure. One consequence of this is that it is difficult to perform optimisation trade-offs between components of the system because of the rigid contractual boundaries. This results in non-optimum designs built, as argued above, with obsolete components, which leads to very poor performance per kilogramme. Here is the first vicious spiral because poor performance per kilogramme requires even bigger payloads.

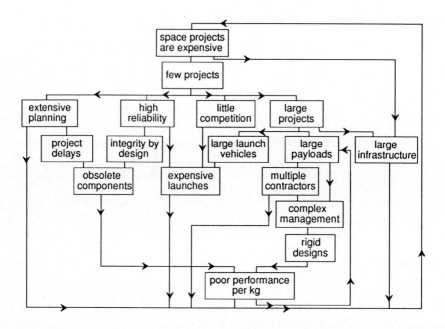

When all of these arguments are brought together, the resulting vicious spiral reinforces the opening premise:- "space projects are expensive". Any perturbation, like a launch vehicle failure, tends to cause more passes around the spiral, reinforces this belief and the costs spiral away.

It is important to recognise that there is no malicious act in this spiral. It is a consequence of reasonable decisions being taken at each stage of the design and planning of these projects. It is because of this that revolutionary changes in the procedures and practices are needed to reverse the cost drivers.

The virtuous spiral

There are five major changes needed to be made to force the costs onto a downward spiral:

- users must determine needs, not space agencies;

- failures must be tolerated;

- appropriate technology must be used;

- missions must be dedicated to fewer payloads;

- projects must have a short duration and small, integrated team.

1   Users determine needs

The essential difference between a project driven by a space agency and one driven by the user is the measure of success. Space agencies tend to measure success by inputs, such as the advance in technology that is achieved or the size of the budget. Users measure success by outputs, such as the data generated or the service provided.

It is instructive to observe the circumstances under which space agencies are able to take a more constructive view and behave like a user. The most quoted example is the Apollo programme in the 1960s and a similar success, although on a smaller scale, was the European Giotto mission to Comet Halley. In both cases, the space agency was presented with a firm target date for the mission and a clear objective and, in both cases, the response of the space agency was excellent.

2   Failures tolerated

A top tennis player tries to win the match, not just the point, and typically hits one in ten of his first services out or into the net. He knows that, to be competitive, he must take risks and accept that he will have failures.

The analysis of the positive feedback mechanism concluded that everyone is behaving reasonably when taking the individual decisions that collectively lead to such an unreasonable consequence. In order to introduce the acceptance of failure, it will be necessary to change the motivation which drives each individual decision. This was recognised by David McLelland in his researches of business practice in the 1950s. He wrote:

- "If the penalty for failure exceeds the reward for success, then people will plan not to fail, not plan to succeed".

In order to be able to reward success, it is necessary first to ensure that projects are driven by users. As long as they are driven by the space agencies, it is always preferable to take the safe option (delay the launch, use the conventional component, reduce the specification) rather than risk a failure.

The Report of the Advisory Committee on the Future of the US Space Programme, more usually known as the Augustine Report, went some way towards recognising this with the statement:

-    "We should insist on perfection as a very real goal but should not make it more advantageous to avoid failures than to achieve success:".

The insistence on perfection is fundamentally wrong. The perfect system will never be built.

3   Appropriate technology used

It is normal to demand that all components and sub-systems are fully space qualified. The level of qualification that should be adopted needs to be appropriate to the stress to which the component will be subjected and to its criticality to the mission.

A clear example of the inappropriate use of specification is the level of radiation tolerance demanded of electronic systems. It is common to specify a total dose of 100 kRad for components to be used on low earth orbit spacecraft which will be subject to a radiation dose of no more than 1 kRad per year. Most commonly available CMOS devices are able to tolerate of the order of 5 to 10 kRad and thus would be acceptable, especially if qualified for the military temperature range. The requirement to achieve 100 kRad excludes most of the devices that are taken for granted in the design of terrestrial systems, leaving many satellites equipped with no more computing power than a modern washing machine.

Many sub-systems are only required to operate before launch and do not need to be fully space qualified. One example is the valve used to control filling of the gas container for a cold gas propulsion system. It was realised during the development of the Space Technology Research Vehicle by the UK Defence Research Agency that the conventional, space-qualified valve would cost $10K but would only have to be used once, before launch. A standard laboratory valve with a much better specification was found at a cost of $150.

Another striking example is the trailer used to transport the Pegasus vehicle to the aircraft from which it is launched. Orbital Sciences commissioned a truck builder to manufacture this trailer. For only $150,000, Orbital received a superbly engineered trailer rated for highway use at 100km per hour.

The general principle that should guide the choice of components and sub-systems is to make maximum use of military or civil devices that already exist. Designing special purpose sub-systems is always expensive and, by appropriate choice of specification, it is often possible to make use of existing reliable and well-engineered products and expertise.

4   Missions dedicated to fewer payloads

Another statement made in the Augustine Report is that:

- "... the Committee supports the concept of simultaneous flight of instruments .... This approach leads to the requirement for a large spacecraft, which is less costly on a per instrument basis."

Were this to be true, much of the work done on small satellites would have to be discarded. The statement is not true for two reasons.

The first concerns the procedures used to plan and manage the programmes. Conventional space projects are locked into the vicious spiral, where the cost is so high that failure is not acceptable so even greater cost is incurred to avoid it. If small satellites are loaded up with the management overheads of large satellites, then it may well be true that they are not economic. However, if appropriate procedures are employed, it is possible to reduce the costs massively and also to reduce the duration of the project.

This then relates to the second reason to reject the Augustine statement. Large, multi-payload satellites are like a convoy, only able to move at the speed of the slowest element. If any part is delayed, the overall project is delayed. As well as failing to meet the needs of the users, this has knock-on effects on the costs. This leads to the last of the five changes needed to get onto the virtuous spiral.

5   Projects have short duration and small team

The cost of the project is typically proportional to its duration and to the number of people involved. Any delay in the project means that the team keeps working, and spending, and any additional complexity or management interfaces means more people generating more documentation.

Part of the reason for the use of technology in space that may be ten or more years behind that used on the ground is that it is necessary to freeze the design early in a long duration project. This is compounded for a complex project with a large team, where early design freeze is necessary to define the interfaces between elements of the spacecraft to allow the distributed team to undertake their detailed design work.

The problem of long projects has an effect on the overall capability of the space industry as well as the cost of each project. Programmes are becoming similar in length to the career of a space engineer so there is little opportunity for applying the experience of earlier projects. This is compounded by the interval between flight opportunities, which may be of the order of 10 years for some project teams.

Project management represents the largest cost element for many projects, especially if international collaboration is involved. Small teams, preferably collocated, working intensively on a short project, are able to minimise the cost of project management.

Way ahead

What could happen if all of these changes in approach were to occur. If it is assumed that space projects are cheap, a different positive feedback picture emerges, a virtuous spiral.

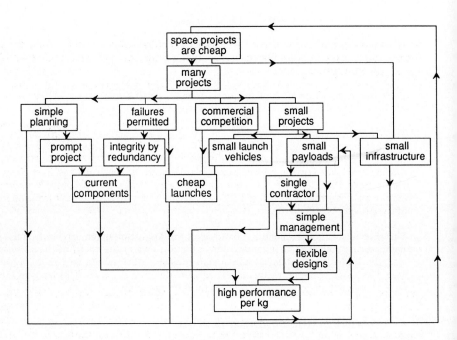

For this to come about, it is necessary to convince the users of space systems, space agencies and contractors that it is desirable. Up to now, most effort has been concentrated on the last two, leading Brian Hughes of American Rocket Company to remark that:

-   "I should like to help because I believe that I am selling a better mousetrap. The trouble is that I am selling it to the mice".

An earlier writer also identified the difficulty of bringing about revolutionary changes and effectively anticipated the problems of the space industry by four hundred years. In "The Prince", Machiavelli wrote:

-   "Nothing is more difficult to undertake, more perilous to conduct or more uncertain in its outcome than to take the lead in introducing a new order of things. For the innovator has for enemies all those who have done well under the old and lukewarm defenders who may do well under the new".

KEY TRENDS OF THE SMALL SATELLITE MARKET

Stéphane Chenard
Euroconsult
Paris

Satellites have historically tended to become larger and heavier, not smaller, filling the mass envelope allowed by new launch vehicles as fast as they appeared. Steady progress toward greater payload fractions, greater performance of payloads and equipment and lower specific cost were offset by the growth of requirements, especially for communications satellites.

However, due to a combination of factors, the population of satellites weighing less than 1,000 kg has visibly begun to recover. Western companies and agencies have announced over 100 programs, totalling an inventory of about 650 satellites to be launched over the next 10 years, with program values ranging from millions to billions of dollars. Though obviously not all will fly and market forecasts in this sector have often proven over-optimistic, growth is likely on the small satellite market, along with a shift from predominantly military to commercial missions.

HOW SMALL IS SMALL

Small satellites tend to be ordered in four families according to their mass. The majority of projects identified to date relate to spacecraft in the 50-500-kg range, for which dedicated launch vehicles recently became available. A recent surge in microsatellites, in the 5-50-kg range, remains to be confirmed beyond 1994. Nanosatellites weighing less than 5 kg still are more fiction than fact, though at least one commercial platform is available and concept studies on ultralight planetary probes and railgun launchers have been carried out by NASA.

Market activity is also higher than expected at the low end of the geostationary communications satellite market, in the 500-1,000-kg range formerly known as the Delta class. Developing countries that have completed their ground communications infrastructure are moving on, while they spurned platforms such as Hughes Aircraft Co.'s HS-394 and HS-399 less than 10 years ago. Orders from Thailand, Malaysia and possibly Argentina, South Africa and the Andean Pact, and new regional systems such as Unicom/Tongasat in the Pacific basin and Cancom in Canada, made possibly by deregulation, are sustaining demand for the 10-15-transponder platforms typical of the early- to mid-1980s well past their expected phaseout.

MARKET DRIVERS

The re-emergence of small satellites appears to be driven by technology, by an institutional shift away from "big science" in the U.S., and in some market segments by financial and operational advantages inherent to small, low-altitude systems.

```
SMALL SATELLITE CLASSIFICATION BY SIZE

BELOW 5 KILOGRAMS (NANOSATELLITES)

Technology theoretically allows significant missions
Exotic concepts but only paper studies so far

5-50 KILOGRAMS (MICROSATELLITES)

Amateur radio
Technology demonstrators
Limited store-and-forward applications
Typically launched as piggyback payloads

50-500 KILOGRAMS (MINISATELLITES)

Includes the majority of current projects
Dedicated launch vehicles available
Cluster deployment likely to become a dominant option

500-1000 KILOGRAMS ("DELTA CLASS")

Constant decline since the mid-1980s
Recent revival remains to be confirmed
```

Small is beautiful - While NASA and the Defense Department had made strategic decisions a decade ago to consolidate vast amounts of resources into multi-ton platforms such as the Great Observatories and the Military Strategic and Tactical Relay (Milstar) series, the pendulum seems to be swinging back. Budget constraints, the complaints of investigators who spent half their professional careers on single projects, and a few public relations disasters and launch failures have allowed the U.S. Congress to force a downsizing of the Earth Observing System (EOS), which NASA recently envisaged would consist of two 14,000-kg platforms, the largest unmanned spacecraft known to date. EOS now consists of five satellites, including two in the Pegasus class. Similar trade-offs are continuing in the U.S. Advanced X-ray Astrophysical Facility and European Polar Platform programs.

Small can be cheaper - Though the specific cost of small satellite platforms is consistent with that of larger satellites, small satellites are generally more expensive by transponder or unit of bandwidth or mass because of their shorter lifetime, and thus of replacement costs and inflation, and of the remaining inelasticity of launch costs. However, these platforms and newly available launch options can permit entry costs an order of magnitude lower than traditional geostationary systems, of the order of $50 million or less.

The ability of dispersed satellite constellations to degrade gracefully and to be built up progressively is also particularly suitable for entrepreneurs who need to demonstrate an appreciable rate of return on investment in a short timeframe, and practically cannot withstand in-orbit losses.

NASA followed about the same logic in restructuring the EOS program, as one of the main benefits of this effort is to reduce annual budget requirements by up to 40% in the first five years of the program. However, the program has become significantly more expensive in its out-years and its total cost has increased, even though some payloads have been abandoned.

Small is possible - While major prime contractors and commercial operators have tended to resist the advances of miniaturization, recent or imminent in-orbit demonstrations may soon overcome their conservatism. In particular, many technology spinoffs from the Strategic Defense Initiative and other U.S. defense programs are currently being declassified. Examples include Earth observation sensors, studied by U.S. contractors for the Air Force's RESERVES program, providing a resolution of 5 m in eight spectral bands from a 500-km orbit and weighing only 112 kg, or less than half the mass of current Spot and Landsat imagers for 2-6 times their resolution.

Spectacular progress has also been achieved at equipment level, with some new technologies enabling gains of up to 10 in on-board data processing capacity per unit of mass and 90 on solar array specific power, along with substantial cost reductions. While light satellites were regarded in the late 1980s as cheap but rustic, commercial platforms available in the $3-10 million range now feature electrothermal thrusters, three-axis stabilization, arcsecond pointing accuracy, on-board Global Positioning System receivers, crosslinks, nickel-hydrogen batteries, memory capacity over 1 Gbyte, encrypted downlinks of up to 1 Gbps and on-board processing power of up to 4 Mips.

Adverse technology trends - At the same time, small satellites may be vulnerable to other technological developments. For example, a quantum leap progress in launch cost, through the introduction of new propulsion techniques, could nullify the advantages of low mass; fiber optic cables using soliton propagation may replace satellites in "bent-pipe" applications; and more agile phased-array antennas and modulation techniques could give large, single platforms the same agility as small distributed satellites.

MARKET SEGMENTS

Five families of applications can be distinguished.

In-orbit technology demonstrators, a traditional role of small satellites, usually associated with the cheapest and lightest among them. Over 100 satellites have been launched for this purpose as part of the U.S. Air Force's Space Test Program (STP). While STP's funding has remained about flat over the past 10 years at $30-40 million per year, an equivalent amount has been invested by the SDI

Organization and the Defense Advanced Research Projects Agency, which funded the development of the Pegasus booster by Orbital Sciences Corp. (OSC) and of the Multiple Access Communications Satellite (Macsat) by Defense Systems Inc. (DSI), both of which became the reference of a number of small satellite proposals.

The UoSAT platforms built by the University of Surrey for technology demonstrations for the Royal Aircraft Establishment and other European customers has also now been licensed to more powerful companies and exported as far as South Korea.

The continuing U.S. programs, greater emphasis on R&D and prototyping in the U.S. defense budget, and the emergence of European military satellites are factors which should sustain this segment of the market. Small technology satellites have competitors in larger platforms such as the European Retrievable Carrier and Get-Away Special cans or other Space Shuttle payloads, but a long user queue remains for these systems.

Gapfillers, overlays and "augmentsats" that complement larger systems. The insistence of the Earth observation community on the continuity of data collection has already convinced NASA, which had been unable to fly ocean color determination payloads at less than many years' intervals, to fund the development, launch and operation of a dedicated Seastar satellite by OSC. The launch of a follow-on is already in the planning phase. To this day, however, Seastar remains something of an exception. A free-flying version of the Advanced Visible High-Resolution Radiometer has been proposed to NASA by the industry without success. A free-flying Total Ozone Mapping Spectrometer is also envisaged, but NASA has already found a cheaper way to keep this instrument available, by piggybacking it on a Russian Meteor-3 satellite.

Finding less strength in numbers than they used to, scientific investigators could also renew with the individualism that small, dedicated platforms allow them, though even the cheapest commercial platforms and launch vehicles are beyond the means of most research laboratories. NASA is attempting to keep its pledge to provide two flight opportunities a year on Small Explorer satellites to the scientific community.

The U.S. Defense Department and intelligence community are following a similar trend, with doctrines that place greater emphasis on being able to respond to sudden surges of activity, characteristic of a less predictable threat environment, and to address demands at the tactical level which the bureaucracy surrounding strategic assets tended to ignore. This, along with the successful demonstration of the two Macsat satellites during the Persian Gulf war, prompted such a flurry of Army, Navy, Marine Corps, Air Force, Coast Guard, Drugs Enforcement Agency and CIA proposals for small communications and intelligence satellites, each often funded from several sources, as to seriously confuse the picture. Congress reacted in 1991 with broad cuts in small satellite budgets, and very little action has followed.

The same doctrinal change which prompted this activity also plays against small satellites, by shifting large amounts of resources, such as EHF capacity on Milstar satellites, toward tactical users.

A few niche applications which do not justify large payloads but require specific orbits. One example is polar communications, primarily with military users such as remote early warning assets or submarines. Demonstrations by the U.S. Global Low Orbit Message Relay and Macsat systems would probably had led to further developments if the threat had not all but disappeared in the Arctic region. A dedicated U.S. Navy program called Arcticom was cancelled in 1991. Other users, such as Arctic oil drilling programs, are likely to be captured by global low Earth orbit communications systems, which would provide capacity at high latitudes.

Startup entrepreneurs - At least six U.S. candidate operators have adopted small satellites as a way to enter commercial markets at a minimum cost. One, Worldspace Corp., proposes radio broadcasting systems. Four others (Orbcomm, Starsys, VITA and Leosat) filed with the U.S. Federal Communications Commission for UHF/VHF mobile messaging and positioning systems. A similar system is under study by CNES in France. This market was tried by Locstar SA and Geostar Corp. without success shortly before them, largely because of the large amount of capital these projects required up front. OHB System GmbH, a German company, also plans to offer commercial data relay services with two microsatellites.

Interestingly, the emergency messaging or search-and-rescue component of these projects could displace these applications from the larger NOAA satellites which now carry COSPAS/SARSAT transponders as piggybacks.

More expensive and sophisticated systems relying on proliferated small satellites because of the flexibility they afford. Mosaics of many low Earth orbit satellites allow services to be patterned more finely after national or even regional markets while still providing global coverage, with a higher rate of frequency reuse than isolated geostationary satellites. Low-altitude systems also allow hand-held terminals with standard FM antennas, as the power required by uplinks is an order of magnitude lower.

Five applicants (Iridium, Aries, Ellipso, Globalstar and Odyssey) are now awaiting FCC rulemakings to enter the mobile and personal communications market with such systems. These systems acount for about one-third of the total inventory of small satellites announced in the next 10 years and, as such, their success or failure will largely reflect on the market. No more than three are generally expected to survive the competition, both between these projects themselves and with terrestrial cellular systems. Despite its generally favourable outcome, the recent 1992 World Administrative Radio Conference also did not dispel all of the many regulatory obstacles to worldwide services, as many attending countries introduced restrictive footnotes in the proceedings.

EFFECTS ON THE SATELLITE INDUSTRY

To what extent the satellite industry will be reshaped remains unclear. Small satellites could remain a sideshow, be limited to a few niche markets, or take over large sections of the market. Traditional market leaders could adapt or be challenged in their position the way mainframe manufacturers were by personal computer companies in the late 1970s.

Should the small satellite market really develop, mass production and techniques which satellite designers are already attempting to transfer from the aircraft and consumer electronics industry would likely drive prices and production cycles down and improve reliability. The few recent examples available show that the recurring cost of communications satellites can fall by up to 75% from the first to the 15th unit produced. This would give a strong leverage effect on the market to the largest constellations envisioned, such as Iridium (77 satellites) or Aries and Globalstar (48 satellites each), and could create a feedback mechanism encouraging further development of the market.

About 30 models of satellite platforms with launch masses ranging from 5 kg to 1,250 kg are commercially available from 23 vendors, about half of whom have never announced orders to date. About half of the next 10 years' inventory is captured by four companies, two of which, Defense Systems Inc. and Orbital Sciences Corp., are relatively new entrants, while more traditional suppliers of communications satellites (Hughes Aircraft Co., General Electric Co., Aerospatiale and Matra) so far appear to have been very little involved.

However, three of these leaders, Space Systems/Loral, OSC and Lockheed Missiles & Space Co., owe their position largely to programs in which they hold equity or which they even initiated. Many of the specialist suppliers which emerged since the late 1980s also appear to be too lightly capitalized to take on the small satellite market as it emerges, given the emphasis placed on standardization, long production series and long-term planning by the principal small satellite operators, and even by NASA and the Defense Department for their research satellites. While OSC and DSI have managed to broaden their foundations respectively through stock offerings and the sale of equity to a bigger company, very little consolidation has otherwise taken place.

Similarly, demand in the Delta class has been captured by proven products from Hughes, Matra Marconi Space and Aerospatiale, rather than by the platforms which companies like Ball Aerospace and Fairchild Space Co., not traditional suppliers of communications satellites, had tailored for it.

EFFECTS ON THE LAUNCH INDUSTRY

Less than a quarter of the satellites announced for the next 10 years are committed to launch vehicles, and even fewer actual contracts have been signed. The Pegasus appears to have the largest market share, through multi-launch agreements with the Defense Department and NASA and because OSC baselined it for its Orbcomm program.

As specific launch costs tend to evolve more slowly than the size and capacity of satellite equipment and generations are shorter for satellites, launch operators could be exposed to greater risk in a real sea change, i.e. if satellites generally became smaller. Several small satellite providers have teamed with launch companies or propose their own launch vehicles, and some offer complete turnkey services including ground segments. Both NASA and the U.S. Defense Department have selected dedicated launch vehicles for their small payloads needs. Substantial competition to the established launch providers may also emerge in the form of decommissioned ballistic missiles, though proposals in this direction by Lockheed and other companies remain mired in regulatory issues.

However, many proposed vehicles remain without the proven track record desired by the insurance community. Further, as the small satellites launch market is likely to be dominated by operators who plan to deploy many identical satellites in a few orbital planes, it in fact appears likely to be captured by established operators of large-capacity launch vehicles offering to deploy these satellites in clusters, at least during the implementation phase of these systems. Cluster deployment relies on relatively simple and well demonstrated techniques, and has already been advertised by Arianespace and McDonnell Douglas. This would stifle the development of most small launch vehicles until the late 1990s, when constellations such as Iridium will require resplenishment launches, at a maximum rate of once per month.

CONCLUSION: MARKET DEVELOPMENT

The actual size of the small satellite market is difficult to predict given the uncertainty of many market drivers, in particular U.S. federal budgets and the availability of financing for commercial programs. The current project inventory is extremely dependent on mobile communications and messaging projects, and thus on competition with terrestrial cellular systems and on the regulatory environment of this market. The fact that all of the programs identified with launch dates beyond 1993 still have to complete their financing or require regulatory or budgetary approval must be another matter of concern. The outlook is also particularly uncertain for the two potentially largest systems planned, Brilliant Eyes (100-500 satellites) and Brilliant Pebbles (1,000 satellites), given Congressional opposition to these two ballistic missile defense programs.

However, the plans announced only need to be partly realized to make small satellites a growth sector of the space industry, even as the overall communications satellite market is expected to flatten for the next few years. Assuming that only one small messaging and one larger mobile communications constellations are devloped in low Earth orbit, that commercial materials processing fails to develop in microgravity, that no ballistic missile defense system is deployed, that STEP and Small Explorer programs remain at their current level and that some regional communications projects are abandoned, a minimum of about 180 satellites in 80 programs would still be deployed in the next 10 years, about 40% more than the traffic of the last 10 years.

SATELLITE LAUNCH MASS FAMILIES

ALL WORLD EXCEPT CHINA AND USSR

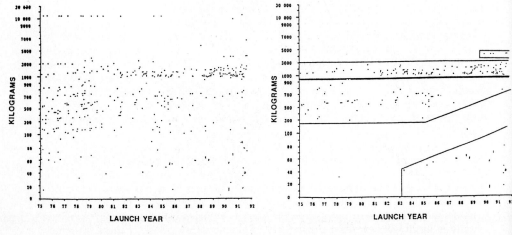

ALL SATELLITES (UNMANNED)   ALL COMMUNICATIONS SATELLITES

SMALL SATELLITE INVENTORY - BREAKDOWN BY LAUNCH MASS

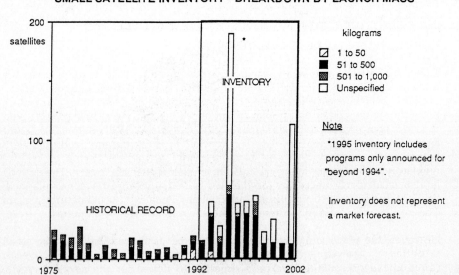

kilograms

☑ 1 to 50
■ 51 to 500
▨ 501 to 1,000
☐ Unspecified

Note

*1995 inventory includes programs only announced for "beyond 1994".

Inventory does not represent a market forecast.

Source: Euroconsult

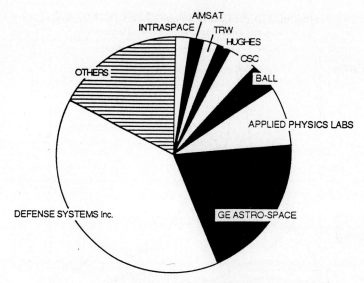

AMSAT
INTRASPACE
TRW
HUGHES
CSC
OTHERS
BALL
APPLIED PHYSICS LABS
DEFENSE SYSTEMS Inc.
GE ASTRO-SPACE

OBSERVED U.S. MARKET, 1975-91
BREAKDOWN BY SATELLITE PRIME CONTRACTOR

1992-2002 PROJECT INVENTORY
BREAKDOWN BY SATELLITE PRIME CONTRACTOR

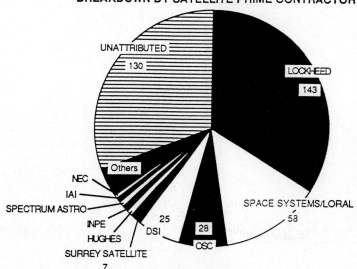

UNATTRIBUTED
130

LOCKHEED
143

Others

NEC
IAI
SPECTRUM ASTRO
INPE
HUGHES
SURREY SATELLITE
7
DSI
25
OSC
28

SPACE SYSTEMS/LORAL
58

Note: Inventory does not represent a market forecast

Source: Euroconsult

INVENTORY IS HEAVILY DEPENDENT ON MOBILE COMMUNICATIONS MARKET

inventory does not represent a market forecast

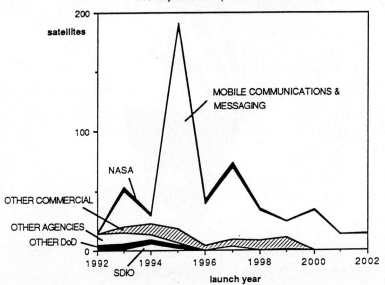

10-YEAR INVENTORY GUARANTEES SOME GROWTH OVER 15-YEAR PAST RECORD

inventory does not constitute a market forecast

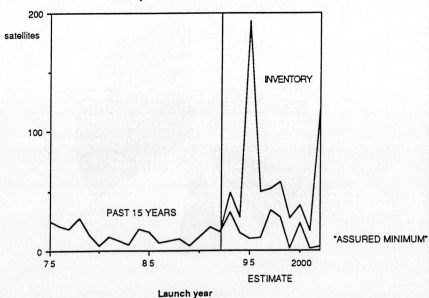

Source: Euroconsult

LONG SATELLITE SERIES HAVE ACHIEVED SUBSTANTIAL ECONOMIES OF SCALE

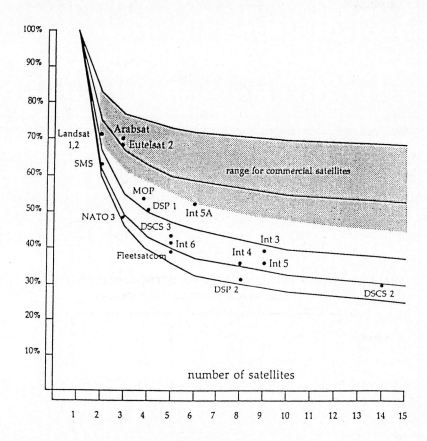

COST PER SPACECRAFT IN PERCENTAGE OF THE COST OF THE FIRST FLIGHT MODEL

Source: Euroconsult

SATELLITES BELOW 1,000 kg : 1992 - 2002

	LAUNCH	OPERATOR	PRIME CONTRACTOR	MASS kg	NUMBER OF UNITS	LAUNCH VEHICLE	MISSION
SAMPEX	June 1992	NASA	NASA	158	1	Scout	Astronomy
S-80/T	June 1992	CNES	Matra Marconi Space NV	150	1	Ariane	Technology
Miniature Seeker Integration Technology	June 1992	SDIO	Spectrum Astro Corp.	170	1	Scout	Technology
Kitsat-A/S	June 1992	Korean Institute of Technology	Surrey Satellite Technology Ltd.	50	2	Ariane	Technology
Oleg-3	June 1992	Israel Space Agency	Israel Aircraft Industries Ltd.	170	1	Shavit 2	Technology
Geoail	July 1992	NASA/ISAS (Japan)	ISAS/NEC	970	1	Delta II	Plasma science
Alexis	July 1992	Los Alamos National Laboratories	Aero Astro Inc.	122	1	Pegasus	Astronomy
Arsene	Aug.1992	Radio Amateur Club de l'Espace (France)	Radio Amateur Club de l'Espace	150	1	Ariane	Amateur radio
SCD-1	Sept.1992	INPE (Brazil)	INPE/Embraer	115	1	Pegasus	Data collection
Lageos	Sept.1992	NASA/Agenzia Spaziale Italiana	Alenia Spazio SpA	406	1	Shuttle	Geodesy
Insat 2B	Oct.1992	Indian Space Research Organization	Indian Space Research Organization	875	1	Ariane	Communications
STEP	Late 1992	Defense Systems Inc.	Defense Systems Inc.	<500	2	Pegasus	Technology
Advanced Photovoltaics and Electronics Experiment	Late 1992	U.S. Air Force/DARPA	Orbital Sciences Corp.	274	1	Pegasus	Technology
Freja	Late 1992	Swedish National Space Board	Swedish National Space Corp.	1050	1	Long March 2C	Plasma science
Thailandsat	1993	Shinawatra Computer Co. (Thailand)	Hughes Aircraft Co.	50	2	Ariane	Communications
Space Technology Research Vehicle	1993	Royal Aircraft Establishment (England)	Surrey Satellite Technology Ltd.	50	2	Ariane	Technology
Technion	1993	Technion Institute of Technology (Israel)	Israel Space Agency	<50	1	Ariane	Technology/Amateur radio
P90-B	1993	U.S. Air Force			1		Technology
Advanced Satellite Communications Technology	1993	U.S. Air Force/DARPA			1		Technology
Tubsat-3	1993	Technical University Berlin	Technical University Berlin	25	1	Soyuz	Technology
X-Sat	1993 ?	NASA	Defense Systems Inc.		1	Space Shuttle	Technology
SSR	1993 ?	INPE (Brazil)	INPE/Embraer	170	2	Long March ?	Earth observation
P90-5/TAOS	Early 1993	U.S. Air Force	Defense Systems Inc.		1	Taurus	Technology
Astro-D	Jan.-Feb.1993	ISAS (Japan)		420	1	M3-SII	Astronomy
Bremsat	Feb.1993	OHB System GmbH	Bremen University (Germany)	<100	1	Space Shuttle	Technology
SAFIR-1	Mar.1993	DARA (Germany)	OHB-System GmbH	55	1	Ariane	Data collection
RadCal	Mar.1993	U.S. Air Force	Defense Systems Inc.		1	Scout	Radar calibration
Commercial Experiment Transporter	June 1993	Orbcomm	Westinghouse Electric Co.		1	Conestoga	Multipurpose
Globcomm	June 1993	Orbcomm?	Orbital Sciences Corp.	150	2	Pegasus	Communications
Sedsal-1	June 1993	SEDS	SEDS		1	Delta	Technology
Safir R	June 1993	OHB System GmbH	OHB System GmbH	55	1	Zenith	Data collection
Seastar	July 1993	NASA	Orbital Sciences Corp.		1	Pegasus	Earth observation
Miniature Seeker Integration Technology	Sept.1993	SDIO	Spectrum Astro Corp.?	170	1	Pegasus	Technology
P90-1	Fall 1993	U.S. Air Force/Naval Research Labs			1		Technology
Vitasat	1993	Volunteers in Technical Assistance Inc.	Surrey Satellite Technology Ltd.	50	2	Scout	Communications
Westar-1	Late 1993	Westinghouse Electric Co.	Westinghouse Electric Co.		1	Conestoga	Multipurpose
Total Ozone Mapping Spectrometer	Dec.1993	NASA			1	Pegasus	Atmospheric science
GOESI	Dec.1993	NOAA	Space Systems/Loral	980	1	Atlas I	Meteorology
Afristar-1	1993	Worldspace Inc.	Defense Systems Inc.		2-Jan	Long March	Communications
Brilliant Pebble demonstration	1994	SDIO	TRW/Martin Marietta	<500	2	Pegasus	Technology
SCD-2	1994	INPE (Brazil)	INPE/Embraer	115	1	Pegasus	Data collection
Sunsat	1994	(South Africa)	Surrey Satellite Technology Ltd.	50	1	Ariane	Astronomy

Name	Date	Operator (Country)	Manufacturer	Mass	Number	Launch Vehicle	Category
Sunsal	1994	(South Africa)	Surrey Satellite Technology Ltd.	50	1	Ariane	Astronomy
Measat	1994	Binyarang (Malaysia)	Hughes Aircraft Co.	1050	2	Ariane	Communications
AMOS	1994	General Satellite Co. (Israel)	Israel Aircraft Industries Ltd.	950	1	Ariane	Communications
P90-A	1994	U.S. Air Force			1		Technology
Westar	1994	Westinghouse Electric Co.	Westinghouse Electric Co.		2	Conestoga ?	Multipurpose
Iridium	1994	Iridium Inc.	Lockheed Missiles & Space Co.	<500	7	Ariane or Delta	Communications
P91-A/Signal Detection Experiment	Early 1994	U.S. Air Force					Technology
Unicom	Early 1994	Unicom			1 or 2	Delta II	Communications
GMS-5	Early 1994	NASDA (Japan)	NEC	725	1	H-2	Meteorology
Miniature Seeker Integration Technology	Mar.1994	SDIO	Spectrum Astro Corp. ?	170	1		Technology
Safir-1	Mid-1994	OHB System GmbH	OHB System GmbH	55	1	Zenith	Data collection
P91-C/SOARS	Mid-1994	U.S. Air Force	Lockheed Missiles & Space Co. ?		1		Technology
OERSE	Mid-1994	French ministry of Defense	Alcatel Espace	50	1	Ariane	Technology
Clementine	Mid-1994	SDIO					Technology
Commercial Experiment Transporter	Aug.1994	NASA	Westinghouse Electric Co.		1	Conestoga	Multipurpose
Fast Auroral Snapshot Explorer	Sept.1994	NASA	NASA	150	1	Pegasus	Plasma science
GOES-J	Dec.1994	NOAA	Space Systems/Loral	980	1	Atlas I	Meteorology
SAC-B/HETE	Dec.1994	Argentina/NASA	John Hopkins Applied Physics Labs.		1	Pegasus	Astronomy
ALTAIR	1994-95	U.S. Air Force	Defense Systems Inc.		1		Technology
Asiastar-1	1994	Worldspace Inc.		150	2-Jan		Communications
S-80	>1994	CNES			8 to 20		Communications
Aries	>1994	Constellation Communications	Defense Systems Inc.		48		Communications
Leosat	>1994	Leosat Corp.			24		Communications
Elipso	>1994	Ellipsat			20		Communications
Iridium	1995	Iridium Inc.	Lockheed Missiles & Space Co.	<500	35	Ariane or Delta	Communications
Starnet	1995	Starsys			24		Communications
Cancom	1995	Canadian Satellite Communications Corp.		800	1 to 4		Communications
Pacificom	1995	TRW	TRW/Defense Systems Inc.		1		Communications
Geosat Follow-On	1995	U.S. Navy			2	Pegasus ?	Geodesy
Theater Launch Detection Experiment	1995	SDIO			1		Technology
Westar	1995	Westinghouse Electric Co.	Westinghouse Electric Co.	800	3	Conestoga ?	Multipurpose
Muses-B/VSOP	Jan.-Feb. 1995	ISAS (Japan)			1	M-5	Astronomy
IndoStar	Early 1995	PT MediaCitra Indostar (Indonesia)		800	2		Communications
Submillimeter Wavelength Astronomy Satellite	June 1995	NASA	Defense Systems Inc.	1100	1	Pegasus	Astronomy
Commercial Experiment Transporter	June 1995	NASA	NASA/Ball Aerospace	180	1	Conestoga	Multipurpose
Clementine	Late 1995	SDIO	Westinghouse Electric Co.		1		Technology
EHF satellite	1995-96	U.S. Army		<500	1		Communications
Ameristar-1	1995	Worldspace Inc.	Defense Systems Inc.		2-Jan		Communications
GOES K-M	1995-2000	NOAA	Space Systems/Loral	980	4-Jan	Atlas	Meteorology
Iridium	1996	Iridium Inc.	Lockheed Missiles & Space Co.	<800	35	Ariane or Delta	Communications
Westar	1996	Westinghouse Electric Co.	Westinghouse Electric Co.		>3	Conestoga ?	Multipurpose
Afristar-2	1996	Worldspace Inc.	Defense Systems Inc.			Long March	Communications
Small Explorer	June 1996	NASA			1	Pegasus	Scientific
Commercial Experiment Transporter	June 1996	NASA	Westinghouse Electric Co.		1	Conestoga	Multipurpose
Far Ultraviolet Spectroscopy Explorer	>1996	NASA		1000	1		Astronomy
Total Ozone Mapping Spectrometer	1997	NASA			1	Pegasus	Atmospheric science

Name	Year	Operator	Manufacturer	Mass	Number	Launcher	Application
Globalstar	1997	Loral-Qualcomm	Space Systems/Loral	<300	24-48		Communications
Asiastar-2	1997	Worldspace Inc.	Defense Systems Inc.		1		Communications
Iridium (replenishment)	1997	Iridium Inc.	Lockheed Missiles & Space Co.	<500	13		Communications
Westar	1997	Westinghouse Electric Co.	Westinghouse Electric Co.		>3	Conestoga ?	Multipurpose
FeLIX	1997	Smithsonian Astronomical Observatories			1		Astronomy
Small Explorer	June 1997	NASA			1	Pegasus	Scientific
Commercial Experiment Transporter	June 1997	NASA	Westinghouse Electric Co.		1	Conestoga	Multipurpose
Republic of China-1	Mid-1997	Space Studies Center (Taiwan)	Space Studies Center (Taiwan)	300	1		Earth observation
Advanced Composition Explorer	Aug.1997	NASA		633	1	Delta II	Astronomy
Brilliant Pebbles	>1997	SDIO	TRW or Martin Marietta	<100	1000		Strategic defense
Odyssey	1998	TRW	Defense Systems Inc.	1250	12		Communications
COLOR	1998	NASA			1	Pegasus ?	Earth observation
Ameristar-2	1998	Worldspace Inc.	Defense Systems Inc.		1		Communications
Iridium (replenishment)	1998	Iridium Inc.	Lockheed Missiles & Space Co.	<500	13		Communications
Westar	1998	Westinghouse Electric Co.	Westinghouse Electric Co.		>3	Conestoga ?	Multipurpose
Near Earth Asteroid Rendezvous	Feb.1998	NASA		700	1	Pegasus	Planetary
Small Explorer	June 1998	NASA			1	Pegasus	Scientific
Westar	1999	Westinghouse Electric Co.	Westinghouse Electric Co.		10	Conestoga ?	Multipurpose
Iridium (replenishment)	1999	Iridium Inc.	Lockheed Missiles & Space Co.	<500	13		Communications
Ellipso (replenishment)	>1999	Ellipsat			20		Communications
AERO	2000	NASA		<500	1	Pegasus ?	Atmospheric science
Iridium (replenishment)	2000	Iridium Inc.	Lockheed Missiles & Space Co.	<500	13		Communications
Iridium (replenishment)	2001	Iridium Inc.	Lockheed Missiles & Space Co.	<500	13		Communications
Brilliant Eyes	>2001	SDIO			50-70		Strategic defense
Iridium (replenishment)	2002	Iridium Inc.	Lockheed Missiles & Space Co.	<500	13		Communications
ALT	2002	NASA			1	Delta ?	Geoscience

Source: Euroconsult

722

SYNTHESE DE LA SESSION
ASPECTS ECONOMIQUES

En prenant en compte les programmes annoncés, la marché mondial des petits satellites dont la masse est inférieure à 1000 kg est estimé à 650 satellites.

Les principales missions sont :

– communications	70 %
– applications militaires (hors communications)	15 %
– applications technologiques et scientifiques	15 %

Une analyse réaliste de ce marché indique un nombre de satellites voisin de 180, correspondant à 80 programmes.

Par ailleurs, il a été noté que la réduction des coûts de ces petits satellites implique de nouvelles approches, adaptées au degré de risque encouru, tant pour ce qui concerne le management, la réalisation des essais, que l'exigence qualité.

SYNTHESIS OF THE SESSION
ECONOMICS

Taking into consideration the programmes that have been announced, the world market for small satellites having masses of less than 1000 kg is estimated at 650 satellites.

The main missions are:

– communications *70%*

– military applications (excluding communications) *15%*

– technological and scientific applications *15%*

A realistic analysis of this market shows a number of satellites close to 180, corresponding to 80 programmes.

It has also been observed that the reduction of the cost of these small satellites implies new approaches suited to the level of risk for management, testing and quality requirements.

SESSION POSTERS

POSTERS

A Study on Business Satellite System Illuminating Europe, North America and East Asia

Shiro Murakami[1], Yuichi Otsu[1], Toneo Kawanishi[2]

[1] Space Communications Research Corporation, Tokyo Japan
[2] National Space Development Agency of Japan

1. Introduction
Demands of communications traffic vary depending on time of the day, day of the week and so on. Especially most traffic of the long distances and overseas communications are concentrated into only a few hours of a day. It might be caused by the time difference. Overseas telecommunications companies usually facilitate the 24-hours-a -day communications capacity, by geostationary satellites or by optical fiber cables.

Business activities in the world are led by Europe, North America and East Asia areas. Communications among them are carried via geostationary satellites, such as INTELSAT satellites, or optical fiber cables, such as TPC(TransPacific Cable) -3 / TAT (TransATlantic) -8 and land lines.

The HEO(Highly inclined Elliptical Orbits) business satellite system is proposed to supplement currently operating systems.

2. Orbit of the Satellite
The HEO is applied. Trajectory of the satellite and its coverage are drawn in Fig 1. The parameters are as follows.

period	12 hours
perigee	1500 km
apogee	39000 km
inclination	63.4 °

Elevation angles in Paris, New York and Tokyo with time of a day is shown in Fig 2. Communications can be performed twice six-hours-period a day at elevation angle more than ten degrees. The first coverage centered 18 JST corresponds to the Europe - East Asia peak traffic hours. The second coverage centered 6 JST corresponds to the USA - East Asia peak traffic hours.

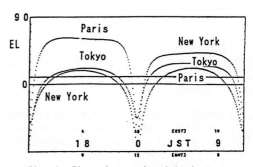

Fig. 1   Trajectory and coverage of
the satellite

Fig. 2   Elevation angle with time

3. Satellite
Assuming Information Rate of 1.544Mbps, 1/2 FEC and an 10% overhead of them are applied, then Transmission Rate will be 3.4Mbps and Required Bandwidth will be 2MHz. When the bandwidth of transponders is 36MHz, 18 carriers can be assigned in one transponder. Required saturation power is 36 W when operated at 3 dB output backoff and transmitting power per carrier is 1W as shown in Fig.4. One typical configuration of the satellite is shown in Fig.3

4. Earth Station

INTELSAT Standard E1 earth station for IBS(INTELSAT Business Service) will be appropriate. The diameter of E1 antenna is around 3.5m and G/T is more than 25dB/K.

The advantage to use such a small earth station is that users can install their own earth stations at the roof-top of the building. That means users can bypass or skip land lines those performances are very poor in some cases.

5. Link Budget

One example of link budget is shown in Fig.4. The carrier frequencies are 14 GHz and 11GHz. Information rate is 1.544Mbps.

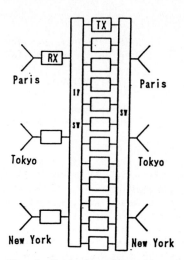

Fig. 3 Typical configuration of the satellite

UPLINK 14GHz		DOWNLINK 11GHz	
Transmit Power 1 W	0.0 dBW	Transmit Power 1 W	0.0 dBW
E/S Antenna Gain	51.2 dB	Sat Antenna Gain	38.2 dB
Feeder Loss	3.0 dB	Feeder Loss	3.0 dB
EIRP	48.2 dBW	EIRP	35.2 dBW
Free Space Loss	207.6 dB	Free Space Loss	205.5 dB
Sat Antenna Gain	40.3 dB	E/S Antenna Gain	49.1 dB
Feeder Loss	3.0 dB	Feeder Loss	3.0 dB
Receiver in Level	-122.1 dBW	Receiver in Level	-124.2 dBW
Rx Noise Temp	27.6 dBK	Rx Noise Temp	26.4 dBK
Antenna	290.0 K	Antenna	150.0 K
Receiver NF	3.0 dB	Receiver NF	3.0 dB
Link Margin	3.0 dB	Link Margin	3.0 dB
C/No	75.9 dBHz	C/No	75.0 dBHz

system	C/No	72.4 dBHz
	FEC	3.0 dB
	Eb/No	13.5 dB

Fig.4 Link Budget

6. Conclusion

Communications system, which could not provide the service on 24-hours-a-day basis but busy-hours-a-day, is proposed considering the traffic profile of long distance calls and the costs.

The benefits of the proposed system are summarized as follows.
1. Economical communications system providing service in busy hours
2. Very reliable communications system skipping land lines those performances are very poor in some cases.
3. A satellite visible from Europe, North America and East Asia at the same time.

Degradation of solar cells caused by periodical passages through Van Allen belt, exhaustion of fuel for attitude control of the non-geostationary satellite shall be studied further.

SATELLITE GROUND SYSTEMS AT ESRANGE

Lennart Marcus

Swedish Space Corporation, Esrange

In northern Sweden, near the town of Kiruna, there are several sophisticated ground systems for satellite support. At Esrange, located at 68° N, 21° E, there are systems for TT&C support, data reception and data processing. The geographic location, north of the arctic circle, is particurly suitable for support of polar orbiting satellites. Communication with spacecraft can be established almost every pass for satellites in circular orbits, and for extended periods of time for satellites in elliptical orbits. Ground based scientific instrumentation as well as instruments flown on balloons or rockets can be used for coordinated measurements. These possibilities have successfully been utilized for magnetospheric and athmospheric research in conjunction with data reception from small satellites.

There are three receiving systems in operation, each capable of data reception in S-band (2.2 GHz to 2.4 GHz) and also in X-band (8.0 GHz to 8.4 GHz). In addition, an UHF system is available for data reception or telecommand opertions. Various demodulation schemes can be handled, and the systems can smoothly be adapted for special requirements. In S-band, phase modulation (PM) is most commonly used, and in X-band, high bit rate data is downlinked using a variety of phase shift keying (PSK) modulation schemes.

TT&C activities are supported by two separate ground systems, both with S-band (2.0 GHz to 2.1 GHz) uplink capabilities. One system utilizes separate downlink and uplink antennas. The uplink antenna is pointed in the same direction as the downlink antenna by means of means of real time pointing angle transfers. This system is part of the CNES 2 GHz network, and includes telemetry, telecommand, ranging and angular measurement equipment. Data from the various equipments is assembled into blocks, according to CNES standards, and transmitted to the user via the CNES communication network.The other TT&C system is intended for general purpose support and is designed for simple interfacing to user equipment. The system consists of a single downlink/uplink antenna, and includes modulation and demodulation equipment, as well as a broadband solid state power amplifier. All interfaces to the system, are defined at low frequency "video signal" level.

These high performance systems are designed to receive data from and transmit telecommands to earth resources satellites, but are very well suited for small satellite missions.The user may install any equipment that is specific for the mission in equipment areas, which are supplied with electrical power and air conditioning facilities. An extensive infrastructure is available, allowing maximum flexibility for the user. Data processing for specific missions is normally performed by dedicated equipment which is integrated into the ground system for the duration of the mission. Processing equipment, including software, is most often supplied by the user to be operated by Esrange personnel. Installation and connection of user equipment to the system is simple, and data can be transferred to/from the user via the public telecommunication networks. International voice and data communication is performed via terrestial links and satellite systems.

During the Swedish "Viking" scientific satellite mission, all equipment for operations of the satellite, data processing and data presentation was installed at Esrange and operated by Esrange personnel. Scientists were able to acess and manipulate their instruments in real time, allowing maximum scientific output. The concept with an integrated science and control facility has proven to be very successful, and will be used again in the next Swedish small satellite project, "Freja".

The Esrange facilities are universal, and are available for immediate use. Adaptation for special demands can easily be performed with short notice. Scientists and user personnel may reside for extended periods of time within the Esrange complex, which includes all facilities for a good standard of living.

Condensed antenna performance specifications.
Two identical 9 m receive only antennas:
S-band; 2.2 GHz to 2.3 GHz, RHCP or LHCP, G/T: $\geq$ 21 dB/°K
X-band; 8.0 GHz to 8.4 GHz, RHCP, G/T: $\geq$ 31 dB/°K

One 13 m receive/transmit antenna:
S-band; 2.2 GHz to 2.4 GHz, RHCP and LHCP, G/T: $\geq$ 23 dB/°K
X-band; 8.0 GHz to 8.4 GHz, RHCP or LHCP, G/T: $\geq$ 33 dB/°K
Transmit S-band; 2.025 GHz to 2.120 GHz, RHCP or LHCP,
                  max. EIRP 67 dBW
One 6 m transmit only antenna:
Transmit S-band; 2.025 GHz to 2.120 GHz, RHCP or LHCP,
                  max. EIRP 67 dBW
One 7 m UHF receive or transmit antenna:
Receive UHF; 400 MHz to 465 MHz, RHCP and LHCP,
          G/T $\geq$ 4 dB/°K
Transmit UHF; 400 MHz to 465 MHz, RHCP and LHCP,
                  max. EIRP 48 dBW

RAPUNZEL - GLUON - MICOSS - POLARCOM

Dr. Ing. N. BALTEAS,
Kayser-Threde, Munich, D

Abstract

RAPUNZEL is a tether Low-Cost small satellite system for environmental and scientific studies. GLUON is a low-cost reentry capsule. MICOSS is a scientific small satellite for Corona observations. POLARCOM is a Low-Cost polar and LEO communication satellite system.

All systems are under development or under study by Kayser-Threde, a medium size company. On the example of this four very different applications, the practical effectivity of small satellite missions, the challenge and advantage of Low-Cost space access will be shown.

SARA : SATELLITE AMATEUR DE RADIO-ASTRONOMIE

A. COLMON
ESIEESPACE – France

SARA a été conçu et réalisé par ESIEESPACE, une association amateur implantée à l'E.S.I.E.E. (Ecole Supérieure d'Ingénieurs en Electrotechnique et en Electronique). Sa mission est d'écouter l'activité de la planète Jupiter dans la bande décamétrique (2 à 15 MHz). Cette expérience a été proposée par l'observatoire de Meudon. La durée de vie de 10 ans doit permettre une écoute continue.

Lancé le 16 juillet 91 depuis Kourou par le vol 44 d'Ariane, en temps que passager auxilliaire à côté d'ERS1, SARA est maintenant opérationnel.

SARA montre qu'il est possible de concevoir des satellites simples avec des moyens très limités, que ce soit en temps ou en argent.

Cette présentation montre les différentes étapes de la conception, de la construction et des tests de SARA. Nous insistons également sur la gestion du projet au sein d'une structure aussi légère qu'une association. Les premiers résultats du vol seront commentés.

TESTS TECHNOLOGIQUES DE COMPOSANTS EN ORBITE

A. COLMON
SODERN – France

SODERN étudie la possibilité de tester des composants en orbite sur des micro-satellites. Pour les futurs capteurs d'attitude (capteurs de terre, viseurs d'étoiles) toute une gamme de composant doit être évaluée.

SODERN travaille dans le domaine de l'optronique et a besoin, à ce titre, d'évaluer de nouveaux détecteurs : matrices à transfert de charges (CCD), barrette CCD, matrices CID, matrices à domaine spectral étendu. Les besoins en traitements de ces nouveaux capteurs sont en augmentation rapide : traitement d'images, compression d'images... Les processeurs nécessaires à ces traitements ne sont pas actuellement disponibles dans des versions spatiales.

L'utilisation d'un micro-satellite est préférée aux simulateurs pour s'affranchir des problèmes de représentativité des modèles. La comparaison avec des tests au sol sur les mêmes composants aidera au recallage de ces modèles.

Le coût des essais en vol est concurrentiel de celui des essais au sol, dans la mesure où il est possible d'essayer simultanément un grand nombre de composants de différents constructeurs.

COMPLETE TURN-KEY SERVICE FOR SMALL PAYLOADS

Antonio FABRIZI
FIAT SPAZIO, Roma

Based on the availabilty of the new small launcher being developed by BPD (FIAT Group) for the Italian Space Agency, FIAT SPAZIO is developing a "commercial turn-key service for small payloads".

The small payloads market is generally different from the medium and large satellites market, where large Organizations or Agencies usually develop the satellites, which are then launched through commercial launch service Organizations and finally operated in most cases by the same Organizations of development (ESA, Eutelsat,...).

The small payload user is often a scientific organization not necessarily experienced in space platforms or vehicles, and sometimes even only interested about data. For these users, that in some cases have also limited resources, it is important to have flight opportunities or even data opportunities, with the availability of whatever is needed for the mission through a single contact point, who can provide the most cost effective mission approach.

FIAT SPAZIO is developing such TURN-KEY SMALL MISSIONS by making available a menu of services where the user can choose and optimize his needs.

These services are based on the FIAT Group Companies and on selected Partners capabilities, which, in addition to the launcher, include mission engineering and planning, standard small platforms, earth observation sensors, store and forward telecommunication packages, small ground stations which can be operated directly by the users, data acquisition and processing, etc.

This paper provides technical and programmatic information on the TURN-KEY SERVICE proposed by FIAT SPAZIO.

TECHNOLOGY DEVELOPMENT FOR LOW COST MICROSATELLITES

S. CECCHI - L. ZUCCONI

Carlo Gavazzi Space SpA, via Gallarate 139 Milano, Italy

INTRODUCTION

This paper deals with the technology for microsatellites and describes the CGS technological initiatives in Italy to promote microsatellite programmes.

To introduce the content of this work it is however necessary to clarify the mission scenario potential applications and the budget requirements for a microsatellite programme.

Small satellites injected in circular or elliptical Earth orbits with mass up to 150 kg are the type of systems that we consider of interest for our initiative and classify as microsatellites.

This type of spacecraft is characterized by very low budget requirements, very short duration of the development phase and relies on the availability of very low cost launch systems.

CGS MICROSATELLITE ACTIVITIES

In 1991 CGS have initiated a profitable collaboration with OHB-System, Bremen in the definition and realization of the SAFIR-1 microsatellite (fig. 1).

The main characteristics of this satellite are reported in table 1 and CGS involvement is based on the definition and realization of the three bands TT&C subsystem [1,2].

Following this experience, CGS has planned the development of standard products capable of being reused in various microsatellites missions.

These products are characterized by very simple architectural solution (i.e. no redundancies are planned) low cost implementations based on good quality commercial components with manufacturing and validation techniques aiming at very low recurring costs.

MICROSATELLITE ON BOARD COMPUTER

In line with these objectives we are currently developing the microsatellite On-board Computer, here called CDM, performing the following functions (fig. 2):

- Data management

- Attitude and orbit control
- Interface with the space link
- Housekeeping and power management.

This product is designed with the purpose of accommodating as much as possible specific mission requirements; this is achieved with the implementation of a mission specific application S/W maintaining the H/W configuration as standard as possible.

The block diagram of the envisaged architecture is shown in fig. 3.

Moreover sophisticated S/W techniques are implemented to enable failure recovery and easy system reconfiguration.

FUTURE ACTIVITIES

In parallel CGS is running a market survey for the identification of available products which may be easily customised and adapted to new applications; this background activity is pursued with the objective of preparing a technological demonstration programme.

This programme shall make use of a microsatellite in a low earth orbit (800 km) which will carry a payload made of components and products which are newly developed and requiring a qualification procedure before their space utilisation.

The in-orbit demonstration programme shall focus on the following development areas:

- electronic equipment for microgravity payload
- electric propulsion (ion and arcjet propulsion)
- solar GaAs cell generators
- power storage
- thermal control (passive and active)
- attitude control (passive and active)
- position and orbital tracking (if possible using GPS receiver)
- study of single event upsets in solid state memory devices
- device qualification in harsh radiation environment
- software reloading and mission reconfiguration from ground.

CONCLUSIONS

With this initiative Carlo Gavazzi Space intends to achieve a sound capacity in the field of microsatellites products manufacturing and to develop capabilities for in-orbit technology demonstrations to fulfil internal needs and provide opportunities for external industrial customers.

REFERENCES

[1] A. Ginati, G. Lehmann, M. Fuchs: "SAFIR a new SAtellite For Information Relay", 42nd Congress of the IAF, Montreal, October 5-11, 1991.

[2] SAFIR-1 TM/TC Subsystem Specifications.

TABLE 1
SAFIR-1 MAIN CHARACTERISTICS

- Sun synchronous orbit: 98.04°, 700 km

- Project life   : 3 years

- Size   : 450 x 450 x 450 mm

- Mass   : 55 Kg

- Power   : 15 W average, 25 W peak

- Stabilization   : Gravity Gradient

- Pointing accuracy   : ± 5°

- Up link frequencies   : 152 MHz, 434 MHz, 1626 MHz

- Down link frequencies: 152 MHz, 434 MHz, 1529 MHz

- Data rates   : 300 bps, 1200 bps, 9600 bps

- Modulations   : FSK, BPSK

- Operations   : half-duplex, bentpipe mode,
                          stand-by mode.

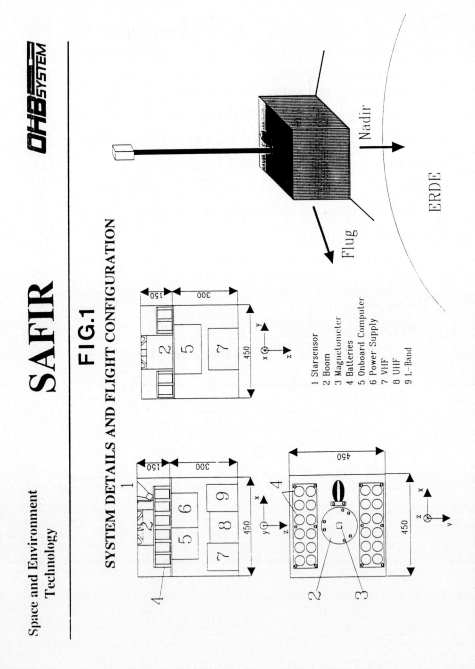

Space and Environment Technology

SAFIR

FIG.1

SYSTEM DETAILS AND FLIGHT CONFIGURATION

1 Starsensor
2 Boom
3 Magnetometer
4 Batteries
5 Onboard Computer
6 Power Supply
7 VHF
8 UHF
9 L-Band

Nadir

ERDE

Flug

FIG.2

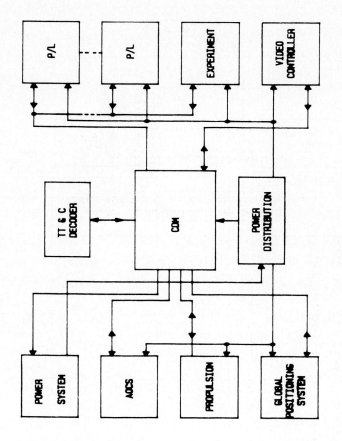

A CDM IN A SATELLITE SYSTEM CONTEXT

743

FIG.3

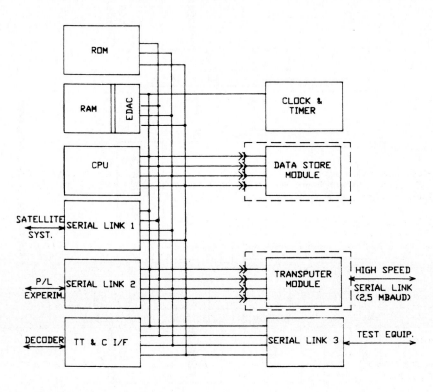

CDM BLOCK DIAGRAM

LIGHT SATELLITES FOR MONITORING POLLUTION ON EARTH

par
P. Naudy, P. Ortolo,

DASSAULT AVIATION, France

Satellites have today demonstrated the enormous contribution of space to Earth monitoring. Every evening, TV broadcast news offer us a beautiful overlook of our planet from space. Pollution monitoring is the next logical utilization of space technology.

1 : Why light satellites for monitoring pollution on Earth ?

In no way, can light satellites replace large ones. Large satellites have proved their major role in weather forecasting and full-time global Earth monitoring. However light satellites could be the logical complementary part for specific and on the spot applications.

Deforestation, holes in the ozone layer, desertification, chemical and nuclear clouds, oil spills, acid rains, pollution by hydrocarbons are phenomena that a large world community is now seriously considering. However the monitoring from space of these phenomena requires, most of the time, specific instrumentation for each of them : sensors, periodicity, resolution, data processing are specific.

The major interests of light satellites for monitoring pollution on Earth can be summarized in four points :

* **cost aspects :** dedicated to a specific mission, the cost of a single light satellite or of a limited constellation is much lower than any kind of large satellite. In this way, specialized organizations or private companies could afford to place in orbit their own light satellite for their own application.

* **suitable orbit :** to achieve a specific task, a light satellite has the possibility to be placed on a suitable orbit for its mission. This statement obviously requires a dedicated launcher. Such a satellite should be able to perform its mission in better conditions than any large and multi-purposes monitoring satellite.

* **alert aspect :** some pollution on Earth, like deforestation or hydrocarbon pollution, evolves slowly. Others, resulting from accidents, are developing more quickly : this include, for examples, nuclear clouds and oils spills. Again, specific light satellites can be launched quickly, in appropriate conditions, to monitor the development of such pollution. This alert aspect of a light satellite is a real complementary element to monitoring a global Earth pollution.

* **lifetime :** A light satellite has a typical lifetime of roughly two years. This period is adapted to the large majority of pollution on Earth resulting from artificial disasters. The lifetime of larger satellites, which can reach 6 to 10 years, is less adapted to such specific missions.

2 : What is the contribution of Dassault Aviation to light satellites ?

Due to the evolution of the market and their own competence in industrialization of small series, Dassault Aviation is betting on light satellites. The company is developing a light platform adapted either to military or civilian purposes.

Characteristics of the platform :

Performance :

* Attitude Control : geocentric pointing - precision : +/-6°
* Transmission Data Rate : 19.2 kbits/s
* Storage Capacity : 4 Mbytes
* Available Mass for the Payload : 8 kg
* Available Power for the Payload : 8 W average/orbit
* World-Wide Coverage

Features

* Dimensions : 500 mm x 500 mm x 580 mm
* Satellite Total Mass : 50 Kg
* Honeycomb Structure Mass : 6.4 kg
* Ultra-light and Non-Polluting Separation System : mass 2.2 kg - miniature pyrotechnic expansion tube
* Passive Attitude Control : Gravity Gradient
* Passive Thermal Control
* Non Regulated 18V Bus
* Battery Capacity : 150 Wh
* Communication Frequency Range : UHF
* 80C86 Computer

Advantages

* The structure is designed to receive equipment on shelves : the equipment is mounted on the lower and upper satellite plates
* Equipment consumption is optimized in line with the needs of the mission : at any moment, only the required equipment is powered on. Thus, taking into account this management and also the large battery capacity, large amount of power can be delivered to the payload when necessary.
* Launch is possible on the (ARIANE 4) ASAP platform.

(*) given for sun synchronous LEO

Programs for large monitoring satellites are already engaged and this is a good point. Programs for light satellites have now to be decided to realize on the spot missions.

There is no point in a trade-off between large and light satellites. They are the complementary elements of a flexible and global system for monitoring pollution on Earth. Suitable utilization of light satellites should come from cooperation, at an international level, between the scientific community and industry. The first having to define the need, the second to build the satellites adapted to this need.

A SOFTWARE TOOL FOR THE DESIGN OF LOW EARTH ORBIT SATELLITE SYSTEMS FOR COMMUNICATIONS AND RADIOLOCATION

Jean Jacques DE RIDDER et Gérard MARAL
Ecole Nationale Supérieure des Télécommunications (TELECOM Paris),
BP4004, 31028 Toulouse Cedex, France

Heinrich MEYR and Peter ZUMEGEN
UNIVERSITY OF AACHEN
ERT 5240 - RTWH
Aachen Sommerfeldstrasse 24
D - 5100 Aachen, Germany

Interest for alternative communications systems using either multiple low earth orbit or high elliptical orbit satellites has increased during the past few years. The market seems quite promising. However it is not clear what performance can be achieved by such systems. Moreover, given the performance, the design of any system is an iterative and lengthy procedure as a result of the numerous parameters that are to be considered.

Compared to the well mastered geostationary satellite systems for which operational experience has accumulated over the years, only a limited experience on such systems is available today. This reflects into an increased design complexity. The decision for the set up of a satellite communications system, and the set up itself of the system must take place in a reduced interval of time : any delay increases the risk that competition takes over the market. Hence it is most important for an operator or a satellite manufacturer to bring down the design time of the system to a minimum.

Software tools have been for a long time used to facilitate the design of satellite communications systems. However the designer has to set up the system configuration and run various independent software tools in a lengthy iterative manner before he ends up with a satisfactory design (Cf. figure 1). Need is obvious for an integrated tool which would allow rapid system design and optimisation from the service requirements.

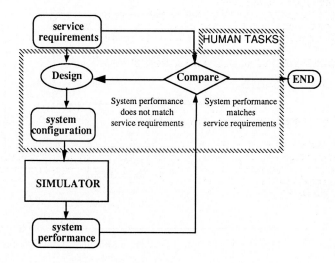

Figure 1 - Conventional design procedure of satellite communications systems

An expert system is felt to be the proper tool for analyzing the service specifications and translating these into candidate system configurations. This poster displays the architecture of such an expert system based software named XEOSCAD (eXpert Earth Orbiting Satellite systems Computer Aided Design and simulation). With XEOSCAD the candidate sytem configurations are simulated (Cf. figure 2). Then the expert system compares their performance to the service requirements and proposes the designer the proper parameter of configuration changes to meet the objectives. XEOSCAD is expected to save time and money during the design phase of satellite communications systems.

We expect a strong synergy effect to be gained by providing a framework which allows an integration of the various tools dedicated to specific tasks. Such a framework is provided by the XEOSCAD architecture presented in this poster

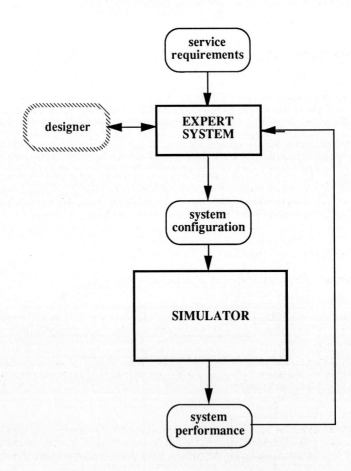

Figure 2 - Expert system aided design procedure of satellite communications systems

OPTIMISATION DE L'AVIONIQUE D'UN MICROLANCEUR

J.-V. LEGRAND

Dassault Aviation (France)

Ce document présente le résumé d'une conférence proposée dans le cadre du symposium CNES/ESA « Small Satellites Systems and Services », qui a eu lieu en juin 1992. Il propose une approche du dimensionnement et des compromis à effectuer pour la conception des systèmes de guidage/pilotage d'un microlanceur.

1. DETERMINATION DES OBJECTIFS

– Analyse du besoin

Les missions envisagées sont examinées (micro satellites d'applications civiles et militaires), et caractérisées en termes de spécifications sur le système (essentiellement orbite utile et précision requise sur celle-ci).

– Analyse des contraintes

Les contraintes sont de deux ordres :

- techniques : le tir est envisagé à partir d'un avion porteur, ce qui limite la masse du lanceur et contraint la séquence de tir (alignement inertiel par exemple) ;
- économiques : l'approche délibérément commerciale conduit à limiter au minimum les paramètres tels que risques de développement et prix de lancement.

2. CONCEPTION AVIONIQUE

La démarche de conception est détaillée selon les étapes suivantes :

– Analyse fonctionnelle

L'analyse des scénarios de mission, mais aussi de mise au point et d'essais, permet de dégager les fonctions dévolues à l'avionique : localisation, guidage, pilotage, télémesure, gestion lanceur, etc.

– Projection matérielle

Un premier avant-projet matériel, utilisant au maximum des éléments sur étagère (limitation du risque et du prix de développement), est réalisé et les fonctions y sont projetées ; il repose sur l'utilisation d'une centrale inertielle à gyrolasers et d'un bus numérique multiplexé, facilitant les essais et l'évolutivité.

– Vérification des performances

Ce système avionique est alors positionné précisément par rapport aux objectifs de performances, masse et coût. Des simulations numériques vérifient en particulier l'adéquation du système de guidage/pilotage ; l'aménagement de la case à équipements permet un contrôle global de la faisabilité mécanique. Des paramètres sensibles sur l'architecture sont alors dégagés.

3. COMPROMIS

L'étude de la sensibilité de ces paramètres permet d'aborder l'optimisation de certains paramètres du lanceur lui-même :

– Contrôle d'attitude

Hors de l'atmosphère, celui-ci peut être par spin ou 3 axes, ce qui influe sur la précision de localisation.

– Stratégie de guidage

Optimisation de l'allocation de précision entre localisation et guidage, selon le type de propulsion du dernier étage (poudre ou liquide).

4. CONCLUSION

Cette étude démontre la faisabilité avec les technologies actuelles, d'un système avionique remplissant le cahier des charges.

Utilisations potentielles du système DORIS

Pour les petits satellites

François NOUEL
Division Mathématiques Spatiales
CNES
18, avenue Edouard Belin
31055 TOULOUSE CEDEX

Quels que soient les services assurés par un satellite ou une constellation de satellites, leur utilisation opérationnelle exige de connaître la trajectoire : exploitation de la charge utile, maintien à poste, manoeuvres, navigation, autonomie...

L'apparition conjuguée de systèmes de poursuites permettant de réaliser à bord des mesures de localisation et de micro-calculateurs puissants embarquables permet de concevoir l'aspect trajectographie d'une façon différente du concept actuel à travers l'exploitation de Centres de Contrôles. En effet, il est désormais possible de disposer à bord et en temps réel d'une orbite évitant ainsi une boucle longue avec le sol.

Les systèmes actuels tels que GPS, DORIS et probablement TDRS peuvent remplir cette fonction. Nous insisterons sur le système DORIS en le décrivant brièvement et en rappelant les applications scientifiques réalisées avec SPOT2 et TOPEX/POSEIDON dans le cas d'une orbite précise. Nous insisterons sur l'extension de DORIS -en cours de développement- au calcul d'orbite à bord dans le cadre de SPOT4.

Partant de là, il est alors possible d'envisager divers concepts de trajectographie suivant les besoins de l'utilisateur, d'identifier l'apport de DORIS (actuel ou adapté) en termes de facilité d'exploitation et de réduction des contraintes opérationnelles.

LE VOILIER SOLAIRE EUROPÉEN, VITRINE DE L'APPROCHE PETITS SATELLITES

J.-Y. PRADO

Union pour la Promotion de la Propulsion Phonique, Toulouse – France

Résumé:

Depuis une dizaine d'années, le projet animé par l'U3P (Union pour la Promotion de la Propulsion Photonique) d'organiser une course de voiliers solaires entre la Terre et la Lune et d'en être un des concurrents a progressé méthodiquement et les conditions de lancement effectif de cette première spatiale devraient pouvoir être atteintes courant 1992.

Le voilier solaire envisagé par l'U3P appartient manifestement à la classe des petits satellites autant par sa masse (moins de 250 kg au lancement) que par les principes de base de son financement (sponsorisation par des entreprises privées issues de tout secteur économique).

Actuellement, il est prévu que la course se déroule entre 3 candidats (Américain, Européen et Japonais), lancés simultanément en passagers secondaires d'un vol ARIANE 4. Une option de lancement par PROTON est également envisagée.

Les études de Phase A ont été présentées au cours d'une revue en octobre 1991 et la phase B est en cours de montage.

Cette phase B présente l'originalité d'être conduite par une association d'entreprises créée spécialement à cette effet: le "Voilier Solaire Européen" (VSE) qui, outre l'U3P, compte 8 membres actuellement (CHRISTOL CONSULTANTS, SEXTANT AVIONIQUE, STERIA, MATRA MARCONI SPACE, BOLLORE TECHNOLOGIES, DUPONT DE NEMOURS, SODERN et PROGESPACE). D'autres adhésions sont en cours de discussion.

Dans le papier proposé, les principaux éléments de la course et de son organisation seront rappelés. La phase B n'étant pas achevée à la date du symposium, seuls les résultats disponibles seront présentés. En conclusion, les domaines de participation possible des industriels intéressés au secteur des petits satellites seront discutés.

Par son impact médiatique important, le Voilier Solaire Européen véhiculera l'image du dynamisme des industriels qui auront su attacher leur nom à cette entreprise.

QUELLES CLASSES DE "PLATEFORME"
POUR L'OBSERVATION DE LA TERRE A L'AIDE DE MINI-SATELLITES

G. Bellaïche, D. Breton et D. Séguela

CENTRE NATIONAL d'ETUDES SPATIALES *

Abstract

This paper describes the opportunity of using mini-satellites for Earth-Observation missions.
First, it defines the kind of missions it deals with, and then how mini-satellites may have their place between dedicated satellites of 2 to 3 tons and very large platforms (8 to 10 tons).
Finally, it presents the mission-sytem requirements and try to give an envelope of the 2 associated platform types specifications.

Résumé

Ce papier décrit les possibilités d'utilisation de mini-satellites pour des missions d'Observation de la Terre.
Il définit tout d'abord les missions concernées, puis la place qui pourrait être dévolue à ces mini-satellites dans les différentes stratégies actuelles (satellites dédiés de 2 à 3 tonnes et grosses plateformes de 8 à 10 tonnes).
Enfin, il présente les besoins mission-système et tente de donner une enveloppe de spécifications pour 2 types de plateforme associés.

1.- QUELLE OBSERVATION DE LA TERRE ?

L'Observation de la Terre (au sens le plus large) à partir de l'orbite basse peut, en ce qui concerne les contraintes instrumentales sur le segment spatial, être classée en 3 thèmes principaux :

- l'imagerie des terres émergées qui nécessite une haute résolution spatiale (typiquement quelques mètres), et le maintien d'un cycle orbital précis.

- la caractérisation globale de l'atmosphère et des interactions surface de la terre-atmosphère, qui se contente d'une résolution spatiale moyenne ou faible (1 km ou plus) sur un grand champ d'observation, sans imposer un cycle orbital précis, mais tout en nécessitant une continuité d'observation sur une période suffisamment longue.

- l'océanographie et l'observation des glaces qui, souvent liées à l'atmosphère, ont des caractéristiques et des contraintes du même type; il faut cependant mentionner le cas spécifique de l'altimétrie (circulation océanique et suivi des glaces), qui nécessite une précision centimétrique imposant une très bonne restitution de l'orbite et le maintien précis du cycle orbital.

Les conditions d'exploitation constituent un critère supplémentaire très important de classification des missions; il semble en effet nécessaire d'établir une distinction entre l'exploitation à des fins opérationnelles ou commerciales, et l'exploitation à des fins scientifiques ou expérimentales.

En effet dans le premier cas, le système doit être suffisamment robuste au niveau du maintien du service, impliquant des contraintes strictes au niveau fiabilité et renouvellement en orbite.

Ainsi si le premier thème est plutôt à vocation opérationnelle et commerciale, le second lui comprend 2 sous-thèmes :
- l'un à vocation opérationnelle : la météo
- l'autre à vocation plutôt scientifique : l'environnement.

Quant au troisième, s'il a eu jusqu'à ce jour un caractère plutôt scientifique, il a maintenant vocation, notamment pour l'altimétrie, à devenir opérationnel.

2.- QUELLE PLACE POUR LES MINI-SATELLITES ?

Laissant de côté les satellites orbite haute tels les METEOSAT européens, les principaux satellites d'Observation de la Terre actuellement en opération sont : LANDSAT, SPOT, TOPEX-POSEIDON (08/92), NOAA, ERS, UARS, et JERS, ces 3 derniers couvrant quasiment tous les domaines des 3 thèmes décrits ci-dessus.

Parmi ces satellites, seuls LANDSAT, SPOT et NOAA ont aujourd'hui un caractère opérationnel.

Tous ces satellites sont de la classe 1.5 à 3 tonnes en orbite.

Pour demain, 2 tendances se profilent aujourd'hui :

- des satellites multi-missions emportant des instruments permettant de couvrir l'ensemble des thèmes, comme la "PPF" européenne telle qu'envisagée par l'ESA, emportant jusqu'à 2.4 tonnes d'instruments (mission POEM).

- des satellites dédiés emportant les instruments permettant de couvrir individuellement chacun de ces thèmes ou sous-thèmes, et s'adaptant de manière optimale aux besoins spécifiques du thème : EOS des USA, emportant jusqu'à 1 tonne d'instruments en est une illustration; de même, une alternative à la PPF actuellement à l'étude en Europe, permettrait de réaliser la mission POEM à l'aide de 3 satellites dédiés emportant également jusqu'à 1 tonne d'instruments chacun.

En complément de ces 2 approches, il peut y avoir place pour des mini-satellites (200 kg à 1 tonne hors tout), qui permettraient :

- de remplir individuellement une mission complète d'un thème, par exemple l'altimétrie opérationnelle.

- de remplir une fonction particulière d'un thème, lorsque celle-ci peut être efficacement disjointe d'une mission principale, par exemple la fonction collecte de données du sous-thème météo.

- de compléter une mission principale assurée par un satellite d'une des classes décrites ci-dessus (multi-missions ou dédiés) de manière à (si la co-registration avec d'autres instruments n'est pas nécessaire) :
  * remplacer un instrument défaillant.
  * assurer un potentiel de croissance à la mission principale (instruments optionnels ou élargissement de la couverture).
  * effectuer des évaluations technologiques en vol de nouveaux concepts instrumentaux.

3.- QUELS BESOINS MISSION-SYSTEME ?

On peut tout d'abord donner les besoins système "génériques" des 3 thèmes énoncés ci-dessus, appliqués aux mini-satellites :
  * une couverture globale et répétitive impliquant des orbites basses fortement inclinées entre 60 et 100°.
  * une bon éclairement terrestre pour les instruments de type "optique visible et MIR", impliquant pour les satellites héliosynchrones une heure locale voisine de 10 heures TU.
  * un phasage terrestre précis pour les instruments registrés par rapport au sol, impliquant un maintien d'orbite d'une centaine de m en altitude.
  * un fonctionnement quasi-permanent et global impliquant une grande capacité énergétique et, pour les données, un stockage de masse et des liaisons bord-sol hautes cadences de plusieurs Mbits/s, ainsi que dans certains cas, une dissémination quasi temps réel de ces données.
  * un couple durée de vie/fiabilité du satellite n'imposant pas une trop forte redondance bord (robustesse du système plutôt que du satellite seul).

Mais on peut indiquer des missions telles celles assurées par les radars (imageurs ou altimétriques) qui s'accommodent fort bien d'une heure locale quelconque.

De même les instruments de collectes de données ou certains instruments d'environnement ne nécessitent pas un phasage terrestre précis.

Comme à l'accoutumée dans le domaine spatial, essayant toujours d'avoir un retour maximum du kg en orbite, on optimise au maximum le satellite pour son besoin mission spécifique.

C'est pourquoi il s'avère difficile de fédérer tous ces besoins en une ou plusieurs classes de "satellites", et donc de définir une ou plusieurs classes de plateformes types répondant de façon optimisée à l'ensemble des besoins.

4.- QUEL TYPE DE PLATEFORME ?

Malgré cette difficulté, on peut tenter de donner des "spécifications enveloppe" permettant à un ou deux types de plateformes de s'adapter à la plupart des missions.

Ces spécifications sont alors de 2 natures, celles communes à toutes les missions et inhérentes au concept de mini-satellites, et celles plus spécifiques aux différents besoins mission.

Ainsi, les premières (génériques) définissent une plateforme :
* héliosynchrone fonctionnant autour de 10 heures (l'héliosynchronisme est ici dictée par une simplification du système bord et non par de réels besoins mission), et si possible adaptable aisément à l'orbite 6h-18h.
* permettant d'emporter jusqu'à 300 kg d'instruments, et en tout état de cause conduisant à un satellite hors tout d'1 tonne maximum.
* disposant d'une ressource énergétique moyenne sur l'orbite de l'ordre de 800 W, dont typiquement 500 dévolus à la charge-utile.
* ayant une durée de vie de 2 à 4 ans avec une fiabilité de l'ordre de 0.7.

Quant aux secondes, elles permettent d'aboutir à 2 classes de plateformes :

- une plateforme dite "rudimentaire" sans système de propulsion (pas de maintien de trace ni d'orbite), délivrant un pointage géocentrique grossier à typiquement ± 1°; cette version peut être associée à certaines missions d'environnement ou de météo, notamment celles à caractère prospectif.

- une plateforme plus sophistiquée qui, en plus des spécifications génériques ci-dessus aura une capacité de :
* maintien d'orbite (altitude et inclinaison) et de phasage terrestre (typiquement ± 2 km à l'équateur), et pouvant voler entre 400 et 900 km d'altitude (emportant donc un sous-système de propulsion).
* pointage géocentrique du satellite avec une précision de l'ordre de ± 0.1° sur les 3 axes.
Cette version est elle plutôt associée aux missions de type imagerie haute résolution et altimétrie océanique.

Il va de soi que ces "deux" plateformes ne peuvent être que des concepts, chaque besoin et donc chaque charge-utile conduisant à un satellite "matériel" adapté; ces plateformes doivent être assemblées comme de véritables "puzzles", en utilisant toujours les mêmes équipements et les mêmes concepts sous-systèmes; de même, il ne faut pas voir le satellite dit "rudimentaire" comme une simple version détarée du satellite sophistiqué, mais plutôt considérer ces deux versions comme 2 filières de plateformes, à coûts récurrents largement différents.

5.- CONCLUSION

On montre qu'à côté des satellites d'Observation de la Terre classiques (2 à 8 tonnes en orbite), il y a place pour des mini-satellites spécialisés de 200 kg à 1 tonne hors tout.

On montre par contre qu'il est très difficile (pour l'Observation de la Terre à partir de l'orbite basse), de fédérer les besoins mission-système afin d'aboutir à une seule plateforme type; toutefois on peut définir 2 concepts de plateforme qui pourraient permettre de couvrir la plupart des missions pouvant être dévolue à ces mini-satellites; on en donne les spécifications typiques.

MARCHE POTENTIEL AUX ETATS UNIS ET EN EUROPE D'UN SYSTEME DE LOCALISATION ET DE MESSAGERIE EN ORBITE BASSE

par

Jean Luc Bessis   Philippe Courrouyan

Collecte Localisation Satellites

Les systèmes LEOMSS (Low Earth Orbit Mobile Satellite Service) dont les marchés potentiels vont être évoqués ici sont des systèmes spécialisés de messagerie bi-directionnelle et de localisation à distance.

La quantité d'informations que chaque émetteur est à même de transmettre ou de recevoir reste faible, mais est largement suffisante pour la plupart des applications potentielles de ces systèmes.

L'idée force derrière les systèmes LEOMSS est de fournir un service fiable, adapté et abordable à une grande variété d'utilisateurs et d'applications.

Cette idée se traduit dans les faits par la mise en oeuvre de solutions techniques relativement simples et éprouvées et qui offrent des services uniques en leur genre aux différents clients.

Ces services répondent à deux questions de base qui, pour chaque marché et chaque utilisateur, se traduisent par des produits et services spécifiques.

Ces deux questions sont : Où et Comment ?

Des études de marché, qui ont été menées de manière intensive en Europe et aux Etats-Unis, font apparaître une demande forte pour de tels systèmes. Chaque segment de marché, comme cela était prévisible, a une sensibilité propre quant aux éléments composant les systèmes : le type d'émetteurs et les coûts associés, le temps de réponse des systèmes et leur couverture géographique .

La sécurité des biens au sens large est un des thèmes les plus porteurs pour les LEOMSS.

Les statistiques récentes publiées par les compagnies d'assurance françaises mettent en évidence une augmentation des vols de véhicules de 50 % de 1989 à 1991.Cet augmentation correspond pour les compagnies concernées à une perte de l'ordre de 5 Milliards de Francs par an.

Au plan européen, les pertes consolidées des compagnies d'assurance s'élèvent à 20 Milliards de Francs, aux Etats-Unis à 17 Milliards de Francs.

Ces chiffres parlent d'eux-même et conduisent les intervenants du marché à vouloir mettre en place un système fiable qui permette la récupération des voitures volées, ces véhicules représentant à eux seuls plus de 45% des dépenses des compagnies d'assurance.

Le marché potentiel est de l'ordre de 200 Millions d'unités aux Etats-Unis et 160 en Europe. Le marché adressable dans un premier temps se limite aux véhicules de haut de gamme, il représente à lui seul près de 45 Millions de véhicules.

Dans le même ordre d'idée, le marché de la location d'engins de chantier est soumis à des pertes qui avoisinent les 280 Millions de Francs par an, suite à des vols d'engins.

En 1991, en Europe, une des plus grosses compagnies de location de voitures a perdu près de 55 Millions de Francs suite à des vols de véhicules jamais retrouvés. Là aussi, le besoin d'un système adapté est plus que fort chez les industriels de la profession. Par ailleurs, la même société a perdu près de 50 000 journées de location suite à des retours de véhicules laissés en dehors des parkings prévus à cet effet, ou retournés dans une autre agence que celle prévue.

Ceci nous conduit à évoquer une autre application des systèmes LEOMSS, celle de la gestion des mobiles. Gestion exceptionnelle plus que gestion quotidienne et répétitive. En effet, la plupart des contrats de location de véhicules se passsent sans encombre, dans un autre domaine, la plupart des transports de conteneurs, de caisses mobiles, et plus généralement de frêt se passent sans problème particulier. Pourtant les 5 à 10 % de cas qui sont problématiques sont une des causes principales de mauvais résultats globaux d'exploitation.
Les marchés adressables dans le domaine de la location d'engins de chantier, et de véhicules sont de l'ordre de 5 Millions d'unités en Europe et aux Etats-Unis.
Quant au marché de la gestion de frêt, il est lui de l'ordre de 7 Millions d'unités sur la même zone.
Surveillance des mobiles, gestion des mobiles : deux applications de base des systèmes LEOMSS, applications pour lesquelles les marchés sont en attente de la mise en oeuvre opérationnelle des systèmes.

Une étude récente a montré qu'en 1991, le nombre d'appels reçu par une société d'assistance automobile américaine était de l'ordre de 50 millions. En Europe, ce sont plus de 100 Millions d'appels qui sont reçus chaque année par l'ensemble des spécialistes de la profession. Les systèmes de communication classiques sont en pleine croissance, toutefois le besoin d'un système dédié existe auprès de ces sociétés. D'une part, pour fidéliser et identifier rapidement leurs adhérents en difficulté, et d'autre part pour gérer au mieux leur flotte de véhicules d'intervention. La centralisation offerte par les systèmes LEOMSS et l'unification des moyens de communication est un plus certain pour les compagnies d'assistance.
Le marché adressable pour les LEOMSS au titre de l'assistance routière est de l'ordre de 100 Millions d'unités pour les Etats-Unis et l'Europe.
Cette notion d'assistance s'étend aux particuliers, que ce soit pour des raisons de santé, d'âge ou d'activité. La mise en place d'un fil d'ariane permanent et fiable entre elles et un centre hospitalier, un organisme de sauvetage, ou un autre particulier correspond à un besoin réel de ces populations.
Chacun des marchés qui ont été étudiés avec soin, fait apparaître des besoins différents en terme de temps de réponse. Les deux premiers marchés décrits (surveillance et gestion des mobiles) sont captables même avec une heure ou deux de délai, tandis que celui d'assistance nécessite une fourniture quasi temps-réel de la position ou du message à l'utilisateur. Ceci se traduit par le fait qu'une configuration initiale réduite (deux à cinq satellites) des systèmes LEOMSS sert une partie non négligeable de la clientèle. Au fur et à mesure de la mise en place des systèmes dans leur configuration finale, les autres marchés seront servis et le service amélioré par les premières applications.

La multiplicité des marchés adressés (industriels puis grand public) et les fonctionnalités de base des systèmes LEOMSS sont synonymes d'une promesse de réussite pour de tels systèmes dans un futur proche, à condition que le coût d'investissement et de fonctionnement pour l'utilisateur soit raisonnable. Un abonnement mensuel de 50 à 100 Francs et un terminal intégré pour quelques milliers de Francs seront la clé du succés..

GEOSYNCHRONOUS POLAR ORBITING SATELLITE CELLULAR SYSTEM

M K Saha
42 Ossulton Way
London   N2 0DS
United Kingdom

Abstract:

The demand for ubiquitous services having no pockets of radio silence on any part of the Earth's surface can hardly be satisfied by Geosynchronous Equatorial Orbit (GEO) or Elliptical Orbit (EO) or Combined GEO-EO systems. The IRIDIUM system, a low earth orbiting system, appears to be a promising candidate to meet the demand. Although IRIDIUM system concepts are innovative and attractive, a large number of satellites with dynamic management of beams and operating modes are required in the system to form the constellation. Higher altitude orbits would require a smaller number of satellites in a constellation to provide continuous coverage. A system based on the IRIDIUM concept but in a circular polar orbit at geosynchronous altitude (GPO) is under study. Some features of the system are presented here.

Only six satellites, in circular polar orbit at geosynchronous altitude, could be distributed in such a way that the constellation with only two orbital planes separated by 104.5 degrees, each containing only three equispaced satellites, would provide continuous coverage as compared to that provided by 77 satellites of the IRIDIUM system in 7 orbital planes. This GPO constellation provides coverage at any point on the Earth's surface with an elevation angle not less than 10 degrees. Unlike IRIDIUM, the crowding of satellites to the extent of 3 or 4 satellites at a time at the poles has been eliminated in this type of constellation. Also, intersatellite links may not be required since a double hop would be available at any point on Earth's surface if the ground stations are suitably distributed. However, the transmission delay in this system would be degraded compared to IRIDIUM.

Each spacecraft in the IRIDIUM system has 37 cells providing a coverage radius of about 18.6 degrees while that in GPO would be about 66.7 degrees. In order to provide the same service quality as IRIDIUM to the ground based equipment or mobile units that are planned to be used in the IRIDIUM system, the number of cells, spacecraft antenna gain, the frequency re-use and hence spacecraft power in the GPO which are interdependent are under study to configure and contain the spacecraft within the constraints for launch by Araine or Delta.

Cell design for the GPO system considered a range from 37 cells/spacecraft to 469 cells/spacecraft with 7 cell pattern re-use as IRIDIUM. Relative gain advantage of the GPO spacecraft antenna for the outermost edge cell in 66.7 degrees coverage compared to 18.6 degrees coverage for IRIDIUM ranges from about 14dB to 25dB for the range of cell numbers from 37 to 469 respectively. While 37 cells GPO system can have nearly 6 times frequency re-use capability like IRIDIUM, 469 cells GPO system could provide 67 times re-use with worldwide available capacity comparable to IRIDIUM and significantly less frequent handovers (cell edge to edge time 17.6 minutes against about 100 seconds in IRIDIUM). The design of the spacecraft antenna in GPO within the constraints and the provision of the additional spacecraft HPA power to take advantage of the high re-use capability, after compensating for the range loss with the spacecraft antenna gain advantage relative to that of the IRIDIUM, are considered to be a formidable challenge.   Nevertheless, the GPO system implementation cost is envisaged to be less compared to any other currently planned system for similar services.

ODIN
A Swedish Small Satellite Project for Astronomical and Atmospheric Research
F.V. SCHELLE

Spacecraft

The drawing shows Odin with the Sun illuminating the four solar panels from below. In between, these are shields to protect the sideways pointing antenna from the sun. Star trackers and payload elements are mounted on top of the upper platform. Subsystems are mounted on both platforms.

Type	3-axis stabilized with reaction wheels, star trackers and gyros
Mass	205 kg (140 kg bus and 65 kg payload)
Size	Height: 1.8 m, width: 1.1 m stored and 3.3 m in operational state
Power	260 W from deployable fixed arrays
Cooling	Closed Stirling cycle coolers
Pointing	± 15 arcsee in staring mode
	± 1.2 arcmin scanning (reconstructed)
Datalink	> 500 kbit/s to Esrange tracking station
Storage	> 80 Mbyte in solid state memory
Launch	1996 on a Pegasus launch vehicle
Orbit	Circular sunsynchronous, 700 km altitude with ascending node at 18:00
Period	98.7 minutes per orbit

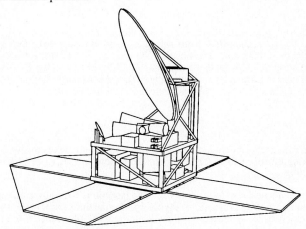

Payload

Antenna

Type	Offset Cassegrain
Diameter	1.1 metre
Surface	10 μm rms
Material	CFRP skins on honeycomb

Radiometer

The radiometer package has one receiver at a wawelength of 3 mm and four in the submm band (0.5 mm)

Type	Single sideband heterodyne receivers
Frequencies	119 GHz, 422 GHz, 488 GHz, 553 GHz and 575 GHz
Coverage	15-20 GHz in each submm band
Bandwidth	100 MHz to 1 GHz
Resolution	0.1 MHz to 1 MHz
Sensitivity	1 K in 1 MHz with S/N = 5 after 15 min
Mixers	Cooled Schottky mixers
LO	Local oscillators based on Gunn diodes and frequency multipliers
LNA	Cooled HEMT low noise amplifiers
Spectrometer	1000 channel hybrid autocorrelator

Optical spectrometer

This instrument has four wawelength bands and views the limb through optics separate but aligned with the submm antenna.

Type	Grating spectrometers
Wawelengths	200 - 800 nm and 1270 nm
Resolution	Optical : 1 nm, IR : 10 nm
Aperture	10 cm^2
FOV	0.02° x 2°

Main Scientific Themes

Odin will work in unexplored bands of the electromagnetic spectrum, around wawelengths of 0.5 mm and 3 mm. These contain emission lines from important molecules such as water vapour, molecular oxygen, ozone and carbon monoxide. The lines will be used as tools to study processes in the Earth atmosphere and in astronomical objects. Complementary information on the Earth atmosphere will come from spectral lines at ultraviolet and optical wawelengths. Major scientific issues relate to star formation processes, interstellar chemistry and atmospheric ozone balance.

Astronomy

The main objective is to perform detailed studies of the physics and the chemistry of the interstellar medium by observing emission from key species. The following classes of objects will be main targets for observations :

– *Giant molecular clouds and nearby dark clouds*: The purpose is to improve our understanding of the chemistry and the cooling processes of the interstellar medium and thereby the conditions for star formation in particular by measuring lines from oxygen and water molecules. Detection of protostars.

– *Comets*: Studies of the physics of outgassing of water, the size of active regions and density estimates both in short and long period comets.

– *Planets*: Height distribution of trace elements in the atmospheres of Jupiter and Saturn. Detection of minor constituents brought up by convection would provide information not only on the dynamics but also on the physics and chemistry of the deep atmospheres.

– *Circumstellar envelopes*: Studies of the dynamics and chemical composition of outflows.

– *Nearby galaxies*: Estimates of star formation activity from observations of CO and H_2O.

Aeronomy

This research will address scientific problems areas in the atmosphere and mesosphere by making measurements of various trace species. The scientific goals can be summarised as follows:

- *Stratospheric ozone science*: To clucidate the geographical extent of and mechanisms responsible for ozone depletion in the « ozone hole » region and to study dilution effects and possible heterogeneous chemistry even outside of the polar regions due to sulphate aerosols.

- *Mesospheric ozone science*: To establish the relative role of odd hydrogen chemistry and the effetcs of ordered and turbulent transport and corpuscular radiation.

- *Summer mesospheric science*: To establish the variability of mesospheric water vapour including an assessment of the required fluxes for aerosol formation in the polar mesosphere.

- *Coupling of atmospheric regions*: To study some of the mechanisms that provide coupling between the upper and lower atmosphere, eg downward transport of aurorally enhanced NO with its effects on ozone photochemistry and the vertical exchange of minor species such as odd oxygen, CO and H_2O.

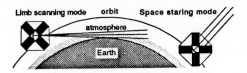

Operating modes

The Odin spacecraft is designed to serve both astronomy and aeronomy. For aeronomy the spacecraft follows the Earth limb - scanning the atmosphere up and down from 15 to 120 km at a rate of up to 40 scans per orbit. When observing astronomical sources Odin is continuously pointing towards the object for up to 60 minutes.

Spectral lines

The radiometer package covers transitions of aeronomical interest from the following molecules :

CIO, CO, NO_2, N_2O, H_2O_2, HO_2, H_2O, $H_2^{18}O$, NO, N_2O, HNO_3, O_3 and O_2.

and atomic and molecular transitions of astrophysical interest from :

CI, CO, $H_2^{18}O$, H_2O, H_2S, NH_3, H_2O, H_2CO, O_2, CS, ^{13}CO, H^2CS, SO, SO_2.

The optical spectrometer is aimed at studying the following species in the Earth atmosphere :

Aerosols, CIO, O_3, O_2, O_4, NO, and NO_2.

LANCEMENT ARIANE 5 PAR GRAPPES D'UNE CONSTELLATION DENSE DE MINISATELLITES SUR ORBITE BASSE INCLINÉE

A. GIRARD, J. JARLIER
Aérospatiale - Cannes

L'émergence de projets spatiaux utilisant des constellations de nombreux objets placés sur des orbites basses leur assurant une couverture mondiale homogène a conduit à imaginer des scénarios de mise en orbite de ces flotilles de petits satellites par des lancements en grappes sur les lanceurs lourds disponibles.

Il est toutefois nécessaire d'atteindre plusieurs plans orbitaux nettement différenciés. Le coût de changement de plan orbital par un incrément de vitesse est bien évidemment prohibitif, pourtant dans le cas des constellations conçues avec plusieurs plans d'inclinaison identiques mais de nœuds ascendants différents, existent des stratégies utilisant la régression orbitale différentielle pour atteindre plusieurs plans orbitaux définitifs, au prix d'une utilisation raisonnable d'ergols de propulsion, en quantitté comparable à celle qui devrait être imposée pour la déorbitation en fin de vie.

Ces stratégies ouvrent ainsi la possibilité d'utiliser Ariane 5 pour la mise en orbite de plusieurs douzaines de satellites. Ce très grand nombre nécessite alors de définr quelles structures porteuses et quelles stratégies d'espacement, de transfert et de mise à poste sont à mettre au point pour ouvrir ce marché au futur lanceur Ariane 5, qui est actuellement le lanceur occidental offrant le meilleur prix au mètre cube en orbite, le volume disponible étant une quantité plus précieuse que la masse en orbite basse.

LE SYSTEME GLOBALSTAR

D. ROUFFET
Alcatel-Espace
A. GIRARD
Aérospatiale

A l'occasion des évolutions de réglementations des fréquences allouées aux services de communications avec les mobiles par satellite, l'Alliance entre Aérospatiale, Alcatel-Espace, Alenia et Loral en association avec Qualcomm, s'est engagée dans le projet Globalstar.

Le système Globalstar est destiné à fournir, en complément des futurs réseaux cellulaires terrestres de téléphonie avec les mobiles, un accès global depuis un téléphone portable léger aux réseaux téléphoniques terrestres classiques, ou via ces réseaux à un autre téléphone portable.

La connexion entre un portable et le réseau terrestre s'établit par l'intermédiaire d'une station sol (ou gateway) via un satellite en visibilité du portable et de la station. Une flotte de 48 petits satellites arrangés en une constellation coordonnée permet d'avoir toujours un ou plusieurs satellites en visibilité mutuelle du portable et de la station sol. Le mouvement des satellites oblige, lorsqu'on atteint la limite de couverture, à procéder à un basculement de la liaison au travers d'un autre satellite mieux placé, mais sans requérir de liaisons intersatellites.

L'impact de ce concept sur les satellites, tant au niveau de la charge utile que de la plate-forme, sera exposé et les architectures possibles illustrées.

World-wide "instantaneous" messaging - the telex users' Iridium?

Mark Bennett and Dr Chris Elliott, Smith System Engineering Ltd, UK

What is the system?

Nanosat emerged from a study carried out by Smith for the UK Ministry of Defence. The aim was to explore low cost message passing systems that could offer a performance similar to a telex terminal with high integrity and using lightweight, low power mobile terminals. Low cost was interpreted as including development, manufacture, deployment and, above all, operational costs.

The system would use several polar orbiting constellations of satellites, each using UHF direct sequence spread spectrum communications to each other and to ground terminals of similar construction to the satellites. Messages from a ground terminal would be repeated to every satellite and ground terminal in the system until reaching their destination or timed out.

It is assumed that the satellites can communicate over a range of 2000km and that there are of the order of 100 satellites randomly positioned in each orbit. Telex-like bandwidth assumes that over 90% of the potential data rate is used by the satellites for repeating messages. Ground terminals are based on a lap-top computer with an additional circuit card electrically and functionally equivalent to a satellite.

The satellites each have a mass of ~1kg, consume ~1W of power and use omnidirectional antennas. No station keeping, attitude control or constellation management is required.

Is the technology plausible?

The critical subsystems of the satellite are:

- antennas and RF;

- data handling;

- power generation and conditioning.

The satellites are assumed to operate in the low UHF band, typically of the order of 400MHz. Each satellite has three mutually perpendicular dipole antennas. Two of these are excited in quadrature when transmitting to form a conventional turnstile antenna. When receiving, the signal from each pair is detected and the strongest signal is selected after detection. This combination of transmit and receive antennas allows communication between two satellites with any relative orientation.

The transmitted signal is encoded using binary phase shift modulation to generate a spread spectrum with a direct sequence chip rate of approximately 1MHz. Data is superimposed on this at a bit rate of approximately 1kHz. The baseline design assumes that the transmitted bit pattern is generated by software using the on-board processor. The receiver is also assumed for the baseline to be implemented in software with a low noise front end amplifier feeding a 1 or 2 bit ADC, the data from which is read by the on-board processor. It is important to note that the spread spectrum parameters are similar to those employed by the Global Positioning System (GPS).

All on-board data handling is assumed for the baseline design to be carried out by a single Inmos transputer. This device offers 32 bit data handling at 10MIP and has been used to implement a GPS receiver capable of simultaneously acquiring and tracking several satellites. The transputer has been shown to be adequately radiation hard for low Earth orbit and has successfully flown on research satellites. It has more than adequate computing power to carry out data handling as well as executing the transmitter and receiver software and, because of the design of its clocking circuits and all-static configuration, can be slowed down to reduce power consumption during periods of low compute load (such as transmit).

Transmitter power of 1W gives a signal/noise ratio of 10dB at a range of 2000km, assuming worst case relative orientation of the satellites and a receiver noise figure of 5dB. The transputer requires a maximum power of 0.5W (less during transmit) and therefore it will be assumed that an average power of 1W is required.

If it is assumed that the satellite uses silicon solar cells of efficiency 12%, is in eclipse for 50% of the orbit and receives no energy from Earth reflection, a projected area of approximately 120cm^2 of solar cells is needed. This corresponds to a sphere of diameter approximately 12cm. A battery with a storage capacity of 1W hour will be needed. Even allowing for limited depth of discharge, a suitable battery will be small compared with the satellite and weigh less than 0.3kg.

The complexity of each satellite is similar to that of a sonobouy. These are mass produced at a cost of a few hundred US dollars each to military standards (capable of withstanding a drop from 1000m into the sea). It is thus not unreasonable to assume that each satellite should cost no more than US$10,000. The cost of deploying several hundred satellites in a single orbital plane is small compared with that of a plausible launch vehicle.

Where does it lead?

No attempt has been made to optimise the design. It was intended to explore the limits of "small" in smallsat and to show that even 1kg satellites may have operational value. The most interesting aspects of the project are the questions that it asks.

Conventional thinking is to assume that operational communications satellites must offer, as a minimum, low latency duplex communications suitable for voice channels. The only exception to this is the use of store-and-forward messaging systems which might take several hours to deliver their messages, depending on the latitude of the source and destination.

There is a class of applications which falls between these two extremes but which is ill-served by existing infrastructure. Nanosat ground terminals can be very low mass and thus particularly suitable for Search and Rescue use. A voice terminal would be too bulky for a mountain climber and store-and-forward messages too slow if you have broken your leg at 8000m. Newspaper journalists frequently need to get copy to their Editors against publication deadlines and are not near a conventional telephone. Small terminals with wide-band spread spectrum emission are of considerable interest for covert operations.

Telex and fax are essential tools of business. Neither need duplex operation or voice bandwidth and may well be paying a high price to obtain these from conventional satellite channels. Nanosat illustrates that there might be another solution to their requirements which is cheaper, more portable and more robust.

AUTONOMOUS ENVIRONMENTAL MONITORING SERVICE BASED ON MICROSATELLITE SYSTEM

Brunella Pavesi and Giuseppe Rondinelli

TELESPAZIO S.p.a. - Via Tiburtina 965 - 00156 Roma, Italy

ABSTRACT

TELESPAZIO is developing the first professional system program using TEMISAT micro-satellite.
The service offer will be dedicated to Environmental Monitoring for data collection and distribution from autonomous Networks.

1. INTRODUCTION

The collection of environmental data requires the deployment of many sensors over wide areas usually difficult to be reached or lacking in communications infrastructures.
A satellite system for environmental monitoring services can offer a unique opportunity for an efficient solution.
In particular making use of the existing technology it is possible to provide the required communications capability using a microsatellite system.

2. THE TEMISAT PROGRAM

The TEMISAT Program foresees the implementation of a Data Collection and Distribution Service for geophysical environment monitoring, throught a micro-satellite named TEMISAT (TElespazio MIcro SATellite) and based on Autonomous Managed Network.

This network will apply very innovative and effective communications technologies to environmental protection service.

The principal application are:

- Basin Level Monitoring
- Oceanographic Monitoring
- Snow Level Monitoring
- Traffic Monitoring
- Monitoring of the structures (Buildings, Dams, ecc..)
- Geological Monitoring
- Seismic Monitoring
- Climatic monitoring

The service shall be provided on a daily basis to private and public users located on the Italian territory and on the surrounding European and Mediterranean Regions.

The environmental data shall be collected on ground by measurements aquired throught sensor subsystems and logged by autonomous and automatic terminal until uploading request from Temisat. Then the data will be trasmitted from Temisat to User Collection Centers.

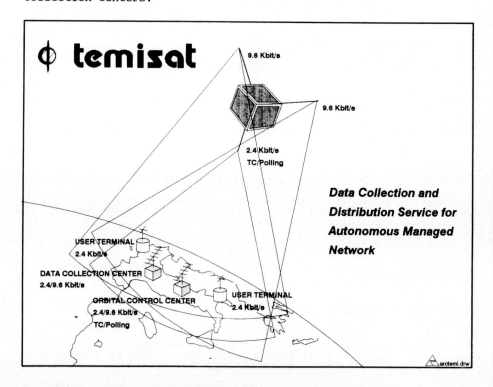

3. TEMISAT SYSTEM CHARACTERISTICS

The system is composed essentially by three main segments:

- A Space Segment consisting of two Micro-Satellites.

These are professional micro-satellites which for the first time introduce a low cost satellite based TDMA/SCPC access scheme.

The espected operational life of each satellite is 5 years, the two satellites are being manufactured by KAYSER and will be put in orbit within two years starting from the first launch.

The principal characteristics of the satellites are:

* High Reliability
* Fully Redundancy
* Store and Forward service
* Direct or on Request Access

The satellite will be injected in a Circular Orbit at a Nominal altitude of 950 Km with an inclination of 82.5°.

- A Ground Support Segment consisting of a Mission Control
  Center.

This Center will process, manage and store the mission data and prepare the User Routing Matrix that contains the polling sequence, the syncronization and the addressee identification codes.

The Mission Control center is responsible for :

* Mission Planning
* Polling Optimization

- A User Segment Consisting of two different types of
  terminals: Collection Center Terminal and User Terminal.

The User terminal and the user station are designed to collect data from various sensors to prepare them for the data trasmission enable on Temisat request during the contact time.

More than 1000 User Stations are planned to be used in the final Network topology.

The principal characteristics of the User Terminal are:

* Standard Interfaces
* Low Power Consumption
* Easy Installation

Data Collection Center is able to receive the down-link data from Temisat corresponding to all the User Terminals belonging to its CUG. It is also possible from this center to transmit command packet to the satellite, these command will be delivered to the proper user terminal together with the polling.

The principal characteristics of the Data Collection Center are:

* High Flexibility
* Close User Group (CUG) Control
* Low Cost and Low Complexity

4. STATE OF ART

The Temisat program is in the advanced phase, the first Unit is planned to be launched from Plesetsk as copassenger of METEOR Satellite by the Russian Launcher TSYCLON in May 1993.
The second Unit is being manifactured together with the first unit; it will be stored on ground for about two years and then will be launched to assure the Service continuity.

RUSSIAN LIGHTSAT SYSTEM "GONETS"
(MESSENGER)

by Alexander PARFENOV

SMALSAT ASSOCIATION - Moscou

ABSTRACT

The "SMALSAT" Association was founded to design, launch and operate a global satellite communication network supported by low orbit satellites normally designed and manufactured by the founding institution.

The new company was established in 1991 by the Association of Applied Mecanics, the Association of Precision Instruments and the "SOYUZMEDINFORM" Association. The Association of Applied Mecanics designs and manufactures 100 % of Russian communication satellites and 65 % of all Russia-made satellites. The Association of Precision Instruments designs and manufactures both space and ground-based electronic components of satellite communication systems. The "SOYUZMEDIN-FORM" Association is the main organisation in management, advertising and distribution of services.

For about two years now "SMALSAT" has been engaged in a major effort to develop and deploy a low orbit satellite communication system called "GONETS" (Russian for "Messenger").

Its services above all comprise :

- telex and fax,
- electronic mail,
- slow scan and compressed video,
- SCADA, environmental monitoring,
- future capability to determine location of any object.

The system has the following main advantages :

- low cost of space and ground-based components as compared with the existing geo-stationary communication networds,
- low-cost of launches because of the possibility to put into orbit 6 satellites at a launch,
- mini-terminals,
- ability to operate in all mobile vehicles, including aircrfat and marine means of transportation
- ability to operate in polar regions inaccessible to other satellite communication systems,
- ability to operate in regions with under or undevelopped communication infrastructure,
- ability to transmit digital information at 9,6 Kbit/sec or 64 Kbit/sec depending on the type of terminals.

The reliability of the system lies in its backbone which is an already existing gouvernemental satellite communication network. The configuration of the main network, hardware and software have undergone extensive testing for over twenty years.

Prospective users of the system are above all :

-   banks and broker offices,
-   ecologic monitoring services,
-   hydrometeorologists,
-   geophysicists,
-   ATC and other traffic controllers,
-   individuals working in regions with undevelopped communication infrastructure (physicians, geologists, rescue workers, businessmen, etc...)

The system garantees the confidentiality of the relayed data as well as protection against unauthorised access to the channels.

"GONETS" incorporates 36 low-orbit communication satellites (1500 km away) storing and transmitting information in packet mode to provide communication services to 1.000.000 users with 20 minutes maximum waiting time.

The deployement of the system will be preceded by a "demonstration project". The demonstration project is planned for July 13, 1992 when two satellites will be placed into orbit.

"GONETS" will be deployed in several stages, the first scheduled for 1994 when 6 satellites will be launched. It is envisaged to launch series of 6 satellites until the deployment (36 satellites) is completed in 1996. The Cyclon carrier rocket will be used to launch 6 satellites at a time until the system is deployed within 6 launches.

The number of satellites in orbit can be enlarged in accordance with the imperative requirements.

CONCLUSIONS
Table ronde de synthèse

Tout d'abord, je voudrai dire que je suis un président de session heureux. J'ai eu en effet le privilège de voir surgir au cours de ma session l'un des scoops majeurs de ce colloque : l'annonce par Brunella PAVESI du lancement du satellite TEMISAT pour la collecte de données d'environnement. Sans doute souhaitons-nous tous davantage de détails. Aussi ai-je proposé en votre nom à tous que ces détails soient inclus dans les actes finaux du colloque.

Si vous m'autorisez maintenant à prendre un peu de recul, je voudrai reposer dans le contexte « Analyse Système » une des questions majeures de ce colloque : pourquoi veut-on faire et lancer des petits satellites ?

Je proposerai d'y répondre en termes généraux : pour arriver à des résultats comparables à ceux qu'on obtiendrait avec de gros satellites mais dans des conditions plus satisfaisantes. Exemple : pour des missions scientifiques, en payant moins ou en payant moins de contraintes comme l'ont rappelé plusieurs orateurs et en particulier ce matin José DORADO. Pour des missions technologiques ou commerciales, en fournissant un service équivalent mais à un moindre coût, ou bien à coût égal avec un meilleur service.

Dans le domaine des télécommunications, la référence est le satellite géostationnaire. Il est loin, le plus souvent il est gros, et parfois bas sur l'horizon. Avec de petits satellites en orbite basse, on peut espérer réduire les coûts de fabrication et de lancement et avoir des satellites au zénith de l'usager avec des temps de propagation plus faibles.

J'ai dit « espérer ». Peut-on réussir ? La réponse a plusieurs aspects : techniques, économiques, humains. Rien de nouveau là par rapport aux satellites géostationnaires sauf que nous manquons d'expérience. L'expérience que nous avons semble indiquer que nos méthodes de travail sont à réviser. Par exemple Jackie RADBONNE, et d'autres, ont montré la nécessité d'équipes intégrées au formalisme d'échange simple et moins structuré.

Des équipes légères avec des procédures simplifiées, cela est incompatible avec un grand nombre d'experts munis d'outils de conception ésotériques. Il faut des outils d'investigation simples, peut-être même grossiers au niveau des grands choix systèmes. Par exemple, José RADZIK et Jean-Jacques DE RIDDER nous ont montré comment on pouvait évaluer rapidement l'intérêt ou non d'un contrôle d'orbite par rapport aux objectifs de mission.

Il faut aussi des moyens d'investigation nouveaux. Par exemple, un des problèmes à prendre en compte est la variabilité de la couverture. J'ai été frappé de voir que Martin DECKETT, dans sa présentation d'ORBCOM a confirmé que le bon outil d'évaluation n'est plus la couverture géographique instantanée, mais la statistique de visibilité, ce qui est exactement ce que fournit l'outil logiciel que nous avons développé sur le site de Toulouse de TELECOM-PARIS sous contrat CNES et qui s'appelle LEONART. Beaucoup d'entre vous ont pu le voir en démonstration sur le stand de TELECOM-PARIS et apprécier ses performances.

Plus fondamentalement, les systèmes à petits satellites ont un caractère révolutionnaire, et c'est peut-être ce qui nous gène, car c'est une remise en cause. Il me semble toutefois qu'il ne faut pas refuser l'innovation mais l'accompagner et la maîtriser. Il faut d'ailleurs en souligner la fragilité : l'expérience acquise par de petites entités se dissout avec la disparition de ces équipes une fois l'objectif atteint ou manqué, au contraire des grosses organisations dont la pérennité est plus certaine.

Un des enjeux de notre action devrait être de mettre en œuvre des outils permettant de garder la mémoire de chaque expérience, heureuse ou malheureuse. C'est notre ambition dans le concept que nous avons présenté en session poster, qui s'appelle XEOSCAD pour « eXpert Earth Orbiting Satellite Systems Computer Aided Design » fondé comme son nom l'indique sur des outils d'intelligence artificielle.

Je conclurai en disant que pour moi ce colloque confirme la validité de l'un de nos axes de recherche à Toulouse qui vise :

– à développer une méthodologie d'investigation et d'évaluation,
– à mettre en place des logiciels conviviaux au service d'équipes de conception entreprenantes,
– sans oublier d'en enseigner à nos élèves l'existence et leur utilisation.

Je répète : il s'agit de faire avec de petits satellites mieux ou aussi bien, que l'existant, mais moins cher.

Round table discussion

First of all, I would like to say that I am a happy session chairman. During my session, we had the privilege of hearing one of the major scoops of the symposium, Brunella PAVESI's announcement of the launch of the TEMISAT satellite for the collection of environmental data. It goes without saying that we would all like more details so, on behalf of all of you, I have suggested that these details should be included in the final proceedings of the symposium.

If I may take a step back, I would like to repeat one of the major questions of the symposium in the "Systems Analysis" context: "Why do we want to make and launch small satellites?"

I have an answer to put forward in general terms: "To obtain results comparable to those possible with large satellites but in more satisfactory conditions". E.g. for scientific missions, by paying less or having fewer constraints, as several of our speakers reminded us, in particular José DORADO this morning. For technological or commercial missions, by providing equivalent service for a lower cost, or alternatively, having the same cost but a better service.

In the telecommunications field, the reference is the geostationary satellite. It is far away, usually big, and sometimes low on the horizon. With small satellites in low orbits, we could hope to reduce production and launch costs and have satellites at the user's zenith with shorter propagation times.

I said "hope". Can we succeed? The answer has several aspects: technical, economic and human. There is nothing new with respect to geostationary satellites except our lack of experience. The experience we have seemed to indicate that our working methods need revising. For example, Jackie RADBONNE and others have shown the need for integrated teams with simplified, less structured forms of exchange.

Light teams with simplified procedures would be incompatible with a large number of experts possessing esoteric design tools. We need simple, perhaps even crude, investigation tools for making the overall system choices. José RADZIK and Jean-Jacques DE RIDDER, for example, showed us how the interest (or not) of orbit control could be quickly assessed with respect to the mission objectives.

New means of investigation are also needed. E.g. one of the problems to be taken into consideration is variability of coverage. I was struck by Martin DECKETT's confirmation in his presentation of ORBCOM that the right assessment tool is not the instantaneous geographical coverage, but visibility statistics, which is exactly what is provided by the software tool we have developed at the Telecom Paris' establishment in Toulouse under a CNES contract called LEONART. Many of you will have seen the demonstration at the Telecom Paris stand and been able to appreciate its performance.

From a more fundamental point of view, small satellites have a revolutionary character, and it is perhaps this that bothers us, as it calls our previous ideas into question. It seems to me, however, that innovation cannot be refused but must be accompanied and controlled. Another point to be highlighted is the fragility of this innovative work: the experience gained by small groups is dissipated with the disbanding of the team once the objective has been attained or missed, whereas a long life is much more certain for large organizations.

One of the important challenges in our action should be to bring in tools enabling all experience, whether good or bad, to be stored for future reference. This is the ambition of the concept we presented in a poster session called XEOSCAD for "eXpert Earth Orbiting Satellite Systems Computer Aided Design", which is based, as its name implies, on artificial intelligence tools.

I would like to conclude by saying that, for me, this symposium has confirmed the validity of one of our lines of research in Toulouse, which aims to:

– develop investigation and assessment methodology;
– provide user friendly software for enterprising design teams;
– without forgetting to inform our pupils of its existence and utilization.

I repeat, the aim is for small satellites to do better, or as well, as existing systems, but cheaper.